MINISTRY OF DEFENCE (NAVY)

BR 67(3)

Admiralty
Manual of Seamanship

VOLUME III

Revised 1983

LONDON: HER MAJESTY'S STATIONERY OFFICE

© *Crown copyright 1983*
First published 1955
Third Edition 1983

ISBN 0 11 771269 8*

BR 67(3)

ADMIRALTY MANUAL OF SEAMANSHIP

VOLUME III

Superseding BR 67(3) dated 1964

March 1983   *By Command of the Defence Council*

MINISTRY OF DEFENCE

Directorate of Naval Warfare

N/DNW 40/76

Note

Since June 1983, the responsibilities of the Marine Division of the Department of Trade have been transferred to the Marine Directorate of the Department of Transport.

Entries which have been listed under Department of Trade in the Index on page 524 should now be read as Department of Transport.

University of Strathclyde Libraries
Main Library
CheckOut Receipt

01/08/06
04:43 pm

Item:Passage planning / Nautical Institute.
Due Date (yyyy-mm-dd):
20060912   170000

Item:Admiralty manual of seamanship /
Ministry of Defence (Navy).
Due Date (yyyy-mm-dd):
20060912   170000

Please retain this receipt

0060912 17000 0

0060912 17000 0

Preface

The *Admiralty Manual of Seamanship* is in four volumes. *Volume I* is the basic book of seamanship for officers and men joining the Royal Navy. *Volume II* contains more technical detail and is a general textbook and reference book for ratings seeking advancement and for junior officers. *Volume III* is intended mainly for officers. It covers such essential seamanship knowledge as the handling of ships and also information on a variety of subjects that could be classed as advanced seamanship, such as aid to ships in distress. *Volume IV* provides information required for Royal Navy purposes only and is not available to the public.

The chapters in each volume are arranged in the following four Parts, dealing generally with the subjects shown.

PART I: *Ship Knowledge and Safety*. Types of ship and their construction; firefighting; stability; control of damage; lifesaving.

PART II: *Seamanship*. The uses of rope; rigging; sailing boats and power boats; anchors and cables; evolutions such as towing, salvage and lifting or moving heavy loads.

PART III: *Ship Organisation*. General organisation of a ship; naval communications; ceremonial; ship upkeep and ship husbandry.

PART IV: *Shiphandling and Navigation*. Steering; elementary navigation and pilotage; handling of ships in different conditions; the Rule of the Road.

It is hoped that Volumes I to III may also prove useful outside the Royal Navy, to all who put to sea in ships or boats.

Acknowledgements for information and assistance in preparing this work are due to the following organisations and companies:

Beaufort Air-Sea Equipment Ltd
Bridon Fibres and Plastics Ltd
British Standards Institution
Cargospeed Equipment Ltd
The College of Nautical Studies
  (Southampton)
Coubro and Scrutton (M & I) Ltd
Cunard-Brocklebank Ltd
GEC Mechanical Handling Ltd
E.C. Goldsworthy & Co. Ltd
International Maritime Organization
J. W. Automarine Crestbury Ltd
Lloyd's Register of Shipping
Marlow Ropes Ltd
The Nautical Institute

Ocean Liners Ltd
Overseas Containers Ltd
Pains-Wessex Schermuly
The Royal National Lifeboat Institution
The School of Maritime Studies
  (Plymouth)
William R. Selwood Ltd
Shell International Marine Ltd
Siebe Gorman & Co. Ltd
Society for Underwater Technology
Three Quays Marine Services
Unimarine Ltd
Watercraft Ltd
Westgate Shipping Ltd

Contents

vii

PART I

SHIP KNOWLEDGE AND SAFETY

CHAPTER 1

Stability of Ships

The factors which affect the stability of a ship are outlined in Volume II. In this chapter stability is dealt with in more detail in order to show how the stability of a ship is determined, and how it can be restored or improved, under various conditions of loading or damage. A comprehensive treatment of the subject is given in BR 2170, *Ship NBCD Manual*.

TRANSVERSE STABILITY

Righting moment

The following facts are basic to an understanding of stability (Fig. 1–1):

1. The position of the centre of gravity G of a ship will vary with her condition of loading. If she is symmetrically loaded, it will lie somewhere on the middle plane of the ship.

2. If the ship moves under the influence of any external force (e.g. wind or wave), the position of the centre of gravity for any particular condition of loading will remain fixed, apart from a slight movement caused by the shifting of any liquids with a free surface.

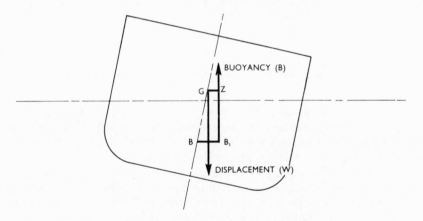

FIG. 1–1. Righting moment

3. The centre of buoyancy B is the geometric centre of the underwater part of the vessel and usually lies directly below the centre of gravity when the ship is steady, but when the ship is heeled it will move to a position B_1 in the centre of the submerged volume of the ship.

4. The forces of weight and buoyancy are each equal to the ship's displacement W, and they act vertically in opposite directions.

5. The force of buoyancy acting upwards through B_1 when the ship is heeled will produce a moment tending to right the ship, and this moment

3

is calculated by multiplying the displacement W by the righting lever GZ, which is the horizontal distance between the forces of weight and buoyancy.

6. The righting moment depends chiefly on the angle of heel and the movement of the centre of buoyancy; it will increase with an increase of the angle of heel up to a certain critical angle, but thereafter it will decrease with any further increase of the angle of heel, and will eventually change to a capsizing moment.

Transverse metacentre and transverse metacentric height

In most ships, for small angles of heel of up to about 10 degrees, the line of action of the force of buoyancy B_1 will cut the middle line of the ship at a fixed point M which is called the *transverse metacentre* (Fig. 1–2).

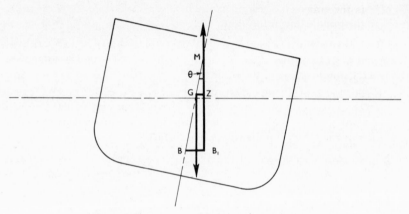

FIG. 1–2. Transverse metacentre and metacentric height

The height of the metacentre M above the centre of gravity G is called the *metacentric height*; it gives a measure of the *initial stability* of the ship, i.e. her stability at small angles of heel. The greater the metacentric height, i.e. the lower the position of G, the greater the stability.

In triangle GMZ of Fig. 1–2, the angle θ at its apex is equal to the angle of heel, and the righting lever GZ will be equal to $GM \sin \theta$ (provided that θ is small and GM is positive, as in this example). If the metacentric height GM is known, the righting moment can be found by multiplying the righting lever GZ by the ship's displacement W.

When a ship is heeled, the position of her transverse metacentre depends upon the shape of her waterplane (the plane through the hull at the waterline) and on the position of the centre of buoyancy B_1, which in turn depends on the draught of the ship and the underwater shape of her hull. At angles of heel of over, say, 10 degrees the position of the transverse metacentre will not be fixed but will change with the angle of heel. The designer must therefore arrange the dimensions of her hull to ensure not only a reasonable margin of initial stability at all normal conditions of loading, but also a reasonable margin of stability over the probable angles of heel to which the ship may roll in a heavy sea. In general it can be assumed that if a ship is of conventional form and has a reasonable margin of initial stability at all ordinary conditions of loading, she will also have sufficient stability to right herself from any angle to which she may be heeled in the normal course of events.

Position of transverse metacentre

The height of the transverse metacentre above the centre of buoyancy (BM in Fig. 1–2) depends solely on the form of the ship at and below her waterline, and it will therefore vary with the beam of the ship, her waterplane area, her coefficient of fineness and her draught. This is shown by the formula:

$$BM = \frac{I}{V} = k\frac{lb^3}{lbd} = k\frac{b^2}{d} \quad \text{(approximately)}$$

where:

I is the transverse second moment of area of the waterplane about the middle line of the ship;

V is the volume of the ship's displacement;

k is a constant depending upon the underwater form of the ship; and

l, b and d are the length, beam and draught, respectively, of the ship.

It will therefore be seen that the distance BM is directly proportional to the square of the beam, and inversely proportional to the draught.

The position of the metacentre is determined by the designer when he plans the ship. As soon as the lines of her design are settled the ship's hydrostatic particulars are calculated, usually by computer, and relevant data such as the height of the initial metacentre above the keel are produced for each of a number of possible waterlines.

Degree of transverse stability

The degree of initial stability, as measured by the ship's transverse metacentric height at any particular condition of loading, depends on the relative positions of her transverse metacentre and her centre of gravity. The position of the transverse metacentre is determined by the designer; it depends entirely on the underwater shape of the hull and, as it will change only as the draught of the ship changes, the seaman has little control over its position. The centre of gravity, however, depends largely on the disposition of the fuel, water, stores and any cargo or ballast which the ship may be carrying, and it can therefore be altered by the seaman to provide the necessary margin of initial stability.

A ship with a large transverse metacentric height has a high resistance to rolling forces, and so will roll with a short, rapid motion; such a ship is said to be *stiff*. A ship with a small transverse metacentric height does not offer so much resistance to rolling, and so will roll with a long, slow motion; such a ship is said to be *tender*.

A ship's initial stability, as measured by her transverse metacentric height, should not, however, be taken as a measure of her seaworthiness. A ship that is too stiff can be just as dangerous as one that is too tender, because rolling that is too rapid and violent may shift her cargo, strain her hull and even unseat her machinery.

The degree of transverse stability is therefore arranged to suit a ship's characteristics and the duties or trade on which she is engaged. Passenger ships must not be too stiff, or the comfort of their passengers will suffer; nor should cargo vessels be too stiff, or their cargo may shift when they are in a seaway. Warships, on the other hand, must be sufficiently stiff to ensure a reasonable margin of stability should they be flooded by underwater damage; but they must not be too stiff, or the accuracy of their armament may be impaired by too violent rolling. The stability of vessels intended for fixed routes, such as cross-Channel ferries, ocean liners and vessels sailing on inland waterways, is often designed to suit the kind of seas they will probably encounter, and this must be borne in mind if it is intended to use such vessels elsewhere.

Stability at large angles of inclination

The simple expression for the length of the righting lever GZ (shown in Fig. 1–2), viz. $GZ = GM \sin \theta$, applies only to small angles of inclination up to about 10 degrees for ships of normal shape. At greater angles of inclination the breadth of the waterplane changes and the position of the transverse metacentre M is no longer fixed. Furthermore, the position of the centre of gravity G depends upon how the vessel is loaded regardless of her displacement.

To take account of the variable positions of M and G a series of intricate calculations is used to estimate the righting levers at different displacements for various angles of inclination (usually every 10 degrees or so from about 10 degrees to 80 degrees). From the values thus obtained a *cross curve of stability* is drawn for each angle of inclination, on a combined graph as shown at Fig. 1–3. Because the position of G is variable, the righting lever used in these curves is measured from a fixed position in the ship, the keel K. Thus the righting lever is represented by KN in the inset to Fig. 1–3, and for this reason the cross curves of stability are known as KN *curves*. The curves have to be drawn over a large variation of displacement for merchant ships, to take account of their greatly differing conditions of loading.

From the KN curves the true righting lever GZ can be calculated for any displacement and angle of inclination by estimating the position of G for the condition of loading and using the formula:

$$GZ = KN - KG \sin \theta.$$

A typical stability curve

From the cross curves of stability *curves of statical stability*, sometimes known as *righting-lever curves* or *GZ curves*, can be drawn for specified conditions of loading. These curves give the length of the righting lever GZ for various angles of heel, and each shows graphically the degree of stability of the ship in the condition for which the curve was drawn.

A typical stability curve is shown at Fig. 1–4 and its general features are described below.

1. At small angles of heel (up to about 10 degrees) the curve is approximately a straight line, and the angle which it makes with the base line is governed by the metacentric height, since $GZ = GM \sin \theta$ when θ is small. If, at $\theta = 1$ radian (57.3 degrees), a perpendicular of length equal to GM is set up to the point M, then the GZ curve is tangential

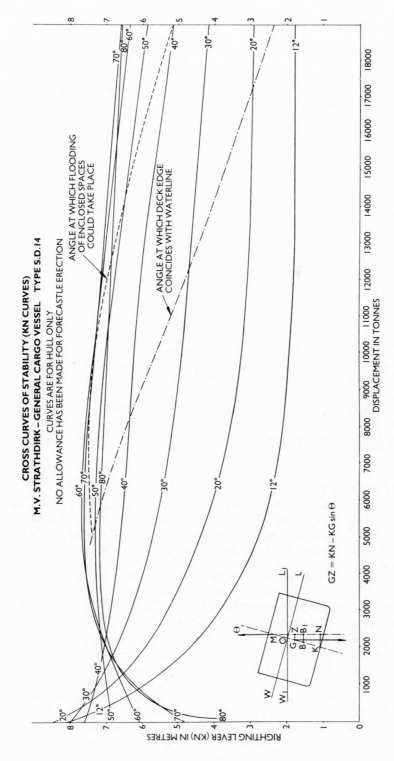

FIG. 1–3. Typical example of cross curves of stability

B

to the line drawn between point M and the origin, for small angles of heel.

2. As the angle of heel increases above 10 degrees the steepness of the curve increases, and it is steepest at the angle at which the freeboard deck-edge becomes immersed. At this point, known as the *point of contraflexure*, the shape of the curve changes from convex to concave.

3. As the angle of heel increases still further, the steepness of the curve decreases, until it becomes horizontal at an angle of heel called the *angle of maximum righting lever*.

4. Thereafter the curve descends, at first with increasing steepness and then at a steady angle of descent, until it crosses the base line at a point called the *vanishing angle*, at which there is no righting lever and beyond which a capsizing lever is set up. This point defines the limit of the *range of stability* for the ship for that particular condition of loading; it is sometimes just called the *range*.

The angle of maximum righting lever is the largest angle of *steady heel* which a ship can take up without capsizing when inclined by a slowly applied constant heeling-moment, because under these conditions the righting moment must balance the heeling moment. These conditions are only theoretical, however, because it is assumed that the sea is calm and there is no wind. Actually, when a ship is inclined to her angle of maximum righting lever by a steady heeling force, set up by a wind or asymmetrical flooding for example, a slight increase in the force or a slight movement of the ship may cause her to capsize. The angle of maximum righting lever must not therefore be regarded as an angle at which the ship is safe under the influence of a steady heeling force; it represents, in still water, the angle at which the ship has no further margin of stability against capsizing. Furthermore, if a heeling moment less than the maximum righting moment were suddenly applied, it could possibly capsize the ship.

Rolling in still water

The meaning of the term *period of roll* of a ship is described in Chapter 15. The period depends on the degree of transverse stability of the ship in any one condition of loading, and also upon the disposition of weights about her longitudinal centre-line: but for any one condition the period of roll of a ship, within small angles (of, say, from 10 to 15 degrees) each side, will be the same irrespective of the angles to which she rolls; in other words, her periods for rolls of, say, 10 and 5 degrees will be the same for any one condition of loading. For large angles of roll the period increases with the angle of roll because of the change of metacentric height at large angles of heel.

The period of roll is inversely proportional to the righting moment or, in other words, the greater the righting moment the shorter will be the period of roll. The period of roll is also affected by the disposition of weights in the ship. Two ships may have the same displacement and metacentric height GM (i.e. equal righting moments), but if significant amounts of weight are placed at the ship's sides in one and concentrated at the centre-line in the other, the former will have a greater period of roll than the latter because of the greater moments of inertia.

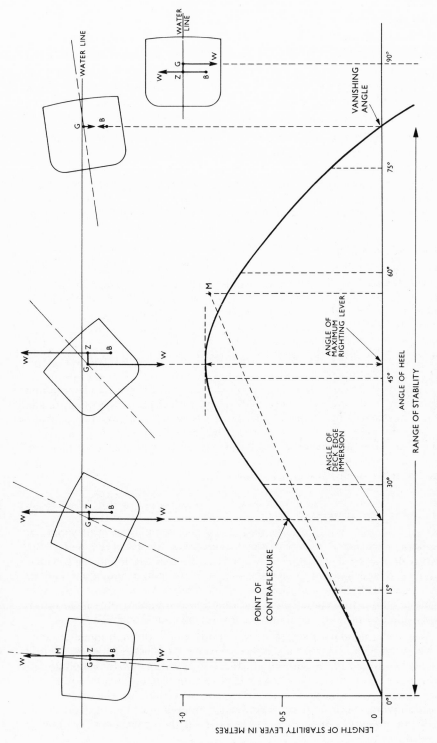

FIG. 1–4. Typical stability curve, showing the length of the righting lever for various angles of heel

If there were no resistance to rolling, the motion would continue indefinitely. Resistance to rolling in *still* water is caused by:

surface disturbance, i.e. resistance caused by the actual displacement of water close to the ship by the movement of her hull from side to side;

eddy resistance caused by flat parts of the hull or projections such as rudder and bilge keels; and

frictional resistance between the water and the hull surface.

Of these, the first is the greatest; the second about one-fifth of this; and the last so small that it can be ignored.

In general, the resistance of the water tends not only to reduce the roll of a ship (the more violent the roll, the greater the resistance), but also to increase the moment of inertia and so increase the period of roll. The effect is greater when the ship is under way and increases with increasing speed.

Rolling in a seaway

The relationship between the period of roll and period of encounter with the waves is described in Chapter 15. From the seaman's point of view the most important lesson is to realise that, in a beam sea, if the period of roll is synchronous with the period of encounter a dangerous situation can arise. If the rolling is excessive, particularly in a ship in which the metacentric height GM is small, and she appears reluctant to recover at the end of a roll, her course should be altered to break the synchronisation between the waves and the period of roll.

If the period of roll is large in comparison with the period of encounter the ship will probably roll only slightly and with the same period as in still water. Passenger ships are usually designed to have small transverse metacentric heights and long periods of roll, so that they have this quality of being steady in a beam sea. Such ships will roll independently of the waves, which will probably break against their sides, but without much inconvenience because passenger ships normally have a high freeboard.

Inclining experiment

When a ship is built, or has undergone considerable reconstruction, an *inclining experiment* is carried out to determine the actual position of the centre of gravity of the ship 'as inclined'. At the same time the displacement of the ship is calculated. When the weight of the ship in the light condition has been established and the position of the centre of gravity has been determined for the 'as inclined' condition it is a comparatively simple matter to calculate its position accurately for any other condition of loading.

The inclining experiment is usually carried out with the feed-water tanks, fresh-water tanks, ballast tanks, fuel tanks or bunkers either completely empty or pressed full, with or without all stores on board but with no ammunition or cargo. The experiment is conducted in still water, preferably in a dock or basin, and on a calm day. If there is any wind the ship should be placed head to wind. All machinery is stopped, pumping systems are drained and, with the exception of those men required for the experiment, her crew is landed.

Long pendulums, about 4 to 6 metres long, are suspended from points in the middle line of the ship through suitable hatchways or in the holds. At a convenient distance below each point of suspension a horizontal batten is fixed (*PQ* in Fig. 1–5) with the centre-line of the ship marked on it, against which the inclination of the ship can be measured. At least two pendulums are required, one forward and one aft. A known weight of ballast, sufficient to incline the ship 2 to 3 degrees, is placed on the upper deck and symmetrically disposed about the fore-and-aft centre-line. The ship should then be floating perfectly upright.

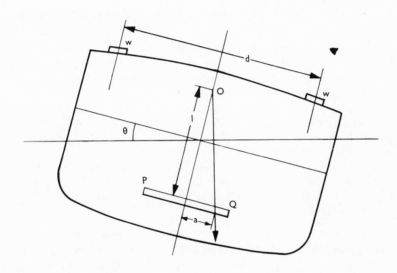

FIG. 1–5. The inclining experiment

The weights are then shifted a measured distance across the deck from one side to the other and, when the ship is steady, the deflection of each pendulum is measured. The weights are then returned to their original positions and the ship resumes the upright position. The weights are next moved the same measured distance the other way across the ship and again the pendulum deflections are measured. The mean of the pendulum deflections is taken and then the metacentric height *GM* can be calculated from the formula:

$$GM = \frac{w \times d}{W \times \tan \theta}$$

where:

w   is the inclining weight;

d   is the distance it has been moved across the ship;

W   is the displacement of the ship (including the inclining weight *w*); and

$\tan \theta$ is $\dfrac{\text{mean of pendulum deflections}}{\text{length of pendulums}}$ $\left(\dfrac{a}{l} \text{ in Fig. } 1\text{–}5\right)$.

The formula can be written:

$$GM = \frac{w \times d}{W \times \dfrac{a}{l}} \qquad \text{or} \qquad GM = \frac{w \times d \times l}{W \times a}.$$

The distance of the metacentre above the keel for this condition of loading is obtained from the hydrostatic particulars, and so the exact position of the centre of gravity can be determined.

METHODS OF IMPROVING TRANSVERSE STABILITY

The transverse stability of a ship can be improved structurally by increasing the ratio of her beam to her draught, which will result in raising the position of her metacentre and thus increasing her metacentric height. A ship's stability at large angles of heel can be improved by increasing her freeboard, provided that the additional structure does not unduly raise her centre of gravity and so reduce her metacentric height. Transverse stability can also be improved by adding ballast low down in the ship or by removing topweight from her; both methods will result in lowering her centre of gravity and so increasing her metacentric height, but whereas the former will increase her draught and reduce her freeboard, the latter will have the opposite effect. Free-surface liquid — that is, liquid which is free to move from side to side of a partially filled tank or compartment — will result in reducing the metacentric height.

Ballasting and removal of topweight (Fig. 1–6)

Many fine-form cargo vessels are very tender in the light-load condition, or *flying light*, and some may even have a negative metacentric height. To offset this tenderness they have to be ballasted by flooding specially designed ballast-compartments and, in some cases, by flooding designated cargo-compartments. Many vessels, notably submarines, are provided with permanent or semi-permanent ballast in the form of pig iron.

The effect of ballasting low down is to lower the centre of gravity without materially affecting the position of the metacentre, thus increasing the metacentric height. The amount by which the centre of gravity is lowered is given by the formula

$$\frac{w \times h}{W + w}$$

where:

w is the weight of the ballast;

h is its distance below the original centre of gravity; and

W is the original displacement of the ship.

Another effect of ballasting, which may be disadvantageous, is to increase the draught of the ship.

Removal of topweight also lowers the centre of gravity and, as it decreases the draught of the ship, it may be preferable to ballasting in ships in which an increase of draught would be a disadvantage. The amount by which the

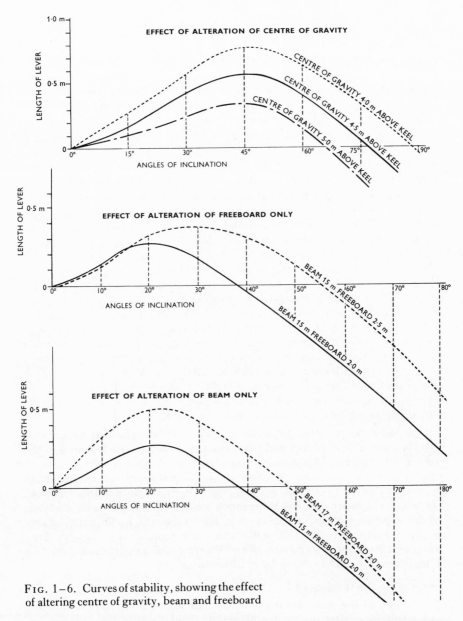

FIG. 1–6. Curves of stability, showing the effect of altering centre of gravity, beam and freeboard

centre of gravity is lowered by the removal of topweight is given by the formula

$$\frac{w \times h}{W - w}$$

where:

w is the topweight;

h is its height above the original centre of gravity; and

W is the original displacement of the ship.

It is a common mistake to suppose that a ship is made steady by ballasting or the removal of topweight. Steadiness is obtained by having a small metacentric height; the metacentric height is increased by ballasting low down or removing topweight and the ship is made stiffer and therefore more lively. In this connection it is of interest to recall that in the last century many of the old 64-gun ships were converted to 38-gun frigates (or *razées*, as they were then called) by removing the upper deck together with its guns and topsides and fitting lighter masts and yards. The removal of this topweight considerably increased the metacentric height, and the ships rolled so violently that they often sprang their topmasts. This failing was overcome to a certain extent by increasing the size, and therefore the weight, of the masts and yards, thereby decreasing the metacentric height by adding topweight.

An opposite effect to that of ballasting arises from the consumption of fuel, water and stores if they are stowed below the ship's centre of gravity. This is particularly evident in the case of fuel, because the fuel tanks of most ships are built into their double bottoms, and the effect of using up the oil fuel is then the same as that of removing ballast. A ship's margin of stability is likely to be seriously reduced by the consumption of much of her fuel unless it is countered by ballasting (which may include water compensation of fuel tanks, see page 16), or anticipated by the disposition of the cargo. In the early years of this century a cargo vessel was provided with little information about her stability, her loading being left to the judgement and experience of her master. This lack of information sometimes led to dangerous situations in which a ship, though perfectly stable on sailing, was in a precarious state on arrival at her destination because of her loss of stability through the consumption of fuel and water during the voyage. Notable examples were the Baltic traders when carrying deck cargoes of timber, which often arrived in this country with negative stability and heeled to an angle of loll.

In modern cargo ships, particularly when fully laden, it may be the case that the expenditure of fuel and other consumables causes a lowering of the metacentric height. This must be considered in conjuction with the rise of the centre of gravity which is the other adverse effect caused by the expenditure of consumables. In a typical general-cargo vessel of gross tonnage 10 000, her centre of gravity may rise by as much as 300 millimetres during a voyage while the position of her metacentre may fall by about 50 millimetres, making a total reduction of some 350 millimetres in her metacentric height. Even when corrected for free-surface effect this may still amount to a reduction of metacentric height in the order of 150 millimetres.

Increasing the freeboard

The weight of the structure involved by increasing the freeboard of a ship will result in raising her centre of gravity, and because her draught and displacement will be increased by a small amount her metacentre will be lowered slightly. The immediate result will therefore be to decrease slightly her metacentric height and therefore her initial stability, but at large angles of heel the result will be to increase her righting moment, the angle of her deck-edge immersion, and her range of stability.

Girdling

Girdling means increasing the ship's beam with the object of increasing her metacentric height.

The modern method of girdling is to attach permanent sponsons which span the waterline along the parallel lengths of the ship's sides. This method of increasing stability is frequently used in the conversion of vessels, particularly tankers or bulk carriers, for use as ultra-heavy-lift ships or pipe-laying vessels for the off-shore oil industry.

In the days of sail one of the chief tactical considerations in an action was to gain the weather gauge, so that the final approach to the enemy could be made from windward and his freedom of manoeuvre thereby restricted. This necessitated fighting the lee guns, and ships of the line had to be stiff enough to resist being heeled by a beam wind sufficiently to submerge the ports of their lowest tier of guns. Moreover, the maximum angle of elevation of these guns was only 12 degrees and therefore, with her crew manning the guns on the lee side, the heel of the ship to leeward had to be limited to 12 degrees. In practice the designers of those days limited the heel to 7 degrees in a 'topsail wind', which corresponded to a wind of force 5 to 6 on the Beaufort scale.

Towards the end of the seventeenth century the stability of ships of the line was unfavourably criticised by our seamen, and our ship designers were then faced with a difficult problem, because removal of topweight would impair the ship's fighting efficiency, and ballasting would increase her draught and reduce the freeboard of her lower gun-ports. In the event they resorted to girdling, which consisted of fitting a wooden belt, from one-third to one-half metre thick, around the ship at her waterline and extending approximately one metre above and below it. This virtually increased the beam of the ship and so raised the position of her metacentre without materially altering her draught or the position of her centre of gravity. The rise of the metacentre was roughly equivalent to the thickness of the girdling, or half the increase of beam. An added advantage of the girdling was that it provided what was virtually an armour belt at that most vulnerable part of the ship — 'between wind and water'.

Effect of free-surface liquids

When a tank is *slack*, i.e. when it contains some liquid but is not full, the metacentric height is reduced by an amount depending solely on the extent of the free surface of the liquid and its density relative to that of sea water. A few centimetres of liquid in the bottom of a rectangular tank would therefore reduce the metacentric height by as much as would several metres, and it is therefore important to ensure that ballast tanks are either pressed up (i.e. filled) or completely drained.

Several methods may be used to calculate the loss of metacentric height due to free surface. One such method is by the formula:

$$\text{Loss of } GM = \frac{dI}{V}$$

where:

d is the relative density of the liquid compared with that of the water in which the ship is floating;

I is the second moment of area of the free surface about the longitudinal axis through the centre of its area; and

V is the volume of displacement of the ship.

The second moment of area of the free surface of a liquid in a rectangular tank is given by the formula:

$$I = \frac{l \times b^3}{12}$$

where l and b are the length and breadth respectively of the tank.

It will therefore be seen that if a tank is divided by a longitudinal partition into two equal parts, the loss of metacentric height due to the free-surface effect will be reduced to a quarter of that of the undivided tank. The deep tanks of cargo ships, and any large tanks which extend athwartships, are therefore divided by one or more longitudinal partitions.

Pressing up a tank or completely draining it will therefore make a ship more stable, but it must be emphasised here that any attempt to improve a ship's stability while at sea must be made with great caution. Pumping, flooding and draining operations take some time to carry out, and in the process the free-surface effects of the slack tanks may well cancel a margin of stability, particularly if it is small and the tanks are large. Many losses of ships have been attributed to attempts to improve their stability by pumping, flooding or draining while the ship was in a seaway. Modern warships are fitted with water-compensation arrangements whereby the fuel used is replaced by salt water. The salt water has a higher relative density than the fuel and, as fuel is consumed, the centre of gravity is lowered thus giving an improvement in stability. Furthermore, the tanks never become slack and so free-surface effects cannot arise.

A certain amount of ullage has to be left in fuel tanks when filling them, to allow for the expansion of the oil with any rise in its temperature, and in oil tankers this results in a considerable reduction of the metacentric height because of free-surface effects, even though the ships are designed with a high degree of compartmentation and each tank is usually divided into three parts by longitudinal bulkheads. In tankers the absence of double bottom tanks lowers the overall centre of gravity of the cargo compared to vessels with double bottom tanks; this has the beneficial effect of increasing the metacentric height. Consequently tankers usually tend to be stiff and, in certain circumstances, some free-surface effect may be considered an advantage in reducing this stiffness.

Another danger is that of free water on decks, particularly in cargo vessels with well decks enclosed by high bulwarks. Such ships are fitted with large *freeing ports* to allow any water shipped in a seaway to drain quickly over the sides. If this were not done the effect of the free-surface water, combined with the loss of metacentric height due to the added weight of water at so high a level, might seriously reduce the ship's margin of stability. This is particularly the case with oil-rig supply vessels which, with a large area of after deck and a relatively low freeboard, tend to be wet especially with a following sea. The added weight of the entrapped water not only raises the centre of gravity and reduces the stability, because of the height of this body of water and its free-surface effect, but also causes a considerable change of trim aft which reduces the righting lever because of the hull form of this type of vessel. A vessel may also ship water through the freeing ports and it is not unknown for the flaps of freeing ports to be secured for the sake of comfort, thus endangering a vessel should she ship a very heavy sea.

Free communication between compartments

If two compartments are in *free communication*, i.e. connected by a pipe, trunk or open valve, liquid will flow between them and they virtually become one compartment when considering free-surface effect. When a ship is heeled, free surface in a compartment in free communication with another will extend across the breadth of both compartments. When an off-centre compartment is holed and open to the sea, the initial weight of flooding is progressively increased as the ship heels towards the damage. It is important therefore that valves, etc. which give access between compartments or to the sea are closed when not in use, to prevent large movements of liquid as the ship heels.

Bulk cargoes

A bulk cargo, such as grain, can produce an effect similar to that of free-surface liquids, but modified by the inertia of the individual particles and the friction between them. For example, a heavy roll to one side may shift the cargo, but it will not necessarily shift back with a roll to the opposite side. Bulk cargo ships are usually built with upper wing tanks (see page 69) which reduce the area of the holds at the upper levels and thus constrain the volume of cargo which can shift. In addition, arrangements may be provided to ensure that the cargo can be pressed up to the tops of the holds between the deck-head beams. The regulations for the carriage of grain, prescribed by the *International Convention for the Safety of Life at Sea*, 1974, require that ships should have sufficient stability after a specified shift of cargo in all cargo spaces. If vessels have sufficient initial stability after the assumed shift of cargo then no further action is required, but if the resulting stability is insufficient then measures must be taken to restrain the shift of cargo. Such measures include the use of *shifting boards* to further subdivide the cargo, or a certain proportion of the cargo may be bagged and laid on platforms over the bulk cargo. The bagged cargo will have little tendency to shift and by its weight will tend to prevent the bulk grain shifting.

Ships built for carrying bulk cargoes are usually designed with a higher margin of stability than those designed for carrying general cargoes, for the following reason. The centre of gravity of a bulk cargo is unalterable and lies at the centre of its volume, and when the ship is fully loaded she will therefore have a high centre of gravity; with a general cargo the position of the ship's centre of gravity can be kept reasonably low by stowing the heavier kinds of cargo in the lower holds. It should be noted, however, that ships designed specifically for carrying ore, which has a high relative density, usually have deeper double bottoms (see page 69) to raise the centre of gravity so that the vessels are not unduly stiff.

HOISTING OUT A HEAVY WEIGHT

The angle to which a ship will be heeled when hoisting out a heavy weight by one of her derricks is given by the formula

$$\tan \theta = \frac{w \times d}{W \times GM}$$

where:

θ is the angle of heel;

w is the weight in tonnes to be hoisted out;

d is the horizontal distance in metres between the stowage position of the weight and its position when slung outboard from the derrick head;

W is the displacement of the ship in tonnes; and

GM is her metacentric height in metres.

When hoisting a heavy weight in or out by a derrick make sure that the ship has a sufficient margin of initial stability, because as soon as the weight is slung its effect will act through the head of the derrick, thus increasing considerably the height of the centre of gravity of the ship and reducing her metacentric height correspondingly. Moreover, when the weight is slung outboard, the farther the ship heels the greater will be the heeling moment of the weight, and measures must therefore be taken to ensure that the ship remains as upright as possible throughout the operation. Ships which may have to deal with heavy lifts are provided with special ballasting arrangements to ensure the necessary degree of stability and resistance to heeling when hoisting the weights in and out. Always work the derrick slowly, and as smoothly and steadily as possible.

LONGITUDINAL STABILITY AND TRIM

Longitudinal metacentre

The longitudinal metacentre M_L of a ship is found in a similar manner to that in which her transverse metacentre is found. In Fig. 1–7 the ship is assumed to have been tipped forward by some external force so that the longitudinal centre of buoyancy (LCB) has moved forward to B_1, thus producing a longitudinal righting moment, $W \times GZ$; where W is the displacement of the ship and GZ is the length of the longitudinal righting lever.

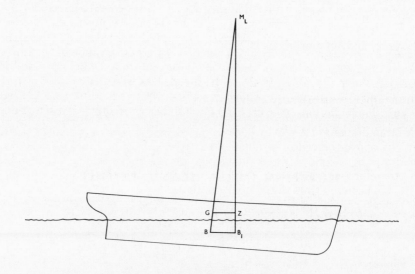

FIG. 1–7. Longitudinal metacentre

The height of the longitudinal metacentre above the centre of buoyancy of an average ship is given very roughly by the formula

$$BM_L = \frac{l^2}{12d}$$

where:

l is the length of the ship; and

d is her draught.

It will therefore be seen that the ship is far stiffer longitudinally than transversely.

Longitudinal centre of buoyancy and of gravity

When a ship is steady her LCB will lie at a position a little before or abaft amidships, and its position will change as the draught of the ship is changed. Under the same conditions a ship's longitudinal centre of gravity (LCG) lies directly above her LCB.

Longitudinal centre of flotation

When a ship is steady her *longitudinal centre of flotation* (LCF) lies at the centre of area of her waterplane, and it is about a transverse axis through this point that the ship trims. If a weight is added to a ship directly above her LCF she will sink bodily and on an even keel, but if the weight is added before or abaft her LCF the ship will trim by the head or by the stern, respectively, as well as sink bodily. Like the longitudinal centre of buoyancy (LCB), a ship's LCF lies at a position a little before or abaft amidships, depending on the hull form, and its position will change if the draught of the ship is changed. If, without changing her trim, the draught of a ship is increased, her LCB and her LCF will usually move aft; the latter more so than the former. Both will also change position with any change of trim because this will change the waterplane area. In a warship the centres of buoyancy and flotation are usually abaft amidships.

Tonnes-per-centimetre immersion

The *tonnes-per-centimetre immersion* (TPC) is the weight required to increase the mean draught of a ship by one centimetre, and it is assumed to be placed directly above the centre of flotation or disposed symmetrically before and abaft it. The weight required will change with a change of waterplane area, and therefore with a change of draught, and for any particular draught the TPC can be found from the following formula:

TPC = the increase in displacement due to a uniform
        increase in the draught of one centimetre

$$= \frac{1.025A}{100} \text{ tonnes,}$$

where A is the waterplane area in square metres.

Trim and change of trim

Trim is the inclination of a ship in a fore-and-aft sense, and it is usually measured by the difference between her draughts forward and aft. If the draughts are the same the ship has no trim and she is said to float on an *even keel*; if the draught forward is the greater she is said to trim *by the head*, and if the draught aft is the greater she is said to trim *by the stern*.

Change of trim is a change in the difference between the draught forward and the draught aft, caused either by shifting weights forward or aft, or by adding or removing weights before or abaft the ship's centre of flotation. If a weight is moved forward or aft there will be no change in the ship's displacement or mean draught, and she is then assumed to incline about the transverse axis through the centre of flotation corresponding to her displacement. If a weight is added or removed, however, her displacement and draught will be altered; and, provided the change of draught is not great, the ship can be assumed to trim about the transverse axis through the centre of flotation corresponding to her new displacement and draught.

When weights are shifted, added or removed, the positions of the centres of gravity, buoyancy and flotation will change in relation both to the ship and to one another; the waterplane area will also be changed. But, unless the changes of weight are very considerable, the relative changes of position of the various centres will be very little, and in practice they are disregarded unless very accurate estimations are required.

The total change of trim is divided between the ends of the ship in the ratio of their distances from the centre of flotation. For very approximate calculations the draughts forward and aft may be assumed to change by half this change of trim with the centre of flotation assumed to be amidships. If, for example, the total change of trim is 50 millimetres by the head, it is assumed that the draught forward will be increased by 25 millimetres and the draught aft will be decreased by 25 millimetres.

Moment to change trim one centimetre

The longitudinal moment to change trim one centimetre (MCTC) depends on the displacement of the ship, her length and her longitudinal metacentric height; it will therefore vary with her condition of loading and is expressed in tonne metres. The relationship between these factors is shown by the formula

$$\text{MCTC} = \frac{W \times GM_L}{100l}$$

where:

W is the displacement of the ship in tonnes;

GM_L is the longitudinal metacentric height in metres; and

l is the length of the ship in metres.

The change of trim caused by shifting a weight forward or aft can be found from the formula

$$\text{change of trim} = \frac{w \times d}{\text{MCTC}}$$

where:

w is the weight in tonnes; and

d is the distance in metres the weight has been shifted.

EXAMPLE

A ship with a displacement of 2000 tonnes has a length of 70 metres between perpendiculars and a longitudinal metacentric height of 75 metres. Thirty tonnes of fuel are pumped from one tank to another which lies 20 metres farther forward. Before pumping was begun her draughts were 3.2 metres forward and 3.5 metres aft. Given that her centre of flotation is amidships: find her draughts after pumping is completed.

$$\text{MCTC} = \frac{2000 \times 75}{100 \times 70} = 21.43 \text{ tonne metres.}$$

$$\text{Total change of trim} = \frac{30 \times 20}{21.43} = 28 \text{ centimetres}$$

$$= 0.28 \text{ metres by the head.}$$

Therefore her new draughts will be:

Forward 3.2 + 0.14 m = 3.34 metres;

Aft   3.5 − 0.14 m = 3.36 metres.

If a weight is added before or abaft the centre of flotation the change of trim is found by assuming that the weight was first added directly above the centre of flotation and then shifted forward or aft to its position.

EXAMPLE

The ship in the foregoing example in her original condition has a tonnes-per-centimetre immersion of 3.5. A weight of 31.5 tonnes is then placed in her No. 2 hold at a distance of 13.6 metres before her centre of flotation. Given that her centre of flotation is amidships: find her new draughts.

$$\text{Mean sinkage} = \frac{31.5}{3.5} = 9 \text{ cm} = 0.09 \text{ metres}$$

in which condition her draughts would be:

Forward 3.2 + 0.09 m = 3.29 metres;

Aft   3.5 + 0.09 m = 3.59 metres.

$$\text{Total change of trim} = \frac{31.5 \times 13.6}{21.43} = 20 \text{ centimetres}$$

$$= 0.2 \text{ metres by the head.}$$

Therefore her new draughts will be:

Forward 3.29 + 0.1 m = 3.39 metres;

Aft   3.59 − 0.1 m = 3.49 metres.

If a weight is removed from a position before or abaft the centre of flotation the change of trim is found by assuming that the weight was first shifted to the centre of flotation and then removed.

EXAMPLE

A ship is about to discharge cargo as follows: 150 and 100 tonnes at 55 and 25 metres respectively before the centre of flotation, and 70 and 80 tonnes at 15 and 50 metres respectively abaft it. Her draughts are 8.532 metres forward and 8.578 metres aft, in which condition her tonnes-per-centimetre immersion is 24 and her moment to change trim one centimetre is 205 tonne metres. The ship's length is 135 metres and the centre of flotation is 65 metres from the stern. Calculate the draughts after the cargo has been discharged.

The moment of each parcel of cargo is found by multiplying its weight by its distance from the centre of flotation. The forward moment is the sum of those before the centre of flotation and the after moment is the sum of those abaft it. The difference between the forward and after moments is the total moment which causes the ship to change trim.

$$\text{Forward moments } 150 \times 55 \ = \ 8\ 250$$
$$100 \times 25 \ = \ 2\ 500$$

$$10\ 750 \text{ tonne metres.}$$

$$\text{After moments} \quad 70 \times 15 \ = \ 1\ 050$$
$$80 \times 50 \ = \ 4\ 000$$

$$5\ 050 \text{ tonne metres.}$$

$$\text{Total moment} = 10\ 750 - 5\ 050 = 5\ 700 \text{ tonne metres.}$$

$$\text{Change of trim} = \frac{\text{Total moment}}{\text{MCTC}} = \frac{5\ 700}{205} = 27.8 \text{ cm}$$

$$= 0.278 \text{ metres.}$$

The change of trim will be by the stern because the forward moments are greater than the after moments. Furthermore the change of draught will be greater forward than aft, in the ratio of the distances of the bow and stern from the centre of flotation.

The draughts will therefore be:

$$\text{Forward } 8.532 - \left(0.278 \times \frac{70}{135}\right) = 8.532 - 0.144 = 8.388 \text{ metres;}$$

$$\text{Aft} \qquad 8.578 + \left(0.278 \times \frac{65}{135}\right) = 8.578 + 0.134 = 8.712 \text{ metres.}$$

The decrease in draught is then found by dividing the sum of the weights by the tonnes-per-centimetre immersion.

$$\text{Change of draught} = \frac{150 + 100 + 70 + 80}{24} = \frac{400}{24} = 16.6 \text{ cm}$$

$$= 0.166 \text{ metres.}$$

The ship's draughts after discharging the cargo will therefore be:

Forward 8.388 − 0.166 = 8.222 metres;

Aft   8.712 − 0.166 = 8.546 metres.

Change of draught when passing from salt water to fresh water

The draught of a ship passing from salt water to fresh water will increase, because salt water is denser than fresh water. The increase is usually small and can be calculated from the formula

$$S = \frac{W}{T}\left[\frac{d_s - d_f}{d_f}\right]$$

where:

S is the sinkage in centimetres;

W is the displacement in tonnes;

T is the tonnes-per-centimetre immersion in salt water;

d_s is the relative density of the salt water; and

d_f is the relative density of fresh water.

For pure fresh water d_f is 1.0 and for salt water d_s is generally taken as 1.025, so that the formula may be written as:

$$S = \frac{W}{T}\left[\frac{1.025 - 1.0}{1.0}\right] = \frac{W}{T} \times \frac{0.025}{1.0} = \frac{W}{40T} \text{ centimetres, or}$$

$$S = \frac{W}{4T} \text{ millimetres.}$$

The estimation of this change of draught is important for a seagoing ship when loading her cargo some miles up a river, because when loading to her marks it determines to what extent the ship can be immersed above her appropriate load line and still conform to *The Merchant Shipping (Load Line) Rules,* 1968 (as described in Chapter 3) when she reaches the sea.

In practice, cargo ships are assigned a *fresh-water allowance,* which represents the change in millimetres of the mean draught of the ship in her deep load condition when she passes from salt to fresh water or vice versa. At river mouths, however, the water is neither entirely fresh nor entirely salt; and, when estimating the change of mean draught, allowance must be made for the different relative densities of the river water, salt water and fresh water. This is done by finding, by means of a hydrometer, the relative density of the river water at the place where the ship is lying and then calculating the change of mean draught by means of the formula

$$C = \frac{A \times d}{D}$$

c

where:

C   is the change of mean draught when passing from the river to the sea;

A   is the fresh-water allowance assigned to the ship;

d   is the difference in relative density between sea water and the river water; and

D   is the difference in relative density between salt water and fresh water.

EXAMPLE

The relative density of the water at a certain river port is 1.008. To what extent can an outward-bound ship with a fresh-water allowance of 150 millimetres immerse her load line?

As fresh water is the datum its relative density is 1.0 and given that the relative density of the sea water off shore is 1.025, the change in draught will be:

$$\frac{150 \times (1.025 - 1.008)}{1.025 - 1.0} = \frac{150 \times 0.017}{0.025} = 102 \text{ millimetres.}$$

EFFECTS OF LOADING AND TRIM

When a vessel is being loaded she must be so trimmed that she will handle well, both in a seaway and in narrow waters, and will have sufficient buoyancy at bows and stern to ride the seas; and any concentrations of weight which may place undue stresses on her structure must be avoided.

Handling qualities

Any ship which is trimmed at all by the bows will probably be difficult to handle, both in a seaway and in narrow waters, because her pivoting point will then be shifted well forward and so will reduce the effect of her rudder. Most ships handle best when trimmed a little by the stern, and when flying light this trim is usually increased to ensure that the propeller and rudder are sufficiently immersed.

The trim of a cargo vessel with her machinery amidships is much easier to estimate and control than that of a vessel with her machinery aft, because in the former vessel the permanent weight is at her centre of flotation and will exert little moment before or abaft it, whereas in the latter vessel, which has her permanent weight right aft, the changing effect of its moment about the centre of flotation as cargo is loaded into the holds is difficult to estimate. In such a vessel the danger lies in loading her down to her marks and then finding her trimmed by the head, when nothing can be done to correct it except reloading the cargo, because by flooding the after ballast tanks the ship will be brought below her marks. To guard against this it is good practice to fill the forepeak tank or No.1 ballast tank before loading, thus enabling any trim by the head to be corrected by pumping out these tanks.

Pitching

Any concentration of weight forward in a ship will reduce the buoyancy forward and increase the inertia of the bows, which will result in the ship being sluggish by the head and failing to rise to the seas. She will be liable to ship heavy seas when steaming head to sea, which may not only strain her structure but also stave in her hatches. Any concentration of weight forward and aft will increase the hogging stress and may result in her breaking her back.

While a concentration of weights amidships will ensure that the bows and stern are buoyant it will increase the stresses of sagging, and the resultant lively pitching may also strain the ship's structure.

A rough compromise between these two extremes is to put 60 per cent of the total weight of cargo in the midship holds, and distribute the remainder between the forward and after holds. The distribution of the cargo by volume, and therefore to a certain extent by weight, is of course governed by the shape of the ship, because the taper at bows and stern makes the forward and after holds much smaller than the midship holds.

Shearing force and bending moment

It has been considered so far that the forces of weight and buoyancy acting on a vessel are concentrated respectively at the centre of gravity and at the centre of buoyancy. They are in fact spread along the length of the vessel and, furthermore, they are not uniformly spread. This irregular variation of forces gives rise to a *shearing force* and a *bending moment,* both of which vary along the length of the vessel. Shearing force is the tendency for consecutive sections of the ship to slide over each other and it is bending moment which exerts the force of compression or tension on the parts of the ship's structure.

The distribution of weight in a ship varies with the condition of her loading and with the expenditure of consumables during a voyage, and the forces of buoyancy at sea vary because of the form of the waves in the seaway. It is a ship design problem to ensure that the fabric of the hull can withstand the forces generated by the worst conditions of the sea and of loading. Warships and passenger vessels can more easily withstand these forces because of the degree of subdivision of the hull by transverse bulkheads and the limited variation of weights embarked. However, cargo ships have less subdivision and much greater variations of weight. Restriction of cargo weights and distribution may be necessary to limit to safe values the maximum still-water shearing forces and bending moments. Such limitations and any special related instructions are included in the ship's *Stability Information Booklet* (see page 26).

Summary

The trim of a ship should be arranged so that she floats on an even keel or is trimmed a little by the stern; she should never be trimmed by the head. The cargo should be distributed symmetrically before and abaft the ship's tipping centre, and the greater part of its weight should be amidships to ensure that her bows are buoyant and that she is stiff longitudinally, and to avoid exceptional shearing stresses at her main transverse bulkheads.

STABILITY PROBLEMS IN WARSHIPS AND CARGO SHIPS

Stability problems in a warship are very different from those arising in a cargo ship. A warship's officers are not greatly concerned with loading problems because the stowage of ammunition, fuel and stores is fixed in the design of the ship. The difference between deep-load and light-load conditions is relatively small; and the manner in which fuel tanks must be emptied, and any necessary ballasting or water compensation, is detailed by the designer. Provided the designer's instructions are followed, the embarkation, disembarkation or consumption of fuel, stores and ammunition will not greatly affect the ship's stability. However the ship's officers must be capable of dealing quickly and effectively with the threat to stability and buoyancy caused by an inrush of water if the ship is damaged below the waterline, for example by collision, grounding or a weapon.

The officers of a cargo ship, on the other hand, must see that the cargo is loaded so as to ensure that their ship will have a reasonable margin of stability throughout a voyage, that she will handle well, and that any loss of stability from the consumption of fuel and stores can be countered if necessary by ballasting. Their problem, though important, is not urgent, and they can usually devote time to it. Should their ship be damaged below the waterline there is little that can be done to regain any lost buoyancy or stability. Because of the large spaces into which a cargo ship is divided, and the lack of watertight subdivision, pumping or counter-flooding are of little avail. Probably the most that can be done is to strengthen the bulkheads by shoring them to prevent the flood water from spreading to other parts of the ship.

STABILITY DATA FOR A CARGO SHIP

A merchant ship's stability data are presented in a booklet particular to the ship. The method of presentation generally follows a standard form recommended in the *Stability Information Booklet*. Additional requirements for ships loading grain are recommended in *The IMO Grain Rules Guidance Booklet*. Both booklets are published by the Marine Division of the Department of Trade.

A ship's *Stability Information Booklet* provides the following data: general particulars and plans showing cargo spaces, storerooms and tanks; special notes regarding loading and stability of the ship; hydrostatic particulars; capacities and centres of gravity of cargo spaces, storerooms, crew and effects; capacities, centres of gravity and free-surface moments of all tanks; cross curves of stability; deadweight scale; loading conditions and statical stability (*GZ*) curves for specified sailing conditions; and flooding and damaged stability information. The more important of these items are described below.

Hydrostatic particulars

A ship's *hydrostatic particulars* were formerly presented as a series of curves on a combined graph called the *hydrostatic curves*. Nowadays it is the practice to present the *particulars* in tabular form, usually in increments of 0.2 metres, over the range from the lightest to the deepest draught. The information given in the particulars is listed and described below, and an example is shown at Fig. 1–8.

Displacement. This column gives the displacement, in tonnes, of the vessel in salt water for a given draught. A separate column for fresh-water displacement is usually given, taking the relative densities of salt water and fresh water as 1.025 and 1.0 respectively.

TPC (tonnes-per-centimetre immersion). This shows the weight, in tonnes, required to be added or removed to change the mean draught by one centimetre at any particular draught in salt water. This, too, may also be given for fresh water.

Draught	Displacement tonnes		TPC tonnes		MCTC tonne metres		KM(T) Above keel	VCB Above keel	LCB Fwd of aft perp	LCF Fwd of aft perp
metres	SW	FW	SW	FW	SW	FW	metres	metres	metres	metres
2.0	3 695	3 605	20.13	19.64	127.2	124.1	15.719	1.034	71.650	70.728
2.2	4 100	4 000	20.30	19.80	129.6	126.4	15.307	1.138	71.560	70.577
2.4	4 509	4 399	20.44	19.94	131.8	128.6	14.241	1.242	71.464	70.433
2.6	4 919	4 799	20.57	20.07	133.9	130.6	13.385	1.346	71.372	70.297
2.8	5 331	5 201	20.71	20.20	136.0	132.7	12.642	1.450	71.284	70.165
3.0	5 745	5 605	20.83	20.32	137.9	134.5	12.058	1.554	71.198	70.037
3.2	6 163	6 013	20.94	20.43	139.8	136.4	11.570	1.658	71.113	69.914
3.4	6 584	6 423	21.06	20.55	141.6	138.1	11.134	1.762	71.030	69.792
3.6	7 005	6 834	21.18	20.66	143.3	139.8	10.772	1.856	70.950	69.670
3.8	7 431	7 250	21.28	20.76	145.0	141.5	10.449	1.970	70.873	69.548
4.0	7 859	7 667	21.39	20.87	146.7	143.1	10.150	2.074	70.797	69.426
4.2	8 288	8 086	21.48	20.96	148.5	144.9	9.892	2.178	70.723	69.305
4.4	8 719	8 506	21.59	21.06	150.3	145.6	9.663	2.282	70.651	69.186
4.6	9 150	8 927	21.69	21.16	152.0	148.3	9.455	2.386	70.579	69.065
4.8	9 586	9 352	21.79	21.26	153.8	150.0	9.281	2.490	70.507	68.942
5.0	10 022	9 778	21.89	21.36	155.6	151.8	9.127	2.594	70.437	68.814
5.2	10 460	10 205	21.99	21.45	157.6	153.8	8.987	2.698	70.369	68.684
5.4	10 903	10 637	22.09	21.55	159.7	155.9	8.873	2.804	70.289	68.550
5.6	11 346	11 069	22.19	21.65	162.0	158.0	8.774	2.909	70.229	68.411
5.8	11 790	11 502	22.29	21.75	164.4	160.4	8.687	3.013	70.159	68.268
6.0	12 235	11 937	22.41	21.86	167.1	163.0	8.617	3.117	70.087	68.105
6.2	12 684	12 375	22.52	21.97	169.9	165.8	8.556	3.221	70.015	67.932
6.4	13 135	12 815	22.64	22.09	172.7	168.5	8.504	3.325	69.943	67.745
6.6	13 590	13 259	22.77	22.21	175.7	171.4	8.466	3.431	69.865	67.532
6.8	14 047	13 704	22.90	22.34	178.7	174.3	8.436	3.538	69.784	67.309
7.0	14 507	14 153	23.03	22.47	181.6	177.2	8.414	3.646	69.700	67.077
7.2	14 968	14 603	23.17	22.60	184.6	180.1	8.399	3.752	69.614	66.855
7.4	15 432	15 056	23.30	22.73	187.6	183.0	8.390	3.859	69.527	66.641
7.6	15 900	15 512	23.43	22.86	190.5	185.9	8.388	3.967	69.439	66.439
7.8	16 369	15 970	23.55	29.98	193.5	188.8	8.395	4.073	69.349	66.253
8.0	16 841	16 430	23.67	23.09	196.4	191.6	8.405	4.180	69.259	66.076
8.2	17 315	16 893	23.78	23.20	199.3	194.4	8.417	4.288	69.169	65.910
8.4	17 794	17 360	23.90	23.32	202.1	197.2	8.437	4.394	69.079	65.756
8.6	18 273	17 826	24.01	23.42	204.9	199.9	8.461	4.501	68.990	65.608
8.8	18 754	18 297	24.12	23.53	207.5	202.4	8.489	4.609	69.902	65.468
9.0	19 238	18 769	24.22	23.63	210.1	205.0	8.522	4.715	68.814	65.336
9.2	19 723	19 242	24.32	23.73	212.6	207.4	8.557	4.822	68.727	65.209
9.4	20 209	19 716	24.43	23.83	215.1	209.9	8.595	4.930	68.641	65.089
9.6	20 700	20 195	24.52	23.92	217.5	212.2	8.636	5.038	68.556	64.976
9.8	21 191	20 674	24.61	24.01	219.9	214.5	8.679	5.145	68.472	64.869
10.0	21 683	21 154	24.70	24.10	222.2	216.8	8.725	5.251	68.368	64.769

Positions of draught marks on ship

Aft   Up to 7.4 metres – 5.5 metres forward of aft perpendicular
        Above 7.4 metres – on aft perpendicular

Forward Up to 10.0 metres – 0.15 metres aft of line of stem

NOTE. The hydrostatic particulars given above have been developed with the vessel floating on waterlines which are level, and on a length of 134.112 metres between perpendiculars.

FIG. 1–8. Example of the hydrostatic particulars for a general cargo ship

MCTC (moment to change trim one centimetre). This is the longitudinal moment in tonne metres required to change the vessel's trim by one centimetre at any particular draught in salt water. This information is also sometimes given for fresh water.

KM(T) (transverse metacentre). The height, in metres, of the transverse metacentre above the keel is shown for any particular draught.

VCB (vertical centre of buoyancy). This column shows the height, in metres, of the centre of buoyancy above the keel for a particular draught.

LCB (longitudinal centre of buoyancy). This column shows the longitudinal distance, in metres, of the centre of buoyancy, at any particular draught, from a specified position in the ship (usually the after perpendicular).

LCF (longitudinal centre of flotation). This column shows the longitudinal distance, in metres, of the centre of area of the waterplane, at any particular draught, from a specified position in the ship (usually the after perpendicular).

KM(L) (longitudinal metacentre). The height, in metres, of the longitudinal metacentre above the keel may be shown for any particular draught.

Cross curves of stability

A typical graph of *cross curves of stability* (*KN* curves) is illustrated at Fig. 1–3. The curves, each of which represents a certain angle of heel, are plotted on a horizontal axis of displacement and a vertical axis of righting lever measured from the keel (*KN* on the inset to Fig. 1–3). The graph gives the length of the righting lever (*KN*), in metres, for any displacement at various angles of heel. From this graph and with knowledge of the position of the centre of gravity for a certain condition of loading, the statical stability, or *GZ*, curve can be drawn for that condition.

Deadweight scale

The deadweight scale is a combination of linear scales which shows the relationship between draught, freeboard, displacement, deadweight, tonnes-per-centimetre immersion and moment to change trim one centimetre for both salt water and fresh water. The data specifying the positions of the load line disc, load lines and tonnage mark (if applicable) are also shown on the scale. A typical deadweight scale is shown at Fig. 1–9.

Curves of statical stability

Curves of statical stability (*GZ* curves) are drawn on a horizontal axis of degrees of heel from zero to beyond the range of stability. The vertical axis represents the length in metres of the righting lever (*GZ*). The curve is drawn for a particular displacement for which the height of the centre of gravity (*KG*) has been calculated. Thus curves can be drawn for any particular condition of loading and these will show at a glance the degree of stability of the ship throughout the range of heel. Two typical examples of curves of statical stability together with the details of the condition of the ship are illustrated in Figs. 1–10 and 1–11.

These curves are drawn by the shipbuilder for various specified sailing conditions: *light ship,* i.e. with no water, fuel, stores or cargo on board;

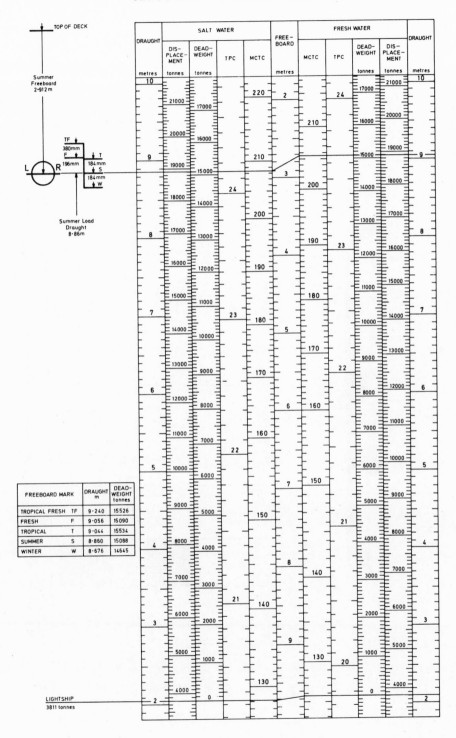

FIG. 1–9. Typical deadweight scale

CONDITION No 2   BALLAST DEPARTURE

Compartment	Colour key	Capacity m³	Stowage factor m³/tonne	Weight tonnes	LCG from Aft Peak metres	Horizontal moment from Aft Peak tonne metres	VCG above base metres	Vertical moment above base tonne metres	Free surface corr'n
CONSUMABLES:									
Fuel oil				996		67 722		1 164	3361
Diesel oil				122		4 400		220	300
Lub oil				61		2 241		533	18
Fresh water				489		11 260		1 330	497
Stores, spares, crew				152		11 170		1 955	
TOTAL CONSUMABLES				1820		96 793		5 202	4176
WATER BALLAST IN:									
No 1 DB Tank across			0.9756	294	112.703	33 135	0.622	183	
No 2 DB Tank P & S			"	416	89.154	37 088	0.631	262	
Fore peak			"	461	129.055	59 494	8.836	4 073	
Aft peak			"	111	3.082	342	7.849	871	
No 3 Hold			"	1780	68.821	122 501	4.926	8 768	
TOTAL WATER BALLAST				3062		252 560		14 157	

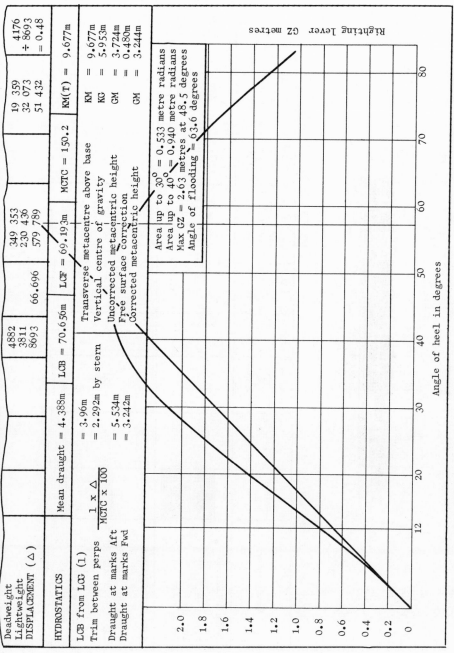

Deadweight			4882		349 353		19 359	4176
Lightweight			3811		230 436		32 073	÷ 8693
DISPLACEMENT (△)			8693	66.696	579 789		51 432	= 0.48

| HYDROSTATICS | Mean draught = 4.388m | LCB = 70.656m | LCF = 69.193m | MCTC = 150.2 | KM(T) = 9.677m |

LCB from LCG (1)   = 3.96m

Trim between perps $\dfrac{1 \times △}{MCTC \times 100}$ = 2.292m by stern

Draught at marks Aft   = 5.534m
Draught at marks Fwd   = 3.242m

Transverse metacentre above base   KM = 9.677m
Vertical centre of gravity   KG = 5.953m
Uncorrected metacentric height   GM = 3.724m
Free surface correction   = 0.480m
Corrected metacentric height   GM = 3.244m

Area up to 30° = 0.533 metre radians
Area up to 40° = 0.940 metre radians
Max GZ = 2.63 metres at 48.5 degrees
Angle of flooding = 63.6 degrees

Righting lever GZ metres

Angle of heel in degrees

FIG. 1–10. Typical condition sheet and the curve of statical stability for a cargo ship in the condition of *ballast departure*

CONDITION No 5   LOADED ARRIVAL

HOMOGENEOUS CARGO AT 1.5858 m³/tonne

Compartment	Colour key	Capacity m³	Stowage factor m³/tonne	Weight tonnes	LCG from Aft Peak metres	Horizontal moment from Aft Peak tonne metres	VCG above base metres	Vertical moment above base tonne metres	Free surface corr'n
CONSUMABLES:									
Fuel oil				83		3 221		608	94
Diesel oil				18		695		135	2
Lub oil				31		1 111		209	18
Fresh water				246		6 189		599	497
Stores, spares, crew				114		8 680		1 449	
TOTAL CONSUMABLES				492		19 896		3 000	611
CARGO AS DEPARTURE		21 424.3	1.5858	13 510		997 011		98 164	
WATER BALLAST IN AFT PEAK			0.9756	111	3.082	342	7.849	871	331

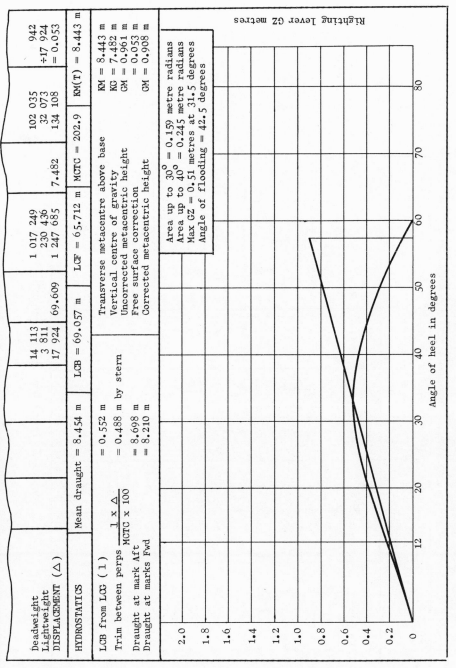

					102 035	942
Deadweight					32 073	÷17 924
Lightweight					134 108	= 0.053
DISPLACEMENT (△)	14 113					
	3 811					
	17 924	69.609	7.482	1 017 249		
				230 436		
				1 247 685		

HYDROSTATICS	Mean draught = 8.454 m	LCB = 69.057 m	LCF = 65.712 m	MCTC = 202.9	KM(T) = 8.443 m

LCB from LCG (1)   = 0.552 m

Trim between perps $\dfrac{1 \times \triangle}{MCTC \times 100}$ = 0.488 m by stern

Draught at mark Aft   = 8.698 m

Draught at marks Fwd   = 8.210 m

Transverse metacentre above base   KM = 8.443 m

Vertical centre of gravity   KG = 7.482 m

Uncorrected metacentric height   GM = 0.961 m

Free surface correction   = 0.053 m

Corrected metacentric height   GM = 0.908 m

Area up to 30° = 0.159 metre radians

Area up to 40° = 0.245 metre radians

Max GZ = 0.51 metres at 31.5 degrees

Angle of flooding = 42.5 degrees

Righting lever GZ metres

Angle of heel in degrees

FIG. 1–11. Typical condition sheet and the curve of statical stability for a cargo ship in the condition of *loaded arrival*

EFFECT ON TRIM DUE TO FILLING TANKS WHEN SAILING AT A MEAN DRAUGHT OF 6.5532 metres IN SALT WATER

Compartment	Added weight tonnes	Change of trim mm	Sinkage mm	Change of draught at marks mm Aft	Forward
No 1 DB Tank across	294.000	757 F	129	− 234	+ 501
No 2 DB Tank Centre	231.848	283 F	102	− 41	+ 242
No 2 DB Tank P	208.000	257 F	92	− 31	+ 218
No 2 DB Tank S	208.000	257 F	92	− 31	+ 218
No 3 DB Tank Centre	271.272	164 A	119	+ 198	+ 39
No 3 DB Tank P	214.376	125 A	94	+ 154	+ 33
No 3 DB Tank S	214.376	125 A	94	+ 154	+ 33
No 4 DB Tank P	56.388	103 A	25	+ 74	− 26
No 4 DB Tank S	49.784	91 A	22	+ 66	− 23
No 5 DB Tank P	17.780	39 A	8	+ 26	− 11
No 5 DB Tank S	17.780	39 A	8	+ 26	− 11
Fore Peak	461.000	1621 F	203	− 573	+ 998
Aft Peak	111.000	408 A	49	+ 244	− 152
No 3 Hold	1780.000	126 F	783	+ 722	+ 845
Tunnel Side Tank P	212.120	564 A	93	+ 354	− 183
Tunnel Side Tank S	186.070	492 A	82	+ 310	− 160
Fresh Water Tank Inner S	25.400	52 A	11	+ 36	− 14
Fresh Water Tank Outer S	29.718	60 A	13	+ 42	− 17
DB Lub Oil Drain	10.160	20 A	5	+ 14	− 5
DB Oily Bilge S	2.540	5 A	1	+ 3	− 1
DB Fuel Oil Drain S	3.810	6 A	2	+ 5	− 2
DB Piston Drain	4.166	7 A	2	+ 5	− 2
Dirty HO Tank S	31.699	55 A	14	+ 40	− 13

Compartment	Added weight tonnes	Change of trim mm	Sinkage mm	Change of draught at marks mm Aft	Forward
Clean HO Tank P	26.812	43 A	12	+ 33	− 9
Clean HO Tank S	23.386	42 A	12	+ 32	− 9
Clean DO Tank P	9.408	17 A	4	+ 12	− 4
Dirty DO Tank P	9.317	15 A	4	+ 11	− 3
Alternator LO Tank P	10.516	20 A	5	+ 14	− 5
Reserve LO Tank P	5.669	10 A	3	+ 8	− 3
Clean LO Tank P	9.530	17 A	4	+ 12	− 4
Renovating LO Tank P	9.906	16 A	4	+ 12	− 4
Cylinder Oil Tank P	16.388	26 A	7	+ 20	− 6

EFFECT ON TRIM DUE TO PLACING 100 tonnes AT THE CENTRE OF EACH CASE

Compartment	Added weight tonnes	Change of trim mm	Sinkage mm	Change of draught at marks mm Aft	Forward
No 1 Upper Deck Hatch	100.000	263 F	44	− 83	+ 173
No 2 Upper Deck Hatch	100.000	152 F	44	− 29	+ 118
No 3 Upper Deck Hatch	100.000	38 F	44	+ 26	+ 65
No 4 Upper Deck Hatch	100.000	86 A	44	+ 85	− 2
No 5 Upper Deck Hatch	100.000	299 A	44	+ 187	− 102

$$\text{Change of draught} = \text{Bodily sinkage} \;{}^{+}_{-}\; \frac{\text{Trim X LCF from Fwd or Aft end at present draught}}{\text{Length between perpendiculars}}$$

$$\text{Bodily sinkage} = \frac{\text{Weight}}{\text{TPC}}$$

$$\text{Change of trim} = \frac{\text{Weight X LCG of compartment from LCF}}{\text{MCTC}}$$

FIG. 1–12. Typical trim table for a cargo ship in the half-laden condition

ballast departure, i.e. with fuel, stores, fresh and feed water on board, and with ballast tanks full, but with no cargo; *ballast arrival,* i.e. similar to ballast departure but with fuel, water and stores reduced to approximately 10 per cent of their departure quantities; *loaded departure,* i.e. fully loaded with fuel, water and stores, and with all holds fully loaded with homogeneous cargo at a specified average stowage factor; *loaded arrival,* i.e. similar to loaded departure but with the fuel, fresh water and stores reduced to approximately 10 per cent of their departure quantities. If a vessel is likely to engage in any other particular trade, e.g. carriage of timber or iron ore, departure and arrival curves drawn for these types of cargo may also be included.

Trim tables

The effects on the trim and draught of the ship, of loading and discharging cargo, and of filling and emptying tanks, can be estimated from trim tables.

It is usual for trim tables to be drawn up by the designer for three conditions of loading of the ship, i.e. light ship, half-laden and fully-laden. An example, for the half-laden condition of a ship, is shown at Fig. 1–12.

The trim tables show the capacity of each tank, in tonnes of the commodity for which it is designed, and its effect on the mean draught, trim, and draught forward and aft. The tables also show the same effects for placing a weight of 100 tonnes at the centre of each cargo hatchway and thus the overall effect of loading or discharging cargo from each hold can be estimated.

STABILITY DATA FOR A WARSHIP

Apart from the possible results of action damage, the variations in the loading of a warship are very small in comparison with those of a cargo vessel, and the stability data supplied to a warship therefore differ in form from those provided for a cargo vessel and are not nearly so detailed.

In wartime a warship must always be maintained in the highest possible condition of stability to ensure that she has the best chance of surviving even when seriously damaged below water. To fulfil this requirement it is usually necessary in destroyers and smaller vessels, where the weight of fuel and ammunition forms a greater proportion of the ship's displacement than in larger vessels, to arrange for the consumption of the fuel in a particular manner and also to water-compensate certain tanks as the fuel is used. These instructions are included in the stability data.

It may occasionally be necessary in special circumstances to use a warship for carrying cargo, but this should be done with discretion and only after a careful review of all the circumstances, because, apart from considerations of space, the carrying of cargo will probably reduce her stability to an extent which will leave an insufficient margin to enable the ship to withstand damage.

All stability data provided for a warship will be found in the *Ship Equipment File* and there is an additional copy in the *NBCD Class Book* peculiar to the ship. Further information and worked examples on stability may be found in BR 2170, *Ship NBCD Manual.*

Hydrostatic particulars

The following hydrostatic particulars for a warship, over a suitable range of mean draught, are presented in tabular form: tonnes-per-centimetre immersion, displacement, height of transverse centre of buoyancy above the keel (*KB*), height of transverse metacentre above the keel (*KM*), position of the longitudinal centre of flotation, position of the longitudinal centre of buoyancy, moment to change trim one centimetre, and the approximate alteration of displacement for one metre change of trim.

An example of hydrostatic particulars is shown at Fig. 1–13. The table is self-explanatory with the possible exceptions of 'abaft 11 ord' and 'Approximate alteration of displacement for 1 metre change of trim'. The term '11 ord' is the ship designer's convenient method of defining the centre of length between perpendiculars; he uses 21 ordinates in his calculations, which makes '11 ord' the centre. The alteration of displacement for one metre change of trim is the change in displacement of the ship if her trim differs from the designed trim at the same mean draught. If there is excessive trim, caused perhaps by heavy damage at one end, the imposed change of displacement must be calculated. For this purpose, first find the displacement at normal trim for the new mean draught and then the change in displacement at the new mean draught. Multiply the change in displacement by the number of metres by which the actual trim differs from the designed trim. This gives the approximate total change of displacement, which must be added to the displacement if the new trim is by the stern and subtracted if it is by the bow.

Fuel tank capacities

A tabular statement is provided which gives the positions of all tanks and the weights of fuel they contain.

Stability statement

A warship's *stability statement* is a form of certificate stating that the stability of the ship is satisfactory, and is based on information determined at an inclining experiment. The statement is normally made out for three particular conditions of loading: the *deep condition,* the *light* or *light-seagoing condition* and the *light-harbour condition.*

For each of these conditions the statement gives the following particulars: mean draught, metacentric height, angle of maximum righting lever and any necessary instructions on liquid limitations.

Curves of statical stability (*GZ* curves)

For each of the conditions referred to in a warship's stability statement, *GZ*, or righting lever, curves are provided.

Examples of damage and flooding

For large warships examples of damage and its control are provided, and for smaller ships examples of flooding and its effect are given.

Pumping and flooding board

Large warships are supplied with a *pumping and flooding board* (Fig. 1–14), which consists of a series of deck plans up to the level of the deep waterline.

HYDROSTATIC PARTICULARS

Mean Draught	Tonnes-per-centimetre immersion	Displacement	KB	KM	LCF abaft 11 ord	LCB abaft 11 ord	Moment to Change Trim 1 centimetre	Approximate alteration of displacement for 1 metre Change of Trim
metres	tonnes	tonnes	metres	metres	metres	metres	tonne metres	tonnes
3.0	8.86	1702	1.809	6.082	4.956	1.830	46.0	36.1
3.2	9.36	1880	1.922	5.986	6.375	2.196	52.7	52.1
3.4	9.62	2068	2.044	5.898	6.786	2.602	55.7	57.0
3.6	9.83	2266	2.158	5.816	7.021	2.980	58.0	60.6
3.8	10.00	2464	2.275	5.734	7.198	3.306	59.7	63.0
4.0	10.15	2667	2.394	5.681	7.320	3.599	61.1	65.0
4.2	10.25	2865	2.509	5.646	7.412	3.849	62.3	66.6
4.4	10.34	3061	2.632	5.603	7.473	4.078	63.3	67.7
4.6	10.42	3271	2.745	5.570	7.512	4.276	64.3	68.7
4.8	10.50	3480	2.864	5.547	7.533	4.468	65.0	69.4
5.0	10.57	3696	2.983	5.532	7.536	4.630	65.8	69.8
5.2	10.60	3912	3.090	5.522	7.533	4.788	66.5	70.1
5.4	10.65	4140	3.215	5.517	7.515	4.926	67.2	70.2

FIG. 1–13. Typical table of hydrostatic particulars for a warship

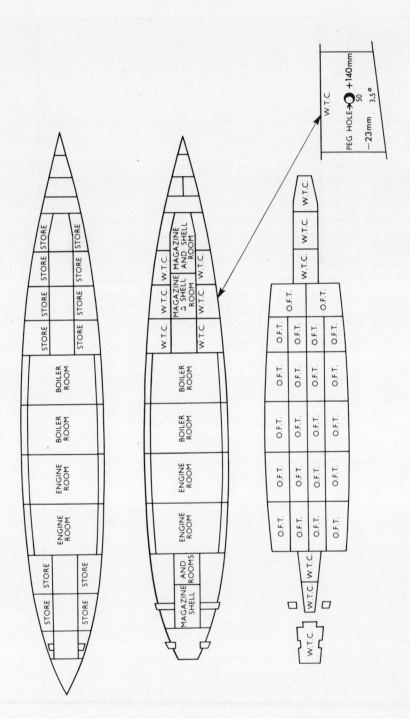

FIG. 1–14. Typical flooding board for a large warship

On it are shown the watertight subdivision of the ship, the capacity of each compartment in tonnes of salt water, and its effect, when flooded, on the ship's heel and trim in the light or light-seagoing condition. Symbols indicate the method of pumping out each compartment. Colour washes are used to indicate the normal contents of a compartment (e.g. stores, water, oil, etc.) and the methods by which compartments can be flooded. Coloured pegs are used to indicate controlled or uncontrolled flooding, water or oil present before damage, and counterflooding.

Once it is known which compartments are flooded, the figures for each compartment can be added up, to give the total *flooding-board heel and trim*. If the ship is stable, she can be restored approximately to the upright by transferring liquids within her, by counterflooding, or by both. Some ships are fitted with rapid-flooding compartments with direct access to the sea for deliberately flooding compartments on the high side. This decreases reserve of buoyancy and increases draught, but is relatively quick. Transfer of liquids from the low to the high side is slow, but has double the effect of counterflooding and does not reduce reserve buoyancy.

Fig. 1–15 shows part of a flooding board. Suppose that tanks *P3* and *P5* are flooded, producing a flooding-board heel of 2.4 + 3.8 degrees, a total of 6.2 degrees. The two methods *could* be used as follows.

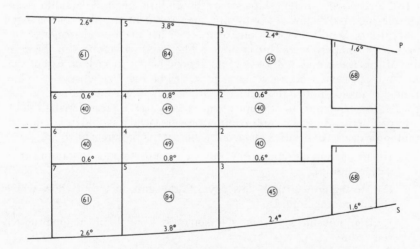

FIG. 1–15. Example of the use of a flooding board

Transferring liquids. The ship can be restored to the upright by transferring liquid from tanks *P1* and *P7* (total capacity 129 tonnes) to the empty tanks *S2*, *S4* and *S6* (total capacity 129 tonnes), thereby providing heel to starboard of 1.6, 2.6, 0.6, 0.8 and 0.6 degrees, a total flooding-board heel of 6.2 degrees.

Counterflooding. The ship can be restored to the upright by filling the empty tanks *S3* and *S5,* thereby providing starboard heel of 2.4 degrees and 3.8 degrees, a total of 6.2 degrees.

In practice, counterflooding would not be used against a heel of only 6.2 degrees. Also, when restoring heel it is possible to recover some trim by using tanks diagonally opposed to the flooding.

D

FLOODING AND COUNTERMEASURES

When practicable the list of a damaged ship should be corrected by transferring liquid from one compartment to another, because this does not entail any loss of the ship's reserve of buoyancy. This method is, however, rather slow and involves additional free-surface effects during the transfer; in warships, therefore, where a quick return to the upright may be essential, counterflooding may be preferable.

Counterflooding is a fast method of curing a list, and in large warships suitable wing compartments are fitted with flooding valves so that they can be filled direct from the sea. If a ship is badly damaged and listing 10 degrees or more, counterflooding should be carried out immediately.

But it should be realised that counterflooding has its disadvantages. It reduces the reserve of buoyancy and sinks the ship lower in the water, and so decreases her speed and manoeuvrability. It should only be used as necessary to get the ship back to a manageable state as quickly as possible, which generally means reducing the list to about 6 degrees, at which angle the ship can be manoeuvred and fought. Thereafter measures such as transferring liquids, repairing damage and pumping out compartments will further reduce the list, and may even allow some reserve of buoyancy to be regained by pumping out compartments which have been counterflooded.

In destroyers and smaller ships, where there is little longitudinal subdivision, damage incurred below the waterline may result in the ship taking large quantities of flood water into one or more of her main compartments: her machinery compartments, for example. The free-surface effect of the large area of this water may reduce the metacentric height to such an extent that the ship will have a negative metacentric height and float unstably, lolling from side to side under the influence of the waves or wind. In such a case it would be dangerous to attempt to correct any heel by transferring liquids or by counterflooding. The only countermeasures which should be attempted, until some degree of positive metacentric height has been regained, are:

1. Isolate, subdivide and pump out any compartments containing free-surface liquids.

2. Fill, to the crown, tanks low down in the ship, including those which already contain liquids.

3. Jettison movable topweight symmetrically from about the longitudinal centre-line.

To summarise, transference of liquids should be regarded generally as being the best method of correcting a list. When it is essential that the damaged ship should be returned to the upright as quickly as possible, counterflooding is preferable, but it should be done as soon as possible after the ship has listed, and its use should be restricted to the minimum necessary to bring the ship to a safe or manageable state. Later, when other measures are in hand, it should be reduced as much as possible. In small ships it is imperative to distinguish between the conditions of *list* and *loll,* because the remedies for each are so different; if the ship is in a state of loll it must be corrected before any measures are taken to counter list. The two conditions are described in detail in Volume II.

STABILITY AND TRIM OF SUBMARINES

This section is not intended as a treatise on the stability and trim of submarines, but merely to indicate the great differences between the problems of stability of these vessels and those of surface ships.

Transverse stability

The transverse stability of a submarine floating on the surface can be estimated in a similar manner to that of a surface ship. From Fig. 1–16 it can be seen

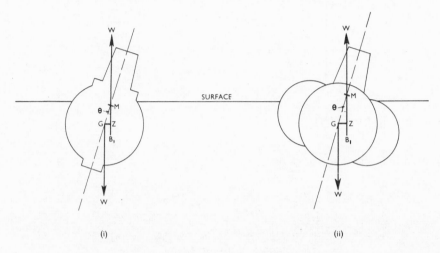

(i)   (ii)

FIG. 1–16. Transverse stability of a surfaced submarine

that, as the vessel heels, her centre of buoyancy B moves to B_1 on the low side, producing a righting moment, $W \times GZ$, where $GZ = GM \sin \theta$ for small angles of heel. At larger angles of heel the saddle-tank type of submarine (Fig. 1–16(ii)) is likely to have better stability than the single-hull type (Fig. 1–16(i)) because of the broader waterplane area of the former.

When a submarine is completely submerged (Fig. 1–17) she has no waterplane and therefore no waterplane inertia, and her metacentre M will then coincide with her centre of buoyancy B. Moreover, B will become a fixed point irrespective of any angle of inclination, because the underwater form of the vessel will not change as she heels. In order, therefore, to provide the necessary righting moment when the submarine is heeled, her centre of gravity G must be below her centre of buoyancy B, as shown in Fig. 1–17(i) and (ii), thus providing the righting lever GZ, which will be equal to BG $\sin \theta$. The distance BG can be taken as constant, if any small movement of G due to free-surface liquids is disregarded, and the GZ curve will therefore become a curve of sines as shown in Fig. 1–17(iii). From this curve it will be seen that the angle of maximum GZ is 90 degrees, that at this angle $GZ = BG$, and that the range of stability is 180 degrees.

The length of BG gives a measure of the stability of a submerged submarine, and corresponds to the metacentric height GM of a surface ship. The BG of a submerged submarine is usually less than her GM when on the surface, except in single-hulled vessels, where the reverse is usually the case.

SURFACE

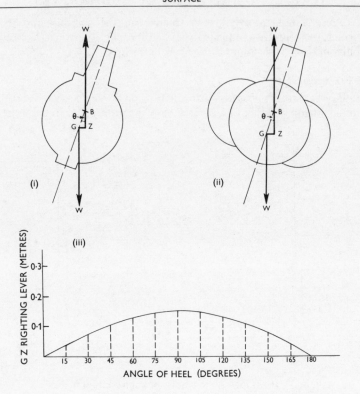

FIG. 1–17. Transverse stability of a submerged submarine

Longitudinal stability and trim

The longitudinal stability of a submarine when on the surface can be estimated, in the same way as that of a surface vessel, from the formula:

$$\text{MCTC} = \frac{W \times GM_L}{100l}$$

as described on page 20.

When the submarine is submerged, however, her longitudinal metacentre M_L will, like her transverse metacentre, coincide with her centre of buoyancy, and her longitudinal metacentric height GM_L will then be equal to BG (see Fig. 1–18). Since the length of BG is usually only about 150 millimetres her longitudinal righting moment is very small indeed, and consequently she is very tender longitudinally when submerged. This tenderness makes it necessary to limit and to control accurately the movement of any weights along the vessel; it is, however, an advantage because it enables her trim to be controlled by fairly small hydroplanes and ensures that she can change depth rapidly, which would not be practicable if she had the longitudinal stiffness of a surface ship.

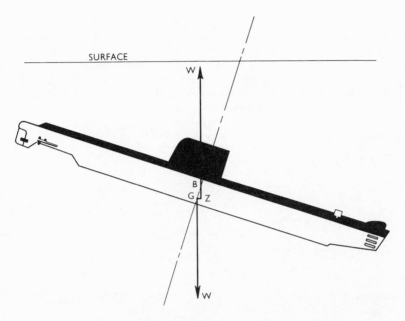

FIG. 1–18. Longitudinal stability of a submerged submarine

GROUNDING

A ship may ground accidentally. On the other hand, she may be beached deliberately, possibly to prevent total loss (see page 179). The problems of salvaging stranded ships are dealt with in Chapter 7. The remarks that follow relate to the stability of a grounded ship; they indicate the dangers involved in dealing with this aspect of grounding, and some possible precautions.

A grounded ship is in a very similar condition to a ship being docked. She is no longer a floating body; the upward pressure of the ground on the ship's bottom has exactly the same effect as if an equal weight were removed at that level, i.e. the centre of gravity rises and GM is less. The greater the pressure on the bottom, the greater the rise of G. The greater the fall of tide, the greater the pressure; and it reaches a maximum just before the ship grounds along her length.

In dry docking, a stage is always reached when this virtual rise of G is equal to GM — when metacentric height becomes nil. Before this stage is reached the ship is prevented from heeling by either shores or side-docking keels. Whether a grounded ship becomes unstable or not depends on her stability at the time of grounding and on how far the water falls after grounding. If a ship grounds near low water, stability is not likely to be endangered by grounding alone. Even if grounding is near high water, if the ground is fairly even and soft most ships will settle into a bed of their own making and not fall over. The danger comes when a ship grounds on a hard and uneven bottom and the tide has some distance to fall. The ship may then become unstable as the tide falls and lie over on her side, with resultant damage and further flooding as the tide rises, causing complete loss of the ship.

The principal maxim to remember is that the normal seamanlike precaution of filling bottom compartments to weigh down the ship and minimise working and pounding on the bottom is equally effective in giving a greater measure of stability as the tide falls. This, together with the emptying of high tanks and the removal of any other weight above the centre of gravity, should materially help to prevent a stranding from becoming a much more costly salvage job or perhaps a total loss.

CHAPTER 2

Pumping and Ventilating Systems in a Warship

The maintenance of pumping and ventilating systems and water services of a warship is normally the responsibility of the Marine Engineering department, but the seaman should have a good knowledge of these systems and how they can best be used for the various purposes for which they are designed. In Volume I, Chapter 3, there is a brief outline of the functions of these systems, and in the present chapter the more important details are described. In particular, the seaman should be familiar with his ship's pumping and flooding systems in order to understand the control of her stability. Information on stability is given in the previous chapter and also in Volume II. The use of pumps and water services such as the ship's *salt-water main* for firefighting is described in the chapters on this subject in Volumes I and II. Further information on all these subjects is given in BR 2170, *Ship NBCD Manual.*

PUMPING ARRANGEMENTS

Pumping out compartments

To avoid penetrating the main transverse bulkheads below the waterline, most warships are so designed that there are independent pumping arrangements for the main transverse watertight subdivisions. In modern warships the pumping-out arrangements differ between the main machinery compartments and the remainder of the ship as described below.

Main machinery spaces. Fixed salvage eductors powered from the salt-water main are provided for pumping out these compartments. At least two eductors are fitted in each machinery space, providing a pumping capacity of 100–200 tonnes per hour.

All other compartments. Portable pumps and portable eductors are provided for pumping out all compartments other than the main machinery spaces. The eductors are powered from the salt-water main and the pumps may be either diesel driven or electrically driven. Some of the electrically driven pumps are submersible. Compartments which are normally closed in action, and into which it is not practicable to introduce suction hoses or submersible pumps, are fitted with standpipes which rise to the lowest accessible deck above.

Salt-water services

The salt-water services in a ship are supplied from a main service pipe which is called the *salt-water main* (see Volume I, Chapter 5). In small ships this is a single-line pipe system running the full length of the ship, but in larger ships it takes the form of a ring main with suitable cross-connections and single-line extensions to the ends of the ship. The salt-water main is supplied through *rising mains* from fixed pumps described later in this chapter.

Numerous branches are taken from the salt-water main, each having an isolating valve close to the main, for supplying hydrants for fire and wash-deck purposes, domestic services, pre-wetting, magazine spraying and other services.

Under action conditions the system can be isolated into sections by suitably placed valves, each section being supplied by its own pump. This limits flooding or loss of pressure from a damaged section of the main and enables hoses to be rigged from branch connections off the rising mains to connections on the undamaged part of the salt-water main.

When the pumps are working on the salt-water main in normal conditions, it is usual for some water to be continually drawn off for sanitary and other services. In action, however, when the salt-water main is isolated into sections, there may be no draw-off and this may cause the pumps to overheat. To obviate this, arrangements to enable each pump to discharge overboard are fitted.

The salt-water main is intended to work at a pressure of 7 bar but damage may cause a considerable drop in pressure and so most appliances for use on the main are designed to work at pressures down to about 3 bar. The normal pressure of the main may be excessive for some subsidiary services, such as sanitary systems; reducing valves are therefore fitted in the branch connections from the main to these services.

In aircraft carriers an additional salt-water main, running just below the flight deck, is fitted to supply the flight-deck firefighting arrangements. In ships of the *Invincible* Class the flight-deck main is connected by rising mains to the ship's salt-water main; independent pumps are not fitted and both mains are supplied by the ship's fire pumps.

Function of pumps

The principal functions of the pumps and eductors (see page 48) in the pumping, flooding and draining systems are:

1. To supply water for domestic services such as sanitary arrangements, bathrooms and washing decks.
2. To supply water for the cooling of weapon, electrical, air-conditioning and other equipment.
3. Routine pumping out of compartments in which water collects during normal service, such as machinery spaces, bilges, gland spaces and sonar compartments.
4. Routine transfer of water for de-ballasting, etc.
5. To supply water under pressure for firefighting, spraying of magazines and hangars, and for pre-wetting of weatherdeck structure to reduce residual contamination after NBC attack.
6. To pump out flooded compartments after action or other damage (i.e. for *salvage duties*).
7. To flood certain compartments to correct heel and trim.

In modern ships, built-in pumping systems are provided for all these functions except salvage purposes. Experience has shown that built-in salvage systems are not only vulnerable, but are unreliable when a ship has been damaged. For salvage purposes, modern ships are provided with portable pumps driven by either electric motors or diesel engines.

The total capacity of the salvage pumps could not cope with the influx of water from even moderate damage. Thus the main factors in keeping a damaged warship afloat are its watertight subdivision and its damage control organisation. Once the flooding has been contained within watertight boundaries, temporary repairs can be made to the hull and the flooded compartments can then be pumped out.

TYPES OF PUMP

The following principal types of pump are used in HM ships.

Main circulating pumps. These are fitted in the engine rooms of steam-driven ships and are intended for circulating sea water through the condensers, but they also have a secondary function which is the pumping of large quantities of water out of the compartments in which they are fitted.

Submersible salvage pumps. All ships are provided with portable pumps for salvage duties, but in some large ships fixed submersible pumps are also fitted in machinery spaces to remove flood water from these compartments. The pumps take suction from the bilges, or they can be used to transfer salt water for the control of heel. The pumps can be controlled locally or by remote controls from the deck above.

Fire pumps. These are single-duty non-submersible pumps designed and fitted to supply only the salt-water system. The pumps are electrically driven and they are sited throughout the ship, both inside and outside the main machinery spaces.

Bilge pumps. These are small-capacity pumps, usually electrically driven, fitted in machinery spaces for the routine clearing of bilges.

Similar small pumps are fitted outside the machinery spaces in large ships, for the routine pumping out of certain compartments such as bathrooms and laundries below the waterline.

Fire and bilge pumps. In older ships these fixed pumps are sited in machinery spaces. They can be used to pump out the bilges, to pump water from one tank to another or to provide water to the salt-water system. They are either electrically or steam-turbine driven.

Hull and fire pumps. Also fitted in older ships, these pumps are sited *outside* the machinery spaces and can be used for pumping out compartments, transferring ballast or for supplying the salt-water system. The pumps are electrically driven.

Portable pumps. Various types of portable pump are provided for fire-fighting and salvage duties. They are driven by gas turbine, diesel engine or electric motor, and the electrically driven pumps may be either submersible or non-submersible. The diesel driven and gas-turbine driven pumps are provided primarily for firefighting although all types of portable pump may be used for either purpose if required and circumstances permit.

Air-driven submersible pumps are provided to ships fitted with a low-pressure air main and where there is liable to be a pumping problem associated with flammable liquids or vapours such that the use of other types of pump would be hazardous.

Eductors. An eductor is a device employing the *venturi* principle to create a suction which is used to pump liquids. Water under pressure from the salt-water main is passed through the bore of the eductor in which there is a constriction (or venturi). A rigid pipe or flexible hose is connected to an inlet on the side of the eductor adjacent to the discharge side of the constriction. The drop in pressure as water passes through the constriction creates a suction which draws liquid through the side inlet and this is expelled from the eductor together with the salt water from the main. Eductors are simple to operate and, having no moving parts, require little maintenance. They are provided in various capacities and are fitted throughout ships for routine pumping out of compartments such as bathrooms below the waterline, de-ballasting and salvage purposes. Portable eductors are also supplied, in addition to portable pumps, for salvage duties.

SPRAYING, FLOODING AND DRAINING ARRANGEMENTS

Spraying

Spraying arrangements are fitted in all magazines and flammable stores, and in all main machinery spaces of modern ships. There are also systems for spraying the hangars of aircraft carriers, and the helicopter hangars of smaller ships.

Magazines. The spraying system in a magazine consists of a grid of pipes fitted with a number of sprinklers so as to cover the whole of the ammunition stowage. The spraying arrangements may be manually operated or automatically operated (each sprinkler is fitted with a *quartzoid bulb* which bursts in the heat of fire and allows water to spray out). The grid is supplied from the salt-water main and, in some installations, a pressurised fresh-water reservoir is incorporated to supply the initial demand and allow time for extra pumps to be connected to the salt-water main.

Machinery spaces. The spraying system in machinery spaces is manually operated and consists of a high-level grid of sprinklers. In large machinery-spaces additional grids may be fitted at lower levels. Inductors are fitted which enable AFFF foam compound to be used with these systems.

Hangars. The sections of between-deck hangars in aircraft carriers are each fitted with a grid of sprinklers which are fed from a ring main. In ships of the *Invincible* Class, the hangar-spray ring main is part of the ship's salt-water system and, when spraying is in operation, additional fire pumps are started by controls at the Ship Control Centre. The large amount of water discharged by hangar spray arrangements would adversely affect the ship's stability if it were not drained quickly and for this reason large scuppers are always fitted.

Helicopter hangars of smaller ships are fitted with a much simpler system comprising two or four overhead spray pipes fed from the salt-water system and controlled by a stop valve operated from outside the hangar.

Flooding

In large warships flooding arrangements are fitted to certain compartments for the purpose of counteracting heel or trim. Air escapes are fitted to all compartments for which there are flooding arrangements. Where a compartment is flooded from the salt-water main, special care must be taken to ensure that the compartment is not subjected to excessive pressure.

Flooding bonnets are provided for the sea inlets of compartments such as magazines so that they can be flooded when the ship is in dry dock. The bonnets are secured directly to gratings on sea inlets by the use of hook bolts, and hoses are then rigged between the bonnets and the shore hydrants.

Draining

Scuppers are fitted at intervals at the outboard edges of the weather decks, and deck drains are fitted, if necessary, in spaces or compartments on other decks if they are well above the waterline. The scupper or drain pipes are led within and close to the ship's side, and they emerge through it just above the waterline, where they discharge through storm valves of the positive-closing type.

In machinery spaces, sumps for collecting bilge water are fitted to the inner bottom. Certain compartments situated low down in the ship are drained into drain tanks or into bilge tanks which are fitted with suction pipes and so can be pumped out, sluice valves being fitted wherever a watertight bulkhead is penetrated.

Bathrooms drain either directly overboard or, more commonly in modern ships, into drain tanks which can be cleared by eductors or pumps.

FRESH WATER

Storage

Fresh-water storage tanks are usually compartments in the ship's structure, low down in the ship. They can be filled through the *fresh-water filling main* either from water-boat connections forward and aft on the weather decks or from the ship's distilling plant. Funnels are fitted in the filling lines just above the tanks to prevent a build-up of pressure in them. Water is transferred in the ship through the fresh-water filling main by fresh-water pumps.

Distribution

The distribution system most used nowadays is the continuous-running-pump system in which the fresh-water pumps discharge continuously into the *fresh-water distribution main,* each pump being provided with a pressure-controlled leak-off back to the tank. Some ships are fitted with the pressure-tank system, in which the pumps are controlled by the air pressure above the water in each of two pressure tanks. The main is usually divided into two or more sections, with valves for isolating the sections or connecting them together.

Hot water

One or more hot-water systems are provided, according to the size of ship, each with its own circulating pump and its steam, electric or oil-fired water heater. Water is circulated in a flow-and-return loop by convection, assisted where necessary by a booster pump. Where more than one system is fitted they can be cross-connected.

Special emergency electrically heated hot-water tanks are provided in such places as the Sick Bay and the Emergency Operating Station.

Drinking water

Cooled fresh water is supplied for drinking, in accommodation spaces, dining halls and at other convenient points.

VENTILATING AND AIR-CONDITIONING SYSTEMS

A modern warship is a complicated assembly of compartments and, in general, the only way of providing the necessary supply of air is by means of mechanical ventilation, i.e. by electric fans (either centrifugal or axial flow) which draw fresh air from outside and distribute it within the ship by means of trunking. Foul air is removed from the ship by means of a complementary system of exhaust fans and trunking.

Ventilation in the tropics

Efficient ventilation in tropical climates is difficult because of the very high humidity of the atmosphere and the consequent need both to cool and to dry the air within the ship. High humidity prevents free evaporation of sweat from the skin, which is one of the body's heat regulators, and in consequence heat exhaustion is brought on more quickly.

For these reasons ordinary mechanical ventilation as described above will not meet the need and many of the compartments in a modern warship are fitted with *air-conditioning* which is a modified form of mechanical ventilation. Examples of these compartments are operational spaces, accommodation spaces and compartments containing electronic equipment.

Tropical conditions — mechanically ventilated compartments

Although the air movement produced by mechanical ventilation gives a sensation of cooling to the person experiencing it, such systems cannot actually cool the air. These systems are normally designed so that the temperature within the compartment does not exceed the external air temperature by more than 5.5 °C.

Tropical conditions — air-conditioned compartments

The requirements of air-conditioning systems are determined by a scale known as *effective temperature*. This is an artificial temperature which takes into account the true temperature (dry bulb), the humidity and the speed of air movement within a compartment, and indicates the degree of comfort experienced within the compartment. Air-conditioning systems in HM warships are designed, as described on page 52, to produce an effective temperature of 25.5 °C.

Cold weather conditions

In cold weather it is necessary to provide heating inside the ship. Air heaters — electric, hot-water or steam — are incorporated into the ventilation or air-conditioning system and they have sufficient capacity to maintain a compartment temperature of 18 °C when the outside temperature is −10 °C. In some systems the air supply may be reduced to lessen the heating load. In modern ships with single-speed fans this is achieved by the use of suitable dampers, and in older ships by selecting the low speed of two-speed fans.

Mechanical ventilation systems

Three types of mechanical ventilation system are in use and these are described below.

Forced supply/natural exhaust. This type of system is used for compartments where a good supply of fresh air is required and where neither great heat nor harmful gases and smells are generated. Ships entirely without air-conditioning are extremely rare in the Fleet but in those that do exist, a forced-supply/natural-exhaust form of ventilation is used for living spaces, offices, some workshops and some store rooms. Exceptionally, for any compartments remote from the weather deck a forced exhaust may be necessary.

Natural supply/forced exhaust. This type of system is installed for compartments containing combustibles, or where flammable or noxious gases or smells are generated. Such compartments are hangars, paint and dope stores, vegetable and tobacco stores, and compartments containing substances that present a high risk of fire and explosion. If any of the gases are heavier than air, then low-level exhaust arrangements are fitted.

Forced supply/forced exhaust. This type of system is used for compartments where heat is generated, for example machinery spaces, galleys and laundries, and workshops with heat-generating equipment. It is also used for the Emergency Operating Station if air-conditioning is not provided. The arrangements in these compartments are so designed that the rate of supply is slightly less than the rate of exhaust to ensure that no hot air escapes into adjacent compartments. The supply is concentrated at positions where the occupants normally work and at other positions which provide havens for men to obtain relief from the hot air around them. The exhaust is concentrated at the places where most heat is generated, thus ensuring that the overheated air in the vicinity does not escape into other areas and so raise the temperature throughout the compartment.

In a modern warship fitted predominantly with air-conditioning, the fitting of mechanical ventilation is confined to such places as machinery spaces, galleys, bathrooms and WCs, and store rooms only occasionally occupied. Even in some of these compartments a limited amount of cooled air may be supplied in addition to the main uncooled supply.

Compartments which are infrequently occupied and which do not require a constant supply of air, such as unoccupied store rooms, are ventilated when required either by fixed fans or by portable air hoses led from nearby connections specially provided in the permanent ventilation system. Certain store rooms that are seldom entered require ventilating at regular intervals, and to ensure this a routine should be laid down.

Air-conditioning systems

An essential feature of air-conditioning is that a proportion of the air handled by the system is fresh air drawn from outside and the remainder is air recirculated from within the ship itself. The air from these two sources is mixed and passed through an *air treatment unit* (ATU) where it is filtered and cooled (or sometimes heated) before being distributed throughout the compartments by supply trunking.

The effect of treatment in the ATU is to remove impurities by filtration and to reduce both the temperature and humidity to an acceptable level. In order to prevent the escape of cool treated air and the ingress of hot humid air, it is very important that external doors and openings in the air-conditioned parts of the ship are opened only when essential.

A typical arrangement of an air-conditioning system is shown in Fig. 2–1. The air cooler within an ATU is normally a finned-tube heat exchanger having a supply of fresh water that has been chilled by a refrigerating plant elsewhere in the ship. In a few cases the cooler is directly connected to the refrigerating plant and the heat-exchanger tubes convey the actual refrigerant. The former system is more common because it is more adaptable and because modern warships are fitted with a system of chilled-water mains for other cooling purposes. The system described above is known as the *centralised air-conditioning system.*

Two other types of system are also used. In one the fans and trunking deal only with the fresh air, and cooling is achieved by chilled-water fan-coil units which circulate the air within the compartments. In the other, a *self-contained air-conditioning unit,* comprising a circulating fan and a small refrigerator-type cooler built into a common casing, is installed in any compartment where required.

Heaters are fitted in the ATU or trunking, or sometimes in both, for use in cold climatic conditions.

Air supply terminals

A ship's air supply terminals consist of punkah-louvres, distributors, linear grilles, bellmouths and slots.

The *punkah-louvre* directs a stream of fresh air from the supply trunk in any direction within a cone of about 85 degrees angle, and it has an effective range at normal working pressures of some two to three metres, depending on its size. This air stream is of great advantage in hot climates. In cooler weather the punkah-louvre can be adjusted to direct the air stream away from the occupants of the compartment. The modern louvre is so made that if the ball is reversed the jet is changed to a diffused air supply.

Distributors and linear grilles are usually employed in air-conditioned compartments to ensure that the air entering a compartment is diffused within it.

Bellmouths, for delivering large volumes of air, are used only in hot compartments such as engine rooms.

Slots in the trunking are specially useful where curtains of air are required for shielding personnel from radiated heat, as in galleys. The air can be delivered from any suitable direction.

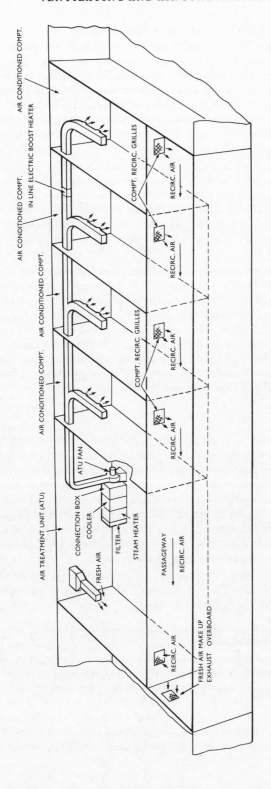

FIG. 2–1. Typical air-conditioning system for a group of compartments

Arrangements for preserving watertight integrity

Main transverse and longitudinal watertight bulkheads are not penetrated by ventilation trunking below the highest 'all-red' deck. Watertight trunking is provided in modern ships wherever the trunks are a potential source of further flooding, and they are fitted as necessary with watertight slide-valves. Suitable positions for operating the valves are chosen to facilitate the control of flooding or fire in the event of damage. In some cases the trunking is made watertight to well above the red-risk zone but no watertight valve is fitted because watertight integrity is then guaranteed by the height of the trunk.

Supply inlets and exhaust outlets are fitted above the weather decks in positions least likely to be affected by seas and spray. The exhaust outlets are usually higher than the supply inlets and they are kept as far from them as possible so that the foul air from the exhaust will not be drawn back into the ship and recirculated. Inlets and exhausts are fitted with hinged watertight covers, the latest types of which are known as *quick-acting hinged watertight covers* (QAHWTC).

The need to preserve watertight integrity, and also to meet the threat of NBC attack, has led to the development of the *section system* of ventilation. This consists essentially of splitting the ship into well-defined sections and confining the arrangements of any one ventilation system within one section of the ship. In large ships a section would usually be bounded by two main transverse bulkheads, but in smaller ships, e.g. frigates, a section may extend through several such bulkheads. The closing down of the ship against NBC attack is greatly facilitated by having only a few openings, which may be closed by the QAHWTCs mentioned above.

Citadel

Citadel is the term applied to the main group, or to each group, of interconnecting compartments which can be conveniently grouped together within an unbroken gastight boundary. Each citadel should be provided with a means for recirculating the air. An important feature of a citadel is that within it the air pressure can be raised slightly above the normal, so that if there is any small breach in the citadel the pressure tends to blow away and outwards any harmful agents, and to prevent their entry. The pressure is built up by sucking in air through *air filtration units* (AFUs), so ensuring that the air within the citadel is filtered and pure.

Normally the citadel (or citadels) in a warship embraces the bridge superstructure including the compass platform and any other superstructure which can reasonably be included.

Organisation of ventilation

The control of ventilation in a ship, especially in the tropics, requires an efficient organisation to ensure on the one hand that there is adequate ventilation for the ship's company, and on the other that the watertight and gastight integrity of the ship is maintained. The ventilation and integrity patrols require an intimate knowledge of the section of the ship in which they work. Ventilation routines have to be prepared to meet the requirements of the different climates and the different tactical conditions in which the ship may be employed.

Immediately the ventilation inlets on the weather decks are shut down, heat and humidity within the ship increase appreciably, so it is important that the inlets should be left open for as long as possible before the higher States of Readiness are assumed.

The jet from a punkah-louvre should be directed in such a way that no annoyance is caused to people in the vicinity, but the maximum flow must be maintained in order to keep up the rate of change of air in the compartment. The practice of fitting cloth filters to punkah-louvres should be discouraged, because the filters impair the air flow, especially when they become clogged with dirt, and so cause high internal temperatures and humidities.

Punkah-louvres operate correctly only within certain limits of air pressure in the trunking, and fitting additional home-made supply terminals may therefore impair the whole system. The fitting of home-made deflector plates to supply openings should not be permitted, nor should any tampering with the relief valves in the ventilation trunking be allowed.

Ventilation systems must be inspected and thoroughly cleaned out at regular intervals, say once every three months, otherwise their performance deteriorates considerably. This regular cleaning and inspection is the responsibility of the ship's Ventilation Party. Certain systems are fitted with metallic gauze or fabric filters and these must be inspected and cleaned much more frequently if the ventilation system is to perform its task. Flameproof filters are extremely delicate, and must be handled very carefully to prevent damage.

CHAPTER 3

Types and Design of Merchant Ships

One of the chief justifications for the existence of warships has always been the need to protect merchant shipping and to ensure that trade by sea can be carried on peaceably. By the use of warships in times of war, each nation attempts to safeguard its own seaborne supplies and to disrupt those of its enemies. There is thus ample reason why a naval officer should be well acquainted with the types, design and functioning of merchant shipping generally.

There is such a wealth of types, however, that only a broad outline of the main types, and the principal factors affecting their design and operation, can be described in this chapter. HM ships should take every opportunity at sea and in harbour to communicate with merchant ships, and should cultivate a liaison with their officers and their various organisations whenever possible.

Before continuing, the reader may wish to examine the tonnage terms and definitions which are given under *Tonnage Measurement* on page 84.

CLASSIFICATION OF MERCHANT SHIPS

In a very broad sense merchant ships can be classified in two ways:

1. As either *liners* or *tramps*.
2. As either *passenger* or *cargo* ships.

A *liner* is any ship which sails to schedule on a definite route for a specific destination, with advertised dates of departure from, and arrival at, nominated ports along her route. She can thus be a ship carrying passengers or cargo or both and therefore the term liner not only includes ocean-going passenger or cargo ships but also cross-Channel ships and some coasting vessels.

A *tramp* is a ship which does not keep to a fixed route or sail to any particular schedule. She is usually purely a cargo vessel which is hired out by her owners under contract to a charterer who, by the terms of his contract, provides her with cargo and specifies her ports of call and the approximate dates of her arrival and departure. Her routes and ports of call are governed solely by the availability of suitable cargoes and, as these must vary considerably both seasonally and geographically, she may roam over the oceans for a long time before returning to her home port.

The interests of passengers, as regards both safety and comfort, are protected by law, and any British ship which carries more than 12 passengers must have a passenger certificate issued by the Department of Trade (Marine Division); she can therefore be classed as a passenger ship although she may carry cargo as well. To qualify for the certificate the ship must be surveyed annually and must conform to certain minimum standards for hull structure, watertight subdivision, lifesaving appliances, fire protection, firefighting and radio equipment. These standards are modified to a certain degree in vessels

56

such as cross-Channel ships, coasters, ships engaged in the pilgrim trade, pleasure steamers and vessels plying in sheltered waters.

Seagoing ships which carry cargo and fewer than 13 passengers do not require a passenger certificate and such ships can be classed as cargo vessels. They are, however, generally built to the minimum standards of construction laid down by the *Classification Societies* (described later) for the purposes of insurance, and have to conform to certain minimum legal standards of accommodation and of lifesaving, firefighting and radio equipment.

All vessels of 500 tons or more gross tonnage must have a SAFCON (safety construction) certificate which is required by the SOLAS (Safety of Life at Sea) convention. A vessel which is classed by a Classification Society will automatically comply with the SAFCON requirements and be issued with a certificate. Other vessels are surveyed by the Department of Trade to ensure that the requirements are satisfied before a certificate is issued.

TYPES OF MERCHANT SHIP

Within the broad classification of merchant ships already given, the following well-established types are readily distinguishable.

PASSENGER SHIPS

In the past, passenger liners were designed for the transatlantic, South African and Australasian trade, but the development of world-wide air travel has now made this type of vessel almost obsolete. One of the last remaining examples of this type is SS *Queen Elizabeth 2* which is now used for holiday cruise purposes. Ships are now purpose built for the passenger cruise trade, examples being MVs *Cunard Princess* and *Cunard Countess*.

The design of these vessels is specialised with a large number of decks to provide the necessary high-class amenities, e.g. sun and observation decks, lounges, bars, dining saloons, galleys etc., in addition to the passenger accommodation. The comfort of passengers is very important and so stabilisers are usually fitted, and in larger vessels bow thrusters are fitted to assist manoeuvrability.

The statutory requirements regarding construction, such as the spacing of bulkheads, are contained in *Merchant (Passenger) Ship Construction Rules*. The ship must also comply with the latest SOLAS and IMO (International Maritime Organization) requirements.

GENERAL CARGO SHIPS

The list of goods which may be classed as general cargo is endless and this has led to the development of a wide variety of ships to satisfy this trade. In general, however, these vessels commonly have five holds with the main machinery situated between No. 4 and No. 5 holds, a deadweight tonnage of up to 14 000 tonnes or so, and a service speed of between 14 and 22 knots. The navigating bridge and accommodation are built into the superstructure which is sited aft over the machinery space. Cargo-handling machinery is always fitted, and ranges from simple derricks to derrick cranes, cranes or heavy-lift derricks depending on the ship's type of trade.

A typical example of these vessels is the 'SD 14', designed and built by Austin and Pickersgill Ltd, which is illustrated at Fig. 3–1. In common with most general cargo vessels, the ship has a single propeller and is diesel powered.

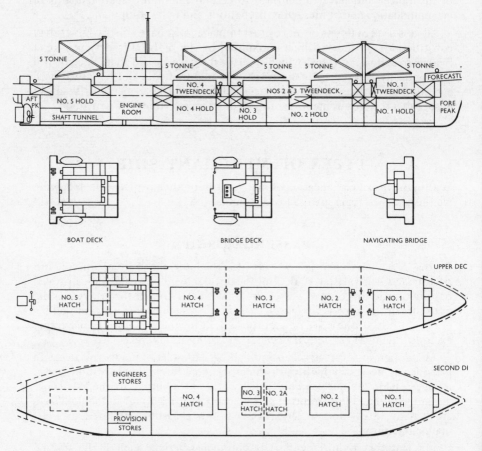

FIG. 3–1. Profile and plans of a typical cargo vessel — the 'SD 14' (Length 141 m, beam 20.5 m, draught 8.7 m, deadweight 14 400 tonnes, speed 14 knots)

'Tween decks (Fig. 3–1)

'Tween decks is the space above the holds and below the upper deck. It is subdivided and numbered in the same sequence as the main holds, and is used for the stowage of cargo. In some cases there may be subdivision by a further deck and then the lower compartment is called the *lower 'tween deck.*

Deep tanks

Many cargo ships are equipped with one or more *deep tanks* which are situated amidships, extend the full width of the ship and have their tops level with the 'tween decks. These tanks serve the double purpose of enabling the ship to carry a part cargo of liquid in bulk and of improving her seaworthiness when in ballast or lightly loaded.

The tanks are usually divided longitudinally by one or more liquid-tight bulkheads so that different liquids may be carried and the free-surface effect of the liquids be reduced. Their use is not, however, confined to the carriage of liquids alone; they can be used for carrying bulk cargo or general cargo, and for this reason they are fitted with large removable lids or hatches.

Deep tanks are particularly useful for water ballast when the ship is lightly laden, because when completely filled with sea water they give the ship the necessary immersion without unduly lowering her centre of gravity. Ships which are not fitted with deep tanks and have all their ballast tanks in the double bottom are liable to be unduly stiff when lightly laden, because all the weight is concentrated low down in the ship.

Refrigerated cargo

For the carriage of certain cargoes, e.g. meat, vegetables and dairy produce, refrigeration is necessary to maintain the optimum temperature during passage. The temperatures required vary within the range -10 °C, for frozen meat, to 12 °C, for bananas.

Refrigeration is provided to all the holds of a ship fully employed on this type of trade, and the ship is commonly called a *reefer*. When only part of the cargo space is refrigerated, this facility is limited to the holds adjacent to the main machinery space and the ship may be called a *semi-reefer*.

CONTAINER SHIPS

The conventional cargo ship spends a great deal of time loading and discharging individual parcels of cargo, whereas a container ship has a much faster *turn-round*. This is because of the ease of handling cargo ready-packed in standard-sized containers. Each stage of container transport, e.g. road and rail transport, port handling and accommodation on board ship, has been designed to provide a completely compatible system which has world-wide applications. Containerisation has cut insurance claims substantially in recent years because the cargo is continuously protected.

A wide variety of cargo, including mail, machine parts, partially assembled aircraft, motor vehicles and refrigerated foodstuffs, is suitable for carriage by container. The cargo is packed, secured and padded within the container to prevent any movement. This practice, known as *packing,* is carried out by the manufacturer at his works or by an agent at a central depot.

The containers are of a suitable size for delivery by road or rail to a container berth where they are loaded by special handling equipment into the container ship. The reverse procedure takes place at the port of discharge and the containers are subsequently *stripped* (unpacked) by the final recipient or an agent.

Modern container ships vary in size from 2000 to 60 000 deadweight tonnes and may carry in excess of 2000 containers. The containers are constructed to conform to International Standards Organization (ISO) specifications and there are two standard sizes: 6.1 × 2.44 × 2.44 metres (20-foot container) and $12.2 \times 2.44 \times 2.44$ metres (40-foot container). The capacity of a container ship is often referred to by the *Twenty-foot Equivalent Unit* (TEU) which is used to indicate the number of 6.1-metre containers a ship can accommodate, e.g. a 400-TEU ship can take 400 of the 6.1-metre containers, or 200 of the 12.2-metre containers, or a mixture of both within the total limitation. Containers are described in more detail in Chapter 4.

Container ship types

Five recognised groups of ship are capable of carrying containers. They are:

Fully containerised ships (Fig. 3–2). These are ships designed and built to carry only containers and they may be partially or fully refrigerated.

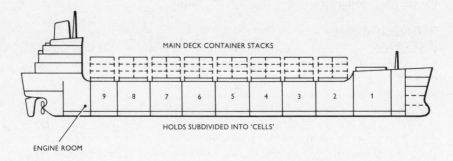

FIG. 3–2. Profile of fully containerised ship

Partial container ships. In these ships only part of the cargo capacity is specially designed for the carriage of containers. The remaining capacity is devoted to the carriage of cargo by the roll-on/roll-off (ro-ro) principle. This type of cargo includes motor vehicles and any goods packed in lorries or trailers. The rollable cargo is loaded and discharged through a stern door and over a stern ramp. The stern door and ramp may be fitted on the centre-line but they are more usually offset to one quarter of the vessel. One of these ships is illustrated later, at Fig. 3–5, and described under the heading *Roll-on/roll-off vessels* on page 63.

The above two types are true container ships and, in keeping with modern ship construction, the bridge accommodation areas and domestic services are contained in an island superstructure sited aft over the machinery spaces. The hull design is such that, when under way, as much water as possible is kept off the upper deck; this is achieved by incorporating a pronounced flare into the design of the bows. The other types are:

Convertible container ships. These ships embody special features in which the whole or part of the vessel's capacity may be used for containers and the remaining capacity used for general or bulk cargo.

Ships of limited container capacity. In this type of ship some container handling and securing devices are installed but the ship is in all respects a general cargo vessel.

Ships without special container stowage arrangements. These ships treat the container as a larger-than-usual parcel of general cargo which is secured on deck by traditional methods.

Container stowage

The holds of fully and partially containerised ships are divided vertically into cells and each cell is fitted with guides to facilitate the stacking of containers up to six deep and ten wide. Heavy web frames separate the cells to provide support for the overall structure and to give the ship rigidity.

The individual container cell, Fig. 3–3, is formed by four of the vertical guides located one at each corner, running from the hatch coaming down to the tank top. The primary function of the guides is to locate the containers in their stacked position within the cell; the secondary purpose is to restrain the containers horizontally and absorb any forces created in a seaway.

Refrigerated cargo is cooled by a duct system which circulates cold air into and out of each container. The cooling arrangements are mechanically coupled to the appropriate containers as they arrive in the cell. The conditions within selected containers can be monitored in a remote control room and the automatic temperature controls adjusted accordingly.

Other containers may be stacked up to four high on the upper deck, thus using all available stowage space. The limiting factors for deck stowage are ship stability, deck loading and suitable securing methods.

Loading and discharge

Loading is achieved by lowering the containers, one on top of the other, to form a stack within each cell. Once plumbed over the cell it is unnecessary to move a container horizontally during loading. Discharging is the reverse of the loading procedure. The handling of containers is described in Chapter 4.

During loading and discharging the ship is kept upright to prevent the jamming of containers in cell guides. This is achieved by an automatic transfer pump which moves water ballast from one side of the ship to the other at a rate equivalent to the loading or discharge of containers. A computer system is installed in container ships which gives a rapid assessment of the effect of cargo stowage on the vessel's trim, stability, and longitudinal and torsional strength limitations.

Ship safety

Fully and partially containerised ships are fitted with arrangements to smother the machinery and cargo spaces with carbon dioxide (CO_2) gas in the event of fire. All enclosed spaces are continuously monitored by deck head fire-detectors which raise the alarm, and indicate the location of a fire, at consoles fitted in the machinery control room and navigating bridge.

Facilities are provided for the adequate ventilation of containers carrying hazardous substances and these containers would normally be stowed forward in No. 1 hold. The marking of such containers is specified by the *International Maritime Dangerous Goods Code,* which is compiled by IMO, and these markings are described on page 114.

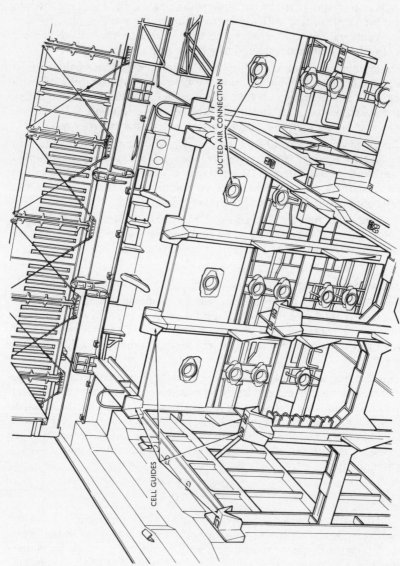

DUCTED AIR CONNECTION

CELL GUIDES

FIG. 3–3.　The cellular construction of the hold of a fully or partially containerised ship
The area of one cell is shown by the indicated cell guides

ROLL-ON/ROLL-OFF (RO-RO) VESSELS

The roll-on/roll-off type of vessel is designed to accommodate a variety of wheeled vehicles which enter and leave the ship over ramps through watertight doors at either the bow or stern, or both. No port craneage is required for the cargo as it is loaded and discharged ready-packed in its vehicle. Some ships also carry standard containers and these are loaded and discharged by special low-loading tractors designed to operate in the restricted height of the vehicle deck. These ships usually ply on short sea routes although, due to port congestion, the ro-ro principle is being applied to larger ships for long ocean voyages.

The most common type of ro-ro ship is the passenger/vehicle ferry which is illustrated in profile at Fig. 3–4. An essential feature is the long clear decks which are uninterrupted by bulkheads. Deckhead heights must be sufficient to accommodate the various types of vehicle; cars being stowed low down in the ship and commercial vehicles on the higher decks.

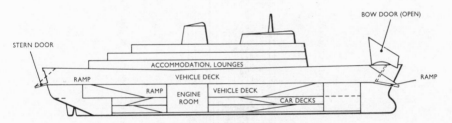

FIG. 3–4. Profile of a ro-ro passenger/vehicle ship

Ramps are fitted at the bow and stern to facilitate loading and discharging, and fixed or hydraulically operated movable ramps or lifts give access to the lower decks. Movable ramps have the advantage of providing a greater loading area. Some vessels are built with the stern door and ramp set at an angle to the fore-and-aft line to enable ro-ro operation alongside a normal quay.

The passenger accommodation which is built into the superstructure varies with the type of trade for which the vessel is designed: vehicle/passenger ferries can accommodate up to 320 cars and 1200 passengers for a short voyage whereas vessels specialising in commercial vehicles have much less passenger accommodation.

Partial container ships. In these ships the space not devoted to containers is used for ro-ro cargo which is loaded and discharged over a stern ramp. The ship profile illustrated in Fig. 3–5 shows how the space is used for each type of cargo. A typical partial container ship has a deadweight capacity of about 18 000 tonnes and a service speed of about 24 knots.

BARGE CARRIERS

A modern and growing development in cargo transport is the use of barge systems which are extensions of the container system but are limited solely

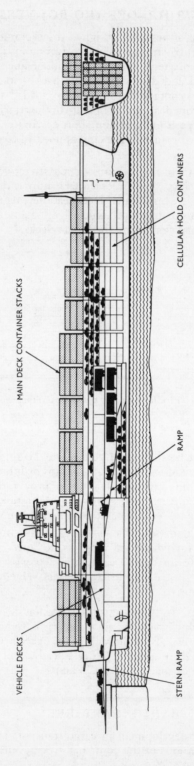

FIG. 3–5. Profile of a partial container ship showing the ro-ro capability

to transport by water. The cargo is packed in barges which are then towed to the barge carrier, taken on board by various methods, transported to their destination and then discharged for final unpacking of the cargo. These types of system are particularly suited to the operation of liner cargo services between ports which are centres of coastal and inland waterways. A faster turnaround of vessels is possible and only the simplest of port facilities are required, i.e. a sheltered anchorage or mooring for the vessel, and the limited wharfage and loading requirements of the lighters.

This section describes the LASH and SEABEE systems which are now well established, and the more recent BACO system. A brief description is also given of the integrated tug/barge concept wherein the barge forms the hull of a vessel which is propelled by a special detachable tug unit. The barge and tug form a composite single vessel and thus the system is analogous to articulated road vehicles in which one tractor unit can service a variety of trailers.

LASH (Lighter Aboard SHip) vessels

·In the patented LASH cargo system any type of cargo is packed in standard-sized lighters. The lighters are then towed to the LASH ship where they are hoisted and stowed on board by the shipboard crane.

The general design of a LASH ship is shown in Fig. 3–6 and is easily recognised by the following prominent features: a short forecastle with the bridge superstructure sited well forward, the heavy gantry crane, the stern sponsons which form the docking well, and the sided funnels. The holds are of cellular construction, similar to those of a container ship, and each cell can accept four lighters stacked on top of each other. A further two tiers of lighters can then be stacked on the hatch covers. The number of lighters carried varies between 60 and 90 and some vessels have additional stowage for up to 550 standard ISO containers. The ships vary in capacity from 30 000 to 50 000 deadweight tonnes and have a service speed in the range of 18 to 22 knots.

The lighters are in effect floating holds with large cargo hatches. They are approximately 18 metres long, 9 metres wide and 4 metres deep with a stowage capacity of about 550 cubic metres or 370 deadweight tonnes. The lighters are fitted with a self-sealing ventilation system which prevents moisture entry when the lighters are in port and which can be connected to the ship's ventilation or air-conditioning system when at sea.

The crane straddles the ship and travels on rails mounted on the ship's side decks. The rails extend from just abaft the bridge superstructure to the sponsons which overhang the stern. The crane legs are fitted with guides which provide continuity with the sides of the holds and the stern sponsons. The lighter is lifted by a load frame, similar to the spreader of a container crane and weighing about 65 tonnes, which is designed to clamp to the corner posts of the lighter. The total lifting capacity is about 500 tonnes which is required to accommodate the combined weight of a loaded lighter and the load frame. The effect of the ship's roll and pitch during hoisting and lowering is compensated by mechanisms built into the hoists of the crane. The hoist and traverse speeds are such that a loading/discharge cycle for one loaded

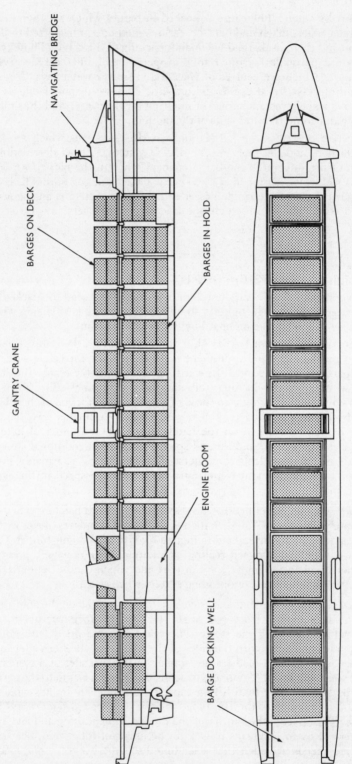

Fig. 3–6. The principal design features of a LASH vessel

lighter takes about 15 minutes and this means that cargo can be handled at up to about 1300 tonnes per hour.

The loading sequence is shown at Fig. 3–7. The loaded lighter is towed to the ship and placed in the docking well where it is automatically clamped to the ship. The crane traverses to the sponsons and lowers the load frame

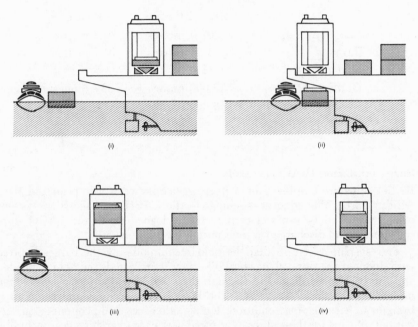

FIG. 3–7. The lighter loading sequence

which automatically clamps to the lighter. The lighter is then lifted into the gantry, the crane moves forward to the required position and stacks the lighter. Discharging is the reverse sequence.

The SEABEE system

The SEABEE system is similar in concept to the LASH system but, whereas in the LASH system the lighters are stowed vertically in cellular holds, in the SEABEE system the barges are stowed horizontally on three decks.

The barges are lifted to the level of the appropriate deck by an elevator constructed between sidewalls at the stern of the ship. The elevator has a lifting capacity of 2000 tonnes and can accommodate two loaded barges. The elevator platform is submerged, the barges are floated in and then raised to the level of the particular deck. The barges are then moved by a transporter system to their stowage. The average time for the load/discharge cycle of a pair of barges is nearly 30 minutes. In addition to accommodation for 38 barges on the three enclosed decks there is also more than 950 TEUs of container stowage which is mainly on the upper deck.

The appearance of a SEABEE ship is very similar to that of a LASH ship, with the superstructure and navigating bridge well forward and with sided funnels abreast each other. There is no transporter crane but the stern is built up to accommodate the elevator. Brief particulars of a typical ship, operated between United States and United Kingdom/north European ports by the Lykes Bros Steamship Co. Inc., are given below.

	SEABEE Ship	Barge
Length overall	267.0 metres	29.7 metres
Beam	32.3 metres	10.7 metres
Draught	11.9 metres	3.8 metres
Deadweight	39 000 tonnes	834 tonnes
Load displacement	58 400 tonnes	—
Service speed	20 knots	—

Barge-container (BACO) vessels

BACO ships are employed on a liner service between European and West African ports. The concept is similar to the LASH and SEABEE systems whereby packed barges and containers are loaded on to the BACO ship, transported and discharged at their port of destination.

This system differs in that the hold accommodating the barges is fitted with doors at the bow of the ship. The ship is ballasted, the hold is flooded and the barges are floated in through the open bow doors. On completion of loading the doors are closed, the hold is pumped out and the ship is brought to her seagoing condition. Unlike other barge and container carriers it is not unusual for these ships to be fitted with cargo-handling gear including cranes of capacity up to 40 tonnes. A typical BACO ship can carry twelve barges, each with a capacity of 800 tonnes deadweight, and has 500–620 TEUs of container stowage, depending on the weight. Brief particulars of such a vessel are given below.

	BACO Ship	Barge
Length overall	204.1 metres	24.00 metres
Beam	28.5 metres	9.5 metres
Draught	6.65 metres	4.25 metres
Deadweight	21 000 tonnes	800 tonnes
Service speed	15 knots	—

The integrated tug/barge concept

In the tug/barge system the barge is built in the moulded form of a normal ship's hull. The stern is designed to accept a special tug unit which can be rigidly connected to the barge thus forming a single composite vessel. The tug is fitted with the propulsion system and navigating equipment, and the composite vessels are capable of full ocean-going service. A tug is capable of servicing a number of barges which can be designed to suit varying types of cargo and can be fitted with the appropriate cargo-handling gear, e.g. cranes, winches, loading/discharge pipelines, pumping equipment, etc. The appearance of a tug/barge vessel depends on the purpose of the barge involved, and the fact that it is an integrated vessel is almost indiscernable. Brief particulars of such a vessel are given below.

	BARGE	TUG
Length overall	190 metres	39.0 metres
Beam	26 metres	16·0 metres
Draught	14 metres	7.6 metres
Deadweight	25 000 tonnes	—
Combination speed	15 knots	

BULK CARRIERS

Bulk carriers are designed to carry a variety of cargoes, such as grain, fertiliser, sugar, salt, ores and raw chemicals, loaded in a loose condition direct into the holds. They have a service speed in the range of 14 to 16 knots and vary in capacity up to 300 000 deadweight tonnes.

Unfortunately bulk carriers are often forced to sail in ballast for parts of their voyages because of international trade patterns and the need for specialised port facilities for loading and discharging. To overcome this disadvantage two further types of bulk cargo vessel have been developed: these are the oil/ore carrier and the oil/bulk/ore (OBO) vessel.

Bulk carrier. A typical bulk-cargo ship is illustrated in Volume I, Fig. 2–21; the arrangement of holds is shown here in Fig. 3–8(i) and (ii). The holds extend over the full width of the ship and are angled at the edges, forming hopper sides to aid the discharge of cargo by mechanical grabs. The wing tanks may be used for a different type of bulk cargo, such as grain, or for water ballast.

Iron ore as a cargo presents certain problems because of its high density. The ship will sink to its load line long before the holds are full, and the centre of gravity becomes very low in the ship. This affects the ship's motion causing a stiff condition in which she recovers sharply from a roll thus subjecting the ship's structure to heavy stresses. Thus the carriage of iron ore in general bulk carriers is limited to certain holds and the remainder are left empty to maintain suitable stability of the vessel. Some ships, specifically designed for this cargo, have narrow holds with raised floors which are flanked by side tanks as shown in Fig. 3–8(iii). All the holds can be used, and the side tanks are empty when the ship is laden and are used for water ballast otherwise. The spaces below the holds are kept dry and, because the vessel's centre of gravity is raised, she has a more kindly motion in a seaway.

Oil/ore carrier. In these vessels the holds are constructed with a cross-section similar to that shown in Fig. 3–8(iii) and are fitted with gastight hatches. When carrying ore, only a limited number of the main centre holds can be used, but when carrying oil all the holds and a proportion of the side tanks can be used for cargo. The side tanks are flooded as required for ballast purposes.

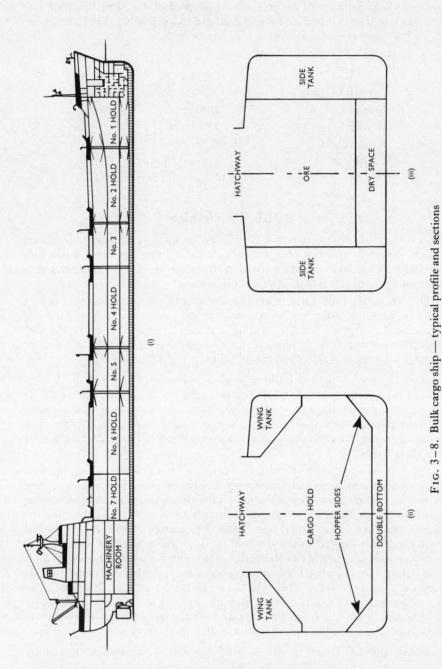

FIG. 3–8. Bulk cargo ship — typical profile and sections

Oil/bulk/ore (OBO) carrier (Fig. 3–9). This type of vessel is designed to accommodate the widest variety of bulk cargoes to overcome the disadvantage of sailing in ballast. The holds are built over a normal double bottom and the floors are not raised. The vessel is additionally strengthened by a double-skinned side which encloses narrow side-tanks. The spaces between

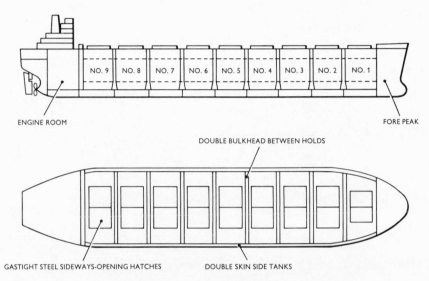

FIG. 3–9. Typical oil/bulk/ore (OBO) carrier in profile and plan

the sloping sides of the holds and the ship's side are also enclosed to form hopper tanks between the side tanks and the double bottom. The holds are fitted with gastight hatches and otherwise they are similar in cross-section to that shown at Fig. 3–8(ii). Only alternate main holds are used when carrying iron ore and these are only partially filled. When carrying oil one or more main holds may have to remain unused and those in use are filled to at least 98 per cent of capacity to overcome the free-surface problems of partially filled compartments. The wing and hopper tanks may also be used for oil cargo. For other bulk cargoes the main holds are completely filled as required and when in ballast the main holds, wing tanks, hopper tanks and double bottom are flooded as required.

Bulk carriers are all similar in appearance with the machinery space and bridge superstructure sited abaft the cargo space. Oil/ore and OBO vessels are fitted with full pumping facilities and can be identified by the upper-deck pipework and the derricks or cranes used for handling hoses. Furthermore, all bulk carriers can be distinguished from tankers by the high hatch coamings.

TANKERS

Tankers are ships specially built to carry liquid cargo in bulk. They vary in size from coasters of about 1200 tonnes deadweight up to the ultra large crude carriers (ULCC) of some 500 000 tonnes deadweight. Fig. 3–10 illustrates

F

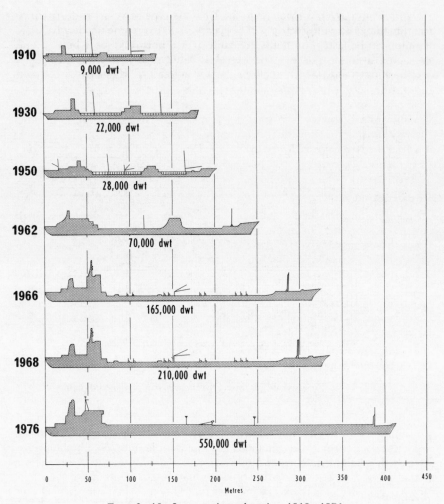

F IG. 3–10. Increase in tanker size, 1910–1976

the increase in size of this type of vessel over the years and the inset of Fig. 3–11 compares the size of a frigate of about 2500 tonnes displacement to that of a very large crude carrier (VLCC) of about 200 000 tonnes deadweight.

Tankers do not necessarily trade over a fixed route although the number of tanker terminal ports at which they can load and discharge is limited. The *lightening* operation, whereby large tankers transfer part of their cargo to smaller tankers before entering ports in which the depth of water is restricted, is discussed on page 126.

The operation of a tanker fleet differs greatly from that of a fleet of general cargo ships. A tanker can seldom obtain a return cargo and it is therefore quite usual for her to discharge a full cargo, load with stores, fuel and ballast, and sail on the return voyage within 18 to 36 hours of arriving at her destination. Similarly the turn-round at her loading port may not take much longer. The limited time in port and the quick turn-rounds complicate the organisation of routine overhauls and running repairs. Moreover, because of the risk of explosion or fire, no work which would cause sparks or other risks can be undertaken in a tanker until she is entirely free of explosive or flammable gases. The efficient and economical running of a tanker fleet demands careful planning of examinations, overhauls, periodical dockings and surveys to ensure that each ship is not out of service for more than one month annually. Many tanker companies now only dry-dock their ships every 18 months to 2 years. Various arrangements have been introduced by the Classification Societies to reduce the time spent on surveys during docking thereby limiting the time the ship is out of service. Some of these arrangements are described on page 81.

Construction

In modern tankers the bridge and accommodation are built into a single superstructure sited over the machinery space and abaft the cargo tanks. Thus these ships appear similar to bulk carriers. However, when laden, the tanker has less freeboard and, in vessels up to 100 000 tonnes deadweight, a *fore-and-aft bridge* or catwalk is built between the superstructure and the forecastle to allow safe passage when the ship is laden. The catwalk is seldom found in VLCCs and ULCCs but these vessels have a railed-off section running fore and aft along the main deck centre-line. The deeper loading of tankers is permitted for the following reasons:

1. The tank openings are very small, being used only for access and to admit light and air at certain times.
2. The tank lids are made of steel or alloy and are as strong as the deck plating. They are very securely fastened by drop-bolts and wing nuts to form a packed oil-tight joint with the hatch coaming.
3. There are no large, open ventilators leading to the cargo compartments.
4. The ship is subdivided into a larger number of watertight compartments than is an ordinary cargo vessel.

The fore-and-aft bridge also forms a convenient support for the numerous pipelines which run along the upper deck, i.e. steam and exhaust lines, steam or foam smothering lines, and the wash-deck line. The cargo loading and discharge lines and the oil-fuel-transfer line were formerly supported on the fore-and-aft bridge but nowadays they are normally mounted on the deck.

The cargo space is divided into tanks which are again subdivided, usually making three tanks abreast, i.e. a rather large centre tank with small wing tanks to port and starboard. The common practice is to number the tanks from forward to aft, and the larger vessels may have twelve tanks or more, thus giving up to thirty-six cargo compartments in all. The cargo space is separated from the forward and after sections of the ship by *cofferdams* which are narrow compartments occupying the whole depth and beam of the ship. These cofferdams ensure complete segregation of the living quarters, machinery spaces and store-rooms from the cargo tanks. Pipes, leads and fittings are not generally allowed to pass through the cofferdams' bulkheads. Cofferdams can be flooded in emergency or for ballast purposes. However, it is modern practice to divide the after cofferdam into a central compartment and two wing compartments, and to site the pumping machinery within the centre compartment. Fuel oil for the ship's propulsion machinery is generally carried

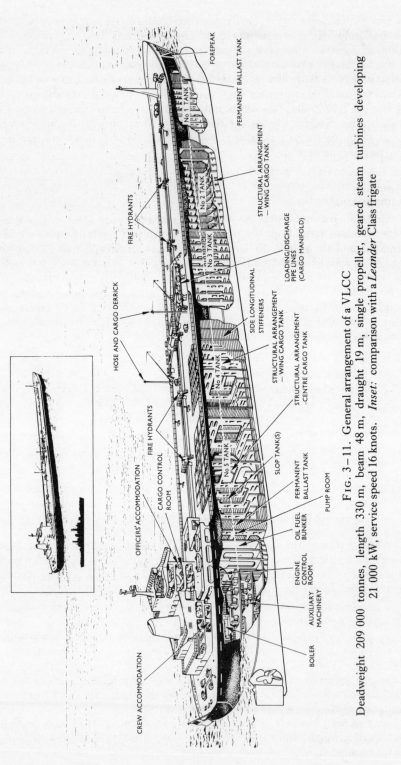

FIG. 3–11. General arrangement of a VLCC

Deadweight 209 000 tonnes, length 330 m, beam 48 m, draught 19 m, single propeller, geared steam turbines developing 21 000 kW, service speed 16 knots. *Inset:* comparison with a *Leander* Class frigate

in a tank which is divided along the centre-line and positioned between the forward cofferdam and the fore peak, and in wing tanks abreast the machinery space.

Fig. 3–11 shows the general arrangement of this type of vessel. The tanker illustrated is a VLCC of 209 000 tonnes deadweight which would carry about 203 000 tonnes of crude oil, the remaining 6000 tonnes being accounted for by fuel oil, fresh water and stores.

Propulsion is generally by steam turbines or diesel engines but in a few cases gas turbines are used. In many modern ships the engines can be remotely controlled from the navigation bridge and in some instances are unmanned, the Engineer Officer keeping his watch at a control console usually situated adjacent to the engine room. In a few of the most modern vessels the console is situated on the bridge deck.

Although their turning characteristics may be comparable to those of a large warship, large tankers need a considerable time and distance to stop. Some idea of the problem may be gained from the typical data for a loaded VLCC of 250 000 tonnes deadweight in deep water, which are listed below.

360-degree turn

Initial speed:	15 knots		
Advance:	1050 yards	Transfer:	1130 yards
Speed remaining:	3.5 knots	Time:	14.06 minutes

Stop

Initial speed:	13.4 knots	
After 30 minutes:	Speed remaining:	3.5 knots
	Distance travelled:	3.5 miles

Emergency stop

Time to stop:	16.5 minutes
Distance travelled:	4 miles

Anchoring

Reduction of speed commences 7 to 8 miles before reaching anchor berth and one hour prior to intended time of anchoring.

When berthing, the speed of large tankers has to be reduced to a crawling pace lest accidental impact should seriously damage the ship or her berth; to assist in this manoeuvre systems are now available which indicate the distance from and rate of approach to alongside berths at close range.

The loading and discharge of crude oil, and details of the handling arrangements are given in Chapter 4.

GAS CARRIERS

Gas carriers are used for the transport of liquefied natural gas (LNG), liquefied petroleum gas (LPG) and some chemicals. A typical gas carrier is illustrated in Volume I, Fig. 2–23. These ships vary in size up to 90 000 tonnes deadweight and have a cargo capacity of between 25 000 and 125 000 cubic metres.

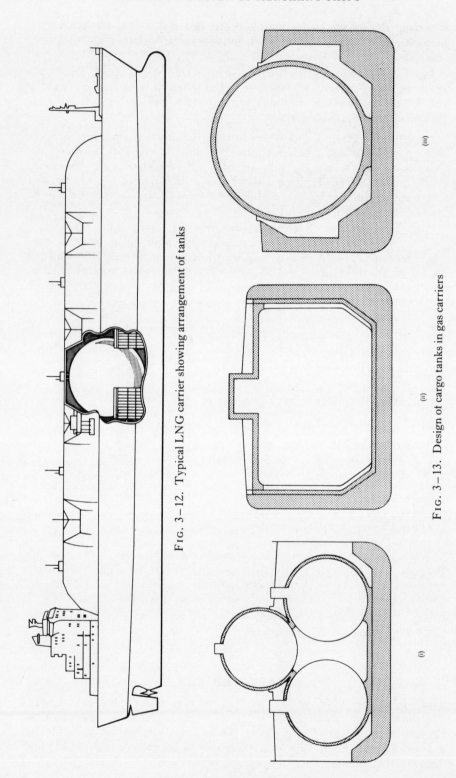

Fig. 3–12. Typical LNG carrier showing arrangement of tanks

Fig. 3–13. Design of cargo tanks in gas carriers

Natural gas occurs in association with oil fields and is predominantly methane. It is liquefied on shore by chilling to below its boiling-point (see table below); this reduces its volume by 600 times and makes it an economical cargo to transport. Petroleum gases, such as butane and propane, generally result from the distillation of crude oil, and these are liquefied in the same manner. Ammonia may also be transported as a liquid by gas carriers.

The design of the tanks and cargo spaces of gas carriers is highly specialised and is still developing. Fig. 3–12 shows the arrangement of a tank and the cargo spaces in a typical LNG carrier. The tanks are individual structures supported by the hull, and their shape and design depend on the working pressure and temperature. Three basic types are in general use:

1. FREE-STANDING OR SELF-SUPPORTING TANK (Fig. 3–13(i)) which has sufficient strength to withstand cargo stresses. May be spherical, prismatic or cylindrical in shape and is fitted with a centre-line washplate to reduce free-surface effect.

2. MEMBRANE TANK (Fig. 3–13(ii)) which is fabricated from stainless steel and carried by load-bearing insulating material which is supported by the ship's structure. In some of these tanks the membrane is double-skinned and the intervening space is filled with insulation.

3. SEMI-MEMBRANE TANK (Fig. 3–13(iii)). Similar in construction to the membrane tank but supported at only the base and sides.

The following particulars of common cargo gases indicate the methods by which they can be carried:

	BUTANE (LPG)	METHANE (LNG)	AMMONIA
Relative density	1.9	0.55	0.62
Boiling-point	−0.5 °C	−161.5 °C	−33.5 °C
Critical temperature*	152 °C	−82 °C	132.4 °C

*Critical temperature is that above which it is impossible to liquefy the gas by pressure alone.

Three methods of transportation are employed:

1. Under pressure at ambient temperatures.

2. At or near the boiling-point of the liquid and at or near atmospheric pressure.

3. At a designed pressure with a corresponding cargo temperature.

All three methods are suitable for LPG as the boiling-point is relatively high, whereas LNG is carried by method 2. The gas is not refrigerated on board ship but, when loaded as a liquid, it is prevented from absorbing heat by the insulating material (usually balsa wood) surrounding the tanks. The insulation serves the dual purposes of keeping the cargo cold and also of preventing any leakage coming into contact with the hull. The extremely low temperatures would alter the characteristics of the steel and make it brittle. To protect the insulation the holds are kept dry by the injection of inert gas (usually nitrogen) under a slight positive pressure. This also prevents the build-up of flammable pockets of gas through cargo leakage.

During the voyage some *boil-off* occurs (for LNG this amounts to approximately 0.4 per cent per day). The vapour is either vented to atmosphere or captured and, if suitable, used as fuel or re-liquefied and returned to the tanks.

Special products carriers

In addition to LNG and LPG there are some three hundred different *special* products requiring transport under a variety of conditions. Special products carriers are used to transport such materials and, in many cases, only small quantities of cargo are involved, in 500- to 5000-tonne lots called parcels. Such vessels are therefore often referred to as *parcel tankers*. They carry refined petroleum products, vegetable and chemical oils, chemicals and molasses for example. Products carriers which accommodate clean oils, i.e. gasolines, fuel oils and similar refined products, are designed and operated as smaller versions of the tankers previously described. For other cargoes the construction and operation of the ships are similar to those of gas carriers. The tanks are insulated and, for some cargoes, have to be heated to maintain the cargo in a liquid state. Typical examples are phosphorus and sulphur which have melting-points of 44 °C and 113 °C respectively. Refrigeration and pressurisation of tanks are also necessary in some cases.

Such vessels may present a safety hazard with their parcels of sometimes explosive or highly reactive chemicals and advice in dealing with potential hazards or in rendering assistance is given in Chapter 7 under *Salvage and Assistance to Ships Carrying Chemical Cargoes.*(See also Chapter 4, under *Dangerous Cargoes.*)

FACTORS AFFECTING DESIGN OF MERCHANT SHIPS

Each type of merchant ship has been evolved to meet the requirements of her particular trade, and certain conditions are imposed on her design, by law, to ensure the safety of the ship, her passengers and her crew.

Among the many factors affecting merchant ship design are the nature of the cargo or the class of passenger to be carried, the maximum length of run between fuelling ports, the speed required, the dimensions of docks to be used and depth of water in the ports and canals to be used, the conditions of climate and weather likely to be encountered, the first cost of construction, and operating costs.

In addition to meeting the owner's requirements, certain features of the construction of a merchant ship, and the extent to which she may be loaded, are subject to certain standards and restrictions which are imposed by international law specified by the International Maritime Organization (IMO), by statutory law of the national authority, and by the rules of the Classification Societies.

It is legally compulsory for all except a few special types of merchant ship to carry permanent marks on each side of the hull indicating the maximum draughts to which the ship may be loaded in different localities at different seasons of the year. These *load lines* are determined by assigning in each case the minimum freeboard permissible, and this freeboard depends on the ship's dimensions, type and structural strength. The maximum permissible displacement of a ship, and thus the extent to which she may be loaded, is therefore limited by law.

Classification Societies, originally formed to meet the needs of marine insurance, have laid down certain rules which must be observed in the construction of ships classed with them. It is authoritatively accepted that vessels built to the standards defined in these rules can be safely loaded to the maximum draught prescribed, subject to the limitations of the maximum permissible still-water shearing forces and bending moments (see page 25). The rules specify the hull scantlings (i.e. standard dimensions for parts of the structure) and therefore virtually determine the minimum weight of the hull structure.

The difference between the maximum displacement allowed and the weight of the hull structure is the weight of the machinery, equipment, bunkers, water, stores, crew, passengers and cargo, and it is the designer's problem to allocate as much as is possible of this weight to earning capacity, i.e. to cargo- and passenger-carrying capacity.

A further factor affecting the general design of a ship are the dues which the owner will be required to pay for the use of harbours, docks, canals and other port facilities. By law all ships must be measured for tonnage, on which such dues are levied, and it is therefore a further problem of the designer to take the best advantage of all the factors which tend to reduce the tonnage measurement.

To summarise, it may be said that in endeavouring to give the shipowner a maximum carrying capacity, the ship designer is restricted by regulations in the following ways: by having to provide for the safety and comfort of the passengers and crew, by having to ensure the safe transport of the ship and her cargo, and by having to minimise the tonnage measurement.

Safety and comfort of passengers and crew. This legislation is enforced by the Department of Trade or delegated to the Classification Society in respect of British vessels, and prescribes:

1. The maximum draught, by the assignment of load lines.
2. Conditions regarding watertight bulkheads, and their spacing, in passenger vessels.
3. The detailed design and arrangement of lifesaving appliances.
4. Structural requirements for restricting the spread of fire, especially in passenger ships.
5. Minimum standards for passenger and crew spaces.
6. Conditions for the stowage of cargoes such as coal, grain in bulk, dangerous goods, flammable or explosive materials or liquids, etc.
7. The minimum standards of radio installations.

Further information on the equipment for fire precautions and lifesaving and the requirements for watertight subdivision is given in Chapter 5.

Safe transport of the ship and her cargo under the normal hazards of the weather she is likely to encounter during her voyage. Vessels are usually classed according to the rules of the Classification Societies to serve as a guide for insuring the ship and her cargo. The fact that a ship is classed is accepted by the Department of Trade as a guarantee that she is structurally sound and efficiently equipped for her service. If a vessel is not so classed the Department's surveyors make the initial survey and subsequently the periodical surveys necessary to ensure that she is maintained in a satisfactory condition.

Tonnage measurement. In order to minimise the harbour, dock and canal dues applicable to the ship she must be designed with the lowest tonnage measurement appropriate to her intended service. (Methods of measuring tonnage are described later in this chapter.) The measurement for tonnage is carried out by surveyors appointed by the Department of Trade or authorised Classification Society.

Classification Societies

The original society for classifying merchant ships according to their strength and seaworthiness was Lloyd's Register of British and Foreign Shipping. It was formed in 1760 by persons engaged in marine insurance, as an association for protecting their interests at a time when no standards of strength and seaworthiness were laid down by law. The British Corporation, a similar but smaller body, was founded in 1890 at Glasgow by shipowners and others with marine interests, but in 1949 it amalgamated with Lloyd's Register. There are several other Classification Societies which publish register books and rules of construction; these are mainly used in foreign countries.

Minimum freeboards, the methods by which they are assigned and corresponding standards of strength have been agreed internationally in the 1966 Load Line Convention. They are laid down by law and, although legally they are administered by the Department of Trade, the assignment of freeboards has been delegated by the Department to certain Classification Societies for ships classed with them. The activities of the Societies go further and include regular detailed surveys of hulls and machinery during the lifetime of a ship, as well as during her building, and they also include the tests of materials.

Lloyd's rules for determining the scantlings for any structural member of a ship's hull are in the form of a series of tables in which the scantlings are given in relation to the main dimensions of the ship, e.g. her length, beam, draught and depth. These tables, being based on the Society's accumulated experience, ensure the production of a thoroughly reliable ship.

A ship built to the scantlings set forth in Lloyd's Rules for the draught required may be designated *100A* in the Register, and the figure *1* is added if the anchors, cables and hawsers are also as prescribed. Thus the designation *100A1* means that the ship and her equipment are in Lloyd's highest class. Ships of special type are similarly classed, as, for example, *Class 100A1 Oil Tanker, Class 100A1 Ore Carrier, Class 100A1 Trawler;* or *Class 100A1 for Vessels in Restricted Service,* e.g. cross-Channel vessels, in which some relaxations of the normal rules for passenger-carrying vessels are permitted. There is also *Class A1 for Restricted Service,* for ships trading in specially sheltered waters such as harbours and estuaries. Vessels built under the Society's special survey are entitled to the distinctive mark of a Maltese cross in front of their classification character.

A steel-built vessel can only retain the classification assigned to her when she was built if she passes a special survey every four years, these surveys becoming progressively more exacting as her age increases. In addition, all vessels are subject to annual or occasional surveys when practicable.

Another classification required by Lloyd's is for the machinery, including main and auxiliary engines, boilers, essential appliances, pumping arrangements and electrical equipment. Subject to compliance with the Society's requirements, the letters *LMC* (Lloyd's Machinery Certificate) are added to the Register, continuance of this classification being subject to periodical surveys as with the hull.

It can be seen that a ship must undergo comprehensive and regular surveys to be classed by a Classification Society. Various arrangements have been introduced by the societies to reduce the time spent out of service for survey. Some examples of the arrangements operated by Lloyd's Register are described below.

Continuous Survey Hull (CSH) enables the complete survey of the hull to be spread over a 5-year period by surveying a portion of the vessel each year.

Continuous Survey Machinery (CSM) enables various items of machinery to be opened during a voyage so that they are ready for inspection by surveyors at the next loading or discharge port.

There is also a system whereby selected Chief Engineer Officers are empowered to examine certain items of their own ship's machinery while at sea; their findings are then endorsed as part of the machinery survey by a surveyor at the next convenient port.

Load lines

With the exception of certain minor vessels, international law requires that all merchant ships shall comply with specified minimum requirements in regard to the height of their freeboard, in order to ensure the safety of life at sea.The freeboard for each ship is assigned according to certain rules to ensure that the ship will have a reasonable reserve of buoyancy, and it determines the maximum draught to which the ship shall be loaded. This draught is required to be marked on the ship's sides by a *load line*.

The methods employed in the assignment are given in a *statutory instrument* called the *Merchant Shipping (Load Line) Rules 1968,* published for the Department of Trade by Her Majesty's Stationery Office, which includes regulations governing the minimum standards of strength to ensure that the structure of the ship can withstand the stresses set up by the loading when she is floated at the prescribed maximum draught. Separate rules are laid down for tankers, sailing ships, and ships carrying deck loads of timber. Exceptional cases are dealt with individually.

To qualify for the minimum freeboard allowed by *Merchant Shipping (Load Line) Rules 1968,* a ship must be built to scantlings which comply with the highest standard of the rules of certain Classification Societies or which comply with standards of strength laid down by the load-line rules. Most passenger vessels, however, cannot be loaded down to the maximum draught permissible for their dimensions because of the limited space available for cargo, and they would be unnecessarily strong if built to these standards. Such ships can be assigned an increased freeboard, and an allowance can be made for the lighter loading by permitting lighter scantlings in the hull structure. The smaller freeboard allowed to tankers has already been explained (page 73).

The freeboard is measured from the uppermost complete deck in which are incorporated permanent means of closing all openings in those parts of the deck exposed to the weather. In flush-decked ships, and in ships with detached poop, bridge and superstructures, this is the upper deck. In ships with a continuous non-watertight superstructure (i.e. shelter-deck vessels) the freeboard is measured from the deck below the uppermost deck.

The amount of the freeboard assigned to a ship depends mainly upon her length; the longer the ship the greater must be her freeboard. Corrections are made to the standard freeboard appropriate to the ship's length in accordance with the ship's form, the extent and height of her superstructure, any excess or lack of sheer or camber, and the ratio of her length to her depth measured from her freeboard deck.

The assigned freeboard is measured, midway between the bow and stern of the ship, vertically downwards from the upper surface of the freeboard deck where it meets the ship's side. It is indicated by a circle bisected by a horizontal line known as the *Load Line Disc* which is permanently marked by chisel or centre-punch on the ship's side and then painted over in white or yellow on a dark background or black on a light background. Additional lines known as *load lines* are similarly marked immediately forward of the assigned freeboard to indicate the *minimum freeboards* allowed in different seasons and localities, in fresh water, and in any other circumstances applicable to the ship, her trade or her route. Typical markings are shown in Fig. 3–14 and described below.

S   indicates the summer freeboard and is the base from which the other freeboards are measured.

W   indicates the winter freeboard, which is greater than the summer freeboard by $\frac{1}{48}$ of summer draught.

WNA   indicates the winter freeboard for voyages in certain areas of the North Atlantic, and is greater than the winter freeboard by 50 millimetres for vessels not exceeding 100 metres in length.

T   indicates the tropical freeboard, and is less than the summer freeboard by $\frac{1}{48}$ of summer draught.

F   indicates the freeboard in fresh water when loaded to the summer draught, salt-water displacement.

TF   indicates the freeboard in fresh water when loaded to the tropical draught, salt-water displacement.

The difference between **S** and **F** is the Fresh Water Allowance (FWA) and equals $\frac{\Delta}{4T}$ millimetres, where Δ is the summer salt-water displacement in tonnes and T is the tonnes-per-centimetre immersion (see also page 23).

The localities and seasons to which the different freeboards apply are internationally agreed and are laid down in the *Merchant Shipping (Load Line) Rules 1968.* These rules necessarily assume that any cargo or ballast is correctly stowed and distributed to ensure that the ship is seaworthy and

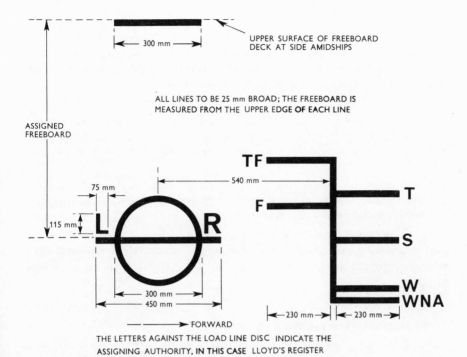

ASSIGNED FREEBOARD

UPPER SURFACE OF FREEBOARD DECK AT SIDE AMIDSHIPS

ALL LINES TO BE 25 mm BROAD; THE FREEBOARD IS MEASURED FROM THE UPPER EDGE OF EACH LINE

THE LETTERS AGAINST THE LOAD LINE DISC INDICATE THE ASSIGNING AUTHORITY, IN THIS CASE LLOYD'S REGISTER

FIG. 3-14. Load line disc and load lines

has a sufficient margin of stability, and the responsibility for this rests with the Master. The *Certificate of Approval* for the load lines assigned to a particular ship is issued by the Department of Trade or the Classification Society concerned, and it must be framed and displayed conspicuously in a public part of the ship. Before any ship puts to sea, particulars of her actual draughts and freeboard immediately before sailing, together with the assigned freeboard, density of the water, fresh-water allowances, etc., must be entered in the ship's official log book. These details must also be entered on the appropriate form which must be publicly displayed before sailing. Methods of calculating changes in draught, trim, etc., are described in Chapter 1.

The assigned freeboard is checked annually by a surveyor of the Department of Trade or the Classification Society concerned, who endorses the Certificate accordingly in the space provided. The Certificate is valid for a period not exceeding five years, and before it can be renewed the ship must be completely surveyed.

International Conference on Safety Of Life At Sea (SOLAS)

Safety of life at sea has been the subject of a series of international conferences, i.e. in 1914, 1929, 1948, 1960 and 1974, which are organised by IMO. The conferences are attended by delegations from governments of nations with a maritime interest and by observers from inter-governmental organisations, e.g. United Nations, International Civil Aviation Organization, World Meteorological Organization, International Hydrographic Bureau, etc.

The conference considers all aspects of safety of life at sea, and its deliberations are published as *The International Convention for the Safety of Life at Sea* which is annexed, together with any particular recommendations, to the Final Act of the conference. When ratified by sufficient subscribing countries the Convention becomes international law.

The Convention covers the following subjects in detail:

General provisions which state the applications and definitions for the Convention, the rules for survey of vessels and the requisite certificates, and the investigation of casualties, e.g. collisions, groundings, fires, explosions etc.

Construction of vessels, including watertight subdivision and stability, machinery and electrical installations, fire protection, fire detection and extinction, and general fire precautions.

Lifesaving appliances, including provision of lifeboats, liferafts, lifejackets and lifebuoys, radio apparatus, and training and emergency procedures.

Radio. Technical and watchkeeping requirements, and the form of logs to be kept.

Safety of navigation.

The carriage of grain and of dangerous goods.

Nuclear ships. Additional regulations applicable to nuclear-powered vessels.

In the United Kingdom the Convention is administered by the Department of Trade or delegated to the Classification Society, and it is by these means that the design, construction, equipment, fittings and operation of ships are required to conform to national law which embodies the Convention.

TONNAGE MEASUREMENT

Tonnage is supposed to have referred originally to the carrying capacity of a ship, in *tuns* of wine, one tun having a capacity of 252 wine gallons and occupying about 42 cubic feet, but the present forms of measurement began with the Merchant Shipping Act of 1854.

The tonnage of a ship can be expressed in terms of weight or volume (capacity). Every merchant ship is required by law to be measured during building for the ascertainment of her tonnage capacity; this tonnage forms the basis on which appropriate dock, harbour and canal dues are assessed.

New rules governing tonnage capacity have come into operation since the publication of Volume I (1979) and these are now described.

Tonnage capacity is a measure of the internal volume of a ship and must not be confused with displacement, deadweight and lightweight tonnages, which are weights expressed in tonnes. Warships are invariably described by their displacement; the term is rarely used for merchant ships because of the great difference in actual weight when fully or lightly loaded.

Tonnage capacity

In 1982, regulations came into force introducing a new system of tonnage measurement giving effect to the IMO Tonnage Convention of 1969. *The Merchant Shipping (Tonnage) Regulations 1982* cater for both new and existing ships: merchant ships of 24 metres in length and over, whose construction began after July 1982, have their tonnage ascertained by the new system of measurement; for existing ships the previously accepted method of measurement remains valid until 1994 when the measurement of all British merchant ships will have to comply with the new system. The previous method of measurement used a volumetric unit of 1 ton = 2.83 cubic metres (100 cubic feet). In the new system no special units are employed because the formulae used in calculating tonnage are made up of several terms, only one of which is volume. The purposes of the new system are: to achieve a unified method of measurement which is relatively simple to apply, and to remove the numerous anomalies of the previous method.

NEW SYSTEM

Gross Tonnage. This value is derived from a formula based upon the moulded (internal dimensions) volume of the entire ship — the hull plus erections and all enclosed spaces. Gross tonnage gives a realistic indication of the ship's size and is expressed, for example, 'Gross Tonnage = 12 000' (not 12 000 *tons*).

Net Tonnage. This is derived from a formula based upon the moulded volume of the ship's cargo spaces, the number of passengers carried, the moulded depth of the ship and the summer draught. Net tonnage gives a general indication of a ship's earning capacity and is expressed simply as the Net Tonnage and not as a quantity of tons.

OLD SYSTEM

Tonnage deck means the deck next below the upper deck except in the case of single deck ships, in which case it means the upper deck.

Underdeck tonnage is the volume of the ship below the tonnage deck and measured to the inside of the frames or sparring, in tons of 2.83 cubic metres. In British tonnage measurement double-bottom spaces are not included, the depths for tonnage being measured to the upper side of the tank-top plating or the hold ceiling.

Gross tonnage is the underdeck tonnage plus the tonnage of between-deck spaces and all permanently closed-in erections above the tonnage deck which are available for cargo, stores or accommodation. It is expressed as tons, gross tonnage.

Register, or Net, tonnage is the figure on which harbour, dock, canal and similar dues are assessed. It is obtained by deducting from the gross tonnage certain allowances for non-earning spaces, principally the propulsion machinery and steering-engine compartments, water-ballast tanks, cable lockers, accommodation for the officers and crew, and navigation spaces such as the wheel and chart houses. Register tonnage is expressed as tons, register (or net) tonnage.

Tonnage Weight

Displacement is the actual weight of a ship expressed in tonnes. The displacement of a warship depends on her condition of loading (whether light, deep, etc.), and a value commonly used nowadays is the *Standard Displacement*, which is the weight of the ship complete when fully manned and equipped with her stores and ammunition on board, but without her fuel. The value for displacement is arrived at by computing the volume of sea water displaced, in cubic metres, and multiplying the result by 1.025 to obtain tonnes.

Deadweight tonnage is the total weight of the cargo, stores, fresh water, fuel and crew which a vessel can carry when loaded down to her marks, and it is measured in tonnes. This is the normal method of expressing the tonnage of oil tankers; for instance a 250 000-tonne tanker carries 250 000 tonnes of cargo, etc., when at her marks.

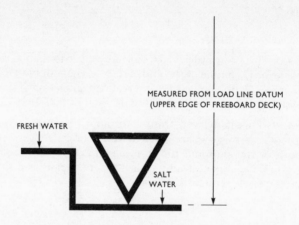

FIG. 3–15. The tonnage mark

Lightweight tonnage is displacement minus deadweight, i.e. the weight of the fabric of the ship, expressed in tonnes.

For comparing the sizes of merchant ships, tonnage figures under the old system are not a reliable guide, because of the variations in the exemptions and deductions allowed on account of differences in details of their construction. The register tonnage is particularly misleading, and so sometimes is the gross tonnage, although it gives a fair idea of the bulk of a ship. A typical example is the open shelter-deck ship, so called because practically the whole of the between-deck space under the shelter-deck is regarded in British tonnage measurement as an *open* space, because there is at least one non-weathertight *tonnage hatch* in it. This space is therefore exempt from measurement, i.e. it is not included in the gross or register tonnage. A ship of the same dimensions without such an opening would have a considerably greater tonnage, because the exemption would not then apply. In the case of countries that have implemented the *tonnage mark scheme* the tonnage hatch in open/closed shelter-deck vessels is permanently sealed. The space in the shelter-deck is still exempted provided the *tonnage mark* (Fig. 3–15) painted on the ship's side is not submerged.

As an example of how tonnage figures compare, those for a medium cargo vessel of standard construction and about 135 metres long would be roughly as follows:

Displacement	18 900 tonnes
Deadweight	15 000 tonnes
Lightweight	3 900 tonnes
Gross Tonnage	8 500 ⎱
Net Tonnage	5 000 ⎰ New System.

Suez and Panama Canal tonnage

The principles governing the measurement of ships by the Suez Canal or Panama Canal rules are the same as for British tonnage, but there are detailed differences as regards the exemption of certain spaces and the deductions allowed for net tonnage. These tonnage figures often vary considerably from the British register tonnages, and usually work out as higher than them by the following percentages, roughly:

Suez:	5 per cent higher than gross
	30 per cent higher than net
Panama:	10 per cent higher than gross
	30 per cent higher than net.

Full details of measurement for these purposes are given in *Measurement of Panama Canal Tonnage* and *Measurement of Suez Canal Tonnage*, published for the Department of Trade by Her Majesty's Stationery Office.

Tonnage of warships

All HM ships are measured by the Department of Trade for tonnage in accordance with both the British rules and the Suez Canal rules, a copy of the *tonnage certificate* being kept on board in the *Ship Equipment File*. An important difference between a warship and merchant ships is that no deduction for crew spaces is allowed in the net tonnage of the former. By agreement between the Ministry of Defence, the tonnage-assigning authority and the harbour authorities, the dues to be paid on behalf of HM ships for the use of British docks and harbours are based on the legal net tonnage reduced by seven per cent of the gross tonnage to allow for crew spaces. This special tonnage figure is inserted on a slip attached to the tonnage certificate.

In the Suez Canal a crew- and navigation-space deduction, limited to five per cent of the gross tonnage, is allowed to warships. Double-bottom spaces are not included in the tonnage, but must be paid for in passing through the canal if they contain more than 15 centimetres depth of oil fuel; they are then paid for on their full capacity.

In the Panama Canal, warships are assessed on their actual displacement. Curves of displacement and tonnes-per-centimetre immersion are included in the Stability Statement kept in the *Ship Equipment File*.

G

REGISTRATION

British ships are required to be registered, and provided with a *Certificate of Registry* issued by the Department of Trade and carried on board. This certificate gives essential particulars of the ship, such as the identification, dimensions, gross and net tonnages, name, port of registry, place and date of build, description, particulars of displacement, particulars of machinery, builder's name, and name and address of the owners. The name of the Master and the number of his certificate are also recorded in the Register and alterations with change of command are endorsed by local Customs Houses in the United Kingdom or by British Consuls if abroad.

There are certain legal prerequisites before a ship can be registered. These include the marking of the approved name on each bow and on the stern; the marking of the port of registry on the stern; the certification of draught marks at bow and stern; and the permanent cutting-in of the official number (which is never altered once the ship is registered) and the register tonnage on the main beam of the ship. This system is unique as long as the vessel remains under the British flag. Should the vessel change flag, that particular country's administration will issue its own official number. Should the flag subsequently revert to British ownership the original number will be re-issued.

CHAPTER 4

Cargo Handling and Stowage

The efficient, economical and safe stowage of a shipment of cargo is a complex problem which needs thorough knowledge and considerable experience of the subject. This chapter is intended only to explain the principles and main features of cargo stowing and handling. It is divided into a *glossary* and the following sections: *general principles* which describes port organisation, cargo-handling gear found in ports, ships' cargo-handling gear, documentation associated with cargo stowage and loading organisation; *containerised cargo* including the different methods of container handling and the stowage of containerised cargo; and *crude oil cargoes*.

Terms and expressions described in the glossary are used in the body of the text without further explanation; a read through the glossary is recommended.

GLOSSARY OF TERMS

Apron.   The quayside between a shed and the edge of a quay.

Backweight rig or *Deadman rig.*   A SWINGING DERRICK with a lazy guy shackled to its head. The lazy guy is then rove through the head block of another derrick rigged to plumb the opposite side of the hold, and a suitable weight is slung on its end. This returns the swinging derrick to plumb the hold after the load has been discharged. No longer in common use.

Bale capacity.   The cargo space available within a ship or a hold, measured in cubic metres from the lower edges of the beams and the inner edges of the cargo battens across the side frames. It is therefore less than the GRAIN CAPACITY (which see) by the amount of space between the beams and the frames.

Between deck, see 'TWEEN DECK.

Bilge and cantline.   The method of stowing barrels or casks with the bilges of the casks of the upper tiers over the cantlines of the casks of the lower tiers.

Bill of lading.   A receipt for goods loaded in a ship. It gives the terms on which the goods are accepted as freight, and is signed by the person who contracts to carry them or by his representative (e.g. the Master of the ship). Although primarily a receipt, a bill of lading is also treated as a negotiable document of title representing the goods to which it relates.

Booby hatch.   A small additional hatchway giving access to a hold.

Breaking bulk.   Shifting the first few packages in a closely stowed hold, the better to get at the remainder.

Breaking-out.   The operation of BREAKING BULK in a hold when starting to discharge cargo.

Broken stowage.   The spaces between items or parcels of cargo when stowed in a hold. It may be due to bad stowage, irregular sizes or shapes of the various items of cargo, the size and shape of the hold, stanchions and similar fittings in way of the cargo, or the need to use a lot of DUNNAGE. An arbitrary allowance for broken stowage, based on experience, is made when planning the stowage of different types of cargo in the same hold.

Bulk cargo.   Any type of dry or liquid cargo such as grain, coal, ores and petroleum which can be stowed in bulk.

Bullrope.   A rope for hauling cargo from the wings or ends of a hold to its centre or vice versa; or a rope used as a steadying line to guide a lift clear of obstructions in its path.

Cargo battens.   Removable wooden battens fitted across the inner edges of the frames in a hold to prevent contact between cargo of a general nature and the ship's side. In addition to protecting the cargo from damage caused by sweating of the ship's sides, they provide an air space for ventilation.

Cargo deadweight.   The weight in tonnes of an item, or parcel, of cargo.

Ceiling.   The wooden deck fitted over the bottoms of the holds of some ships which carry a general cargo. Its purpose is to prevent contact between the cargo and the inner bottom or the tank tops.

Containers.   The standard-sized units into which cargoes are packed for carriage in container ships.

Cordwood.   Small pieces of wood used as DUNNAGE.

Corner casting.   The standard casting built into the corners of all cargo containers complying with ISO specifications. Used for the attachment of handling gear and securing arrangements.

Deadman rig, see BACKWEIGHT RIG.

Demurrage.   The rate or amount payable to the shipowner by a charterer for failure to load or discharge cargo within the agreed time.

Derrick table or *Mast platform.*   A tabernacle built round the foot of a mast for supporting the heels of the derricks and occasionally the winches.

Despatch money.   A bonus paid by the shipowner to the charterer if his ship is loaded or discharged before the period agreed upon.

Drift.   The clearance between the head block of a derrick and the bulwarks, the quayside or any obstruction in its path.

Dunnage.   Baulks of timber, QUARTERING, planks, CORDWOOD and other similar materials, used for shoring, chocking, packing and ventilating cargo.

Dunnage bags.   Inflatable bags used as packing between cargo in a loose stow to prevent movement.

Fiddley.   The space above the boiler and engine rooms of a ship.

Flooring-out.   Spreading DUNNAGE or stowing cargo over the bottom of a hold.

Full and down. Describes the condition of a vessel when her holds are filled to capacity and she is loaded down to her maximum legal draught.

Gantry. An overhanging or spanning structure. Descriptive of the most common type of container-handling crane.

General cargo. A cargo comprising different commodities, as distinct from HOMOGENEOUS CARGO such as grain or liquids in bulk.

Gin fall. Another name for the whip, RUNNER or purchase of a derrick.

Grain capacity. Cargo space available within a ship or a hold, measured in cubic metres from the sides of the ship and the deckheads of the holds. It is therefore greater than the BALE CAPACITY (which see) by the amount of space between the frames and the beams.

Gross weight. The total weight of a case and its contents.

Hand hook. A pointed steel hook with a T-handle used by stevedores for handling cargo. Its use should be strictly confined to handling crates, cases and other similar articles, and it should never be used for handling bales, bags and other 'softly'-packed goods.

Hatch beams. Removable steel beams fitted athwart a hatch to strengthen it and to support the HATCH BOARDS.

Hatch boards. Stout timber boards which fit over the HATCH BEAMS and form part of the HATCH COVER.

Hatch covers. In most modern merchant ships these are of the PONTOON or folding type and generally they are mechanically operated from the weather deck.

Hatch square or *Hatch case.* The area enclosed by the coamings of a hatch.

Hoist or *Sett.* One or a number of items of cargo slung for hoisting.

Homogeneous cargo. A cargo comprising one commodity.

House fall. A variation of the UNION PURCHASE RIG in which one of the whips is led through a head block shackled to a structure on shore.

ISO (International Standards Organization). The ISO exists to make agreements on international standards and in the cargo-handling context determines the standard sizes of CONTAINERS, PALLETS, etc.

Jumbo derrick. A derrick designed for heavy lifts.

Lay days. The period agreed between a charterer and a shipowner for loading or discharging a shipment of cargo. (See also DEMURRAGE and DESPATCH MONEY.)

Lazaret. A store room for ship's stores or provisions, usually situated in the after part of the ship.

Limber boards. Removable boards between the sides and bottom of a hold to give access to the bilges for cleaning or drying them out.

Liverpool rig. A rig used with a single STANDING DERRICK rigged to plumb over the ship's side. The hoist is guided through the hatch by reeving the whip through a tail block fitted with a BULLROPE, and the bullrope is worked from a portable bollard clamped to the hatch coaming.

Lock-up or *Locker*.   A cargo space specially built or partitioned-off from a hold and situated usually in one of the lower or upper 'TWEEN DECKS, where valuable cargo or cargo of a pilferable nature is stowed.

Lower hold.   The lowest of a tier of holds in ships fitted with one or more 'TWEEN DECKS.

Manifest.   A detailed list of a ship's cargo, prepared at the port of shipment; it shows the marks, numbers and descriptions of packages, together with the names of the consignees.

Married gear, see UNION PURCHASE RIG.

Mast platform, see DERRICK TABLE.

Midship derrick.   The derrick which plumbs the hatch in the UNION PURCHASE RIG.

Midship guy.   The guy rigged between the heads of the midship and outboard derricks.

Nett weight.   The weight of the contents of a case or CONTAINER.

Optional cargo.   Cargo of a general nature which, at the option of the consignor, may be discharged at any one of a number of ports.

Outboard derrick or *Yard-arm derrick*.   The derrick which plumbs over the ship's side in the UNION PURCHASE RIG.

Over-carriage.   The carriage of cargo beyond its port of destination by an oversight.

Packing and *Stripping*.   The descriptive names for the packing and unpacking operations of CONTAINERS.

Pallet.   A wooden tray used for slinging a number of items of cargo in one SETT.

Pallet tray or *Master pallet*.   A large pallet capable of loading or discharging more than one pallet at a time.

Parcel.   A number of items of cargo from a common source, or for a common destination.

Pontoon hatch-cover or *Slab hatch-cover*.   A steel hatch-cover unsupported by beams.

Port speed.   The rate at which cargo is loaded or discharged at a particular port. For bulk cargo it is sometimes called the *custom of the port*.

Quartering.   Timber of square cross-section used as DUNNAGE.

Roll on/roll off.   Ro-ro is a system whereby specially designed ships can be loaded and unloaded by driving vehicles containing the cargo, or handling the cargo, directly on and off the ship.

Runner.   The whip or fall of a derrick.

Save-all.   A net rigged to catch any cargo falling between the ship and the quay, or a canvas sheet spread in a hold or on deck to catch any leakage from bagged cargo such as grain.

Separation. The stowage of one type of cargo apart from another as a precaution against fire, and for the prevention of contamination or deterioration of the cargo and damage to the cargo or the ship. Separation may also be used to distinguish between two or more consignments of the same commodity.

Sett, see HOIST.

Shipping ton. A measurement of 1.135 cubic metres (originally 40 cubic feet) used at the option of the shipowner in determining the freightage dues for cargo; it was approximately the space occupied by a ton of well-stowed Welsh coal. The freightage of heavier cargo is computed on its deadweight.

Short-landing. Failure to discharge the whole of a cargo at its destination, due to an oversight. (See also OVER-CARRIAGE.)

Sideloader. A mobile container-handling machine capable of stowing CONTAINERS close together and requiring very little headroom.

Sparring. Planking or other material fitted as a lining to the sides or ends of a compartment to insulate the cargo from the sides or bulkheads.

Special cargo. Fragile or valuable cargo which is consigned to the special custody of the Chief Officer, and stowed usually in the LOCKER or other secure stowage.

Standing derrick. A derrick rigged to plumb one position only.

Stevedore. Strictly, the person who contracts for the handling of cargo into or out of a ship. In general, however, men actually engaged in stowing or discharging the cargo are called stevedores.

Stowage factor. The volume in cubic metres occupied by one tonne of any particular type of well-stowed cargo. It includes allowances for BROKEN STOWAGE and any DUNNAGE required for that particular type of cargo.

Stowage plan. A rough plan of the ship showing the stowage of her cargo.

Straddle carrier. A mobile container-handling machine which transports and stacks CONTAINERS by hoisting them within its four-wheeled legs.

Stripping, see PACKING.

Strong-room. A strongly constructed, fireproof compartment, provided in some ships for the stowage of very valuable cargo or specie.

Supercargo. Short for Cargo Superintendent — an official formerly appointed to a cargo ship by the shipowner or charterer expressly for the supervision of the loading, selling and discharging of her cargo and obtaining other cargoes; he sailed with the ship throughout her voyage. This office is seldom filled nowadays.

Swinging derrick. A derrick rigged to plumb alternately over the hold and over the ship's side.

Tally and *Tally clerk.* To tally is to check each item of cargo as it is loaded or discharged, and a tally clerk is the man who does this job.

Tare weight. The weight of an empty case or vehicle.

Tomming. Shoring cargo to prevent it from shifting.

'Tween deck.   An auxiliary cargo deck below the upper deck. In a hold with two 'tween decks the spaces are called the upper and lower 'tween decks and the LOWER HOLD.

Ullage.   The amount by which a cask, tank or other container holding liquid is not full. For ship's tanks, the ullage is usually measured as the depth vacant at the top of the tank and then coverted to quantity by the use of *Ullage Tables* which are computed for the particular tank.

Union purchase rig or *Married gear.*   A rig in which the whips of two STANDING DERRICKS are joined to the cargo hook. One derrick plumbs the hold and the other plumbs over the ship's side.

Unitised cargo.   Cargo which is ready-packed in units, e.g. containerised cargo, palletised cargo.

Wharfinger.   The operator of a wharf, who has certain responsibilities in regard to goods stowed thereon, the upkeep of the wharf and of the berths alongside it.

Winging.   Stowing cargo so that most of it is distributed in the wings of the hold. This may be done when stowing heavy items of cargo to improve the seaworthiness of the ship.

Wing lead.   An alternative to the BACKWEIGHT method of rigging a SWINGING DERRICK. The whip is led from the head of the derrick through a leading block on the ship's side and thence to the winch. As the whip takes the weight of a HOIST the derrick will tend to swing over the ship's side.

GENERAL PRINCIPLES

PORT ORGANISATION

The cargo traffic through a port may be divided into two categories — *bulk cargo* and *general cargo*. The term general cargo covers a wide range of commodities and, although containerisation is converting a great deal of general cargo to bulk cargo for handling purposes, containerised cargo is still classified within the general-cargo concept. True bulk cargoes are ores, chemicals, fertilisers, oils and petroleum, all of which are cargoes stowed in their loose form (i.e. unpacked) in ships specially designed for their carriage.

It follows that different cargo-handling equipment, handling techniques and berthing facilities are required to deal with these diverse cargoes. The types of berth provided at ports fall mainly into the following categories.

Unit load berths. These include the container-ship berths where containers are loaded, discharged and marshalled by specialised cranes and equipment.

Ro-ro berths. These berths are specially designed and constructed with arrangements to connect to the ship's ramps.

Break bulk berths. These berths handle general cargo shipped by traditional methods.

Specialised berths. These are berths which have particular facilities for handling some commodities usually classified as general cargo but often handled in bulk, such as chemicals, and timber and steel products.

Of these categories the unit load berth reflects the greatest change in port development in recent years. As well as the specialised handling equipment, some of which is discussed later in this chapter, a container berth requires a large storage area for collecting and sorting containers.

Port speed

Each day that a vessel remains unnecessarily in port results in a reduction of the ship's earnings. The earnings of a vessel are determined by balancing the debits against the credits after a vessel has completed a particular voyage. The usual outstanding item of credit is the freightage earned, while the wharfage and dock charges constitute a large debit item. It is this latter item which makes the speed of handling so important.

PORT CRANEAGE

Container craneage

Various types of crane are used to lift and transport containers, of which the major types fall into two groups: the transporter gantry crane which is used to load and discharge containers to and from the ship on to the apron or the flat beds of rail or road vehicles, and the overhead travelling crane usually engaged in the lifting, transporting and stacking of containers in the storage or marshalling area. These two types of crane are assisted in their operations at a container port by other fully-mobile container-handling equipment, e.g. straddle carriers and sideloaders.

The transporter gantry crane (Fig. 4–1). There are several variations of this type of crane but they are all constructed on similar principles. The crane is supported on a wide-spaced four-legged gantry which is mounted on rails and capable of travelling along the edge of the quay. Mounted on the gantry is the transporter beam which projects outwards over the edge of the quay and inwards over the apron. The beam supports a carriage which can be traversed through the gantry legs and along the whole length of the beam. A spreader, which is slung from the carriage by the purchase wires, can be lowered into and hoisted from the cells of a container ship. Guides and coupler latches are fitted at the underside four corners of the spreader so that, when lowered on to a container, the latches automatically engage with the four top corner castings. The latches operate on a twist-and-lock principle and are locked into and released from the container by remote-operated actuators. It is common practice for the spreader to be constructed on telescopic principles so that it may be set up to handle the differing sizes of container. Thus the crane is capable of positioning its transporter beam over the cellular hold of a ship, lifting a container, transporting it, and lowering it on to the apron of the quay. Loading is carried out by the reverse procedure. The outer portion of the transporter beam is pivoted at the gantry and, when not in use, can be topped up to allow unobstructed movement of shipping at the quay. In normal use this type of crane can handle up to about 25 containers per hour.

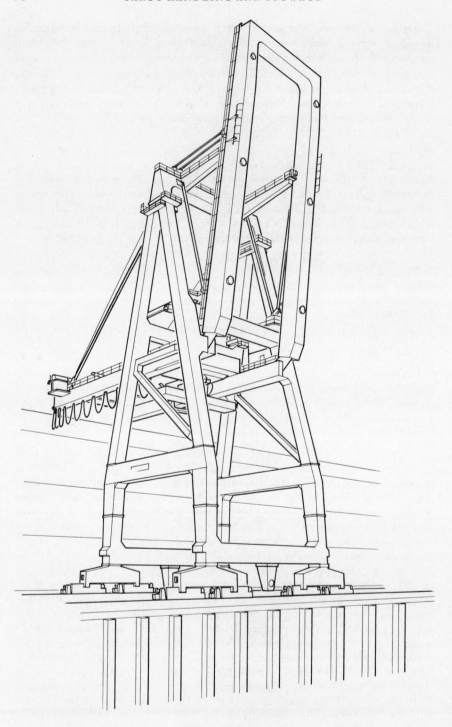

FIG. 4–1. Typical transporter gantry crane showing the transporter beam
topped up

The overhead travelling crane is built on the cantilever principle and has a long transporter beam supported on wide-spaced legs which are mounted on rails. The beam spans the legs and projects beyond them at each end, and the complete structure can travel along the length of the rails. A carriage and spreader, similar to that of the gantry crane, are supported on the transporter beam and can traverse the whole length of the beam. This type of crane can lift, transport and stack containers over the area of the storage premises or marshalling area for which it is designed.

Conventional craneage

There is a vast range of conventional cranes, including floating cranes, with lifting capacities from 3 to 400 tonnes. The types of crane found in a port will be those associated with the particular types of trade of the port, and they can be grouped accordingly. Conventional cranes can handle containers by means of a top-lift container frame, one type of which is illustrated in Volume II, Fig. 6–13.

General cargo. This is handled by jib cranes having capacities of up to 50 tonnes, jib cranes of the luffing type with capacities up to 35 tonnes and double-luffing cranes of up to 50 tonnes capacity.

Bulk cargo. Those cargoes requiring craneage are normally handled by luffing cranes fitted with *clamp* or *grab* attachments most suited to the cargo. In many cases the attachment is specifically designed for handling a particular commodity.

Heavy lifts. Cranes for heavy lifts have capacities up to 180 tonnes and for heavier lifts floating cranes with capacities up to 400 tonnes are used.

SHIP CRANEAGE

Although many modern ships are now fitted with electric or hydraulic cranes, derricks still remain the most common form of cargo-handling equipment. This section deals with the principles of derrick rigs and operation, and then describes their application to a modern derrick crane.

Basic principles

Considerable development has taken place in recent years in the aspects of ship craneage but the original principles of derrick operation still apply. Derricks, and the methods of determining stresses in parts of the rig and safe working loads, are described in Volume II, Chapter 6. The common methods of derrick operation are described below.

Swinging derrick. The swinging derrick is the oldest form of ship cargo-handling gear and its various methods of rigging are shown in Fig. 4–2. The traditional swinging derrick is rigged with a topping lift and two guys in addition to the cargo fall, whereas in modern versions the topping lift and guys are combined into a common topping/slewing rig.

Standing derricks. Various rigs of standing derrick are shown in Fig. 4–3. Of these the *union purchase* (Fig. 4–3(ii)) is the usual type for handling general cargo, particularly in older ships. Two derricks are rigged so that

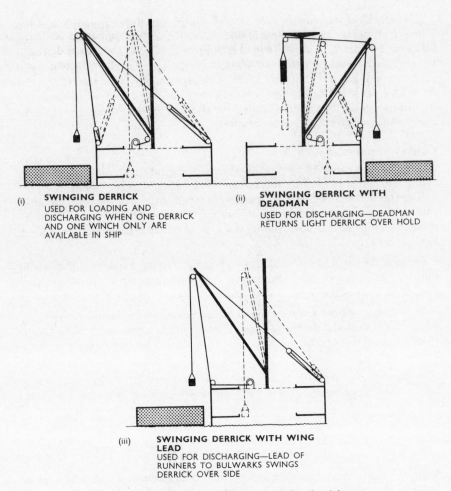

(i) **SWINGING DERRICK**
USED FOR LOADING AND
DISCHARGING WHEN ONE DERRICK
AND ONE WINCH ONLY ARE
AVAILABLE IN SHIP

(ii) **SWINGING DERRICK WITH
DEADMAN**
USED FOR DISCHARGING—DEADMAN
RETURNS LIGHT DERRICK OVER HOLD

(iii) **SWINGING DERRICK WITH WING
LEAD**
USED FOR DISCHARGING—LEAD OF
RUNNERS TO BULWARKS SWINGS
DERRICK OVER SIDE

FIG. 4–2. Various rigs of a swinging derrick

one, known as the *midship derrick*, will plumb the hold, while the other, known as the *outboard derrick*, is turned out over the ship's side to plumb a lighter or wharf. Their whips are joined by a union hook (see Volume II, Fig. 6–24) or by a union plate, either of which prevents undue stresses in the rig. The load is first hoisted by one derrick while the slack in the whip of the other is taken down; when clear of the hatchway or bulwarks, the load is transferred to the other derrick and lowered to the lighter or wharf. Alternative methods using a swinging derrick are illustrated at Fig. 4–3(i) and (iii).

A modern derrick crane

A typical derrick commonly found in general cargo vessels is illustrated at Fig. 4–4. This is one model of the range of Velle 'Shipshape' cranes. In this type the topping lift and guys are combined into a common topping/slewing rig which is led to the two winches, both of which have divided barrels. Both leads to the topping winch pass over the barrel in the same direction (D in

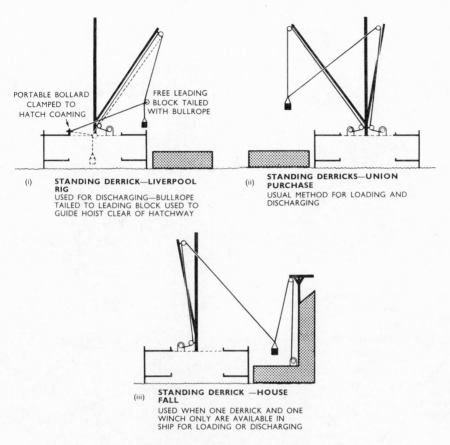

FIG. 4–3. Three types of rig of a standing derrick

Fig. 4–4) while those to the slewing winch pass over the barrel in opposite directions (*E* in Fig. 4–4). The topping winch shortens or lengthens both falls, thus raising or lowering the derrick, while the slewing winch lengthens one fall and shortens the other, thus slewing the derrick in one direction or the other but maintaining the topped height. To provide a wide slewing angle the topping/slewing rig is led through blocks widely spaced on the 'T' of the mast and is connected to the derrick head by a wire bridle as shown in Fig. 4–4 or by stabilising outriggers which are shown in Volume II, Fig. 6–22. Either form of rig stabilises the derrick while slewing and maintains positive control. The purchase arrangements vary from a simple double whip to double multi-parted falls but in all cases the upper block is divided with the halves positioned at each end of the 'T', at the derrick head. This arrangement stabilises the purchase and greatly reduces swinging of the load. These types of derrick are designed and built to suit particular requirements but common safe working loads vary between 10 and 50 tonnes. For heavier lifts it is often arranged that the hooks of two adjacent derricks can be connected by a spreader to handle loads of nearly twice the capacity of a single derrick. The crane is operated at a fixed console or from a portable control box which has a joystick to control the topping and slewing winches and a lever to control

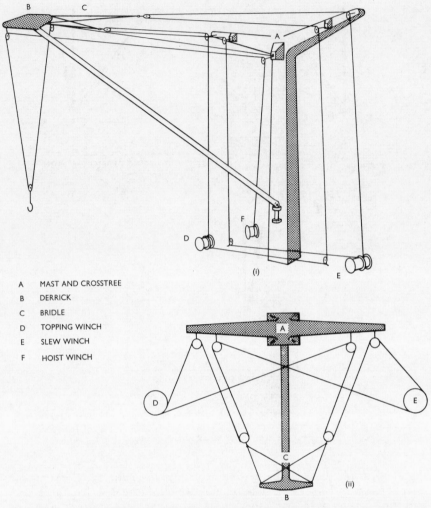

A	MAST AND CROSSTREE
B	DERRICK
C	BRIDLE
D	TOPPING WINCH
E	SLEW WINCH
F	HOIST WINCH

FIG. 4–4. The 'Velle' slewing derrick crane

the hoist winch. The joystick and lever automatically return to the neutral positions when released. All three motions are capable of simultaneous operation and, dependent on the weight of the load, high loading-cycle speeds can be obtained by a skilled operator.

HATCH COVERS

Access to holds for the loading and discharge of cargo is provided by large hatchways. In some vessels two hatchways will be found opening into one hold. The hatchways are as large as possible commensurate with the strength of the ship's structure, for example approximately 13 metres long by 9 metres wide in a typical general cargo ship. The hatchway is surrounded by a *coaming* or raised side which extends below the level of the deck, to support the deck beams and girders.

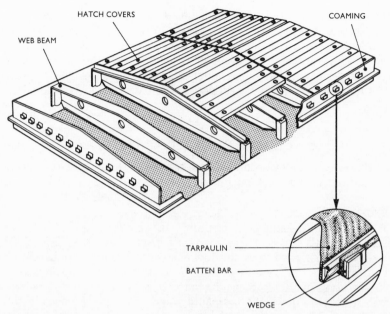

HATCH COVERS

WEB BEAM

COAMING

TARPAULIN

BATTEN BAR

WEDGE

FIG. 4–5. Hatch cover arrangement showing method of securing tarpaulin

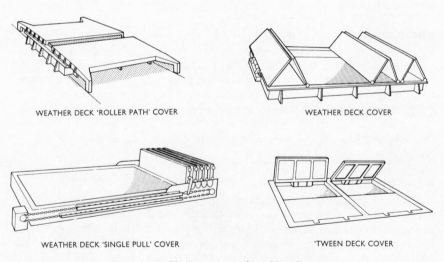

WEATHER DECK 'ROLLER PATH' COVER

WEATHER DECK COVER

WEATHER DECK 'SINGLE PULL' COVER

'TWEEN DECK COVER

FIG. 4–6. Various types of steel hatch-cover

The traditional method of closing hatchways is shown in Fig. 4–5. Web beams are supported by sockets on the inner face of the coaming and these in turn provide support for the hatch covers which are usually of strong timber of convenient sizes for easy removal. The whole is made watertight by covering with tarpaulins which are secured to the outer face of the coaming by batten bars and wedges. This method is now being rapidly superseded by steel hatch-covers (Fig. 4–6).

Mechanically operated steel hatch-covers are generally manufactured by specialist contractors and various types are illustrated in Fig. 4–6. The covers are worked by electric or hydraulic power and they are generally capable of emergency operation in the event of failure of the primary method. The covers are designed to give maximum clear working space when open, and to be watertight and capable of supporting a full deck load when closed.

CARGO DOCUMENTATION

This section outlines the documentation which is essential to the management of the loading and discharge operations of a ship's cargo.

Tallying

Tallying is the checking and recording of all the cargo loaded into or discharged from a vessel. This important part of cargo work, carried out by *tally clerks*, is designed to establish which consignments were handled by a particular ship in the event of a claim for missing cargo. Alphabetical index books are used, one for each hatch and each port of loading, to record the marks, numbers, description, quantity and stowage of goods within a compartment. The complete record of a consignment is generally kept on two facing pages, the left-hand for loading and the right-hand for discharge particulars.

Boat notes and mate's receipts

When a consignment is delivered to a ship a receipt must be given when the goods are on board. Regardless of the method of delivery the consignment is accompanied by an advice known as the *boat note*. When it is confirmed by tally that the goods are on board a *mate's receipt* is given either on a duplicate copy of the boat note or on the shipping company's official form. A receipt is given for only those goods proved to be on board and any discrepancy between the boat note and the tally is recorded on the mate's receipt.

Bill of lading

The bill of lading is the contractual agreement between the Master, or his agent, and the shipper, which specifies the conditions under which the consignment of cargo is carried. The goods are listed by their marks, numbers, description and quantity, and so it can be seen that the mate's receipts play an important part in the compilation of the bill of lading. The bill is not signed by the Master or his agent until all the correct mate's receipts are available. The bill is then delivered to the shipper on tendering his copies of the mate's receipts, and the bill thus becomes the proper receipt for goods proved to be on board. The bill is then forwarded by the shipper to the consignee and when the bill is tendered at the port of discharge the ship is bound to deliver the goods. It follows that separate bills of lading are required for each shipper and each consignee.

With the introduction of container and ro-ro cargo services the bill of lading may not entirely satisfy the need for an overall transit document and a modified form of bill may be introduced. One such form of documentation is the *Through Bill of Lading* (TBL) which is used on some European and intercontinental services.

Manifest

The manifest is a comprehensive list of all the cargo loaded into a vessel at a port of shipment. Against each bill of lading number are recorded the shippers, consignees, marks, numbers, quantity, weight, measurement, freightage paid or payable, and stowage of the items of cargo. It may be prepared by an agent although it is not unusual for ship's officers to compile the manifest from the ship's copies of the bills of lading.

The manifest is of great value in checking the discharge of cargo and in preventing over-carriage. Copies are forwarded to ports of discharge to assist in the planning of stevedoring services and equipment, and a full copy is required by the customs authorities at each port of discharge. Manifests also provide the information needed for the preparation of national trade statistics, e.g. imports and exports.

Cargo plans

The cargo plan is a schematic drawing showing the stowage of cargo in a general-cargo vessel. A blank pro-forma showing the sectional elevation and cargo deck plans is used to record the following cargo information: port of loading, port of discharge, quantity, deadweight and disposition of stow. Additional notations are made for hazardous and special cargoes, heavy lifts and any other particular information.

The cargo of container ships is completely unitised and thus the information described above can be presented in a more simple tabular form. Typical examples of cargo planning for both types of ship are described below.

Plan for a general cargo. Fig. 4–7 shows a typical stowage plan. It is the actual plan for the MV *Strathdevon* loading at three ports in the United Kingdom and discharging at six Gulf ports, and is reproduced by courtesy of The Peninsular and Oriental Steam Navigation Company. The size of the plan has been greatly reduced for presentation in this book and, to show the detail, a section representing No. 1 hold is shown at about two-thirds of its normal size in Fig. 4–8. The plan is coded in colours representing the ports of discharge and detailed study will reveal how the requirements listed above are incorporated in the plan. A table is either drawn up on the plan, or attached to it, showing the disposition of cargo deadweight in the particular holds for discharge at the various ports. The table is shown inset on Fig. 4–7 and from this information the vessel's stability data for the stages of the voyage are calculated.

The initial plan may be subject to considerable revision after it is compiled. The stevedoring contractors may require minor alterations to suit the handling of particular types of cargo, to suit the port facilities or to comply with certain conditions of labour; some cargoes may be delayed in transit, some cancelled and some added. The Master must assess the effects of loading or discharging cargo on the stability, draught and trim as accurately as possible and, since he has the ultimate responsibility for the ship and her cargo, he has the last say in the matter and may require some adjustments to suit any peculiarities or features of his ship. Copies of the initial plan are sent to the loading-port stevedores and to the company's agents.

H

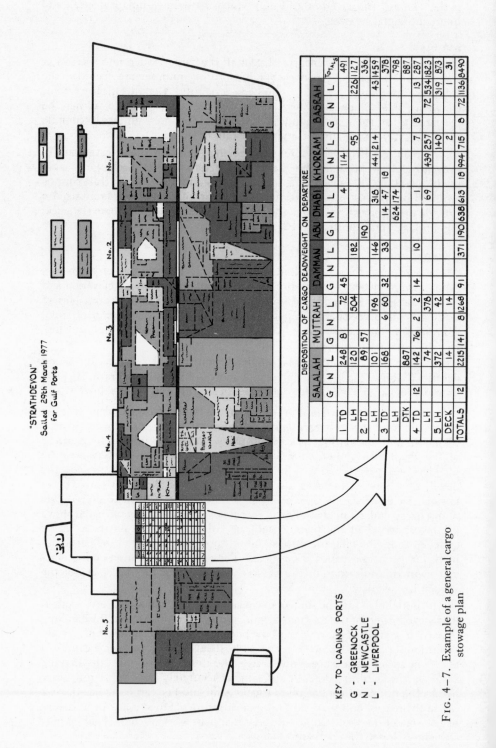

Fig. 4–7. Example of a general cargo stowage plan

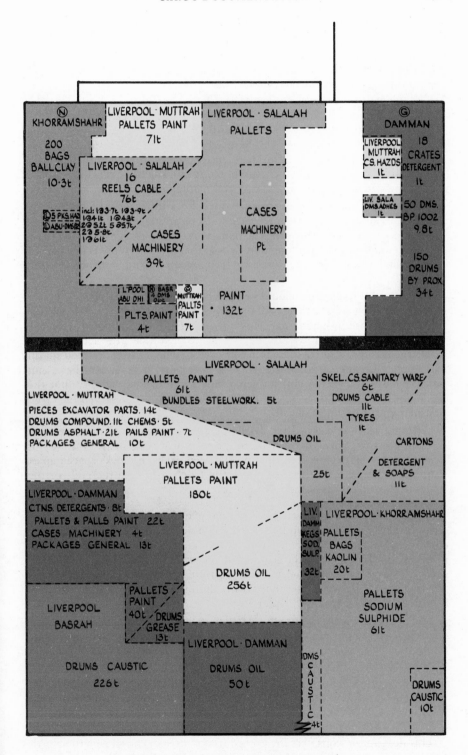

Fɪɢ. 4–8. Detail of part of cargo stowage plan

As the cargo is being loaded the ship's officers, or a plan maker, record the actual details of the stow and prepare an 'as stowed' plan. Copies of this plan and the cargo manifest are then sent to the discharge-port stevedores, the head office of the company, the company's agents and, if the plan has been compiled by a plan maker, to the Master of the ship.

The planner must ensure that the cargo is stowed so that it can be discharged as quickly as possible. Any large quantity of cargo destined for a particular port should therefore be distributed evenly among as many holds as is practicable, so that they can be used simultaneously when loading or discharging. For the same reason the cargo should be stowed at the opposite ends or sides of each hold so that two gangs of stevedores can work in the hold at the same time without getting in each other's way.

When two or more cargoes each destined for a different port are stowed together in the same hold, their stowage must be arranged so that discharging one will not necessitate restowing the remainder. The stowage of such cargoes should therefore be stepped down in tiers so that if one or more is discharged the remainder is stable and can easily be prevented from shifting by using dunnage.

It is essential that cargo should be readily accessible on arrival at the port of its destination so that there will be no delay in discharging and no wasted time and expense in having to restow any other cargo which may be in the way. Cargo is usually stowed in the reverse order to that in which it will be discharged, to prevent the possibility of overstowing a cargo destined for an early port with the cargo consigned to a later port. The 'tween decks and hatch squares are very useful for separating cargo for accessibility, but the hatch square of the upper 'tween decks should always be reserved for cargo destined for the first port of call.

Optional cargo consigned for discharge at two or more ports is the most difficult to stow, particularly if there are several parcels of it. One way of dealing with it is to stow it in the upper 'tween decks in blocks spaced apart from one another, each reaching from the hatch square to the ends or the wings or the bulkheads of the 'tween deck.

Plan for a container cargo. The stowage plan for a containerised cargo is simplified by the use of standard-sized containers into which the cargo has already been packed, very often by the manufacturer. Thus the ship is primarily concerned with the loading of containers of varying weights into predetermined slots, having particular regard to special or hazardous cargoes. The trimming problems associated with the loading or discharge of heavy containers are discussed in Chapter 3.

The method of compiling a stowage plan may vary between container-ship operators, but the principles described below are used completely or in part to produce a stowage plan. Telex (Automatic *Tele*typewriter *Ex*change Service) and computer services play a major role in the compilation of stowage plans and in the general execution of a modern shipping company's business.

The following description of the compilation of a stowage plan is that used by Atlantic Container Line Ltd, a company which operates partial container ships carrying both containerised and ro-ro cargo.

This description considers the procedure for a vessel engaged on the North Atlantic trade and calling at three European ports and three North American ports. One group of ports only is considered; the identical procedure would also occur at the other group of ports.

The company's *co-ordinator* (or *ship planner*) and all the *terminal operators* at the loading ports are interlinked by telex. The terminal operators initially produce their portions of the stowage plan which are passed to the co-ordinator who is ultimately responsible for deciding the stowage of cargo in a particular vessel. The co-ordinator may be sited at the company's headquarters or at one of the container terminals.

In this example the ports designated port 1, port 2 and port 3 are ports of loading but in practice, because container-ship operation is a continuous cycle, the loading ports are also ports of discharge.

During a period, usually one week preceding the arrival of the vessel at port 1, the company's *traffic* (freight) *departments* accept bookings from the market of shippers for cargo to be transported to advertised ports. The essential information required by the traffic departments is the number, weight and size of containers, details of rollable cargo, and the nature of any hazardous or special cargo. This information is collated and passed to the co-ordinator and the appropriate terminal operators by telex. The information is despatched daily as details of cargo become known and the message is known as a *booking telex*.

The co-ordinator and terminal operators each have a stateboard on which is entered the details of the stowage plan for the vessel prior to its arrival at port 1. Thus each operator is aware of the cargo to be discharged and the space available for loading cargo at his particular port.

The information on the stateboards and in the booking telex messages enables the terminal operators to prepare stowage plans for the cargo which is to be loaded at their respective ports. Twenty-four hours prior to the vessel's arrival at port 1, the terminal operator at that port passes his provisional stowage plan in message form, known as the *pre-stow telex,* to the co-ordinator. The co-ordinator, who has copies of the booking-telex messages for all the ports, either approves or amends this pre-stow plan. When the port 1 pre-stow telex has been agreed with the port 1 operator, the co-ordinator sends it to the operators at the subsequent ports. All the stateboards are then updated to comply with this information.

On receipt of the port 1 pre-stow telex, the port 2 terminal operator can prepare his provisional stowage plan and despatch the port 2 pre-stow telex to the co-ordinator, and the same procedure as for port 1 ensues. Subsequently the same procedure takes place between the port 3 terminal operator and the co-ordinator and the whole process is completed before the ship arrives at port 1.

On arrival at port 1 the designated cargo is discharged and that port's cargo is loaded. When loading is completed, port 1 sends a *condensed post-stow telex* to the co-ordinator and the subsequent ports to inform them of the stowage, number, size and destination of the containers and cargo actually loaded. This may differ from the agreed pre-stow telex because cargo may have been delayed or other cargo may have been booked and received after the pre-stow stage. The same procedure ensues at the subsequent loading ports.

```
TO  ACL/SOUTHAMPTON ES798
    ACL/LE HAVRE EF012
    ACL/ROTTERDAM/ER022


POSTOWAGE ATLANTIC CHAMPAGNE 447


01F1
2 203743 22 PP BA ROT
3 201986 22 PP BA ROT
4 207943 16 PP BA ROT    FLAM/LIQUID
5 203298 22 PP BA ROT
6 203964 22 PP BA ROT
7 206656 23 HH BA ROT
01F2
2 208370 23 HH BA ROT
3 202940 22 HH BA ROT
4 204019 20 HH BA ROT
5 205456 22 HH BA ROT
6 207650 22 HH BA ROT
7 206519 19 PP BA ROT
02F1
1 206083 14 HH NY RO
2 208398 23 HH NY RO
3 204793 23 HH NY AM     VIA/RO
4 206842 23 HH NY RO
5 205070 13 HH NY RO
6 205455 18 HH PO ROT
7 208102 10 HH BA ROT
8 207684 23 HH BA ROT
02F2
1 207147 22 HH NY RO
2 208045 22 HH NY RO
3 204302 23 HH NY RO
4 208111 13 HH NY RO
5 207624 20 HH NY RO
6 210805  9 HH BA AM     UFCU VIA/ROT
7 206530  6 HH BA AM     VIA/ROT
8 202866 19 PP BA ROT    OXIDIZING MATERIAL
03F1
1 205663 17HPP BA LH
2 220421 22 HH BA LH
3 203869 13 PP NY LH     POISON
4 203999 24 HH NY LH
```

|1| 2 | 3 | 4 | 5 | 6 | 7 |

FIG. 4–9. Excerpt from a typical full post-stow telex

Loading plans showing full information of the cargo and its stowage at port
1 are prepared by the terminal operator and handed to the Chief Officer.
These loading plans, known as the *traveller*, are handed to the terminal
operators at ports 2 and 3, and they are brought up to date as loading proceeds.
On completion of loading at port 3 a full set of loading plans will have been

compiled for the ship's officers. The requisite information is extracted from these plans and sent by telex to the co-ordinator and all terminal operators, enabling them to update their stateboards. This message is known as the *full post-stow telex*.

Fig. 4–9 illustrates part of a full post-stow telex for a voyage (No. 447) of the SS *Atlantic Champagne* from the North American ports of Baltimore, New York and Portland to Southampton, Le Havre and Rotterdam. The message was originated at the last port of loading and is addressed to the three European terminal operators. The message is divided into sections representing stowage positions within the ship and it is laid out in columns, indicated by numbers in the illustration, which carry the required information as explained in the table which follows.

Column	Information
1 (1 digit)	Position of container or ro-ro cargo within stowage section.
2 (6 digits)	Identification number of container.
3 (2 digits)	Container gross weight in tonnes.
4 (2/3 letters)	Status of the container. PP (Pier to Pier) indicates a container loaded at a depot with various shippers' goods. The container is then stripped at the pier at the port of destination and the consignees collect their goods as though they were conventional general cargo. HH (House to House) indicates a container packed at the shipper's premises (factory or warehouse); it will not be stripped until it reaches the consignees premises. There are variations to these basic rules, which are self-explanatory, e.g. PH, HP, HPP, etc.
5 (2/3 letters)	Port of loading in abbreviated form, i.e. BA (Baltimore) — NY (New York) — PO (Portland).
6 (2/3 letters)	Port of discharge in abbreviated form, i.e. ROT (Rotterdam) — LH (Le Havre).
7	Remarks including details of hazardous cargoes, routeing instructions for onward shipping, ownership of rented containers, etc.

At each port when loading has been completed, the weights of cargo, by section and layer, are calculated and are then sent to the co-ordinator by telex. From this information the co-ordinator calculates the stability data for the condition of loading and this is given to the Master before the ship sails.

STOWAGE PRINCIPLES

Measurement of cargo space

For the purposes of stowing cargo, the internal volume of the holds of a ship is measured by two methods: *grain space* and *bale space*. The unit of measurement is the cubic metre and the capacity of each cargo space, by both methods, is shown on the *General Arrangement and Capacity Plans* and in the *Stability Information Booklet* for the ship.

Grain space. This is the total internal volume measured between the plating athwartships and fore-and-aft, and from the deck to the deckhead. This space is not necessarily associated with the stowage of grain, but is the measurement for any bulk cargo which stows in such a manner as to fill completely the available space.

Bale space. This is the total internal volume of a compartment measured from the inner edges of the frames and from the deck to the lower edges of the beams. It is the measurement used for the stowage of general cargo which takes the form of packages or bales.

Measurement of cargo

Cargo is measured for two reasons: to decide whether its freight charges will be levied on a basis of deadweight or of cubic capacity; and to ascertain the approximate space it will occupy when stowed. Freightage on cargo which stows at less than 4.25 cubic metres per tonne is usually charged by deadweight, and cargo with a greater stowage factor is charged by cubic capacity. The cubic capacity of an irregularly shaped item of cargo is measured as if it were contained in a box of regular shape. The measurement of a cylindrical or circular object, such as a drum or tyre, would be the product of its length or depth and the square of its diameter. Most items of cargo are marked by the manufacturer or consignor with their weight and dimensions, but these are usually checked at the wharf before loading.

Stowage factors

The *stowage factor* is a figure which expresses the amount of space in cubic metres required for the stowage of one tonne of any particular cargo. The figure is not the actual volume of one tonne of the commodity but takes into account the necessity for dunnage, and the form and design of packaging. It is therefore the gross space required for the stowage of one tonne of the commodity.

The available cargo space must be used to the best advantage to obtain maximum profit on the vessel. The stowage factors of the cargo together with the capacity plans of the vessel enable the cargo planner to accomplish this by determining the best stowage for cargo and the space available for further consignments. Stowage factors are not applicable to container ships, because a specified number of containers can be carried, but the factors may have a bearing on the packing of containers.

Stowage factors may vary because of the different forms of packaging, the skill and experience of the stevedores, and any peculiarities of the ship's holds. The examples in the following table show the wide differences of stowage factors and the variations for particular commodities.

COMMODITY	PACKAGING	STOWAGE FACTOR $m^3/tonne$
Antimony	cases	0.48
Bran	bags	2.8–3.6
Cotton	bales	1.4–3.8
Ginger	cases	2.0
Granite	blocks	0.45–0.5
Hay	bales	2.5–2.9

Commodity	Packaging	Stowage Factor $m^3/tonne$
Hemp	bales	3.2
Kapok	bales	5.3
Pig iron	ingots	0.33–0.4
Rubber	cases or bales	1.8
Sugar	bags	1.25–1.45
Tea (China)	½ chests	3.35–3.6
Tea (India)	cases	2.5
Tin	ingots	0.28–0.3
Tinned fruit	cases	1.7
Tyres	bales or loose	3.9–5.5
Wool	bales	1.7

Dunnage

The nature, quantity and total weight of dunnage carried will vary considerably with the nature of the cargo. If particularly heavy items are to be stowed in the 'tween decks or as deck cargo, the decks may have to be shored from the lower hold upwards and each item may require a considerable amount of tomming. Sometimes a temporary 'tween deck may have to be built in a deep lower hold when heavy cargo is to be stowed over crushable cargo, or a temporary bulkhead may have to be built to separate bulk cargo from general cargo. Bins may have to be constructed to protect deck cargo; and if there is much of it, catwalks may have to be built over it to give access forward and aft. These are, however, exceptional cases, and the dunnage usually consists of baulks, planks and quarterings of timber, cordwood, matting, cloths and rope, amounting in all to between 100 and 200 tonnes deadweight in a ship of 7000 tons gross (Old System).

The dunnage deadweight must, of course, be subtracted from that of the ship's cargo when assessing the cargo deadweight available, and similarly an allowance must be made for it when assessing the ship's available cargo capacity.

Broken stowage

The stowage factor for any particular type of cargo includes an allowance for broken stowage, but this allowance applies to that type of cargo alone and does not allow for broken stowage which may result from stowing that particular cargo with other kinds of cargo in the same hold. An allowance must also be made for broken stowage due to the shape of the holds and to pillars and similar fittings in way of the cargo. Furthermore, the stowage factor for a particular cargo may vary from port to port according to the way in which it is packed and the way in which it is stowed by the local stevedores. The planner must therefore make an arbitrary allowance for broken stowage, based on his experience of the various kinds of cargo and the skill of the stevedores at a port. This allowance may vary from 10 per cent to as much as 25 per cent of a ship's bale space.

Marking of cargo

Most items of cargo are marked by the manufacturer or consignor to indicate their origin, destination and sometimes their nature. Dangerous goods which are specified in the International Maritime Dangerous Goods Code (IMDG Code) must be marked with the correct technical name and with special labels indicating the hazard (see page 114). All these markings, however, serve only to identify specific items of cargo before loading or after discharge and are of little use to distinguish one batch of cargo from another when stowed in a hold.

The clear designation of cargo destined for different ports, and sometimes of batches destined for the same port, is essential for its quick discharge and to avoid over-carriage and short-landing. Ships' officers usually devise their own code for this purpose, consisting of colours and designs to distinguish the different consignments. A code in general use is to allot a colour for each port of discharge and a shape such as a square, a circle, a diamond or a cross for particular batches. These designs are sometimes stencilled on each item (or on the boundary items of each parcel) as it is stowed. Other means of distinguishing one cargo from another are by tarpaulins, matting, old rope, and water paints.

SEPARATION OF CARGO

The separation of cargo is necessary in order to prevent one kind from contaminating or damaging another, to minimise the risk of fire or explosion, to ensure that the ship has the required degree of stability, to provide necessary ventilation, to ensure the accessibility of cargo at its port of discharge, to avoid having to restow cargo and to ensure that it can be discharged quickly and efficiently. The following notes apply to the stowage of general cargo in ships; they may partly apply to the stowage of goods in containers and to the stowage of containers in ships. Container practice generally overcomes the majority of cargo separation problems before the containers reach the vessel.

Contamination and tainting

Some commodities are very susceptible to tainting by moisture or odours, and others are very liable to leak or to produce moisture, odours or noxious gases. Examples of the former are flour, sugar, eggs, cheese, tea and pepper, and of the latter potatoes, onions, green vegetables, fruit, wine, grain, wet hides, manure, copra and freshly-sawn timber. Some goods are liable to be damaged or to deteriorate if placed in contact with certain other goods, or even near them, examples being iron and bagged chemicals, cotton and rubber, cotton and coke, cotton and oil, and chrome and manganese ores. Other commodities, again, are susceptible to spontaneous combustion if not properly ventilated, and some will produce moisture or noxious vapours if placed next to a hot bulkhead such as that of a boiler room or engine room; examples are copra, nuts, wool and grain.

Condensation

Cargoes generally fall into two classes: *hygroscopic* or *wet* goods which are mainly vegetable in origin and contain moisture, and *non-hygroscopic* or *dry* goods such as steel products, metal drums, earthenware and sealed packaged goods. With change of temperature during the voyage, the moisture given off to the atmosphere by wet goods condenses, to form '*sweat*' on the ship's structure and on other goods. Thus, certain cargoes must be separated within holds or into different holds, and particular attention must be paid to efficient ventilation of cargo spaces to overcome sweat and its possibly damaging effect on dry goods.

Crushing and chafing

Fragile goods may be crushed if overstowed with heavy cargo, or if stowed in too many tiers without separating them with dunnage, or if there is insufficient vertical separation with dunnage so that cargo in the wings is crushed as the ship rolls. Chafing is caused chiefly by bad stowing, which allows adjacent items of cargo to rub against each other with the movement of the ship. All of these, except overstowing, are mainly the concern of the stevedores and the ship's officers, but the planner can assist to a certain extent by providing what is called *filler cargo*, consisting of small packages of suitable goods which can be stowed between largely different kinds of cargo, and so enable the holds to be stowed compactly, symmetrically and evenly. Examples of filler cargo are bones, cordwood, bundles of wood and matting, and coconut husks; such goods are usually accepted at a lower rate of freight on the understanding that they may be used as filler cargo, but on no account should they be used as dunnage to chock or separate the cargo.

Stability and trim

Separation of the cargo to provide the required degree of stability and trim both at the start of, and throughout, a voyage is most important. Account must be taken of the consumption of fuel, stores and water between ports of call, the discharge of part-cargo at intermediate ports of call, and sometimes the minimum depths of water which the ship may encounter at any port. The stowage should be arranged so that the ship will have the required degree of stability between one port and the next without having to take in or discharge ballast at sea, any necessary ballasting being carried out before the ship sails or while she is in sheltered waters. This is important, because many losses have been attributed to attempts to improve a ship's stability by ballasting while she was in a seaway.

If a ship is filled to capacity with a general cargo entirely for one destination, and provided that the stowage factors of the different types of cargo are not particularly high or low and the ship is not very stiff or tender, the shape and size of her holds and the necessity for stowing light cargo over heavy cargo will usually ensure that on sailing she will have the required degree of stability and trim. If, however, the ship is bound for several intermediate ports of call, the various part-cargoes must be distributed throughout the holds and stowed symmetrically, both fore-and-aft and athwartships. If some of the cargo is particularly heavy, it must be distributed among the holds to avoid any exceptional shearing stresses, and also be divided between the lower holds and the 'tween decks so that the ship is neither too stiff nor too tender (see Chapter 1). The 'tween decks must never be overloaded.

Many British ships are provided with a Ralston's Stability Indicator. This is virtually a pivoted model of the ship which, when weights representing the deadweight of the cargo are added, shows the stability, draught and trim of the ship when loaded.

DANGEROUS CARGOES

The Merchant Shipping Act defines dangerous goods as: those which are liable to spontaneous combustion either in themselves or when stowed with other substances; those which give off explosive gases, poisonous fumes or tainting odours; and those giving off gases which, when mixed with air, are liable to explode.

The international recommendations for the carriage of dangerous goods are prescribed by the International Conference on Safety of Life at Sea (SOLAS) convened by the International Maritime Organization (IMO). These recommendations are published as the *International Maritime Dangerous Goods Code* (IMDG Code). British government regulations controlling the carriage of dangerous goods are contained in *The Merchant Shipping (Dangerous Goods) Rules, 1978*. These regulations are amplified by the IMDG Code and also by recommendations, published by HMSO for the Department of Trade, in a comprehensive book titled *The Carriage of Dangerous Goods in Ships*, commonly known as the *Blue Book*. The book is kept up to date with new information by the publication of amendments and annexes as circumstances require. For the purposes of the IMDG Code dangerous goods are classified as in the table opposite.

The IMDG Code and the Blue Book specify the degree of danger associated with each commodity, the method of packaging, the part of the ship in which it shall be stowed, the method of stowage and the segregation between different parcels of dangerous goods. The principal document is the IMDG Code but the Blue Book contains recommendations for certain specific commodities where the British advisory committee considered that national requirements should override the international recommendations.

Further information relating to the safe handling of ships and cargoes, and the safety of personnel is published in a series of *Merchant Shipping Notices*. These are commonly known as 'M' notices and are obtainable from the Marine Library of the Department of Trade.

Marking and stowage

The packages of dangerous goods, and the containers in which they are packed, are marked by an internationally recognised system of labelling which was originated by the United Nations Organization. The labels are shown in Fig. 4–10 and the number on each refers to the IMO classification of the goods concerned. The labels for packages measure 100 × 100 millimetres and for containers they should not be less than 150 × 150 millimetres.

The disposition of dangerous goods in a ship is strictly controlled but a certain latitude is allowed in the amount of such cargo that may be carried on deck. In general, up to 50 per cent of the upper deck area may be allocated to dangerous goods, depending on the type of ship, freeboard and deck protection, and the provision of suitable securing arrangements. Lashings of wire rope should be used in preference to cordage.

IMO Class	BLUE BOOK Class	DESCRIPTION
1	1	Explosives
2	2	Gases: compressed, liquefied or dissolved under pressure
3	3	Flammable liquids
4.1	4(a)	Flammable solids
4.2	4(b)	Flammable solids, or substances, liable to spontaneous combustion
4.3	4(c)	Flammable solids, or substances, which in contact with water emit flammable gases
5.1	5(a)	Oxidising substances
5.2	5(b)	Organic peroxides
6.1	6(a)	Poisonous (toxic) substances
6.2	6(b)	Infectious substances
7	7	Radioactive substances
8	8	Corrosives
9	9	Miscellaneous dangerous substances, that is, any other substance which experience has shown, or may show, to be of such a dangerous character that the provisions for the carriage of dangerous goods should apply to it
—	10	Dangerous chemicals in limited quantities.

Substances which give off flammable vapours, e.g. petroleum spirit products, should ideally be stowed in a hermetically sealed compartment but if this is not possible great care and attention must be paid to the efficient ventilation of the compartment. To carry explosives, it is general practice to build a magazine, constructed either of wood or of metal with a wooden lining, within a compartment (preferably 'tween decks) which is surrounded by permanent bulkheads.

Dangerous chemicals in bulk

The carriage of dangerous chemicals in bulk gives rise to further dangers, primarily those of asphyxiation or the effect of toxic vapours on anyone entering a tank or an enclosed space. Some 50 or more substances are listed and vessels intending to carry these require a certificate of fitness. The general precautions for these and 40 or more other substances are outlined in appropriate 'M' notices.

FIG. 4–10(i). United Nations labelling for dangerous goods

FIG. 4–10(ii). United Nations labelling for dangerous goods (*cont.*)

STOWAGE OF CONTAINERISED CARGO

Five types of ship capable of carrying containers were listed in Chapter 3. The various methods by which cargo can be loaded or discharged are described below.

Lift-on/lift-off method. This term is used to describe the operation of loading and discharging cargo by means of shore craneage. Where specially designed cranes are sited at selected berths, lift-on/lift-off is the accepted method for fully and partially containerised ships. Containers can also be handled by conventional cranes using suitable spreaders at general berths. This latter method is much slower and would only be used for a limited number of containers which are part of a general cargo.

Roll-on/roll-off method. Certain vessels (ro-ro ships) are specially designed to permit loading and discharge by driving the vehicles containing the cargo, or the mobile cargo itself, directly on board or ashore. This system provides greater flexibility of the types of cargo that can be carried, including trailers, cars, and most wheeled vehicles as well as containers. Although these ships usually require special berths to accommodate the loading ramps, they have the advantage of independence from shore or ship craneage.

Float-on/float-off method (LASH system). In this system the loaded lighters are towed to and from the ship and they are embarked or disembarked by means of the ship's gantry crane. No special facilities are required ashore other than for the conventional operations of loading and discharging cargo into and from the lighters. It is not uncommon for LASH vessels to carry a limited amount of container cargo and in that event they would need the specialised facilities of a container berth.

Containers

Cargo containers are constructed in the form of a rectangular box and there are three main types in general use: the general cargo container, the insulated container and the top-loader.

Standard containers comply with the specifications of the International Standards Organization (ISO), and the containers are thus compatible with the ships and vehicles of all companies or countries which have adopted this standard. As mentioned earlier the two common internationally accepted sizes are $6.1 \times 2.44 \times 2.44$ metres (20-foot container) and $12.2 \times 2.44 \times 2.44$ metres (40-foot container). Normally the larger 40-foot containers form the main deck stack but, if necessary, they can be stowed within the ship after adjustment of the cell guides. The gross (loaded) weight of a container can vary between 3 and 30 tonnes.

Containers are generally built completely of steel or as a steel framework which is clad in aluminium sheet. The interior is lined with plywood and fitted with a wood or aluminium floor. A standard corner casting (Fig. 4–11) is built into the framework at each corner. The corner casting is hollow and has apertures, on the three exposed sides, which are primarily designed to accept the coupler latches of the crane spreader when hoisting or lowering. The apertures are also used for attaching hooks, shackles or locking devices, to secure the containers on ships or transport vehicles.

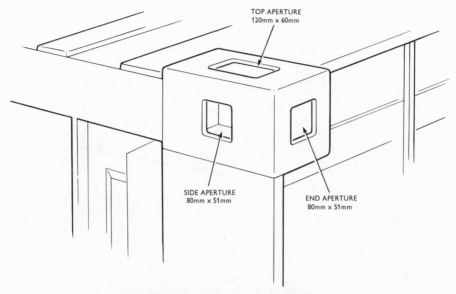

FIG. 4–11. Corner casting

Various containers which demonstrate the versatility of this cargo system are shown in Fig. 4–12.

General-cargo container. This is the most common type of container. It can be packed with all forms of general cargo, either loose or suitably packed. The packing operation comprises securing the goods within the container and chocking with dunnage to ensure the safety of the cargo.

Insulated container. Although similar in appearance to the general-cargo container, this type has heat-insulating material built into the cladding and the doors. Two alternative methods of cooling are commonly used to maintain the optimum temperature for the cargo: in one, arrangements are fitted at the ends of the container for connection to the ship's ducted-air cooling system (see Fig. 3–3); and in the other, an electrically driven refrigeration-plant, which can be connected to the ship's electrical system, is fitted to the container (Fig. 4–12(i)). These containers are used for the carriage of fresh or frozen foods, drugs, photographic materials or any other goods which are sensitive to changes of temperature.

Tank container. To transport liquids in bulk a suitable tank is enclosed within a container framework.

Top-loading container. This container is designed to accept awkwardly shaped or heavy individual loads. The roof of the container is formed by a waterproof cover which can be drawn back to provide access.

Dry-bulk container. This type is used for the carriage of dry-bulk cargo which will flow into the body of the container. Cargo is loaded through the top hatches and discharged through the lower doors at the ends.

Open-sided container. For ease of loading, some containers are built with one or both sides open. After packing, the sides are closed by wire-mesh screens or laced tarpaulin covers.

I

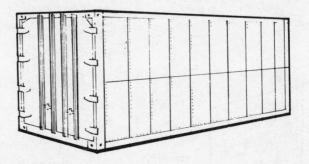

GENERAL CARGO CONTAINER

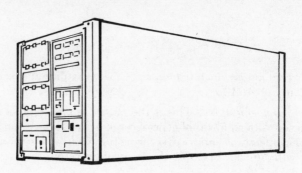

REFRIGERATED CONTAINER (REAR END)

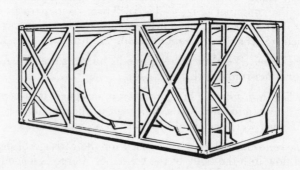

TANK CONTAINER

FIG. 4–12(i). Cargo containers

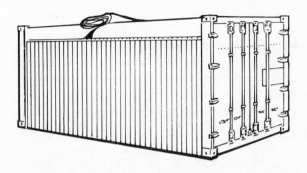

TOP LOADING CONTAINER (TARPAULIN COVERED)

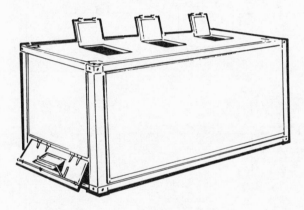

DRY BULK CONTAINER

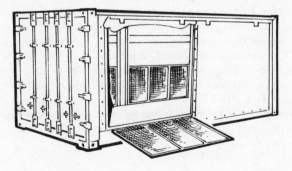

OPEN-SIDED CONTAINER

FIG. 4–12(ii). Cargo containers (*cont.*)

The container principle can be adapted to the carriage of the majority of cargo types and, if demand is sufficient, special containers can be constructed within the ISO specifications to satisfy any particular requirements.

Container loading/discharge sequence

Fig. 4–13 shows the sequence of events in the loading and discharging cycle and illustrates the speed of handling which can be attained when using a container gantry crane.

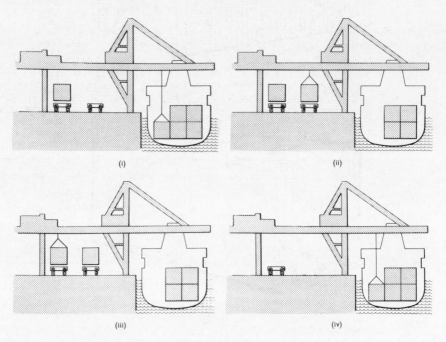

FIG. 4–13. Container loading/discharge sequence

The crane is positioned on the quay abreast the particular cell in the ship's hold. Fig. 4–13(i) shows the spreader of the crane lowered into the hold and engaged with an *import* container; the time for this operation being about 30 seconds. The container is hoisted, traversed over the quay and lowered on to a waiting trailer (Fig. 4–13(ii)). The elapsed time is now of the order of one minute. The spreader is now plumbed over and engaged with a waiting *export* container (Fig. 4–13(iii)) and the import container is driven away. The export container is hoisted, traversed and then lowered into the ship (Fig. 4–13(iv)). The total time for a complete cycle of the loading operation is of the order of 2 minutes.

Container lashings

The containers which are stowed within the ship require no securing other than that provided by the guides of the cellular structure of the holds. However, the containers on the upper deck, frequently stacked up to four high and twelve across, require a rugged securing system which can be quickly applied and released (Fig. 4–14).

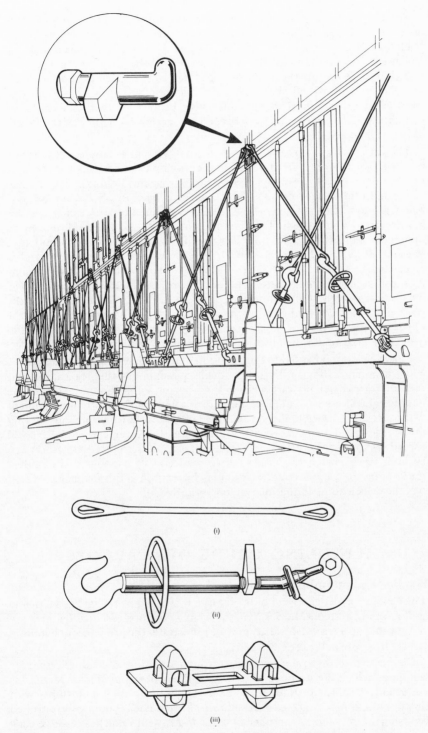

FIG. 4–14. Part of a container stack and the main lashing components
Inset: long hook; (i) diagonal lashing rod; (ii) heavy screw; (iii) bridge piece

Container lashing systems are the subject of much research, and a variety of specially designed fittings is provided to satisfy particular requirements. Each operating company devises a system, using a common range of fittings, which can be applied to all the vessels in their fleet. Each ship is provided with *lashing plans* in the form of a booklet which specifies the container stowage limitations and shows how the common system is applied to that ship. As a general rule no container may be heavier than any container supporting it, i.e. the containers become progressively lighter as the height of the stack increases.

The variety of systems and fittings does not warrant a complete description but brief details are given to illustrate the principles underlying the securing of containers. Fig. 4–14 shows one method of diagonal lashing and a selection of the more important fittings. This system is used in SS *Encounter Bay*, belonging to the fleet of Overseas Containers Limited by whose courtesy this information is published. The *long hook* (Fig. 4–14, inset) locates in an upper corner casting, and provides the means of securing one end of a *diagonal lashing rod* (Fig. 4–14(i)). The other end of the lashing rod is connected to a *heavy screw* (Fig. 4–14(ii)), which in turn is connected by its slip to a deck lashing plate. The heavy screw is fitted with a hand-wheel by which the complete lashing is tensioned. Lateral movement within the stack is eliminated by the *bridge piece* (Fig. 4–14(iii)) which fits into the upper corner castings of adjacent containers, locks the stack together and provides a location for the next tier of containers.

Further research has led to the adoption of another system which dispenses with diagonal lashings. This was made possible by the realisation that container gross weights rarely reach their permitted maximum and that the total weight of a stack could be limited to a lower value without detriment to the service. This led to the development of *twistlocks* which are interlocking fittings designed to engage with and secure the lower corner castings of containers to specially fitted *deck stools*. Stacks of up to three containers can be built up by using twistlocks between successive containers. Individual stacks of up to 45 tonnes total weight may be secured in this manner provided that the deck loading limitations are not exceeded.

HANDLING CRUDE OIL CARGOES

Pipeline and pumping system

The loading and discharge of bulk oil cargo is effected by the tanker's pipeline and pumping system. Many variations having common essential features are employed, and a typical installation which illustrates the principles of handling crude oil is shown in Fig. 4–15.

Connection to the system is made through a number of loading/discharge couplings which are grouped together and known as a *manifold*. Manifolds are usually duplicated, one on each side of the main deck amidships, with the couplings interconnected to separate *deck lines*. Each coupling is controlled by its own gate valve. A number of *cargo lines*, with branches to serve each tank, run through the bottom of the cargo spaces. Direct *drop lines* fitted with control valves interconnect the cargo lines with their associated deck

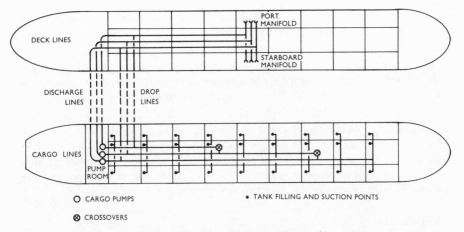

O CARGO PUMPS   • TANK FILLING AND SUCTION POINTS

⊗ CROSSOVERS

FIG. 4–15. Typical cargo pipeline and pumping system

lines. The oil is handled on board by cargo pumps situated in a separate pump-room. These pumps take their suction from the cargo lines and discharge to the deck lines.

The particular installation described above is known as the *direct loading system* and it is used where pipelines and tanks may need to be isolated for the carriage of different grades of cargo. When only one grade is to be carried the system can be linked by the *crossovers*. Only a few of the valves have been mentioned but many more are fitted for complete control of the cargo system.

The pipework so far described is constructed of large-bore pipes up to 600 millimetres in diameter. In addition a smaller (up to 300 millimetres diameter) cargo line, called the *stripping line*, with suction valves in all tanks is ranged along the bottom. The stripping line is connected to a separate stripping pump which discharges to the manifold. The purpose of the stripping system (not shown in Fig. 4–15) is to remove the final residue of cargo which is below the reach of the main cargo-lines.

The pumps

The main cargo-pumps are usually of the centrifugal type to provide a high-capacity discharge of up to 9000 cubic metres per hour for each pump. The stripping pump is generally of the reciprocating type with a capacity of up to 750 cubic metres per hour. This combination of pumps provides a speedy bulk discharge and effective draining of the tanks. Steam or electric power is used to drive the pumps. If electricity is used, the motors and control gear are situated outside the pump room, usually in the engine room, with the drive shafts passing through sealed glands in the bulkhead. This precaution is necessary because of the possible presence of explosive gases in the pump room.

Loading and discharge

Loading. Flexible hoses are connected at the manifold and the cargo is pumped from shore to ship. The valves in the system are set so that the drop lines are open to feed the cargo lines and the selected tanks. The pumps and discharge lines are isolated during loading.

Discharging. The valves are set so that the drop lines are isolated. The ship's cargo-pumps take suction from the cargo lines and discharge to the deck lines and thence ashore, or to a tanker alongside, through flexible hoses connected to the manifold. Finally the residue in each tank is removed and discharged by the stripping system.

Lightening operations. In order that large tankers may use ports with limited depths of water, it is sometimes necessary to lighten the vessels of some of their cargo. This is achieved by transferring part of the cargo to a specially equipped smaller tanker which may discharge at the same port or trans-ship the cargo to some other shallow-water port.

Ventilation

The top of each tank is connected to a ventilation pipeline called the *gas line* which is led to a position well above deck level at the head of a mast or some other structure. The gas line is terminated at its upper end by an equalising valve which has the purpose of balancing the pressure within the tanks with that of the atmosphere.

It is modern practice to maintain a slight pressure of inert gas within the tanks. The gas is derived from the ship's main boiler or, in the case of diesel-propelled vessels, from a gas generator. The oxygen content of the gas is maintained at less than 5 per cent, which is insufficient to support combustion, thus preventing the possibility of cargo-tank explosions.

Tank cleaning

The carriage of crude oil results in the deposit of a waxy asphaltic sediment on the tank bottoms and internal structure, and a film of oil is left on the vertical surfaces. The deposit has the effect of clogging draining systems and of reducing the total amount of cargo that can be discharged.

Water washing the empty tanks has been the traditional method of overcoming this problem but in modern tankers this process is augmented by *crude-oil washing* which has become the primary method. During the discharge of cargo, crude oil is fed to cleaning machines within the tanks by one of the cargo pumps. The machines produce jets of crude oil for washing the tank structure, and as many machines as may be required are permanently fitted in each tank. Crude-oil washing has a solvent effect as well as physically breaking up the residue which is then circulated with the cargo and discharged. Any final residue is then combined with the next cargo.

If the tanks have to be completely cleaned for ballast purposes, for the carriage of other commodities or for docking of the vessel, the tanks are then washed with hot water by the same cleaning machines and washing system. The residue is removed as an emulsion which is allowed to settle so that the oil and water can be separated.

Cargo measurement

It is usual for cargo to be measured by equipment on shore during the discharge operation. However, if the quantity has to be determined on board it is calculated by measuring the *ullage* or distance between the surface of the oil and the tank tops. At the same time the depth of any water at the bottom of the tanks has to be measured. By application of these figures to the *Ullage Tables*, which are computed for each of the tanks in the vessel, the cargo content of each tank can be ascertained.

Ballast and trim

The manner in which sea water is used for ballast depends on the design of the ship. It is common to designate some tanks solely for ballast, e.g. the forepeak and tanks adjacent to the machinery space, and such ballast is known as *segregated* or *permanent ballast*. Designated cargo tanks are used when further ballasting is necessary and this ballast is known as *cargo-tank ballast*.

Small tankers generally have facilities for only cargo-tank ballast. Larger tankers use both types; a ballast pipeline system, fitted with its own pump in the pump room, is installed. This system permits ballasting operations during the loading or discharge of cargo thereby reducing both the turn-round time and the stresses experienced by the hull structure. It is normal for a tanker to be trimmed by the stern when discharging, to assist drainage of the cargo tanks.

When sailing with a part cargo, or when loading or discharging a full cargo at different ports, a cargo plan has to be drawn up in a similar manner to that for a general cargo. From the plan, information is derived to calculate stability data, and calculations are made to ensure that at no time during the voyage do the loading stresses exceed the criteria stated in the ship's *Stability Information Booklet*. Many modern vessels are fitted with electric stress-finding instruments which measure the actual stresses at selected critical positions in the hull.

CHAPTER 5

Safety Arrangements in Merchant Ships

Warships are often called upon to go to the assistance of merchant ships in distress after collision or grounding or when on fire. Tasks such as the rescue of passengers and crew, extinguishing fires, taking in tow and salvage of merchant ships, or the placing of a crew on board an abandoned merchant vessel may arise at any time without warning. HM ships must therefore be prepared for this sort of work. Some knowledge of the construction of merchant ships and of their firefighting and lifesaving arrangements is essential to naval officers and senior ratings. The great variety of merchant shipping precludes a detailed description of these features, but it is hoped that this chapter will provide a general idea of them, and will show the principal ways in which they differ from those of warships. Lifesaving arrangements in HM ships are described in Volume II, Chapter 3.

International Conference on Safety of Life at Sea

The principal maritime nations subscribe to regulations agreed by international conferences which are convened from time to time by the International Maritime Organization (IMO). These regulations include not only those governing the prevention of collision at sea (commonly known as the *Rule of the Road*) but also a wide range of detailed regulations on construction of ships, lifesaving equipment, fire prevention and precautions, etc., which are listed on page 79.

The international regulations are contained in an annex to the *Report of the Conference on Safety of Life at Sea*. The report of the most-recent conference, held in London in 1974, is published by IMO as a book with the title commonly abbreviated to *SOLAS, 1974*. By mid-1979 sufficient nations had ratified the convention for it to become international law and the information in this chapter is mainly based on *SOLAS, 1974*.

The administration of each subscribing country amplifies and enforces the international regulations. In the United Kingdom the various statutory requirements are laid down under the provisions of the *Merchant Shipping Acts* and administered by the Department of Trade. The requirements of construction and seaworthiness are also embodied in the demands of the Classification Societies, such as Lloyd's Register. Even though classification by a society is not compulsory most merchant ships of gross tonnage 500 or more must be surveyed at prescribed intervals to ensure compliance with the regulations.

WATERTIGHT SUBDIVISION

General standards for merchant ships

Watertight subdivision, while increasing the safety of a ship by limiting the inflow of water resulting from bad weather or damage, provides cellular stowage for fuel, water and stores, and also a means of correcting any trim or list, and of increasing the stability of the ship, by pumping or counter-flooding. Too much subdivision, however, limits the space for cargo, hinders cargo operations and communication between different parts of the ship, and complicates the arrangements for draining, pumping and ventilating. For these reasons it is clear that subdivision is not incorporated to the same degree in a merchant ship as in a warship.

No definite rules regarding subdivision were laid down for British passenger ships until 1914, when rules were formulated after the sinking of the White Star liner *Titanic* in mid-Atlantic in 1912 with great loss of life after she had collided with an iceberg. Various 'Bulkhead Committees' have met since then, and the present rules are based on those formulated by the International Conference on Safety of Life at Sea, at their meeting in London in 1960.

Regulations for passenger ships

The regulations for passenger ships prescribed by the 1974 International Conference provide for:

1. A minimum standard of watertight subdivision for various types of ships.
2. The arrangement of such subdivision to ensure that the ship will remain afloat when one or, in certain cases, two or three major compartments are flooded.
3. A sufficient margin of stability for the safe operation of the ship.
4. Precautions to prevent the spread of fire.

The standard of subdivision varies with the type of ship, and the highest degree is required in ships of the greatest length and engaged primarily in carrying passengers.

The following terms are used when fixing the maximum permissible spacing of the bulkheads in any particular passenger ship:

the *bulkhead deck* is the uppermost deck up to which the transverse watertight bulkheads are carried;

the *margin line* is a line parallel to, and at least 76 millimetres below, the upper surface of the bulkhead deck where it meets the ship's side;

the *floodable length* at any point along the ship is the length of the longest full section of the hull, having its centre at the selected point, the complete flooding of which would not quite submerge the margin line;

the maximum *permissible length* of a compartment having its centre at a selected point along the length of a ship is obtained from the floodable length multiplied by the *factor of subdivision*. This factor takes into account the length of the ship and the degree to which she is designed for the carriage of passengers, the value being less as length increases and as passenger-carrying tends to predominate over cargo-carrying. The smaller the factor, the higher is the standard of subdivision; for example, if the factor is *one-half* or less, the flooding of any *two* adjacent compartments will not submerge the ship to her margin line; and, similarly, if the factor is *one-third* or less, the ship will survive the flooding of any *three* adjacent compartments.

To ensure that draught does not exceed that used in determining the degree of subdivision, a passenger ship is marked with a subdivision load line (commonly called a *convention line*) alongside her other load lines, and when she is carrying more than 12 passengers she must not be loaded to an extent that will submerge this mark. Ships in which extra accommodation may occasionally be provided for passengers, e.g. ships chartered for the Islamic pilgrim trade or as troopships, are marked with two, and sometimes three, of these lines to conform with the number of her passengers and the situation of their accommodation. The lines may, for example, be marked C.1, C.2 or C.3 accordingly, and in British ships their positions are assigned by Department of Trade surveyors.

Very close subdivision is not necessarily an advantage because, if too close, a watertight compartment may be so short that damage may cause flooding both before and abaft it. For this reason the regulations specify a minimum spacing between bulkheads.

Longitudinal bulkheads may limit the amount of flooding and help to preserve the waterplane area, but they may also cause the ship to heel badly by confining the flood water to one side of the ship. It is therefore specified that the angle of heel which would be caused by flooding any wing compartment as a result of damage shall neither exceed 7 degrees, nor submerge the margin line under normal circumstances, after any prescribed measures to restore stability have been taken.

Apart from the spacing of transverse and longitudinal watertight bulkheads, the effects of watertight decks, inner skins and similar structures on heel and stability are also required by regulations to be carefully examined.

A typical watertight door in a passenger ship slides across to close, and is a machined fit, metal to metal. There is neither rubber nor clips such as are found on a Service door. Such doors can be closed locally by hand, or by remote control from the bridge. When the doors are closed by remote control, a gong sounds by the door to warn people in the vicinity to keep clear. After being closed from the bridge, the door can still be opened locally by hand, but will close again automatically after a fixed delay of, say, 5 seconds.

A typical bridge control-panel displays drawings of the ship with indicator lights in the various watertight-door positions. Each door can be closed by a switch, and the appropriate indicator light glows when the door is closed.

Regulations for cargo ships

In general the watertight subdivision of cargo ships is determined by the degree of flooding which they must be capable of withstanding under the provisions of the *Merchant Shipping (Load Line) Rules*. In addition to compliance with these rules, codes of construction for ships with particular environmental risks (e.g. chemical and liquid-gas carriers) are published by IMO. The *International Convention for the Prevention of Marine Pollution, 1973* (MARPOL 1973) also recommends particular requirements for tankers to limit the outflow of oil after collision or grounding. These codes and recommendations, in limiting the size of cargo compartments of tankers and controlling the disposition of cargo tanks for chemical and gas carriers, thus also affect the subdivision of these vessels.

FIRE PRECAUTIONS

The regulations governing fire precautions in merchant ships are based on the following principles, as appropriate to the various types of ship and the potential fire hazards involved.

1. Division of ship into main vertical zones by thermal and structural boundaries.
2. Separation of accommodation spaces from remainder of ship by thermal and structural boundaries.
3. Restricted use of combustible materials.
4. Detection of any fire in the zone of origin.
5. Containment and extinction of any fire in the space of origin.
6. Protection of means of escape or access for firefighting.
7. Ready availability of fire-extinguishing appliances.
8. Minimisation of possibility of ignition of flammable cargo vapour.

Construction

For passenger vessels the regulations require that the structure is subdivided into main vertical fire-zones by bulkheads of steel or equivalent material. The bulkheads must be of adequate scantlings and stiffening, and insulated where necessary to resist fire and restrict heat transfer. The mean distance between any two such bulkheads normally must not exceed 40 metres, and the means of closing all openings in them must be fire-resisting and flametight. Further subdivision of these main spaces is required unless automatic fire-alarm and extinguishing systems are fitted.

For cargo ships the regulations prescribe the materials to be used in construction to ensure fire safety and, for tankers, the location of accommodation and machinery spaces with respect to the cargo tanks.

For all vessels, the spaces which require special protection (e.g. control stations or stairways forming vertical escape routes) or in which there is a special fire risk (e.g. machinery spaces and galleys) must be enclosed by fire-resistant bulkheads.

Fire appliances

The minimum standards of firefighting equipment to be carried by British merchant ships are laid down in the *Merchant Shipping (Fire Appliances) Rules, 1965*, the *Merchant Shipping (Fire Appliances) Amendment Rules, 1980*, and the *Merchant Shipping (Fire Appliances) Regulations, 1980*, which are statutory instruments. Ships are surveyed regularly to ensure compliance with the regulations, and guidance for these surveys is given in *Survey of Fire Appliances* published by HMSO for the Department of Trade. The number and type of appliances vary according to:

1. The size of ship.
2. Whether she carries passengers or cargo, or both.
3. The type of cargo carried.
4. Whether she has oil-fired boilers or is motor-driven.

A general description of the types of firefighting equipment usually found in merchant ships is given in the following paragraphs.

Fixed systems

Fire doors. As already mentioned, the doors at the openings in all bulkheads are designed to prevent fire from spreading and they must be fire-resisting and flametight.

Fire main. This system, sometimes known in the Merchant Navy as the *wash-deck service,* supplies hydrants suitably disposed about the ship. Water is delivered to the system by independently driven pumps which in cargo ships are situated in the engine room with an independently driven emergency-pump in a separate compartment, and in passenger vessels are situated in separate compartments. Each pump in the system is capable of supplying two powerful jets of water to any position in the ship. In accommodation, service and machinery spaces one of these jets must be capable of being supplied by a single length of hose, and in passenger vessels these conditions must be met with all bulkhead and fire doors closed. The hydrants are usually fitted with 64-millimetre female couplings. Hoses and branchpipes are usually kept in glass-fronted cupboards adjacent to the hydrants, but in the interior locations of passenger ships carrying more than 36 passengers the hoses are connected to the hydrants at all times, as in HM ships. Additionally, where required in machinery spaces, nozzles are provided which are capable of spraying water on oil. The fire main in ships of gross tonnage 1000 and upwards must have at least one international-type shore connection capable of being used on either side of the ship.

Water-spray, smothering-gas and foam-making systems. Boiler rooms, motor rooms of motor-driven ships and compartments containing large internal combustion engines are fitted with a fixed water-spray, smothering-gas or foam-making installation. Cargo spaces are fitted with a smothering-gas installation and, for cargo vessels only, steam may be used as the smothering agent, provided no explosives are stowed in the hold. Steam smothering is rarely found nowadays and is no longer recommended for new construction.

The majority of merchant vessels are fitted with carbon dioxide (CO_2) smothering systems for the engine rooms and holds. The CO_2 gas is contained in cylinders in the superstructures, or in bulk storage in some refrigerated ships, and its use is controlled by valves mounted on panels which also carry a diagram of the compartments served by the system. Engine rooms, boiler rooms and other working spaces are fitted with audible alarms to give warning that smothering gas is about to be released into the compartments. With these systems it is important that all hands are accounted for and that all openings are closed before injection of the CO_2. It is also important to allow the space to cool, assisted by boundary cooling, before opening the compartment, otherwise re-ignition is liable to occur.

A modern development of smothering systems is to use a *halon* (halogenated hydrocarbon) as the smothering agent instead of CO_2, but otherwise the systems are similar to the CO_2 systems described above. Halons are substances in which some of the hydrogen atoms in a hydrocarbon compound are replaced by atoms from one of the group of elements known as halogens (i.e.

fluorine, chlorine, bromine, iodine, etc.). Whereas CO_2 starves a fire by reducing the oxygen content of the air, a halon breaks down in fire and interrupts the chemical reaction of combustion. Halons are identified by a universal numbering system. IMO has resolved to allow the use of three types of halon extinguishant but only two are approved by the Department of Trade for use in British ships; these are Halon 1211 and Halon 1301 of which the latter is the more widely used. The third, Halon 2402, may be found in foreign ships, notably Russian. The major advantages of the permitted halons are that a much lower concentration (5–9 per cent by volume) is required to extinguish a fire, and that, even though they are anaesthetic, they have a very low toxicity; thus they are much less dangerous than CO_2 to personnel, and limited exposure will cause no harmful or persistent side effects.

Water-spray and foam-making systems are operated from outside the compartments they protect, at positions where access is not endangered by fire.

The modern trend adopted in most tankers is to install a large-capacity foam-making system to protect the cargo tanks. These vessels have two fixed mains, one supplying water only and the other a foam-compound/water mixture. The mains are located on the main deck, one each side of the fore-and-aft bridge, and are fitted with isolating valves and crossovers to enable damaged sections of the system to be isolated. They are supplied with foam and water from storage tanks and fire pumps located at each end of the vessel. The forward fire pump is driven by a diesel engine and is therefore independent of the ship's power supply. The foam is then applied through tank openings, or on to the deck, either automatically by monitors or by hand-operated equipment.

Inert-gas systems. Many tankers are fitted with a system (see also page 126) by which an inert gas under pressure by blowers is forced into the top of each tank, to prevent fires or explosions. This system is a requirement on tankers of 100 000 tonnes deadweight and over, and on combination carriers (oil/bulk/ore or oil/ore) of 50 000 tonnes deadweight and over. It is probable that the requirement will subsequently be extended to smaller vessels. Ships so fitted keep their cargo tanks *inerted* throughout the whole range of normal cargo-handling and ballasting operations. The oxygen level of the inert gas in the tank is normally about 5 per cent with an upper limit of 8 per cent which is insufficient to support combustion.

Sprinkler systems. Automatic sprinkler systems are often installed in spaces provided for the use and service of passengers and crew. These systems are usually supplied with fresh water from a sprinkler tank under pneumatic pressure, supplemented by pumps which automatically come into operation immediately the water pressure in the system begins to fall. The usual method of operation is to incorporate a glass bulb in each sprinkler head. At a predetermined temperature, associated with fire in the compartment, the bulbs explode, allow water to flow from the sprinkler heads affected by the fire and operate an alarm.

Fire detection and alarm systems. These systems which generally detect the presence of smoke or combustion particles are usually fitted to provide surveillance in cargo holds and other spaces which are not easily accessible.

Detector heads fitted in the appropriate compartments operate the alarm and indicate the position of the fire at a central cabinet sited on the bridge or at some position in direct communication with the bridge.

The sprinkler systems described above are all required to be fitted with automatic alarms which indicate at the bridge or other suitable position that they have come into operation; the sprinkler system may therefore be considered primarily as an alarm system.

In some cases the detector system is associated with a CO_2 smothering system. The atmosphere from the protected spaces is sampled for the presence of smoke by a system of pipes which is also used for the injection of CO_2 to the affected compartment.

Portable equipment

Portable fire extinguishers may be of the foam, CO_2, dry powder, soda/acid or gas/water type. The two latter types discharge water, and of these the gas/water extinguisher is most generally provided in spaces occupied by or for the service of passengers and crew. Portable foam and CO_2 extinguishers are placed in boiler rooms, galleys and compartments containing internal-combustion engines, and dry powder or CO_2 extinguishers are provided in spaces containing electrical hazards. One of the extinguishers intended for use in a particular compartment is always stowed near the entrance to that space.

Sand. Bins of sand or other suitable material are provided in the firing spaces of boiler rooms, for smothering and soaking up spills of oil.

Breathing apparatus. Suitable types of breathing apparatus are provided to permit entry to smoke-filled spaces. One type of breathing apparatus commonly in use is illustrated in Fig. 5–1.

Safety lamps of the electric-battery type which have a minimum burning period of three hours are provided for emergency purposes.

Fireman's outfit. This comprises a suit of protective clothing including boots and gloves of electrically non-conducting material and a safety helmet, a suitable breathing apparatus, a fireproof lifeline, a safety lamp and an axe. All ships carry a minimum of two outfits and passenger vessels carry additional outfits dependent on their size.

Emergency arrangements

Emergency source of electrical power. Passenger ships and cargo ships of gross tonnage 5000 and upwards are fitted with an emergency source of electrical power capable of supplying all those services necessary for the safety of passengers and crew in an emergency. The source of power may be a storage battery or a generator, situated outside the machinery casings and sufficiently high in the ship to be unaffected by flooding. The most common form of emergency supply is a diesel generator with a self-contained fuel supply. In cargo ships of less than gross tonnage 5000 an emergency power-supply capable of illuminating the lifesaving equipment and positions must be installed. All emergency power-supply arrangements must be capable of operating with the ship listing up to $22\frac{1}{2}$ degrees and with a trim of up to 10 degrees.

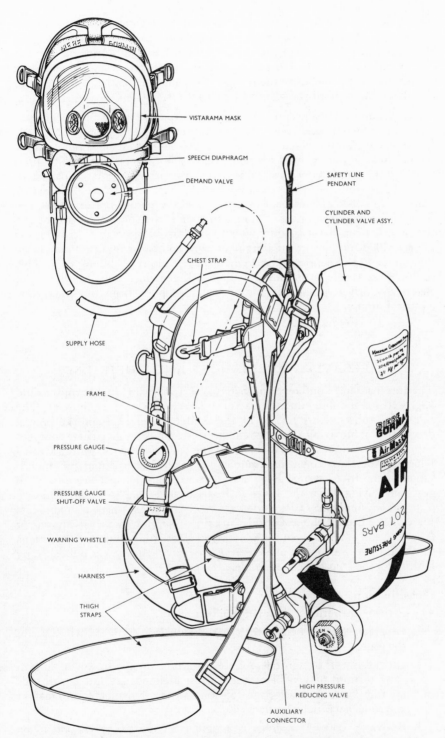

VISTARAMA MASK

SPEECH DIAPHRAGM

DEMAND VALVE

SAFETY LINE
PENDANT

CYLINDER AND
CYLINDER VALVE ASSY.

CHEST STRAP

SUPPLY HOSE

FRAME

PRESSURE GAUGE

PRESSURE GAUGE
SHUT-OFF VALVE

WARNING WHISTLE

HARNESS

THIGH
STRAPS

HIGH PRESSURE
REDUCING VALVE

AUXILIARY
CONNECTOR

FIG. 5–1. Typical breathing apparatus used for firefighting in a merchant ship:
the 'Airmaster' compressed-air breathing apparatus

K

Emergency controls. In all merchant ships the regulations call for means of stopping oil-fuel pumps and forced-ventilation fans from a position outside the space concerned. These emergency controls are usually grouped together at a suitable position which has safe access from the open deck. Many modern tankers have a cargo control room where the emergency controls are installed together with the normal cargo-handling controls.

Fire pumps. Pumps used for firefighting purposes must be independently driven. Sanitary, ballast, bilge and general-service pumps may all be used. Pumps having an occasional duty of pumping oil fuel, such as fuel transfer pumps and the pumps used for tank cleaning in tankers, may also be used provided they are fitted with suitable changeover arrangements. In passenger ships of gross tonnage 1000 and upwards the pumps must be arranged so that a fire in any one compartment cannot put all the pumps out of action, i.e. the positions of pumps must be spread over more than one compartment and the pumps must have separate sources of power. In cargo ships of gross tonnage 2000 and upwards if a fire in any one compartment could put all the fire pumps out of action, a fixed emergency pump must be installed. This could be a diesel-driven pump with a self-contained fuel supply or an electrically driven pump capable of being supplied from the emergency electrical supply.

LIFESAVING APPLIANCES AND THEIR USE

The International Conference on Safety of Life at Sea (1960) permitted and approved for the first time the use of inflatable lifesaving equipment. The rules were subsequently revised by the Conference of 1974 and the general description of lifesaving appliances in the Merchant Navy given here complies with the Convention (SOLAS 1974) of the later conference. In the United Kingdom the Department of Trade issues detailed instructions, in amplification of the International Regulations, controlling the specifications of all gear, and laying down the scales to be used under the *Merchant Shipping (Life-saving Appliances) Regulations, 1980.* The Department also appoints surveyors to inspect ships at regular intervals to ensure that their equipment is correct and is maintained at the required standard. Guidance instructions for these surveys are given in *Survey of Life-Saving Appliances* published by HMSO for the Department of Trade.

Classification

The six main categories of lifesaving appliances are:

1. LIFEJACKETS. These are worn by individuals to support themselves in the water.

2. LIFEBUOYS. If a man falls overboard a lifebuoy is thrown for him to cling to until he can be rescued. Most lifebuoys are fitted with self-igniting lights (but see page 139 for special arrangements in tankers) and some have lifelines attached.

3. BUOYANT APPARATUS. This is a rigid structure strong enough to be thrown from the place where it is stowed into the water without suffering damage, or to float clear of a ship when it founders.

4. RIGID LIFERAFTS. These are similar to inflatable liferafts, except that they do not depend on inflation for their buoyancy.

5. INFLATABLE LIFERAFTS. These are collapsible fabric rafts which can be inflated automatically or manually by means of gas contained in cylinders fitted to the raft.

6. LIFEBOATS. These are specially constructed for this purpose; they may be propelled by oars, sails, mechanical means or power, and each is rated to carry a specified number of persons.

Availability of lifesaving appliances

The general principle governing the provision of lifeboats, liferafts and buoyant apparatuses in a ship is that they must be readily available in an emergency, and hence they must comply with the following conditions.

1. It must be possible to put the entire approved complement of lifesaving appliances of a ship into the water safely and rapidly under unfavourable conditions of trim and 15 degrees of list.

2. It must be possible to load the lifeboats and liferafts rapidly and in good order.

3. The arrangement of each lifeboat, liferaft or article of buoyant apparatus is to be such that it will not interfere with the operation of any other lifesaving appliance.

All the lifesaving appliances on board ship must be kept in working order and available for immediate use before the ship leaves port and at all times during the voyage.

Lifejackets

Every ship must carry an approved type of lifejacket for every person on board. Unless these can be adapted for use by children, a ship must also carry a sufficient number of lifejackets which are suitable for children. Passenger ships must also carry additional lifejackets for five per cent of the total number of persons on board, and these lifejackets must be stowed in a conspicuous position on deck and plainly indicated. Each lifejacket must be marked to show that it has been approved by the national authority and must comply with the following requirements.

1. Must be constructed with proper workmanship and materials.

2. Must be constructed so as to eliminate as far as possible all risk of its being put on incorrectly, except that it shall be capable of being worn inside out.

3. Must be capable of lifting the face of an exhausted or unconscious person out of the water and holding it above the water with the body inclined backwards from its vertical position.

4. Must be capable of turning the body in the water from any position to a safe floating position with the body inclined backwards from its vertical position.

5. Must be of a highly visible colour.

6. Must be fitted with an approved whistle, firmly secured by a cord.

7. Must not be adversely affected by oil or oil products.

8. Its buoyancy must not be reduced by more than five per cent after 24 hours submergence in fresh water.

A lifejacket which depends on inflation for buoyancy may be permitted for use by crews of all ships except passenger ships and tankers provided that: it has two separate inflatable compartments; it is capable of being inflated both mechanically and by mouth; and it complies with the general requirements 1 – 8 above with either compartment inflated separately.

A typical lifejacket approved by the Department of Trade and in general use in merchant ships is illustrated in Fig. 5 – 2.

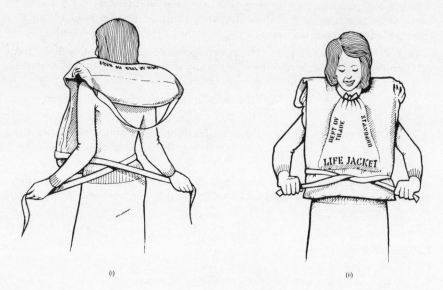

(i)   (ii)

F IG. 5–2. Typical non-inflatable lifejacket

When putting on a lifejacket it should be very firmly secured round the body by its tapes or lines. If fitted with a lifting becket this should be left clear for rescue and not used with the tapes for adjustment of the lifejacket on the body.

If at all possible, every effort should be made to enter the water by climbing down the ship's side using ladders, ropes or even fire hoses. If necessary it is safe to jump into the water from heights of up to 6 metres; the recommended method is to hold the nose between the fingers of one hand and to pass the other arm across the chest to pull down on the lifejacket. It is inadvisable to jump from heights greater than 6 metres when wearing a lifejacket of the non-inflatable type, because on impact with the water the jacket may be forced violently upwards against the wearer's head and so knock him unconscious or even break his neck. If jumping from substantial heights is unavoidable, the survivor should jump with the lifejacket and then put it on when in the water.

Lifebuoys

A lifebuoy is of circular shape and is nowadays usually made of polyurethane foam encased in a plastic cover. Older types may be made of cork or balsa wood covered with painted canvas. To comply with the SOLAS Convention a lifebuoy must:

1. Be capable of supporting 14.5 kilograms of iron in fresh water for 24 hours.
2. Not be adversely affected by oil or oil products.
3. Be of a highly visible colour.
4. Be marked in block letters with the name and port of registry of the ship in which it is carried.
5. Be fitted with beckets securely siezed.

The number of lifebuoys carried in a ship depends on whether she is a passenger or cargo vessel. A cargo ship of gross tonnage 500 and upwards must carry at least 8 lifebuoys, and the number carried by passenger ships varies with their length, from a minimum of 8 for ships under 61 metres long up to a minimum of 30 for ships of 244 or more metres long.

Lifebuoys are placed in conspicuous and handy positions on the upper decks so as to be readily accessible to the persons on board. At least two of the lifebuoys must be capable of quick release from the navigating bridge, and at least one on each side of the ship must be fitted with a buoyant lifeline having a minimum length of 27.5 metres.

Man-overboard markers. A proportion of the lifebuoys carried must be provided with efficient self-igniting lights. In passenger ships the proportion is not less than one-half of the total number of lifebuoys, and in no case must there be less than six lifebuoys with these lights; in cargo ships the proportion is at least one-half of the total number of lifebuoys. For tankers these lights must be of an approved electric-battery type. At least two of the lifebuoys including those capable of quick release from the navigating bridge must be provided with an efficient self-activating smoke signal as well as a self-igniting light. The light and the smoke signal are secured to the lifebuoy by short lanyards so that they remain attached when the lifebuoy is released or thrown overboard.

The light and the smoke signal may be individual items but they are commonly combined. A typical combined unit is the Pains-Wessex 'Man-overboard' lifebuoy marker, which is identical to that described in Volume II, Chapter 3, and illustrated in Volume II, Fig. 3–20.

Buoyant apparatus

Buoyant apparatus is usually constructed in the form of a flat raft either of wood enclosing metal buoyancy tanks, or of glass-reinforced plastic (GRP) incorporating foam buoyancy material. A typical stack of buoyant apparatuses on the deck of a passenger ship is shown in Fig. 5–3 and such equipment is commonly seen on board passenger ships, cross-Channel and other ferries, and pleasure craft.

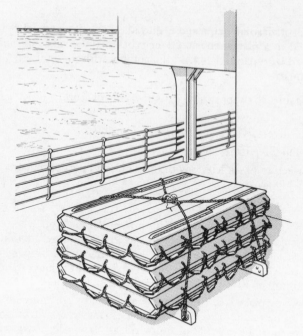

FIG. 5–3. Stack of three buoyant apparatuses on a passenger ship

An approved buoyant apparatus must have satisfied the following conditions. It must:

1. Be of such size and strength that it can be thrown from its stowage into the water without being damaged.

2. Not exceed 180 kilograms in weight unless suitable means of launching without lifting by hand are provided.

3. Be made of approved material and construction.

4. Be effective and stable when floating either way up.

5. Have the air cases or equivalent buoyancy placed as near as possible to the sides of the apparatus, and such buoyancy must not be dependent upon inflation.

6. Be fitted with a painter and have a line securely becketed around the outside.

The number of persons for which a buoyant apparatus is certified is determined by whichever is the lesser of either, the weight in kilograms of iron which the apparatus can support in fresh water divided by 14.5 or, the length of the perimeter in millimetres divided by 305.

Passenger ships engaged on international voyages may in some instances carry buoyant apparatuses for 25 per cent of the total number of persons on board, but generally sufficient is carried to accommodate only 3 per cent of all persons on board. Passenger ships engaged on short international voyages must carry buoyant apparatuses for at least 5 per cent of the total number of persons on board.

Rigid liferafts

Rigid liferafts are permitted by the SOLAS Convention but nowadays they are usually only used for particular applications, notably on board tankers. This type of raft is so constructed that when dropped into the water from its normal stowage neither the liferaft nor its equipment will suffer damage. The raft must be effective and stable, and its equipment must be readily available, when floating either way up. It is fitted with a deck to support the occupants and as far as practicable to prevent the ingress of water, and has a cover of some highly visible colour as a protection from exposure. In passenger ships the total weight of a rigid liferaft and its equipment must not exceed 180 kilograms; in cargo ships this weight may be exceeded if the liferafts are capable of being launched from both sides of the ship or if means are provided for putting them into the water mechanically. There is a painter, and a lifeline securely becketed around the outside and inside of the raft. There must also be efficient means to enable people in the water to climb on board at each opening, and arrangements for towing the raft. A buoyant light of the electric-battery type must also be attached by a lanyard. The liferaft must be so constructed as to be unaffected by oil or oil products and must be stowed so as to float free if the ship founders.

The approved carrying capacity of a rigid liferaft is calculated from the volume of air cases or equivalent buoyancy and from the effective deck-area of the raft. A proportion of a ship's lifesaving equipment may comprise either rigid or inflatable rafts, and the equipment to be carried in them is listed on pages 146–7.

Inflatable liferafts

The requirements of an inflatable liferaft are set out in the SOLAS Convention. In general these are the same as for a rigid liferaft but the inflatable liferaft must satisfy the following additional requirements.

1. The liferaft and its equipment must not become damaged when dropped into the water from a height of 18 metres or the height of its stowage if this is greater.

2. The raft must be capable of being readily righted by one person if it inflates in the inverted position.

3. The raft is to be contained in a valise or container in which it is inherently buoyant.

4. The total weight of the raft, its valise or container and its equipment is not to exceed 180 kilograms.

5. The floor of the raft is to be waterproof and capable of being insulated against cold.

6. The subdivision of the buoyancy compartments and means of inflation are to be such that if only half the compartments are inflated the raft will still support its approved complement of survivors.

7. The gas used for inflation of the raft must not be injurious to the occupants; inflation is to occur automatically by the pulling of a line or some other simple device.

8. Means must be provided of topping up the raft's buoyancy compartments. The raft must be constructed so as to withstand exposure for 30 days afloat in all sea conditions.

9. The raft must be capable of operating throughout a temperature range of −30 °C to 66 °C.

10. The raft must be stowed so that it is readily available in an emergency, and will float free, inflate and break free from the ship if she sinks.

11. If lashings are used to secure the raft in its stowage they must be fitted with an automatic release mechanism.

Liferafts are available in a range of sizes and these are all similar to the naval inflatable liferaft described in Volume II. To comply with the SOLAS Convention the capacities of approved liferafts vary from 6 to 25 persons but a smaller 4-man raft is additionally approved by the Department of Trade for use only in pleasure yachts. The small liferafts, for 4, 6 and 8 persons, are usually circular, and the larger rafts, for 10, 12, 16, 20 and 25 persons, are oval in shape. A typical inflatable liferaft is shown in Fig. 5–4. A further range of liferafts has been specially designed and approved for use in hovercraft.

Passenger ships engaged on international voyages carry liferafts, either rigid or inflatable, for 25 per cent of the total number of persons on board, but in some cases buoyant apparatuses may be substituted for the liferafts. Passenger ships engaged on short international voyages must have lifeboat and liferaft capacity which aggregates to the total number of persons on board, and they must have additional liferaft capacity for 10 per cent of the lifeboat capacity. Most cargo ships carry liferafts, either rigid or inflatable, to accommodate half the total number of persons on board. Cargo ships with no midships superstructure and with a registered length of 150 metres or more also carry, stowed as far forward as is practicable, an additional liferaft with a capacity of at least six persons.

Packing. Liferafts are packed in *valises* or *containers*. The valise is made of neoprene-coated fabric, has a pair of carrying loops and is suitable for stowage in lockers or under bench seats. The folded liferaft with its equipment is enclosed in the valise which is then laced together with a cord which breaks when the raft starts to inflate. A flap retains and protects the painter, a short length of which protrudes from the valise. The standard valise is similar to that shown later, in Fig. 5–6, except that it has no bowsing lines or suspension shackle.

The container is made of rigid GRP material which is durable and gives protection in open weather-deck stowages. A typical container in its stowage is shown in Fig. 5–5. The container is made in two halves which fit together to form a cylindrical enclosure. The liferaft and its equipment are enclosed in a cotton cover or polythene sheet within the container. The lid and base of the container are held together with a sealing gasket and the painter is threaded through a tunnel between the lid and base. Containers are normally stowed on deck chocks or specially built ramps at the ship's sides and at all stowages the end of the painter is secured to a metal strongpoint.

Automatic operation. All inflatable liferafts are required to float free from their stowage, inflate and break free in the event of the vessel sinking. This

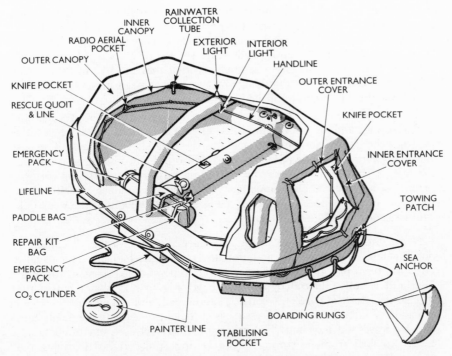

FIG. 5–4. Inflatable liferaft: the Marine Type X manufactured in capacities up to 25 persons by Messrs Beaufort (Air-Sea) Equipment Ltd

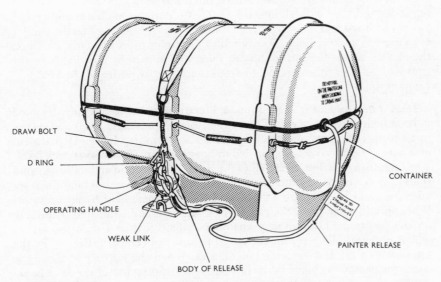

FIG. 5–5. General arrangement for the stowage of an inflatable liferaft in a GRP container on deck chocks

is achieved by making the liferaft buoyant in its valise or container and stowing it in such a manner that it is released when submerged. Containers on chocks or ramps are secured by a *hydrostatic release* which operates when submerged to a certain depth. Valises are stowed on wooden platforms, in collapsible boxes, or on raised gratings, so that they are free to float when submerged. Comprehensive guidance on the stowage, securing and protection of all inflatable liferafts is published by the Department of Trade.

The protruding end of the painter is secured by a *weak link* to a strongpoint at the stowage and pays out as the valise or container floats away. When fully paid out the painter tautens and operates the inflation mechanism. The gas (normally carbon dioxide (CO_2)) is released from the two bottles and inflates the raft. As inflation proceeds the expanding raft breaks the lacing cord or sealing gasket and the raft bursts from its valise or container. Finally when the strain on the painter reaches a force of 227 ± 45 kilograms the weak link ruptures and allows the raft to float free.

Hydrostatic release. The lashing or securing strop of a liferaft container on deck must be secured by an automatic release mechanism. This usually takes the form of a hydrostatic release, one type of which is shown in Fig. 5–5 and is fully illustrated in Volume II, Fig. 3–12. Water enters the mechanism (*body of release*) when it is submerged, and at a depth of between 1.5 and 3.7 metres the water pressure is sufficient to activate the diaphragm which releases the draw bolt. The lashing or strop is released and the container is free to float from its stowage. The D-ring is also released leaving the painter attached to the deck by the weak link.

The container can also be released manually. In the type of hydrostatic release illustrated this is achieved by turning the operating handle to the position marked 'FREE'. This releases the draw bolt and allows the container to roll over the side or be lifted from its stowage.

Launching. Liferafts in containers on ramp stowages can be released manually and they will fall into the water. Containers on chocks and valises have to be lifted and thrown into the water after first ensuring that the painter is secured to a strongpoint. Tension on the painter or, if this fails, a pull on the painter causes the raft to inflate. The raft can then be boarded from the ship by ladder or other means, or from the water by means of the boarding rungs of the raft.

Davit launching. Fig. 5–6 shows a liferaft in its valise specially designed to be launched from a davit. This type is used in passenger ships and its use in some other types of merchant vessel is also permitted by the Department of Trade. The survivors are enabled to board the raft dry-shod at deck level. The liferaft in its valise is carried to the launching position and its suspension shackle is connected to the davit release hook. The two bowsing lines are taken in hand or to suitable cleats and the painter is held by an operator. When lifted by the davit the raft swings outboard and is inflated by pulling on the painter. The buoyancy chambers inflate first and then the arches which automatically erect the canopy. The survivors embark (Fig. 5–7), the lines are cast off and lowering commences. When the raft is just above the water the person in charge in the raft pulls the tripping line of the davit hook. As lowering continues the raft automatically releases itself as soon as it becomes waterborne.

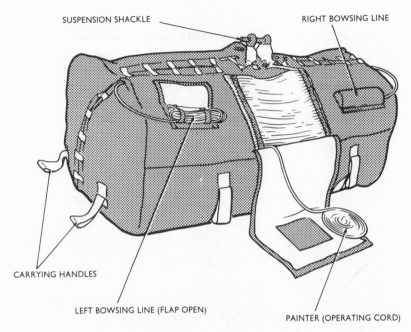

SUSPENSION SHACKLE

RIGHT BOWSING LINE

CARRYING HANDLES

LEFT BOWSING LINE (FLAP OPEN)

PAINTER (OPERATING CORD)

FIG. 5–6. Davit-launched Marine Type Q liferaft stowed in its valise

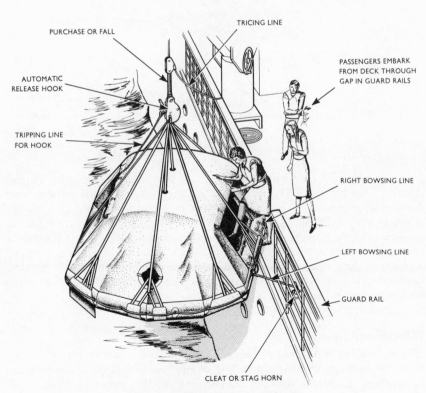

PURCHASE OR FALL

TRICING LINE

PASSENGERS EMBARK
FROM DECK THROUGH
GAP IN GUARD RAILS

AUTOMATIC
RELEASE HOOK

TRIPPING LINE
FOR HOOK

RIGHT BOWSING LINE

LEFT BOWSING LINE

GUARD RAIL

CLEAT OR STAG HORN

FIG. 5–7. Davit-launched liferaft

After each occasion of lowering, the davit remains turned out, the fall is recovered by a tricing line and the next liferaft is hooked on.

Davit release hook. The hook used for davit-launched liferafts is of a special type which automatically releases the raft when it is waterborne. One example is the Mills 'Atlas' release hook which has been designed to meet the requirements of the Department of Trade and other authorities, and is shown in Fig. 5–8. The liferaft suspension shackle is offered to the hook and engaged

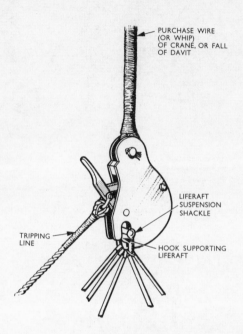

FIG. 5–8. The Mills 'Atlas' release hook for use with davit-launched liferafts

by closing the lever which fits readily into the palm of the hand. In this condition the hook will lift and not release the load. When the raft has been lowered to just above the water the person in charge of the raft pulls the tripping line which opens the lever but the weight of the raft continues to maintain the hook engaged with the suspension shackle. When the raft is waterborne and the load is reduced, the hook is released by spring pressure and allows the suspension shackle to fall away. The hook is normally set to open when the suspended load reduces to 13.5 kilograms but this value can be adjusted to suit any special requirements.

Liferaft equipment

The equipment and its scale of supply for rigid and inflatable liferafts is laid down in the SOLAS Convention and comprises: rescue quoit and buoyant line, knives and balers, sponges, sea anchors, paddles, puncture repair outfit, topping-up pump for inflatable rafts, tin openers, first-aid outfit, water rations and graduated drinking vessel, waterproof torch capable of signalling Morse code, spare batteries and bulb, daylight signalling mirror and whistle, parachute distress-signals and hand flares, a set of fishing tackle, food rations, anti-seasickness tablets, survival instructions, and an illustrated copy of the table of lifesaving signals.

Lifeboats

The detailed specifications for the construction and fitting of lifeboats are laid down in the United Kingdom by the Department of Trade to comply with the general specifications contained in the SOLAS Convention. In this section a general description only is given to show broadly what types of lifeboat are fitted and how they are equipped and used.

Classification of boats. Lifeboats may be propelled by oars, sail, mechanical power or by a compression-ignition engine.

Stability and buoyancy. Every lifeboat must have ample stability in a seaway, and adequate freeboard when loaded with its full complement of persons and equipment. It must have rigid sides and be fitted with internal buoyancy only. Lifeboats with a rigid shelter may be approved, but the shelter must be capable of being readily opened from the inside and outside, and it must in no way impede the rapid embarkation or disembarkation or the launching or handling of the boat.

All lifeboats must have inherent buoyancy, or be fitted with watertight buoyancy tanks or compartments sufficient to float the boat when it is flooded and open to the sea. Additional buoyancy equal to at least one-tenth of the cubic capacity of the boat must also be provided, and for boats with a capacity of 100 persons or more this additional buoyancy must be still further increased. Motor lifeboats must also be provided with additional buoyancy, dependent on the number of extra persons that could be carried if the engine, its accessories and certain other equipment were removed. The buoyancy tanks or compartments may be filled with a non-corrodable buoyant material which is not affected by oil or oil products.

Size. For a lifeboat to be approved under the SOLAS Convention its maximum weight must not exceed 20.3 tonnes when laden with its full complement of persons and equipment, and its carrying capacity must not be more than 150 persons. A typical large motor-lifeboat to carry 145 persons is shown in Fig. 5–9. Lifeboats that carry more than 100 persons must be motor lifeboats, and those with a capacity of more than 60 but not more than 100 persons must be propelled either by motor or by mechanical means.

Propulsion. A motor lifeboat is fitted with a compression-ignition engine. The engine must be kept so that it is ready for use at all times and can be started in all conditions, and must be fuelled for 24 hours' continuous running at a speed of at least six knots (fully loaded) when carried on board passenger ships, tankers, or whale or canning factory-ships; and at least four knots if carried in other types of ship. The engine must be protected adequately from the weather and the engine casing must be fire-resisting.

A mechanically propelled lifeboat is fitted with propelling gear of sufficient power to enable the lifeboat to be cleared readily from the ship's side when launched and to be able to hold course under adverse weather conditions.

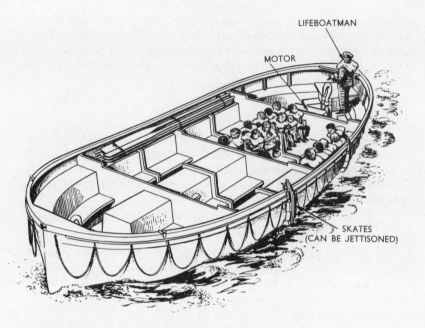

FIG. 5–9. Typical large motor-lifeboat of a passenger ship

The gear must be capable of being worked by untrained persons and must be workable when the lifeboat is flooded. A common form of manual propulsion is by means of levers placed between the thwarts. When the levers are worked backwards and forwards the boat is propelled through the water (Fig. 5–10).

Motor lifeboats and mechanically propelled lifeboats must be fitted with the means of going astern.

In the majority of passenger vessels and tankers, at least one lifeboat on each side of the ship must be a motor lifeboat, and in other cargo vessels at least one of the lifeboats must be a motor lifeboat.

Number of lifeboats carried. The SOLAS Convention lays down the minimum complement of lifeboats which are to be carried on board various types of ship. Some ships are permitted to substitute liferafts for a proportion of their lifeboats, while others are required to carry more lifeboat capacity than the number of persons on board. For example, a cargo ship if damaged is liable to list heavily because of its large cargo spaces and is therefore required to carry sufficient lifeboats on *each* side of the ship to accommodate *all* the persons on board, while a passenger ship is only required to carry sufficient lifeboats on *each* side of the ship for *half* the number of persons on board.

Emergency boats. In passenger ships there must be one boat on each side of the ship kept ready for immediate use while the ship is at sea. These boats must be of an approved type and not more than 8.5 metres in length. If they comply fully with the requirements for lifeboats they may be counted as part of the lifeboat complement.

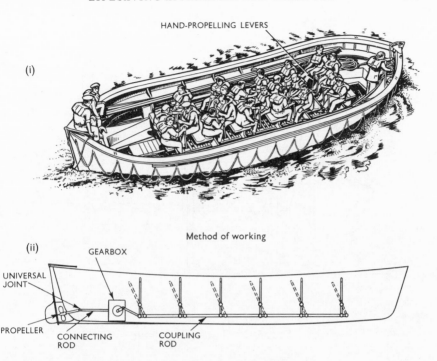

FIG. 5–10. Hand-propelled lifeboat

Stowage of lifeboats. Every lifeboat is normally hoisted at a separate pair of davits, and lifeboats may only be stowed on more than one deck if proper measures are taken to prevent lifeboats on a lower deck being fouled by those stowed on a deck above.

Two types of davits are approved for use in merchant ships: the *luffing* type and the *gravity* type. The luffing davits, one type of which is illustrated in Fig. 5–11, are canted outboard by a crank handle to move the boat to a position where it is ready for lowering. Gravity-type davits (Fig. 5–12) are made in two parts: the fixed part is called the *skid* and the movable part is called the *cradle*. The cradle, which supports the boat, is mounted on rollers and can move up or down the skid. The boat is slung from falls which are rove round sheaves on the cradle and led to a power-operated winch. When the brake of the winch is released the cradle moves by gravity down the skid and comes to a stop at the lower end of the skid. The skid is so shaped that when the cradle reaches the stop it is canted outboard and the boat then continues to lower from the davit head.

In tankers of 1600 tons gross tonnage and upwards, all davits must be of the gravity type. In all other ships the davits must be luffing or gravity type for lifeboats which weigh 2.3 tonnes or less in their turning-out condition, and gravity type for lifeboats which weigh more than 2.3 tonnes.

Skates are usually fitted to the inboard side of each lifeboat (Fig. 5–13) to enable the boat to slide down a listed ship's side without suffering undue damage. When the boat is waterborne the skates can be unclamped and jettisoned.

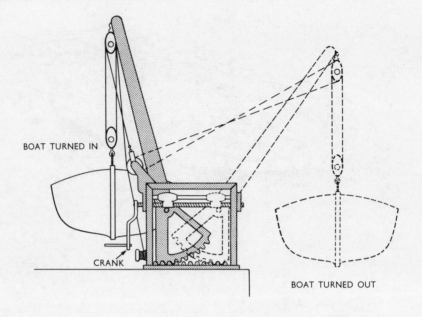

FIG. 5–11. Luffing-type davits

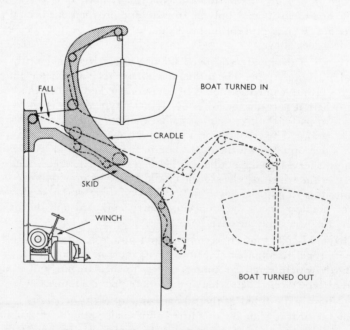

FIG. 5–12. Gravity-type davits

Emergency-boat davits and winches must be capable of quick recovery of the boats. The falls at lifeboat davits must normally be wire although the Department of Trade may permit manila or other approved material to be used in exceptional cases. At least two lifelines must be fitted to the davit span, and the falls and lifelines must be long enough to reach the water with the ship at its lightest seagoing draught and listed 15 degrees either way. The lower blocks of the falls have a suitable ring or long link for securing the blocks to the sling hook, unless there is disengaging gear fitted.

Typical lowering and embarkation arrangements for a large lifeboat in a passenger ship are illustrated in Fig. 5–13. All lifeboats must be provided with means of holding the boat on the ship's side at the embarkation point. One method of achieving this, shown in Fig. 5–13, uses a *tricing pendant* and *bowsing-in tackle* at each end of the boat. The upper end of the pendant is secured to the davit at position *2A* and the lower end to a lug on the lower block of the fall at position *2B*. When the boat reaches deck level at the boat station (where passengers embark) the pendant tautens and takes the weight of the boat. A bowsing-in tackle is then rigged between the ship's side and another lug on each fall block and hauled taut from within the boat (position *3*). When the passengers are embarked and the boat is ready for lowering, the pendant is slipped and the tackles are eased out and removed, and the boat is lowered (position *4*).

Equipment in lifeboats is fully listed in the SOLAS Convention and comprises: buoyant oars and thole pins or crutches, a boat hook, two plugs for each plug hole, a baler and two buckets, a lamp and oil, matches in a watertight container, a mast or masts with orange-coloured sails, a sea anchor, a container of 4.5 litres of suitable oil which can be dispersed when the container is secured to the sea anchor, food rations, water rations and a graduated drinking vessel, parachute signals and hand flares, buoyant smoke-signals, a first-aid outfit, a jack-knife fitted with a tin opener, two buoyant heaving lines, a whistle, fishing tackle, a cover of highly visible colour to protect the survivors from exposure, and a copy of the illustrated table of lifesaving signals.

Lifeboats must be fitted with a rudder and tiller, a lifeline becketed around the outside of the boat, a painter secured forward by a toggle and strop and one firmly secured aft, handholds in the bilge rails, and grab lines to enable persons to cling to the boat should it capsize, a manual pump, and a suitable locker for the stowage of small gear.

Motor and mechanically propelled lifeboats need not carry a mast or sails or more than half the complement of oars but they must carry two boat-hooks. Motor lifeboats must also carry a portable fire extinguisher.

Radio apparatus and searchlights

The SOLAS Convention specifies the number of motor lifeboats which are to be fitted with radio apparatus and a searchlight. The radio apparatus must be fitted in a cabin large enough to accommodate the equipment and the operator. The searchlight must have a power of at least 80 watts and be capable of illuminating a light-coloured object at a distance of up to 180 metres.

Portable radio apparatus. An approved portable radio apparatus for survival craft is carried on board every ship which does not carry on each side

L

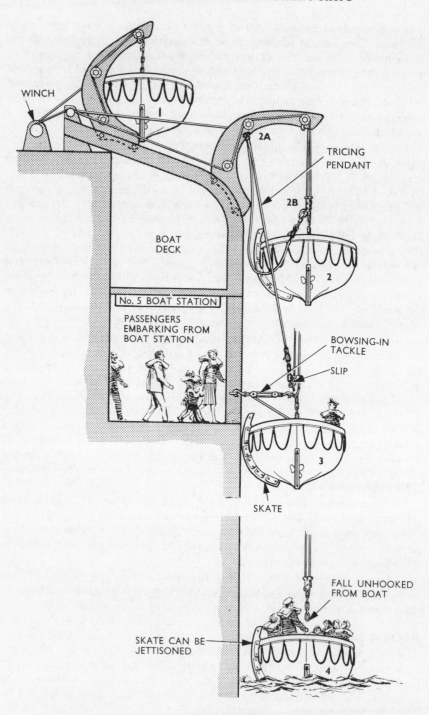

WINCH

2A

TRICING PENDANT

2B

BOAT DECK

2

No. 5 BOAT STATION

PASSENGERS EMBARKING FROM BOAT STATION

BOWSING-IN TACKLE

SLIP

3

SKATE

FALL UNHOOKED FROM BOAT

SKATE CAN BE JETTISONED

4

Fig. 5–13. Lowering and embarkation arrangements for a large lifeboat in a passenger ship

a motor lifeboat fitted with radio. The radio must be: capable of transmitting and receiving on the international distress frequencies, watertight, capable of being dropped into the sea without damage and of floating in sea water, and capable of being operated in emergency by an unskilled person. This apparatus is kept available in the chartroom or other suitable place (but not in the radio room) ready to be moved to one or other of the lifeboats in an emergency. In vessels where there is a considerable fore-and-aft separation between the main transmitter and the survival craft the portable radio apparatus should be stowed in the vicinity of the craft most distant from the radio room.

Certificated lifeboatmen

A certificated lifeboatman is a seaman who holds a certificate issued by the Department of Trade to the effect that he has passed an examination in all the operations connected with launching lifeboats and other lifesaving appliances, in the use of oars and propelling gear and in the practical handling of lifeboats and other lifesaving equipment.

The crews of all passenger ships include such men, the number depending upon the number of lifeboats carried and the prescribed complement of each boat. The following table shows the minimum number of lifeboatmen who must be included in the complement of each boat carried.

PRESCRIBED COMPLEMENT OF LIFEBOAT	MINIMUM NUMBER OF CERTIFICATED LIFEBOATMEN
Less than 41 persons	2
From 41 to 61 persons	3
From 62 to 85 persons	4
Above 85 persons	5

Practice musters and drills

In passenger ships the crew is normally exercised weekly for boat drill and fire drill, and must also be exercised when the ship leaves the final port of departure on an international voyage. The passengers are mustered at their respective boat stations within twenty-four hours of a ship leaving port when on an international voyage.

Different groups of lifeboats are used in turn at successive boat drills, and every lifeboat should be swung out and lowered at least once every four months.

The inspections of the lifeboats and their equipment are so arranged that the crew are practised in the duties they have to perform, including the handling of liferafts if carried.

In cargo ships the crew is mustered for boat drill and fire drill at least once a fortnight, and, if more than 25 per cent of the crew have been replaced, within twenty-four hours of leaving port. At the fortnightly muster all the lifeboats' equipment is examined to make sure that it is complete.

The emergency signal for summoning passengers to muster stations is a succession of seven or more short blasts followed by one long blast on the ship's whistle or siren. In passenger ships on international voyages this signal is supplemented by other electrically operated signals throughout the ship and operable from the bridge. The meaning of all signals affecting passengers, with precise instructions on what to do in an emergency, is clearly stated on cards posted in cabins and in conspicuous places in other passenger accommodation.

Crew muster list and emergency procedure. Before a vessel sails a muster list is drawn up and copies are posted about the ship, and in particular in the crew's quarters. It shows the special duties allocated to each member of the crew in an emergency and the station to which he must go. These special duties include the closing of watertight doors, valves, scuppers, fire doors and other openings; the equipping of the lifeboats and the other lifesaving appliances, including the portable radio apparatus for survival craft; the launching of the lifeboats; the general preparation of the other lifesaving appliances; the muster of the passengers; and the extinction of fire.

The special duties assigned to members of the stewards' department include warning the passengers, seeing they are suitably dressed and have put on their lifejackets in the proper manner, assembling them at muster stations, keeping order in the passages and on the stairways, and ensuring that a supply of blankets is taken to the lifeboats.

Before leaving harbour on an international voyage in a British passenger ship there is normally a muster of all her crew and an exercise in their various emergency and lifesaving duties. In the United Kingdom a Marine Surveyor of the Department of Trade is usually present and checks that the various members of the crew know exactly what would be expected of them in an emergency.

Manning of lifeboats and liferafts

Each lifeboat normally has a deck officer or certificated lifeboatman in charge; a second-in-command is also nominated. The person in charge should have a list of the lifeboat's crew and must ensure that they are acquainted with their duties. One of the crew must be capable of working the engine if the boat is a motor lifeboat; another must be able to work the radio and searchlight installation if carried.

Embarkation into lifeboats and liferafts

Suitable arrangements must be made for embarkation into the lifeboats and liferafts, consisting of a ladder or some such suitable device at each set of davits, and sufficient ladders at the launching positions to enable people to join the lifeboats or liferafts when they are waterborne. There must be adequate illumination at the davit and liferaft stowage and embarkation positions; the water must also be illuminated during the launching, until the operation is completed. Arrangements must be made for warning the passengers and crew that the ship is about to be abandoned. Precautions must be taken to prevent the discharge of water into the lifeboats and liferafts at fixed launching positions, including those under launching devices. There must also be an emergency lamp kept continuously lighted at the exit from each main compartment in the ship occupied by passengers or crew.

Ships' distress signals

All merchant ships which proceed to sea carry at least 12 parachute distress rockets which show a bright red light at high altitude. The red flare is designed to light at a minimum height of 300 metres and to extinguish when it has descended to a height of not less than 50 metres above sea level.

Line-throwing appliances

Every ship must carry a line-throwing appliance capable of throwing a line 230 metres with reasonable accuracy, and the appliance must include at least four lines and four projectiles.

One type of equipment to satisfy this requirement is the Pains-Wessex Schermuly 'Speedline' which is shown in Fig. 5–14. This self-contained unit will project a line 230 metres in calm weather by means of a solid propellant. The line is faked inside the container, and both the line and the propellant are protected from the weather by transparent polythene end-caps. The line is fired by a trigger which becomes operative after the removal of a safety pin. Pictorial instructions are printed on each side of the container. The Speedline is primarily a one-shot disposable unit and thus four complete equipments are normally carried, stowed in suitable positions around the ship. A buoyant head (Fig. 5–14(iii)) is available as an optional extra to the Speedline. The buoyant head has reflective patches and is attached to the rocket by means of a quick-action bayonet fitting, thus enabling the line to be recovered if it misses the target. It is particularly useful for the recovery of swimmers.

ROCKET LIFESAVING APPARATUS

Lifesaving stations

Numerous lifesaving stations are established around the coasts of Great Britain and Northern Ireland for rescuing shipwrecked mariners or assisting vessels in distress by means of RNLI lifeboats or by Coastguard Rescue Equipment. Coastguard Rescue Equipment stations are administered by the Department of Trade (HM Coastguard), and their locations together with details of assistance they can provide are given in a booklet titled *United Kingdom Marine Search and Rescue Organisation* published by HMSO, and also in the relevant volumes of the *Sailing Directions*.

Rocket lifesaving apparatus is used for rescuing the crew of a ship stranded close inshore and thus it is usually provided at stations in the vicinity of cliffs or high land, and in other places where a lifeboat cannot get close inshore.

Description and method of operation

The equipment comprises a rocket and line (Fig. 5–15), a tail block rove with an endless whip, a 12-millimetre jackstay or 24-millimetre hawser, a traveller block and a breeches buoy (Fig. 5–16). Various rocket apparatuses using 41-millimetre, 70-millimetre or 83-millimetre rockets are available to project a line from shore to pass over the ship. Fig. 5–15 shows the Pains-Wessex Schermuly 70-millimetre line-throwing apparatus which is capable of projecting an 8-millimetre man-made fibre line to at least 275 metres in calm weather, or alternatively a 4-millimetre line to at least 500 metres.

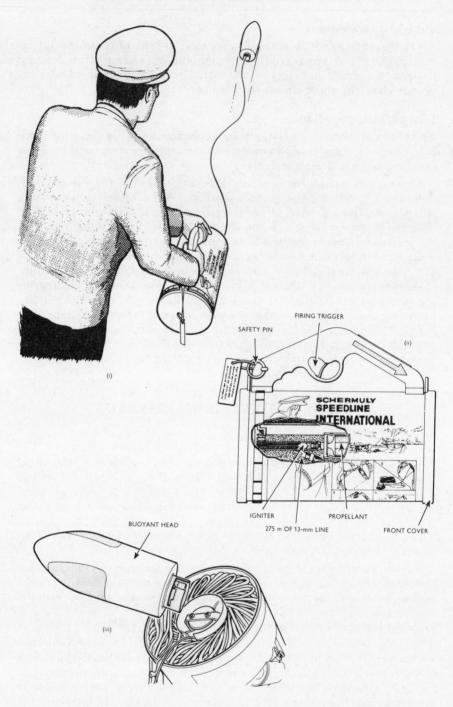

FIG. 5–14. The Pains-Wessex Schermuly 'Speedline' line-throwing apparatus

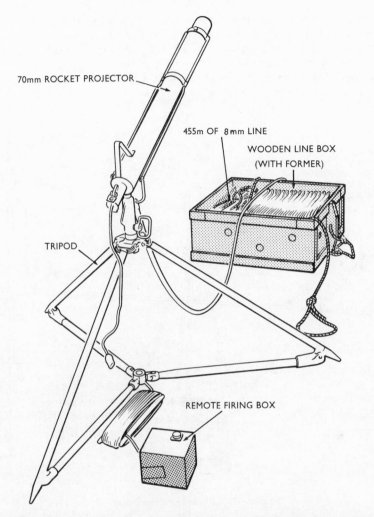

70mm ROCKET PROJECTOR

455m OF 8mm LINE

WOODEN LINE BOX
(WITH FORMER)

TRIPOD

REMOTE FIRING BOX

FIG. 5–15. The Pains-Wessex Schermuly 70-mm line-throwing apparatus

If a particularly heavy gale is blowing directly onshore, initial connection may be made by the ship firing a line to shore. If necessary, after contact has been made, the rescuers hitch a stouter line (usually 8-millimetre) to the initial line, which is then hauled out to the ship. The tail block, which is rove with the endless whip, is then hitched to the stouter line and hauled out to the ship by its crew. When it is inboard the tail block is secured to the mast or superstructure as high as is conveniently practicable.

The 24-millimetre hawser is 220 metres in length and has a becket spliced into it one metre or so from its end. One part of the endless whip is hitched to the hawser by reeving its bight through the becket and making a clove hitch on the bight round the hawser. When the tail block has been secured on board, the rescuers haul the end of the hawser out to the ship by means of the endless whip. When the end of the hawser is hauled on board it is brought up between the two parts of the endless whip and made fast to the same part of the ship as the tail block but just above it and with the tally board close up to the position to which the end of the hawser is secured, as shown in Fig. 5–16. The whip is then unhitched from the hawser, care being taken that the whip is clear of the hawser and free to run through the tail block.

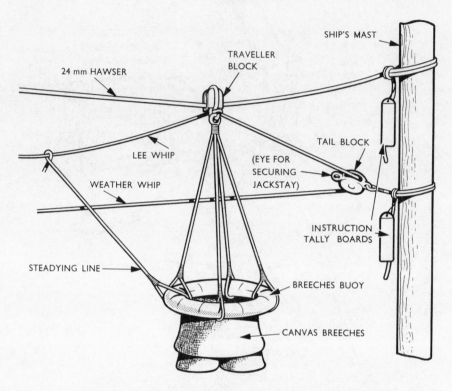

FIG. 5–16. Rocket lifesaving apparatus
The 24-mm hawser rig is illustrated; if the 12-mm jackstay rig is used, the jackstay is shackled directly to the tail block and not bent to the mast as shown for the hawser

The rescuers then set the hawser up taut and fit the inverted single block, which forms the traveller, to the hawser. A bight of the endless whip is then bent to the becket of the traveller; the outhaul part is called the *weather whip* and the other part the *lee whip*.

The breeches buoy, which is a Kisbie buoy fitted with a four-legged sling and a divided canvas trunk in the form of a pair of breeches, is slung on the traveller and a steadying line is rigged from the shore side of the buoy to the lee whip. The traveller with the breeches buoy is then hauled out to the ship by the weather whip.

The first member of the crew to be rescued then steps into the breeches of the buoy, facing shoreward, and steadies himself by grasping the steadying line; the rescuers then haul the buoy ashore by the lee whip. This operation is repeated until all the crew are rescued.

It may sometimes happen that the weather and the condition of the ship are such that a hawser cannot be set up. In such cases the breeches buoy is supported either on a 12-millimetre jackstay which is shackled to the eye of the tail block and passed with it, or solely on the endless whip.

Signals for operating

Each stage of the operation should be indicated by a signal.

By day. The signals made from both shore and ship consist of the horizontal or vertical movement of a white flag. The meanings of these two movements are given below. In the ship a man should be detailed to stand clear of the remainder of the crew and to wave the flag; or, if no flag is available, to wave his arm or his cap.

By night. The signals from both shore and ship consist of the horizontal or vertical movement of a white light.

If the signal is made by waving with a vertical motion (up and down) its sense is *affirmative,* e.g. 'Haul away', 'Line made fast'; but if it is made by waving horizontally (from side to side) its general sense is *negative,* e.g. 'Avast hauling', 'Slack away'.

In poor visibility the signals may be made in the ship by use of the siren, foghorn or a whistle, and they may be made on shore by blowing a whistle. The Morse code letter K (— • —) is sounded for affirmative and the letter S (• • •) for negative.

The following various stages should be indicated by signal:

In the ship: When the rocket line is in hand.
                 When the tail block is secured.
                 When the hawser is secured.
                 When a man is ready to be hauled ashore in the breeches buoy.

On shore: When the tail block is hitched to the rocket line and ready to be hauled on board.

In addition to these signals, communication by flashing light or hand flags should be established between ship and shore whenever possible; in most rescue crews there is a trained signalman. It may also be found convenient to secure a small message-container to the breeches buoy once the rig has been set up.

PART II

SEAMANSHIP

CHAPTER 6

Towing at Sea

Taking a ship in tow, and preparing to be taken in tow, are both commonly practised evolutions in warships. The need to take a disabled ship in tow may occur suddenly in peacetime and perhaps more frequently in wartime. How to prepare the necessary gear on the upper deck, how to pass and secure the tow, and how to slip and recover it, are described in Volume II.

It is obvious, however, that no rigidly standard method of towing or being taken in tow can be laid down, because the method used will depend on the types of ship involved, the condition of the towed ship, the duration of the tow, and such other matters as the urgency of the situation, the weather and the route to be taken. This chapter deals with the subject as a problem in shiphandling, and is also intended to help the Captain and his assistants on the bridge to select the gear and method best suited to the situation. Shiphandling generally is dealt with in Part IV.

Comparison between warships and rescue tugs
Generally speaking, the average warship compares unfavourably with a properly equipped salvage tug for the purpose of towing. Ocean-going tugs have certain features in common. Firstly they are as small as is consistent with good sea-keeping qualities, adequate power and endurance. They are highly manoeuvrable — a short, squat ship is handy at slow speed in a seaway; moreover, the towing deck is under direct control of the bridge, and the distance between forecastle and towing deck is so short that a head-on approach when passing the tow can be adopted if circumstances require it. Secondly, ocean tugs are built with an overhanging and well-padded counter and, if twin-screwed, they are fitted with efficient rope guards. Thirdly, the tug has a low towing deck with overhead towing horses to provide a clear run for the gear, and is fitted with a self-rendering or self-tensioning winch and a shock-absorbing towing hook near her centre of gravity. A modern Ministry of Defence ocean-going tug which possesses many of these attributes is illustrated at Fig. 6–1.

Warships in general are the antithesis of the salvage tug in all these respects, and the problem is aggravated by their widely differing handling characteristics. These handicaps can be minimised by skilful shiphandling, and on many occasions ships of the Royal Navy have carried out successful tows in most difficult circumstances over long distances.

Taking in tow
To recapitulate briefly the process of taking in tow (as described in Volume II), a typical sequence of events would be as follows, given that the ship to be towed is able to prepare the towing gear. On board the ship to be towed the polyamide towing-hawser is laid out on the forecastle, with its inboard end secured to the port (or starboard) cable. The outboard end of the towing hawser is secured to a polypropylene hawser which is used as a messenger

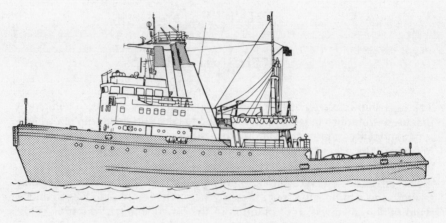

Fɪɢ. 6–1. A Ministry of Defence 'R' Class ocean tug

to take the heavy towing-hawser across to the towing ship. Both the towing hawser and messenger are on the forecastle of the towed ship, faked down ready for running.

The towing ship now approaches and establishes contact, usually by firing a gun line which the towed ship secures to the polypropylene messenger. The towing ship then hauls across the gun line, followed by the messenger and the towing hawser which she secures to her towing slip. The towed ship now veers a suitable length of cable secured to the end of the towing hawser to act as a spring to take the shock of sudden stresses in the tow. The length of cable is adjusted so that a joining shackle is positioned between the hawsepipe and the capstan or windlass; in this way the cable may be parted for ease of slipping the tow in emergency. The tow is secured by allowing the brake of the cable holder or gypsy to take the weight of the tow and by putting a riding slip on the cable to act as a preventer. The cable holder or gypsy is now disconnected and all is ready for the tow to proceed.

A polyamide towing-hawser has been used in the foregoing description; however, composite towing-hawsers (wire and polyamide or polypropylene) are commonly used in commercial practice.

TOWING PREPARATIONS

In addition to making ready the towing gear (as described in Volume II) there are various other preparations that may have to be made.

Communications

In the towing ship it is essential to organise good communication between the bridge and quarterdeck. It will be helpful to station on the quarterdeck an officer or senior rating whose sole duty is to pass a running commentary on the situation aft by telephone to the bridge. Communication between the towing and towed ship is primarily achieved by hand signals (described in Volume II) and by portable VHF radio which enables all parties engaged in a tow to be in contact with one another.

Propellers

When a ship is being towed the drag of each of her propellers may be as much as, or even greater than, the resistance offered by the underwater surface of her hull. The engines should therefore be disconnected from their shafts, when practicable, to allow the propellers to trail, but this is only possible when continuous lubrication can be provided to the shafts.

Radar reflectors

When it is intended to tow a small vessel, or one with a very low freeboard, it is usually helpful to rig her with a mast fitted with a radar reflector. This will enable a check to be kept on her in restricted visibility, and help in her recovery if she breaks adrift or if the towrope has to be slipped in emergency.

Lights

In a manned tow, navigation lights should present no problems. However, in an unmanned tow every endeavour should be made to provide navigation lights throughout the period of the tow. If this cannot be achieved, the towing ship should illuminate the towed ship at night by searchlight when in the vicinity of shipping.

All Ministry of Defence tugs are supplied with a set of propane-gas navigation lights for installation on unmanned towed vessels. The lights will burn continuously for a period of approximately six months.

Provision of electric power

If a damaged and disabled vessel is without steam and electric power it may be possible in calm or moderate weather to supply her by cable with sufficient electric power to enable her to pump out flooded compartments and correct any trim or list, provided that her electrical system is compatible with that of the towing ship. On one occasion a destroyer in danger of sinking was made sufficiently seaworthy by this means to enable her to be towed to port. The cable should be in one continuous length, because it is very difficult at short notice to make a joint in electric cable sufficiently strong and watertight for this purpose. The end of the cable should be bound with tape to make it as watertight as possible, and the cable should be stopped in shallow bights, at intervals of about one metre, to a 12-millimetre wire-rope jackstay, care being taken to parcel the cable at the stops to avoid chafe. If towing at long stay, the jackstay should be slung from the towrope by spring hooks at intervals of 10 to 20 metres.

APPROACH TO THE DISABLED SHIP

Maintaining position while passing the tow

The distance between the two ships should be kept as short as possible while the towing hawser is being passed and secured. The operation will be much more difficult if this distance is allowed to increase rapidly after first contact by line is made. For example, it will be a slow and painful procedure to haul in a heavy wire by hand if the distance exceeds 30 metres; while even with power available, as it normally is, the distance cannot be increased beyond about 90 metres without risk of parting the messenger.

Attitude and drift of the towing and the disabled ship

In any weather conditions other than glassy calm, the nub of the problem of taking in tow lies in the fact that the disabled ship and the towing ship, unless they happen to be ships of the same class and are both undamaged, will almost certainly be drifting at different rates, and when stopped will be lying in different attitudes relative to the wind and sea.

Attitude of disabled ship relative to wind and sea

The direction, relative to the wind and sea, in which a ship will lie when stopped depends upon the position of her superstructure, her freeboard, the shape of the underwater part of her hull, and her trim.

If the ship is trimmed on an even keel the direction in which she will lie depends upon her freeboard and the arrangement of her superstructure. Ships with a high forecastle and a superstructure disposed well forward, such as tugs, will lie with the wind somewhat abaft the beam. Ships with their superstructure disposed more or less amidships, such as aircraft carriers, passenger vessels and some cargo ships, will lie broadside-on to the wind. Ships with their superstructure right aft, such as tankers, bulk carriers and some coastal vessels, may lie with the wind somewhat before the beam.

The more a ship is trimmed by the stern the farther will she lie off the wind; conversely, the more she is trimmed by the head the nearer will she lie to the wind. The lighter a ship is laden the greater will the position of her superstructure and an uneven trim affect her attitude. A deeply laden three-island vessel will probably lie broadside-on to the wind, but the same ship in ballast, trimmed slightly by the stern to give adequate propeller immersion, will probably lie with the wind well abaft the beam.

Damaged plating projecting below the keel will have an effect similar to that of uneven trim, particularly if it is well aft or forward, because of the drag it offers to the drift of the ship to leeward.

Drift of a disabled ship

The speed at which a ship drifts to leeward depends upon the strength of the wind, her draught, her freeboard, and the area of her superstructure; and the more lightly laden she is the faster will she drift. A general cargo ship, averagely laden, may drift in a gale at a speed of as much as 2 knots.

A ship lying with bow or quarter to the wind will tend to sail and so gather a little sternway or headway as she drifts; and this, combined with the effect of the waves, will make her yaw.

Assessing the situation

Time will probably be saved in the long run if the Captain of the towing ship, on first coming up with the disabled vessel, makes a careful and deliberate assessment of the attitude and drift both of the disabled vessel and of his own when stopped. It is therefore good practice to circle a disabled vessel at close range before approaching to pass a line. If uncertain as to how his own ship will lie and drift, he should stop her clear of the disabled ship and note her behaviour before attempting a close approach. If it is obvious that the rates of drift are going to be very different, e.g. a carrier intending to tow a deeply-laden tanker, then the Captain must impress on everyone the necessity to get the tow passed as quickly as possible, and must see that everything is fully prepared before passing the first line. Speed of action and good seamanship are the key to success especially when assisting merchant ships. It must always be remembered that the crew of a merchant ship is usually small — for example, a VLCC may have only nine men on deck.

DIRECTION OF APPROACH — DRIFTING ATTITUDES SIMILAR

If the drifting attitudes and rates of the two ships are expected to be similar, the approach is best made on a slightly converging heading and aiming to pass very close across the weather bow of the disabled ship. There is little danger in a close approach under these circumstances, because the towing ship will make considerably less leeway as long as she is making headway (Fig. 6–2). The course steered during the approach must take this fact into account.

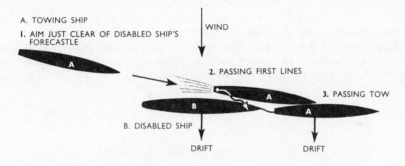

FIG. 6–2. Approach to a disabled ship — drifting attitudes similar

The first lines can be passed from any position, but to avoid long leads of messenger and risk of fouling the propellers it will probably be easiest to pass from aft, as the towing ship's quarterdeck comes within range of the disabled ship's forecastle. As way is taken off the towing ship she should be manoeuvred so as to take up position some 30 metres ahead of the other, and on the same heading, and this heading should be maintained as steadily as possible while the towing gear is being passed.

Should connection not be established when passing to windward of the disabled vessel, it may be difficult to regain a good position by making a sternboard and it will usually be more practicable to go right round and make another approach.

When the tow has been passed and secured, the towing ship should proceed slowly ahead on or near her present course while the gear is being paid out, and should not attempt to turn to the final course until the disabled ship is in tow. The alteration should then be made in very easy stages.

M

DIRECTION OF APPROACH — DRIFTING ATTITUDES DISSIMILAR

It may be the case that the towing ship is expected neither to assume the same drifting attitude as the disabled ship nor to drift at the same rate. In these circumstances a down-wind approach is usually preferable, because most warships will steer quite well at slow speed with the wind astern unless there is a heavy following sea, whereas head-to-wind and -sea they are liable to pay off rapidly and uncontrollably as headway is lost. Furthermore this tendency to pay off when head-to-wind will be accentuated as sternway is gathered with the object of maintaining position on the drifting ship, whereas if approaching down-wind it will be comparatively easy to hold the stern up into the wind with slow astern revolutions while maintaining a slight drift to leeward. But the possibility of washing down the quarterdeck when going astern must be remembered. The following is an example of the down-wind approach.

Disabled ship lying broadside to wind

If the disabled ship is lying broadside to wind the towing ship should approach so that her course with the wind dead astern will lead her about 30 metres from the disabled ship's bows at the closest point (Fig. 6–3). The greatest attention is required during the approach to ensure that own ship's path remains that distance ahead of the other. If the disabled ship appears to be drifting ahead, and narrowing the estimated gap, it is not sufficient to alter a few degrees away, because a further alteration will almost certainly be required later, thus bringing the wind well on the quarter in the final stages.

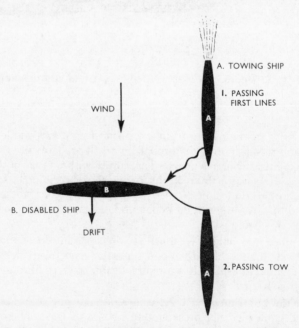

FIG. 6–3. Drifting attitudes dissimilar — approach to a disabled ship lying broadside to wind

It will be better to elbow out so as to run down towards a position considerably farther ahead.

The approach should be made at the slowest speed which will give good steering control. The precise moment and the method of passing the first line is a matter of seamanship on which individual opinions will vary. If the forecastle is considered the best place for the gun or heaving line, being under the direct control of the bridge, great care will be needed to keep the messenger clear of the propellers while the ship moves ahead to take up a position slightly to leeward of the other's bows. No attempt to haul the towing gear across should be made until this position is reached.

There should be no great difficulty in maintaining a position just ahead and to leeward of the disabled ship's bow, given that she is drifting dead to leeward and that propellers can be used, at least on the disengaged side. The towing ship should proceed slowly down-wind while the gear is being paid out, and take the first strain while still nearly at right-angles to the other ship.

Disabled ship lying with wind abaft her beam

If the disabled ship is lying with the wind abaft her beam she will be making headway and it will be dangerous to attempt to pass close across her bows. If a down-wind approach is made the towing ship must keep well ahead of the disabled ship in order not to risk collision (Fig. 6–4, position *1*).

By judicious use of the engines it should be easy enough to ensure that the disabled ship drifts close across the stern, and the first connection should be made as this position is approached (Fig. 6–4, position *2*). If own ship's heading can subsequently be maintained in the direction of the other's drift, the operation of passing the tow should proceed normally; but if, as is more

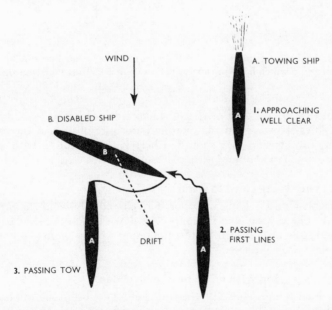

FIG. 6–4. Drifting attitudes dissimilar — approach across the bow of a disabled ship which has wind abaft the beam and is drifting with some headway

probable, own ship can only be maintained stern to wind, she will drift along the other's lee side and the handling of the gear may be difficult (Fig. 6–4, position *3*).

If the tow is successfully hauled across and secured in spite of this relative drift, the towing ship should be brought if possible on to a heading similar to that of the disabled ship while paying out, because unless a more forward position is attained the gear will be unfairly nipped and may part when the first strain is taken.

An approach on a heading similar to that of the disabled ship in these circumstances may therefore be preferable (Fig. 6–5). When in position *2*

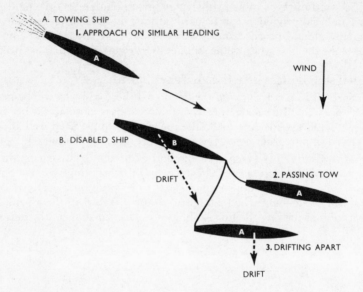

FIG. 6–5. Drifting attitudes dissimilar — approach on a heading similar to that of a disabled ship which has wind abaft the beam and is drifting with some headway

the disabled ship's forward drift can be allowed for by the use of the towing ship's engines. However, if the rates and attitudes of drift of the two ships differ, the towing ship may soon find herself in position *3*, with a rapidly widening gap that will hinder the passing of the tow.

Disabled ship lying stern to wind

If the disabled ship is lying with her stern directly up-wind the problem is simplified. The towing ship can approach down-wind on a similar heading and should have little difficulty in maintaining a position on one bow or the other while the tow is passed.

Disabled ship lying with wind before her beam

If the disabled ship is lying with the wind before her beam she will be making slight sternway, so that a close approach down-wind can be made without danger (Fig. 6–6).

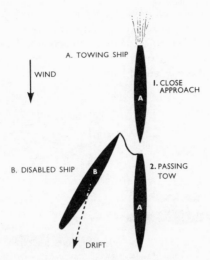

FIG. 6–6. Disabled ship lying with wind before the beam — down-wind approach

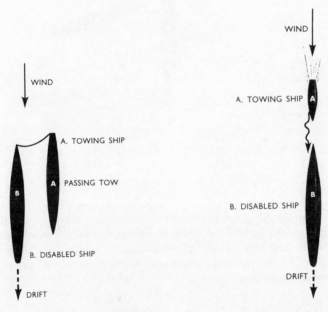

FIG. 6–7. Disabled ship lying bows to wind — beam approach down-wind

FIG. 6–8. Disabled ship lying bows to wind — bow-to-bow approach by tug

Disabled ship lying bows to wind

If the disabled ship is holed forward and is well down by the bows she may lie practically head to wind. An approach down-wind to a point abreast the disabled vessel (Fig. 6–7) may expedite the passing of the first lines, but the towing ship will find it difficult to maintain her position while the tow is being passed, and even more difficult to move away to pay out the tow before taking the strain. In these conditions a tug would probably approach down-wind bow-to-bow (Fig. 6–8). Her handiness and the proximity of the towing deck to the bridge would assist such an approach, but the average warship would find it awkward to pass the tow from such a position. A warship would probably find that an approach across the disabled ship's bows would be more effective (Fig. 6–9). The tow would be passed as she drifts slowly down the side of the disabled ship.

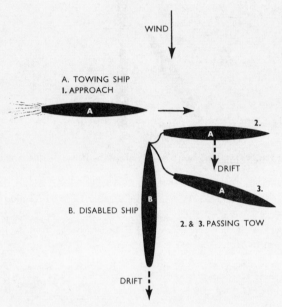

FIG. 6–9. Disabled ship lying bows to wind — crossing approach by warship

The most obvious approach is into the wind and on a heading similar to that of the disabled ship, but this choice will almost certainly lead to trouble. The towing ship will fall off the wind as soon as her engines are put astern, and may then find herself across the disabled ship's bows and drifting rapidly on to her, possibly at a time when it is impossible to use the engines for fear of fouling the towing gear.

DISABLED SHIP TO BE TOWED STERN FIRST

The shiphandling problem will not necessarily be any more difficult when the other ship has to be towed stern-first, though the operation of passing and securing the tow will often be more complicated.

In most cases the other ship will have been damaged forward and will be down by the bows. If this results in a head-to-wind attitude, a down-wind approach should enable position to be maintained quite easily while passing the tow, but great care will be required to keep the towing ship well clear of the disabled ship's exposed rudder and screws.

ESTABLISHING CONTACT

Use of boats or helicopters

Unless the disabled ship is short-handed or abandoned, boat work should be avoided as an unnecessary complication. The first line can be passed more quickly by gun or rocket, while in calm weather it is often possible to approach close enough for a heaving line to be used. Should these methods fail because of the weather conditions it is probable that boat work will also be impossible.

Warships that carry helicopters will find them invaluable as a means to carry across men and equipment to an abandoned vessel, but it is unlikely that they will prove any quicker as a means of carrying across the first lines. The merits and method of passing a tow by helicopter are discussed in Volume II.

By streaming a polypropylene line

There a several different ways of establishing contact by streaming a polypropylene line with its end bent to a small buoy, lifebuoy or other item of buoyant gear. In one method the disabled ship pays out the line from her weather side as she drifts to leeward; the line will then be streamed to windward of her, where it can be grappled and picked up by the towing ship. Alternatively, the towing ship can stream the buoyant line while under way and tow it so that it will lie to leeward of the disabled ship and in the path of her drift, then as the disabled ship drifts over the line she can grapple it and pick it up.

Another method is for the towing ship to bend the end of a buoyant line to a small target or a float rigged with a sail. She then stops to windward of the disabled ship, casts the target overboard and allows it to sail down-wind to the disabled ship, carrying the end of the line with it.

Establishing contact by gun line

The remarks in earlier sections of this chapter, on how to approach the ship to be taken in tow, indicate generally at what stage to fire the gun line. It is usually easier to fire it from aft, so that it is close to the scene of operations. But if the tow is being provided by the towing ship the Captain may prefer to pass the gun line, and the messenger, from the forecastle. He will then have an unobstructed view of the proceedings during the critical early stages when he is manoeuvring his ship to get her as close as possible. The inboard part of the messenger must be prepared in this case by leading it aft from the forecastle, outboard of all, stopped at intervals to the gunwale, and then inboard through the towing fairlead on the quarterdeck, where it is secured to the towrope.

Establishing contact by rocket line-throwing apparatus

Rocket line-throwing apparatus may be used to make the initial connection but the risk of flammable vapour in the atmosphere must be considered. This is particularly important when assisting tankers, and even more so when assisting LNG (liquefied natural gas) carriers. The towing ship should always take up a windward position to fire the apparatus.

Passing the tow

The work of passing and securing the tow is dealt with in Volume II.

SHIPHANDLING WHILE TOWING

Getting the tow under way

When the end of the towrope has been secured, the towing ship should move slowly ahead while veering the towrope to the required scope, and then stop while the towrope is finally secured in both ships. In shallow water care is required at this stage to keep the bight of the towrope off the bottom. The towing ship should then take up the tow, by going ahead very gently so as to subject the towrope as gradually as possible to the stresses of getting the towed ship under way. On reaching a speed of about two knots the engines can be kept moving continuously and speed can be increased gradually until the required towing speed is attained. If a polyamide towrope is used its great elasticity permits a practically horizontal pull to be applied safely for short periods.

Great care and patience should be exercised when taking up a tow because the stresses involved in overcoming the inertia of the towed ship are much greater than those of towing her at a constant speed. The best way to judge the degree of stress in a towrope is to watch its catenary; the shallower the catenary, the greater, of course, is the stress in the towrope, and it increases rapidly as the rope straightens out. The best practical rule for avoiding undue stresses in the towrope, both when taking up the tow and when towing, is never to allow its bight to break surface.

The direction in which the towing vessel should move off initially will be dictated to a certain extent by the relative attitudes adopted by the two ships during the passing of the tow. If possible, she should move off on the heading of the towed ship, and only when satisfied that the tow is taking an even strain should she begin to alter course towards the intended destination. This alteration must be done gradually in steps each of a few degrees, allowing time after each step for the towed ship to come round to the new heading before altering to the next one.

Towing

Provided that the tow is riding comfortably astern and not yawing, there are no particular problems involved in towing. The bight of the towrope should be kept well immersed, and in a swell its length should be adjusted so that both ships rise together on the crests of the waves and fall together in the troughs. Keep the bight of the towrope off the bottom, because if it fouls the bottom both ships will be brought up with perhaps serious results, particularly if the towing course lies across the wind or current.

If the bight of the towrope shows a tendency to break surface, either the towrope should be lengthened or the speed of towing should be reduced. If the weather deteriorates the bight of the towrope should be immersed deeper, provided that there is a sufficient depth of water, and this is best done by veering cable. If there is insufficient water to increase the depth of the bight, speed should be reduced.

Any large alteration of course should be made in steps of a few degrees at a time, so that a steady strain is maintained in the towrope, otherwise its bight will sag and may foul the bottom.

When towing in the vicinity of other shipping, any avoiding action should be decisive and should be taken early. An approaching ship may be confused by the lights of the tow, especially if the tow has a sheer, and an approaching ship on a particular bearing may see different coloured sidelights on the towing and towed vessels.

Keeping the towrope intact

Once the tow is under way and turned towards harbour, the chief concern of both ships should be to keep the tow intact, since it is quite possible that neither ship (unless one is a salvage tug) will have a suitable replacement for the towrope if it parts. Often a parted tow cannot be recovered because, for example, of lack of facilities in the disabled ship. So no precaution that may help to preserve the tow should be neglected. The recovery of a parted tow, even if possible, is always arduous; and the time wasted on recovery and reconnection will be greater usually than that which might have been saved by forcing on at a higher speed than the circumstances warranted.

The condition of the towing gear must be kept under continuous observation in both ships and any signs of chafe or stranding remedied before a serious weakness develops. When chain cable is used at either end, the nip should be freshened at least once every twenty-four hours, speed being reduced during the process. The nip of a wire hawser requires more attention, and should be freshened more frequently. Fairleads and hawsepipes should be kept well greased, and the towing hawser should be parcelled well where it passes through fairleads and hawsepipes. As added protection against chafe a lace-on sleeve protector is used. These sleeves are Naval Store items and are generally only issued to Ministry of Defence tugs.

Speed of tow

A fair assessment of the maximum safe towing speed in calm water can be made from the graphs near the end of this chapter. In these conditions, and provided the tow is handling well, there is no objection to towing at a speed near the maximum that allows a reasonable safety margin for the gear in use. But, at the first sign of deteriorating weather, speed must be reduced drastically in anticipation of the increased stresses.

In a long ocean tow the weather is usually the factor that dictates the speed. The average rate of progress on a long-distance tow may be as little as four knots, and at such low speeds the effects of wind and currents are proportionately very large. Wind charts, ocean-current atlases and weather forecasts should be carefully studied, and the track of the ships should be planned to take advantage of favourable winds and currents and to avoid adverse ones. When towing, the shortest route is not always the quickest.

YAWING OF THE TOWED SHIP

Most vessels when in tow have a tendency to yaw to one side or both sides of the course, but if the yaw is not excessive and the towed ship is able to steer, no difficulty should be experienced. If the towed ship is unable to steer and the yaw is excessive the towrope will be subjected to heavy stresses, particularly at the limit of each yaw, and it may also be severely chafed or nipped. The following factors, singly or in combination, may make a ship yaw or contribute towards her tendency to yaw.

The direction and force of wind and sea relative to her course
Her freeboard, draught, and the disposition of her superstructure
Her trim
Any list she may have on her
Any underwater projections caused by damage to her hull.

The more deeply laden a ship, the less tendency will she have to yaw, and, of the yawing factors, trim has the greatest effect.

Effect of wind and sea

With an undamaged ship in normal trim little can be done to correct yawing caused by wind and sea except to alter course or alter the speed of towing. A ship with a high forecastle and superstructure forward, such as a destroyer or frigate, will tend to bore up to windward, and a ship with her superstructure aft, such as a tanker, will tend to pay off to leeward. In a cross-wind a frigate will probably first fall off to leeward and then bore up into the wind, and so yaw from one side of the course to the other, whereas a tanker will probably pay off to leeward and then ride there at a steady angle of sheer. In a following wind and sea a tanker, particularly one with a counter stern, will tend to yaw more than a frigate; but in a head wind there should be little tendency for either type of ship to yaw.

Effect of trim, list and underwater projections

The more a ship is trimmed by the stern the steadier will she be when in tow; and conversely, the more she is trimmed by the head the greater will be her tendency to yaw. In fact a ship trimmed well down by the head will be unmanageable if towed bows first, and she should therefore be towed stern first.

A ship with a list will tend to sheer off towards her high side, and this tendency will be increased by a cross-wind blowing on that side. But a cross-wind blowing on her low side will tend to steady her.

Underwater projections caused by damage to the hull structure will have an effect similar to that of trim or list. If the projections are before the ship's pivoting point the effect will be the same as if she were trimmed by the head, and vice versa, and if they are to one side of her centre line she will tend to sheer towards that side.

Correction of yaw

Yawing may be corrected or reduced in a number of ways, and the choice of method must depend upon its cause and the circumstances of the tow.

The chief cause of yawing is usually that the ship is not trimmed sufficiently by the stern. Trim is best corrected by transferring liquids or ballast from one part of the ship to another, because then her reserve of buoyancy is maintained. If trim is corrected by flooding or by adding ballast, it should be done with discretion, otherwise the ship's stability, reserve of buoyancy, or seaworthiness may be dangerously affected.

If it is impracticable to alter the trim of the ship, or if her yawing is not due to incorrect trim, one or other of the methods described below should be tried. These have all proved successful in practice, but most of them increase the drag of the towed ship, and may subject the towrope to exceptional stresses or to a bad nip or chafe. An increase of drag may reduce the speed of towing to less than the economical or efficient speed.

Altering the speed. Yawing may be increased or reduced by altering the speed of towing. Yawing caused by list is usually decreased by increasing the speed of towing, and yawing caused by trim is usually decreased by reducing the speed of towing.

Setting the rudder. If a ship's steering gear is damaged her rudder may still be workable by hand, either by gearing or by reeving tackles on the tiller. By setting her rudder at an angle the towed ship may be steadied at a constant angle of sheer to one side or the other of the towing ship's track, but it may then be necessary to alter the lead of the towrope to ensure that it is not subjected to a bad nip or chafe. If the rudder angle or the angle of sheer is large this method may be impracticable because of the increased drag of the towed ship.

Towing another ship astern. Securing a second rescue ship with a hawser astern of the disabled ship, and using this rescue ship as a kind of powered rudder, has been tried with success on a number of occasions. The second ship is secured by her bows to the stern of the disabled ship, and may need to veer some cable on the end of her towrope. She then keeps a slight stress on her towrope and sheers to one side or the other as necessary to keep the disabled ship on course. Smartness in obeying engine orders is a paramount necessity in the astern-towing ship.

On one occasion a ship which had lost her rudder, but which was otherwise undamaged, used another ship as a rudder by taking her in tow, and was able to proceed in a high wind and sea on a fairly steady course without any other assistance.

Shifting the point of tow. A ship which is yawing to one side of the course may be steadied at a constant angle of sheer by shifting the point of tow farther aft on the inner bow. But this is only practicable if the resultant angle of sheer is not too great, and if the towrope is not subjected to chafe.

Towing a drogue. A drogue towed astern of the towed ship may steady her, particularly if she is fairly small with fine lines. Drogues which have proved successful include a bight of 48-millimetre buoyant line; one or two shackles of the ship's cable streamed on a messenger; a provision net, filled with paunch mats, towed on a two-legged bridle; and a multiplane kite otter, as used for minesweeping.

Setting a sail. Setting a sail in the towed ship either right forward or right aft may reduce the yaw. A boat's sail or a small awning can be used with an improvised rig.

Propellers. Although as a rule the propellers of the towed ship should be allowed to trail, it may be that one or more of them, if stopped, will drag in such a way as to reduce the yaw.

SHORTENING-IN THE TOW

Before entering shallow or restricted waters, or handing over to harbour tugs, the tow must be brought to short stay. This will give better manoeuvrability. It will also ensure that the bight is kept clear of the bottom, which is essential if the bottom is rocky or uneven. When the towing ship has a powerful winch aft, shortening-in can be carried out while still retaining headway, though speed should be reduced as far as possible to relieve the strain. Similarly the disabled ship, if she has power, will have no difficulty in retrieving her cable. When neither ship can heave in by power, the towing ship must ease down gradually until both ships are stopped, and then endeavour to haul in the towing hawser by hand. But this procedure will only be practicable if plenty of sea room is available and, in shallow water, if the bottom is free of snags. If shortening-in by hand proves impossible it may be necessary to slip the sea tow at both ends as soon as the disabled ship has been taken over by the harbour tugs.

When towing in restricted waters, make ample allowance for the drift of the tow to leeward and for leeway, in order to keep the towed ship clear of navigational marks and dangers.

EMERGENCY ACTION WHEN TOWING

Slipping and buoying the towrope

The after towing arrangements of a warship incorporate a slip to enable her to slip the towrope in emergency and so regain her freedom of manoeuvre. If the towrope is slipped, its recovery by the towed ship will be difficult and sometimes impossible, and when towing is resumed time will be wasted in recovering the towrope or passing a new one. If in sufficiently shallow water the towing ship should therefore buoy the end of the towrope before slipping it, the buoy being rigged with a stave and flag. A good method is to reeve the buoy-rope as a double whip through a block shackled to the end of the towrope, the buoy-rope being strong enough for weighing the end of the towrope.

Encountering heavy weather

In very bad weather it is probably preferable to turn and run slowly before wind and sea, although some tugmasters prefer to heave-to into wind and sea to maintain control of the tow. Heaving-to head to sea is likely to result in far heavier strains on the gear, although steering may be easier. When running with the gale it may be possible to steady the disabled ship by streaming a drogue. Obviously the ships cannot run if this is likely to bring them near a lee shore.

In extreme weather conditions which the gear cannot be expected to withstand, it may be preferable to slip the tow rather than to hold on until the gear parts. The disabled ship may ride more easily when drifting with the towing gear trailing as a sea anchor, while the towing ship will have freedom to manoeuvre.

Recovery of the entire tow, when the weather moderates, will probably be impracticable unless either the disabled ship can use her windlass or the end of the towrope was buoyed when it was slipped.

Use of oil in heavy weather

Heavy seas breaking on board may often be dangerous, especially if the ship is disabled. Even in the roughest weather, however, seas can be prevented from breaking by spreading a small quantity of oil on the water. Before the decision is taken to spread oil the following other factors must be considered.

Does the risk to human life justify the minor pollution which will be caused?

Because of the low freeboard of tugs, is the possible contamination of the towing deck and the consequent hazard to life and limb acceptable?

Unless there is a danger to life, oil should not be spread within 12 miles of any coast to comply with the stringent 'Oil on Navigable Waters' regulations.

The best oils to use are those of fish, animal or vegetable origin. If they are not available, lubricating oils should be used. Fuel oils should only be spread when their use is absolutely unavoidable and then only in very limited quantities. Only a few litres of oil per hour are required and it can be distributed in many ways, some of which are described below.

1. Fill a suitable tin with oil, punch sufficient holes in its bottom to give the required rate of flow, and place it in a water-closet pan, wash-basin or bath, so that the oil runs or is flushed outboard through the soil-pipes.

2. Take an old wash-deck hose, cut off the connections, sew up one end and prick a number of holes along its length with a sailmaker's needle. Then fill the hose with oil, close its other end with a strong seizing, and stop the hose to the gunwale at the required position.

3. Take a bag, fit it with a two-legged sling, ballast it with a weight of about 3 kilograms and pack it, not too tightly, with cotton-type material. Then with a sailmaker's needle prick a number of holes in the bottom and lower half of the sides of the bag, fill it with oil, close its neck with a strong seizing, and trail it in the water on a line.

Both ships should distribute oil; the positions from which to distribute it depend upon the direction of the wind and sea. If wind and sea are from abaft the quarter, oil should be distributed from each bow and quarter and from amidships on each side. If wind and sea are from between the quarter and the bow, oil should be distributed on the weather side from the bow, from amidships and from the quarter. If wind and sea are from before the bow, oil should be distributed from each bow. If wind and sea are before the beam and the towed ship is yawing badly, the towing ship should sling the bag described above by a bow-shackle on the towing hawser, tail it with a strong messenger, and allow it to slide well down the hawser so that it will distribute the oil ahead of the towed ship within the limits of her yaw.

If oil is used when taking a vessel in tow, the lines and hawsers should, if possible, be kept clear of the oil, otherwise they will become slippery and very difficult to handle.

Beaching a damaged ship

If the towed ship appears to be sinking it may be possible to beach her in time to save the ship. The optimum conditions for beaching are a sheltered bay, a soft and gently shelving bottom, and high water. If the value of the sinking ship warrants the risk, secure the towing ship alongside the lee quarter of the other and push her as far in towards the selected beaching point as practicable before slipping and going astern to clear her. Before attempting the operation the towing gear must be recovered, in order to prevent the disabled ship from anchoring herself before reaching the beach.

When the decision is taken to beach, there may be other ships standing by which are more suitable for the purpose because of their lighter draught or better manoeuvrability. The best control during a beaching will be achieved by securing a light-draught ship on each quarter of the disabled vessel. When the towing ship is of greater draught, or if for other reasons the risk of securing alongside the sinking ship is not justified, the best that can be done is to heave in the tow to short stay and cut adrift when heading in the general direction of the beach, while there is still room to manoeuvre clear. Some remarks on the stability of a grounded ship will be found in Chapter 1.

Taking an anchored ship in tow

If there is little sea, the simplest method of passing a tow to an anchored ship will probably be from alongside her, and on the side opposite to her cable if she has only one anchor down. When the tow has been passed, the towing ship should move ahead and stand off well clear while the anchor is being weighed, keeping the towing hawser fairly taut and off the bottom. It is more likely that this operation will be required in emergency to keep the anchored ship — which, it is assumed, has no power on her main engines — from drifting on to a lee shore in a gale. A warship attempting this feat, particularly in confined waters, will be severely handicapped as compared with a salvage tug.

Should the towing ship approach down-wind and pass the tow from her forecastle, she will then find it very difficult to steer astern. Most warships have astern power that is very inferior to ahead power and many cannot keep up astern revolutions for long periods.

If she approaches head to wind and passes the tow from aft, she will then find it impossible to keep head to wind and will pay off rapidly to one side or the other, possibly colliding with the anchored ship.

The only method that appears to offer a chance of success is to anchor the towing ship to windward of the disabled ship in such a way that, after veering a good scope on her cable, her stern is within line-throwing distance of the disabled ship. The tow is then passed and the towing ship takes the strain by using her engines and at the same time shortening-in the cable. At the appropriate time the disabled ship either weighs or slips her cable and the towing ship goes ahead.

TOWROPES

Composition

In HM ships, polyamide is used for towing because it has greater elasticity than wire and is generally easier to handle. In spite of this great elasticity a shackle or two of chain cable should be used between the towrope and the towed ship, to keep all the cordage outside of hawsepipes and fairleads, and to prevent shock loading. The elasticity of polyamide obviates the need of a deep bight in the tow, as is required with wire towropes.

For ocean towing by tugs not provided with self-tensioning winches the towing hawser is usually composed of polyamide or polyester, wire rope and chain cable; but for emergency tows it is quickest and simplest to use a wire hawser shackled to a suitable length of the towed ship's anchor cable. For emergency tows at short stay, such as for towing a burning vessel clear of shipping in harbour, the spring hawser described in Volume I probably makes the most efficient towrope.

Ministry of Defence ocean-going tugs are fitted with automatic self-tensioning or self-rendering towing winches that allow the towing wire to render or heave-in according to the strain experienced. In addition, they are supplied with polyamide hawsers in lengths up to 180 metres and sizes varying from 40 to 80 millimetres.

Strength

The required strength of a towing hawser depends upon the power available in the towing ship, the intended speed of towing, and the displacement of the towed ship. The following table gives a rough guide for the estimation of the towing pull of modern diesel-powered tugs expressed as bollard pull in tonnes for every 100 kilowatts of shaft power.

Type of Propulsion	Bollard Pull (tonnes/100 kilowatts shaft power)
Open screw	1.54
Screw with Kort nozzle	2.15
Cycloidal	1.41

Thus a conventional tug of 1000 kilowatts shaft power may be expected to exert a maximum bollard pull of 15.4 tonnes in good weather.

The forces required to tow various types of warships and merchant ships in calm weather at various speeds can be found from the graphs in Fig. 6–10(i) and (ii) for locked and trailing propellers respectively. These forces will be greatly increased in rough weather, in heavy swell, when the ship yaws badly or is damaged, or if the ships' bottoms are heavily fouled; for example, a wind of storm force 10 (about 50 knots) would increase the pull required to tow an aircraft carrier by some 25 tonnes. It is emphasised that the tonnage for merchant ships in the graphs is displacement tonnage at deep-load draught, and not gross tonnage. It will be noticed that a lesser towing pull is required for merchant ships than for warships of a similar displacement. This difference is caused by propeller drag; warships generally having two propellers, or sometimes four, whereas merchant ships usually have only one or, at the most, two propellers.

Selection

The choice of towrope depends upon the pull required and the factor of safety that is selected. The factor of safety in turn depends upon the gear available and such circumstances as the duration of tow, the weather, and the urgency of the situation; but the factor of safety should be not less than four. The graphs in Figs. 6–11 and 6–12 show, respectively, the size of steel

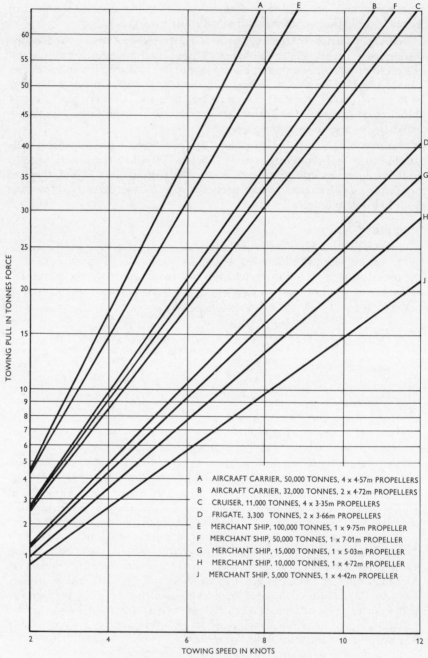

A   AIRCRAFT CARRIER, 50,000 TONNES, 4 x 4·57m PROPELLERS
B   AIRCRAFT CARRIER, 32,000 TONNES, 2 x 4·72m PROPELLERS
C   CRUISER, 11,000 TONNES, 4 x 3·35m PROPELLERS
D   FRIGATE, 3,300 TONNES, 2 x 3·66m PROPELLERS
E   MERCHANT SHIP, 100,000 TONNES, 1 x 9·75m PROPELLER
F   MERCHANT SHIP, 50,000 TONNES, 1 x 7·01m PROPELLER
G   MERCHANT SHIP, 15,000 TONNES, 1 x 5·03m PROPELLER
H   MERCHANT SHIP, 10,000 TONNES, 1 x 4·72m PROPELLER
J   MERCHANT SHIP, 5,000 TONNES, 1 x 4·42m PROPELLER

TOWING SPEED IN KNOTS

NOTE   (1) THESE CURVES ARE FOR CALM WEATHER AND FOR SHIPS 3 MONTHS
            OUT OF DOCK. TO ALLOW FOR FOULED BOTTOMS, BAD WEATHER
            OR YAWING, INCREASE THE FACTOR OF SAFETY.
       (2) THE TONNAGE SHOWN FOR MERCHANT SHIPS IS THEIR
            DISPLACEMENT TONNAGE.

FIG. 6–10(i). Towing pull required for a selection of ships at various speeds in
calm weather — towed ship with locked propellers
Note: A, B and C are no longer applicable to RN (1983)

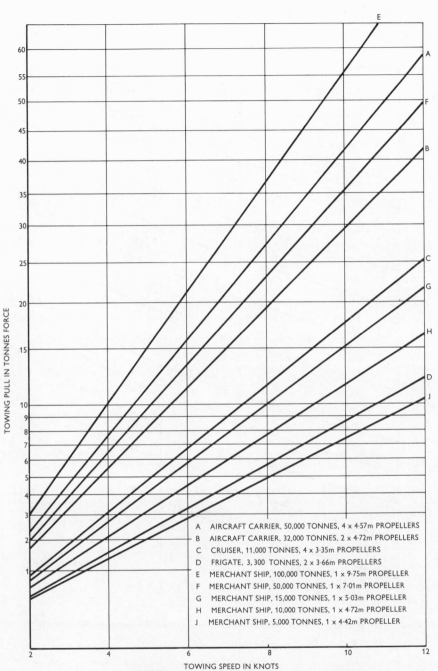

A   AIRCRAFT CARRIER, 50,000 TONNES, 4 x 4·57m PROPELLERS
B   AIRCRAFT CARRIER, 32,000 TONNES, 2 x 4·72m PROPELLERS
C   CRUISER, 11,000 TONNES, 4 x 3·35m PROPELLERS
D   FRIGATE, 3,300 TONNES, 2 x 3·66m PROPELLERS
E   MERCHANT SHIP, 100,000 TONNES, 1 x 9·75m PROPELLER
F   MERCHANT SHIP, 50,000 TONNES, 1 x 7·01m PROPELLER
G   MERCHANT SHIP, 15,000 TONNES, 1 x 5·03m PROPELLER
H   MERCHANT SHIP, 10,000 TONNES, 1 x 4·72m PROPELLER
J   MERCHANT SHIP, 5,000 TONNES, 1 x 4·42m PROPELLER

TOWING SPEED IN KNOTS

NOTE   (1)   THESE CURVES ARE FOR CALM WEATHER AND FOR SHIPS 3 MONTHS
               OUT OF DOCK. TO ALLOW FOR FOULED BOTTOMS, BAD WEATHER
               OR YAWING, INCREASE THE FACTOR OF SAFETY.
        (2)   THE TONNAGE SHOWN FOR MERCHANT SHIPS IS THEIR
               DISPLACEMENT TONNAGE.

FIG. 6–10(ii). Towing pull required for a selection of ships at various speeds in
calm weather — towed ship with trailing propellers
Note: A, B and C are no longer applicable to RN (1983)

N

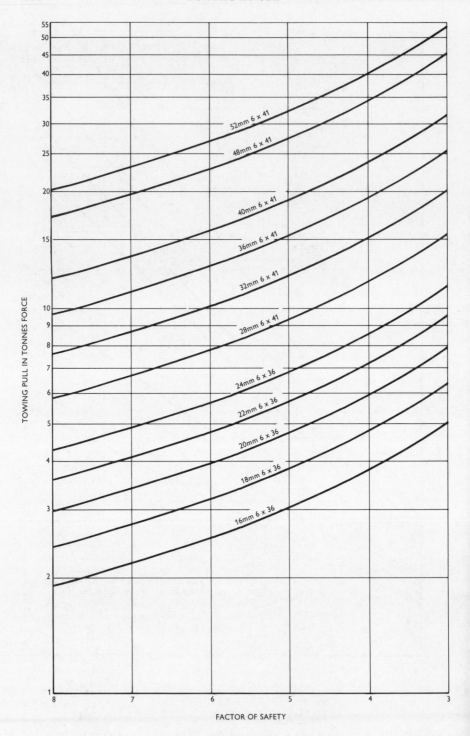

FIG. 6–11. Towing pull and factor of safety for 6 × 36 and 6 × 41 ranges of steel wire hawser

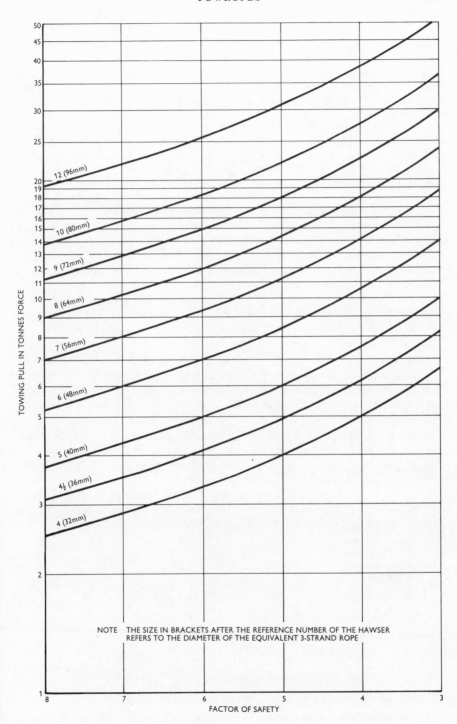

FIG. 6–12. Towing pull and factor of safety for eight-strand plaited polyamide hawser

wire rope and eight-strand plaited polyamide rope which are required for
various pulling forces at differing factors of safety. With these graphs and
the graphs shown in Figs. 6–10(i) and (ii), the seaman who has at his
disposal unlimited towing power and choice of gear can select the type and
size of towrope to suit his particular requirements; and, conversely, the
seaman with limited resources can estimate the safe capabilities of the gear
available.

Length

The length of towrope to be used depends upon the sea room available, the
depth of water, the displacement of the towed ship, the required speed of
towing, the factor of safety used, the weight of the towrope, and the weather.
The chief requirement in towing (except when using polyamide) is to ensure
that when the ships are moving at the required speed there is a sufficient sag
in the bight of the towrope to absorb any sudden fluctuating loads. The
amount of this sag depends upon the pulling force exerted and the length and
weight of the towrope; and the lighter the towrope the longer it must be. The
sag must not be too great, because not only may the bight then foul the
bottom, but the towing ship will have to exert an additional pulling force to
drag the bight through the water and also support its weight. For this reason,
and because the ships are then more manoeuvrable, a short, heavy towrope
is preferable to a long, light one.

The graph shown in Fig. 6–13 gives the length of wire hawser necessary
in calm weather to obtain a required depth of sag in the bight. Having
determined this depth and the factor of safety, and having selected the type
of hawser for the job, the appropriate curve in the graph is taken and the
required length of towrope is read off the horizontal scale at the foot.

The graph shows the length of towrope required if using steel wire rope
of 6 × 36 or 6 × 41 construction only; but because the usual practice is to
use a composite towrope of chain cable and wire rope, the length shown by
the graph can be reduced by an amount corresponding to the length of chain
cable veered, and still maintain the bight of the towrope at the required
degree of sag. The amount of cable to be veered for a given reduction in the
length of towrope can be calculated from the formula:

$$L = k\frac{c}{d}(H - h)$$

where:

L is the length of cable to be veered, in metres;

k is a constant which is 0.35 for 6 × 41 steel wire rope;

c is the size of the chain cable, in millimetres;

d is the diameter, in millimetres, of the wire hawser;

H is the length of towrope, in metres, indicated by Fig. 6–13;

h is the length, in metres, of the wire hawser available.

In rough weather a deeper bight is necessary to absorb the sudden loads
to which the towrope will be subjected, and this is better obtained by veering
cable rather than by veering the hawser. The amount of cable to be veered
can be determined from the graph and by using the above formula. It is

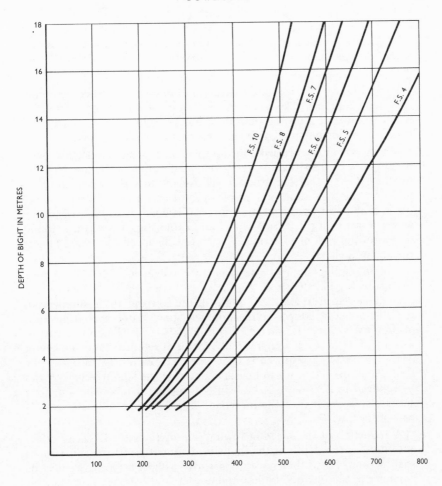

MAXIMUM LENGTH OF TOW IN METRES

I.E. LENGTH NECESSARY WHEN NO CHAIN CABLE IS USED AS A SPRING

FIG. 6–13. Dip of a steel wire towrope in relation to length of tow at various factors of safety

recommended that the bight of the towrope should be immersed to a depth of at least 7 metres in calm weather and at least 11 metres in rough weather.

How to use the graphs

The following example shows how the graphs are used to determine the length and composition of the towrope for a particular towing problem, and the probable safe speeds of towing.

EXAMPLE

There is a requirement to tow a deeply laden merchant ship of about 5000 tonnes displacement, for which the ship's 50-millimetre anchor

188   TOWING AT SEA

cable and a 275-metre length of 32-millimetre 6 × 41 construction steel wire hawser are available. What should be the length and composition of the towrope, and what will be the maximum speed of towing in calm weather?

From Fig. 6–11 it is found that a 32-millimetre, 6 × 41 construction steel wire rope can take a towing pull of 15 tonnes using a factor of safety of four, or a towing pull of 12 tonnes using a factor of safety of five, or a towing pull of 10 tonnes using a factor of safety of six.

The factor of safety used and the speed of towing will depend upon the urgency of the situation, the probable duration of the tow, and the weather. Given that the situation is urgent, that the vessel must be towed at the maximum practicable speed for about 30 miles, that the sea is calm and that the weather forecast is good, it will be reasonable to use a factor of safety as low as four. From Fig. 6–10(i) it is found that a towing pull of 15 tonnes gives a towing speed of about 10 knots (locked propellers).

The lower the factor of safety used the longer must be the towrope to ensure a good depth of bight. As the sea is calm, 7 metres is a reasonable depth to allow the bight of the towrope to be submerged, to which must be added the mean height above water level of the ends of the towrope, say 4.5 metres. From Fig. 6–13 it is found that, with a depth of bight of 11.5 metres and a factor of safety of four, the length of the wire hawser required is 675 metres. However, by means of the formula on page 186, it can be calculated that the length of hawser can be reduced to 275 metres (the length available) if three-and-a-quarter shackles (89 metres) of the merchant ship's anchor cable are used as part of the towrope.

A reduction of the speed of towing will increase the factor of safety and increase the depth of the bight in the towrope. If the ships are in shallow water, or if they have to pass over a shoal patch, there may be a danger of the towrope fouling the bottom and parting. To avoid this the towrope must be shortened, and the graphs and formula can be used to determine the length and composition of towrope required to maintain the depth of bight at the reduced towing speed and new factor of safety.

If, for example, the speed of towing is reduced to 7 knots, reference to Fig. 6–10(i) shows that the towing pull is reduced to 7.5 tonnes. On referring to Fig. 6–11 it is seen that with this reduced towing pull the factor of safety for a 32-millimetre hawser is increased to just over eight. By referring to Fig. 6–13 it is seen that with a factor of safety of eight (the nearest factor of safety) a 490-metre length of hawser is required to maintain a dip in the bight of 11.5 metres, and that this length can be reduced to 180 metres by using only two-and-a-half shackles (69 metres) of the merchant ship's cable. In practice, however, it may be simpler to adjust the length of tow by heaving-in or veering the cable in the towed ship rather than heaving-in or veering the hawser in the towing ship. In this example the same effect is achieved if the towed ship heaves in one-and-a-half shackles (41 metres) of cable, thus making a towrope comprising the 275-metre length of 32-millimetre hawser and one-and-three-quarter shackles (48 metres) of cable.

Summary

The chief requirements for towropes (other than polyamide) may be summarised as follows.

1. The towrope should be long enough and heavy enough for a large part of the bight to be immersed when towing at the required speed.

2. When determining the proportion of cable to hawser in a composite towrope, remember that the larger the proportion of cable the better will be the spring.

3. Remember, also, that the larger the proportion of cable the shorter will be the required length of towrope, and the shorter the length of towrope the more manoeuvrable will be the ships.

4. The rough rule for determining the proportions of cable and hawser required to provide a towrope of a certain weight is that cable, if steel, is about five (or if wrought iron, about seven) times as heavy as wire rope of approximately the same strength.

5. A good rule for towing in moderate weather is: use three shackles (82 metres) of the towed ship's anchor cable shackled to 275 metres of wire hawser of a size about four-fifths the size of the cable. With a 50-millimetre cable, for example, use a 40-millimetre hawser.

CHAPTER 7

Salvage Operations

The salvage of a ship, particularly one which is sunk, or stranded and severely damaged, is usually a complicated operation demanding special equipment and specialist salvage officers. Some salvage operations are, however, well within the capabilities of a resourceful seaman using the normal equipment of a well-found ship or the equipment available at any port. The purpose of the first part of this chapter, therefore, is to provide the seaman with an elementary knowledge which will enable him to undertake the simpler forms of ship salvage or, in more complicated cases, to take such emergency measures as will simplify the subsequent salvage operation or even prevent the total loss of a ship. The second part of the chapter deals with the increasingly important task of the salvage of crashed aircraft which all warships may have to undertake at very short notice.

SOME LEGAL ASPECTS OF SALVAGE

It is, of course, the duty of every seaman to afford every possible aid to vessels in danger, in distress or in want of assistance, and to save life. When property, such as a ship or her cargo, is also saved the salvor or his employer is usually entitled to claim recompense in the form of a salvage award commensurate with the degree of assistance rendered and the value of the property saved.

If the vessel is in immediate danger or dire distress any such aid will obviously be welcomed by her Master and crew and accepted without demur; but if the vessel has not been abandoned and if she or her crew are not in immediate danger it is usual for her Master or owner to come to some form of agreement with the prospective salvor in regard to the degree of assistance required. When offering his services the prospective salvor should bear in mind that salvage awards are made only when the services rendered are successful or have materially assisted in the saving of property, and that no claim can be entertained if the efforts are unsuccessful; moreover, wrongful methods of salvage resulting in further damage or loss of property, or even the loss of the ship, may render the salvor liable in respect of such damage or loss.

It is therefore very important that full agreement on methods to be adopted should be reached between the salvor and the Master or owner of the vessel, but it should be remembered that the Master is at all times responsible for his ship and her cargo, and that a salvor has no right to give him orders. At the same time it may be presumed that if the Master has asked for assistance he is willing to accept advice and to co-operate.

Instructions to naval officers about offering salvage assistance, and the procedure required for the claim of awards for such services, are laid down in *The Queen's Regulations for the Royal Navy*, and a useful aide-memoire is published in BR 45(4), *Admiralty Manual of Navigation*, Volume IV.

Before starting operations the prospective salvor should, if possible, board the vessel and consult with her Master, who should be requested to sign *Lloyd's Standard Form of Salvage Agreement*. If this is impracticable the salvor should make every endeavour to get the Master to agree to sign the form later, as and when convenient and, if practicable, before the salvage operations end. The agreement is usually accepted in its 'open form', that is to say the remuneration payable in the event of salvage being successful is open to arbitration, and the basis of agreement is 'no cure, no pay'. In the case of a vessel abandoned by her crew this matter does not arise. However, it should be noted that an entire ship's company may leave a stricken vessel without legally abandoning their ship — for example, during a fire. A clear intention not to return to the ship is therefore needed for her to be considered abandoned in law.

The *Lloyd's Standard Form of Salvage Agreement* is a salvage contract in which, in the case of HM ships or other Ministry of Defence vessels, the Commanding Officer or other officer binds himself and the Ministry to use their best endeavours to salve the hull and/or cargo of the stricken vessel and to take it to a place of safety. Thus it should not be lightly signed if doubt exists as to whether the operation can be successfully concluded. Lack of the agreement, however, should not inhibit salvage operations while awaiting advice from the Ministry of Defence, except in situations where dangerous cargoes are involved. (See also page 211.)

Any reports rendered during salvage operations should be carefully worded, because many interests are concerned in marine casualties, and the insurance markets react strongly to such reports as may be published. Whoever is in charge of salvage operations should therefore confine himself strictly to details of damage and to the existing situation, and he should avoid any predictions.

SALVAGE AND ASSISTANCE TO SHIPS

EMERGENCY AID TO VESSELS AFLOAT

A vessel at sea which is so damaged that she requires assistance will probably require to be towed to port, but before taking her in tow the extent of her damage should be examined and its effect on her seaworthiness should be considered. If the damage is considerable and the nearest port with good repair facilities is some distance away it is preferable to tow the vessel to the nearest safe anchorage as quickly as possible and there make temporary repairs before attempting the long passage. This may seem obvious, but ships have in fact been lost because this elementary precaution was neglected.

If the vessel is leaking badly she should be beached, because her seaworthiness will rapidly deteriorate as she loses her buoyancy. Also, the deeper a ship sinks in the water the greater will be the water pressure on the leaks and exposed bulkheads, and should the latter collapse the vessel will probably sink. Remarks on the stability of a grounded ship are to be found in Chapter 1.

Firefighting

Fires in the damaged ship may need to be brought under control before any attempt at salvage can be made. Methods and Royal Navy equipment for firefighting are described in the relevant chapters in Volumes I and II, while typical firefighting arrangements in merchant ships are outlined in Chapter 5 of this volume. Details of the firefighting equipment of Ministry of Defence salvage vessels are given on page 211.

Pumps and confinement of flooding

During preparations for towing, all available portable pumps should be transferred to the vessel, even if no immediate need for them is apparent; it is far better to have the pumps at hand and find eventually that they are not needed than to have to stop towing, for them to be transferred, when an emergency arises. If the vessel has electric pumps and her electric generators are out of action, the practicability of providing her with electric power from the rescue ship should also be considered. A quick general survey of the vessel should then be made, flooded compartments should be noted, and immediate steps taken to ascertain whether the leakage is likely to be controllable by the available pumping capacity.

Generally speaking, it is advisable to concentrate on confining the flooding to as few compartments as possible, and where difficulty in pumping out any badly damaged space is anticipated it is best to concentrate on preventing any extension of the damage to surrounding spaces. The compartments to be dealt with first will therefore be those with the least leakage, because conditions will improve with every tonne of water pumped out. These comparatively small leaks should be dealt with promptly so that the available pumps can be concentrated as soon as possible on pumping out the more extensively damaged sections, with the object of restoring the maximum amount of buoyancy.

The nature and extent of the damage having been ascertained, those compartments which are leaking should be inspected to see whether they can be tightened up and reclaimed. Continuous soundings should be taken in all compartments, even though they are remote from the damage, so that early warning of any increased leakage may be obtained. Pumps should be rigged with the shortest suctions possible so that they discharge overboard by the most direct route. A stout line or a light purchase should be attached to the end of the suction-pipe so that it can easily be lifted and cleared if it gets choked. Any leaks which are accessible should be stopped with wooden wedges, plugs, tallow, etc., and all pumps should be concentrated on pumping out the badly damaged compartments as soon as possible after those with the least leakage.

The speed with which a compartment will flood can be appreciated from the fact that, for example, a hole 150 millimetres in diameter and about 2 metres below the waterline could admit up to 6 tonnes of sea water per minute. In other words, this small hole would cause a compartment $6 \times 3.5 \times 2.5$ metres to fill completely in less than 10 minutes.

Emergency stopping of leaks

Access to leaks in the holds of a merchant ship is often impossible because of the cargo there, and temporary measures have to be adopted to stem the inflow of water until more permanent repairs can be effected by divers at the nearest sheltered anchorage. To stop small leaks in seams or rivet holes, bundles of oakum secured to a bottom-line with split-yarn and hauled under the ship and over the leak will often prove effective; the suction draws the oakum into the leaks and water pressure holds it there so long as the compartment is kept pumped out. For larger leaks, blankets and mattresses backed by wooden battens dogged to bottom-lines and then hauled into place will often prove effective.

As soon as the vessel has been anchored or beached in a sheltered spot, these temporary measures should be replaced by more permanent repairs to make the vessel as seaworthy as possible.

Patching of leaks

The construction of large patches to cover extensive damage is usually beyond the resources of the seaman on the spot, but with the means at his disposal he should be able to make small patches to cover less extensive damage. The construction and fitting of a typical small patch are described below and illustrated in Figs. 7–1 to 7–5. The materials selected will depend on what is available at the time. Sizes are quoted for descriptive purposes only.

The following materials are required.

1. Timber for backing.
2. Two 75 mm × 6 mm flat steel bars, equal in length to the breadth of the patch.
3. Two 75 mm × 75 mm steel angle-bars of similar length.
4. Two angle-bars (to act as strongbacks) fitted with long draw-bolts.
5. Sufficient canvas to cover an area 1.5 metres longer and wider than the patch.
6. A quantity of coir fibre, for use as a pudding around the patch. (Oakum can be used instead of coir fibre, but is not so satisfactory as it has no spring when compressed.)

The canvas is first stretched out on the deck and the timber is then cut and laid centrally upon it so as to leave a 750-millimetre margin of canvas all round, as shown in Fig. 7–1. The two flat bars are then laid in position across the planks of timber, and holes are drilled through each bar and plank (two to a plank) and through the canvas backing so that the bars and planks can be firmly secured to each other by steel bolts.

If the pad is to be secured in place by draw-bolts the holes for these are now drilled through the bars, timber and canvas. The holes should be large enough to allow for the wood swelling under water, otherwise it will nip the bolts and make it impossible to adjust them when fitting the pad in its correct position.

The two 75 mm × 75 mm angle-bars are now drilled in a similar manner; the flat steel bars being used as templates. The flat bars are then placed on the timber and the securing bolts driven through. Coir fibre is teased out and laid so as to form a pudding-bolster 225 millimetres in diameter around the edges of the patch, and the canvas is then turned over this and tacked down with flat-headed nails, as shown in Fig. 7–2.

The pad is now turned over, canvas side uppermost, the two 75 mm × 75 mm angle-bars are fitted in place over the protruding bolts, to which nuts are fitted and screwed home, thus completing the pad as shown in Fig. 7–3.

The two strongbacks, cut to the required length, are now fitted with their respective draw-bolts. The hole for the draw-bolt should be drilled slightly nearer to one end of the strongback than the other, so that the strongback will hang vertically when it is pivoted on the draw-bolt. Fig. 7–3 shows the pad complete with its draw-bolts and strongback, and Fig. 7–4 shows the pad fixed in position.

A pad of this type, however, will probably float when placed in the water, and it must therefore be ballasted so that it can be slung over the side and lowered into position. The weight of ballast required is very simply calculated, as the following example shows.

EXAMPLE

	VOLUME (m³)	WEIGHT (kg)
Timber: 2.5 m × 1 m × 60 mm	0.15	90
Pudding: 7 m × 200 mm × 200 mm	0.28	5
Angle-bars, say		25
Total volume and weight of pad	0.43	120
Weight of sea water displaced by pad if entirely submerged, 1.025 × 0.43		440
Actual weight of pad		120
Weight (in water) of ballast required		320
True weight of ballast required, 1.15 × 320		= 370.

Draw-bolts with angle-bar strongbacks provide the most efficient method of securing the pad in position when the hole is long and narrow, or where the plating is light and the frames are widely spaced. However, for a round hole, particularly one with its edges jagged and bent inboard, the pad will have to be secured in position with hook-bolts, as described below and illustrated in Fig. 7–5.

To fit the pad with hook-bolts the outline of the hole is drawn on the canvas backing, and the holes for the hook-bolts are drilled through the timber at suitable intervals round, and well within, the indicated perimeter of the hole. The holes should be large enough to allow the hook-bolts considerable play so that when the pad is in position the hooked ends of the bolts can be placed as required. Such a pad will probably require stiffeners, which should be fitted to the outside of the pad and in such a manner that they are held in place by the hook-bolts.

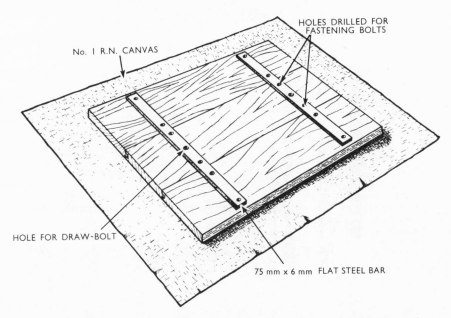

No. 1 R.N. CANVAS

HOLES DRILLED FOR
FASTENING BOLTS

HOLE FOR DRAW-BOLT

75 mm x 6 mm FLAT STEEL BAR

FIG. 7–1. Constructing a simple wooden pad for patching a small hole — first stage

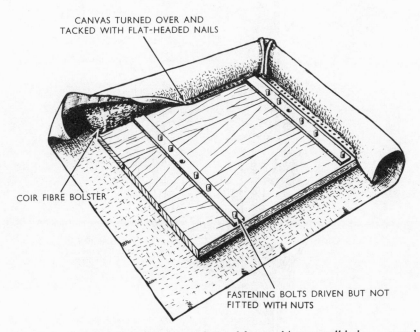

CANVAS TURNED OVER AND
TACKED WITH FLAT-HEADED NAILS

COIR FIBRE BOLSTER

FASTENING BOLTS DRIVEN BUT NOT
FITTED WITH NUTS

FIG. 7–2. Constructing a simple wooden pad for patching a small hole — second stage

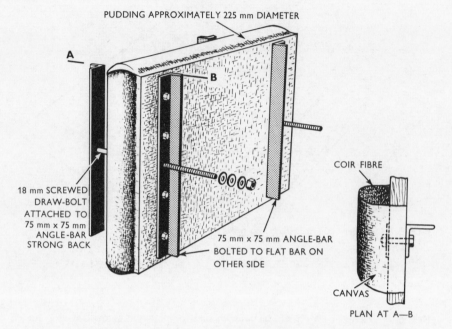

PUDDING APPROXIMATELY 225 mm DIAMETER

A

B

COIR FIBRE

18 mm SCREWED DRAW-BOLT ATTACHED TO 75 mm x 75 mm ANGLE-BAR STRONG BACK

75 mm x 75 mm ANGLE-BAR BOLTED TO FLAT BAR ON OTHER SIDE

CANVAS

PLAN AT A—B

FIG. 7–3. Simple wooden pad — details of construction, showing draw-bolts

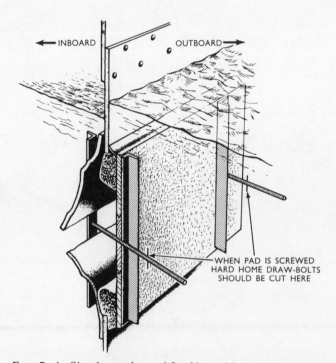

INBOARD   OUTBOARD

WHEN PAD IS SCREWED HARD HOME DRAW-BOLTS SHOULD BE CUT HERE

FIG. 7–4. Simple wooden pad fixed in position with draw-bolts

ANGLE STIFFENERS POSITIONED AND
DRILLED TO TAKE HOOK-BOLTS

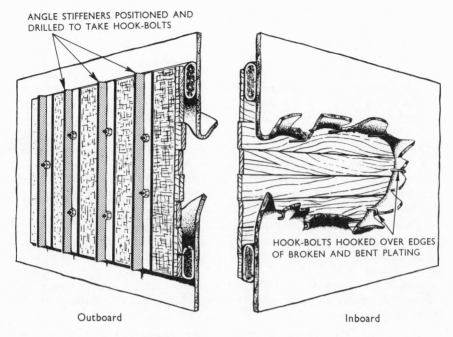

HOOK-BOLTS HOOKED OVER EDGES
OF BROKEN AND BENT PLATING

Outboard   Inboard

FIG. 7–5. Wooden pad for fixing in position with hook-bolts

Use of concrete

Mixture. Concrete, which is a composition of cement, gravel and sand mixed with water, is used extensively in salvage work for temporary repairs and leak-stopping, particularly where the work has to be done by divers and where there is no inflow of water through the leaks — in a submerged compartment, for example, which has been flooded up. It is also of particular value in repairing damage to the bilges of merchant ships where the frame-spaces between the margin-plates and the bottom-plating can be filled and there is no need to construct boxes to hold the concrete until it sets.

In salvage work *Rapid Hardening Cement* is preferable to ordinary *Portland* cement, because it sets more quickly and so will withstand water pressure in a shorter time; good results can, however, be obtained with Portland cement, but the two should never be mixed. Cement by itself has very little strength, and so it must be mixed with coarse and fine *aggregate* in fixed proportions to make concrete. (Aggregate is the term used in the building trade to describe broken stones, gravel and sand; in this context coarse aggregate is gravel of 10-millimetre to 20-millimetre gauge and fine aggregate is sand.) For ordinary concrete work the proportions by volume are one of cement to two of fine aggregate and four of coarse; but for underwater work it is desirable to increase the proportion of cement used, and a good mixture for this purpose is one of cement to one-and-a-half each of fine and coarse aggregate by volume; this provides a quick-setting mixture which will give satisfactory results in a shorter time than would that used for ordinary building purposes.

To make concrete the cement and aggregate are well mixed, and water is added until the mixture is of a consistency which can be easily worked into the corners and crevices of the space to be filled. In deciding on the quantities of materials required for a job it must be remembered that the volume of the mixture will be reduced by approximately 30 per cent when water is added during mixing. For quicker hardening, warm fresh water with a little soda added will help, but it is not essential. Sea water should not be used for mixing concrete unless fresh water is unobtainable, as it weakens the concrete.

When sending a mixture down to a diver the cement must be prevented from washing out so that only sand and gravel remain when it reaches him. The best method is to send the mixture down in buckets or canvas bags, but if large quantities are required an enclosed chute may have to be used. When using a chute, the mixture should be sent down in large quantities at a time to form a continuous stream rather than in dribs and drabs.

Where there is no support for the mixture a rough timber box should be constructed and firmly fixed around the space to be filled. Materials sectionally large enough to support the weight of the mixture must be used until it sets, and the user should bear in mind that when dry the aggregate weighs approximately 2 tonnes per cubic metre and the cement approximately 1.5 tonnes per cubic metre; stout timber, well shored and supported therefore will be required.

Application. To close a gaping fracture with cement the first of the mixture is usually sent down to the diver in bags, which are then middled and wedged in the fracture so that each bag is half-inside and half-outside. When the aperture is thus closed the remaining space is filled in and the whole then shored up. If a large space is to be filled in, much time and material can be saved by packing it with handy-sized pieces of rock, provided that they are then well bonded into the concrete.

To stop small leaks with concrete while they are still under pressure, the leakage is first reduced to a minimum by plugging, and then a drain is provided to carry away the water until the cement is set. A rough water-course is constructed in the ship's bilges to allow drainage from the damage, and for boxes a drainpipe or pipes are provided. The cement is then applied in the usual way, time being allowed for it to set; it is then well shored and the drains are securely plugged.

If large cement boxes are being constructed over the inside of temporary patches to provide additional strength for long sea passages, or against damaged bulkheads for stiffening them, additional reinforcing with odd sections of steel will greatly add to their strength.

Concrete is of little use for a structure which is liable to work in a seaway. It does not bind well with steel which is contaminated with oil, but is most satisfactory on lightly rusted surfaces. If there is any likelihood of grease or oil on a surface which is to be covered with concrete, the surface should, if practicable, be cleaned with petrol or a hot solution of soda.

Use of compressed air

In salvage operations, compressed air is extensively used for driving underwater tools, pumps and other equipment, and it can also be used in certain circumstances to recover buoyancy in flooded compartments which cannot be pumped out. By sealing the flooded space and introducing air under pressure the water is forced out through the fractures, and so buoyancy is restored. The use of compressed air for this purpose in merchant vessels (except in oil tankers) is limited, because their cargo holds have large hatches and numerous openings which can only be sealed by very extensive work. In cargo vessels, therefore, compressed air is only of use in tanks and spaces which are constructed as dry tanks, ballast tanks and oil tanks.

Compressed air can be of considerable value for recovering buoyancy in double-bottom tanks which have been damaged by grounding, but it should be used with discretion, because the building up of sufficient pressure in the tanks to expel the water exerts a considerable strain on the tank-tops. The tank-tops of merchant vessels are constructed and tested to withstand a pressure-head of water equal to that on the bottom-plating when the ship is fully loaded, so theoretically there should be no risk of damage in building up such an air pressure; in a ship with heavy bottom-damage, however, it should be assumed that the tank-top also may have been strained and weakened, and so it must only be submitted to any additional stress with great care. The ship may also be floating at a greater depth than is normal, owing to flooding, and if the use of compressed air could damage the tank-top it should be well shored. In the holds of a fully loaded vessel the risk of damage will be greatly reduced, as her cargo will help to prevent any tendency for the plating to lift when air is forced into the tanks. The usual method of admitting compressed air into a double-bottom tank is by means of a flexible pipe tightly fixed into a wooden plug, which is driven into the breathing pipe of the tank. If possible, a pressure gauge should be provided to indicate immediately if the air pressure is excessive or the water is not being freely displaced.

Oil tankers, with their numerous easily sealed compartments, are particularly suitable for the use of compressed air. The tank lids are so constructed that they are airtight when closed. There are valves which can be closed in the gas pipelines, and the oil compartments are virtually sealed whenever they are filled. However, it must be clearly understood that the use of compressed air in tanks which are not gas-free can lead to the creation of a flammable mixture where none existed before.

AID TO VESSELS BEACHED OR STRANDED

Beaching a ship
If a vessel is so heavily damaged that the leakage cannot be brought under control she should be beached, if possible. For remarks on how to beach a damaged vessel see page 179. In tidal waters it is better to allow the vessel to ground on a falling tide than to drive her on to the beach. How far up she is beached depends on many factors, such as the range of the tide, whether it is necessary for the damaged places to be uncovered at low water, and the estimated time required to repair the damage; but the vessel should not be beached too far up, because this may make refloating her unnecessarily difficult.

Securing a beached or stranded vessel
When a vessel is beached or stranded bow-on or stern-on to the shore, the first task is to secure her so that she will not be driven farther onshore by

the tide or bad weather, or be slewed broadside-on to the waves, or suffer further damage by pounding in a swell or in heavy seas.

Use of anchors and cables. A vessel is best secured with her anchors and cables laid out with as much scope of cable as possible and backed as necessary by other ground tackle. It is emphasised that any ground tackle used should be as heavy and as strong as possible and laid out with as much scope as possible, because the stresses to which it will be subjected are far greater than normal, for the reasons described below.

When a vessel is riding normally to her anchor in a heavy sea she is not forced to leeward by the waves, but merely rises and falls on each wave as it passes her. As she rises on the crest of each wave she surges ahead a little and then drops back as she falls in the trough; this surging, combined with the spring in the bight of the cable, prevents sudden and heavy stresses being transmitted to her anchor. When waves break against a vessel aground in shallow water, however, they exert a considerable force, tending to push her farther shoreward. To prevent this the cables of any ground tackle holding her must be hove as taut as possible, but there is then no bight in the cables to absorb any sudden stresses. Furthermore, that part of the vessel which is seaward may be waterborne and so may tend to rise and fall with the passing of each successive wave, but because the vessel is aground she cannot surge, and so the extra stress is transmitted through the taut cables to her anchors. This extra stress may have one of two results: if the ground tackle is not heavy enough or strong enough, either the anchors will drag or the cables will part; if, however, the ground tackle is sufficiently strong and heavy the vessel may be dragged seaward little by little as each successive wave passes, until the cable is sufficiently slack for its bight to absorb the extra stress. When securing the vessel in a swell the cables of her ground tackle must therefore be sufficiently slack to absorb any extra stresses as the vessel rises and falls, but not too slack, otherwise the waves will slew her bow or stern round. When refloating the vessel, however, these extra stresses can usefully be employed to haul her off, simply by keeping the cables as taut as possible. To prevent broaching, it will probably be necessary to lay out a kedge anchor from forward or aft, or to run quarter or shoulder wires to the bights of the anchor cables.

When laying out ground tackle, the anchors should be placed, if possible, in the best positions both for holding the vessel and for hauling her off.

Scuttling. If the available ground tackle is insufficient for holding the vessel she should be scuttled, and sufficient compartments flooded to hold her steady. Scuttling a vessel will also prevent her from lifting and pounding in a heavy swell. Before opening holds to the sea every available tank should be ballasted and the propeller-shaft tunnel should be flooded. Only if this fails to steady the vessel should selected spaces be made free-flooding. The best method of scuttling is to burn holes with an oxy-acetylene burner in the ship's side above the turn of the bilge between frames and as close to the low-water mark as possible. If oxy-acetylene plant is not available explosives may be used, but any holes thus made will have to be patched and made good again before refloating, so small charges only should be used. The selection of the compartments to be flooded in a merchant ship will necessarily depend on the nature and amount of cargo in the holds, and little guidance can be given in this respect; usually the flooding of two holds will be sufficient to keep a vessel steady, but more may have to be flooded if the weather is bad.

Use of small vessels or craft for dredging

When a vessel is aground on a soft bottom, sand or mud may silt up around her to such an extent that even when lightened she cannot be hauled off. In such circumstances the use of small craft for dredging away the silt by means of the wash from their propellers has proved very effective where the nature of the bottom is suitable.

Dredging by this means may be used for three different purposes: to scour away the sea bed under a stranded ship so that she can settle down deeper and so become waterborne; to dredge a channel seaward through which the ship can be moved to deeper water; and for tunnelling cavities under a beached ship to enable a diver to effect repairs. This type of dredging is effective where the bottom is of sand, soft mud, mud and sand, or shingle and stones, but is useless where the bottom is stiff clay. Disappointment may be experienced where the bottom consists of a layer of sand or silt about half a metre thick which is easily washed away but has hard, stiff clay or rock under it.

The most suitable type of vessel likely to be available for dredging would be a twin-screw tug drawing about 3.8 metres aft and 2.8 metres forward, but a single-screw trawler or similar handy vessel will serve.

Before starting dredging operations an accurate plan of the area around the vessel must be made and frequently checked as the work proceeds, otherwise the displaced silt may settle and bank up in inconvenient places. Dredging craft have, in fact, been known to pen themselves in with banks of their own creation. Such banks are, however, more easily dispersed than the undisturbed sea bed, particularly at full ebb or flood.

The depth at which dredging is effective depends upon the power of the dredging craft and the nature of the work. For dredging a tunnel right under a vessel from one side to the other a powerful craft could not work effectively in a depth more than 2 metres greater than her normal draught, but when it is only desired to free mud from under the bilges of the vessel, and not to extend the dredging as far as her keel, dredging can be effective in depths as great as 8 metres.

Scouring away the sea bed. As an example of the use which can be made of craft for dredging purposes, suppose that a ship lying evenly aground on slightly shelving sand cannot be moved by her own power, or with ground tackle or by towing. Lightening her can still be tried but, as this would probably involve delay and the expense of obtaining a suitable ship for transhipment of cargo, dredging should first be attempted. Before starting operations the stranded ship is secured with efficient ground tackle. Two dredging craft are employed, suitably trimmed by the stern, and each moored for dredging with both bower anchors laid out with a good scope of cable and well spread. The craft then back into position, both on the same side of the ship, one about one-third and the other about two-thirds of the stranded ship's length from the bow; their sterns are then secured close to her side, by means of a strong hawser on the towing hook which is taken right across the ship and made fast to a suitable point on the opposite side, to obtain as much scope as possible. If there is any sea, a short towing spring will have to be used and reasonable clearance from the ship allowed. If there is not much current the foremost dredging craft is secured at an angle of about 70 degrees to the fore-and-aft line of the ship, with her stern directed towards the bow of the ship, and the after craft is secured at the same angle to the fore-and-aft line but with her stern directed towards the ship's quarter.

Manila springs are led from each quarter of the dredging craft, through convenient leads to winches in the stranded ship, so that the craft can be gradually hove along the ship's side as dredging progresses; and headropes are also run out for altering the angle of inclination of the dredging craft. If the depth of water alongside the ship is such that the propeller of the dredging craft is near the bottom, her stern can be held against the ship's side so that her propellers will be about 2.5 metres clear, but in deeper water a greater clearance, say 3.5 metres, must be allowed and the trim of the dredging craft by the stern must be increased as much as safety will permit.

The general object is to tunnel completely under the stranded ship, if possible, and there is a gratifying moment when, perhaps after an hour or two of work, a sudden blow-through of sand, mud and seaweed appearing in the water on the far side of the ship shows that this has been accomplished. With hawser and springs in position, it is well to start slowly and adjust the strain on all parts; too violent disturbance of the sand may cause choked inlets. The positions for the first effort should be chosen so that the removal of the sand from underneath does not throw an undue strain on the hull. If the dredging craft are held at too fine an angle, the flow of water will be deflected along the sides and bilges of the ship instead of scouring in underneath her bottom. Once the silt is blown through to the other side, the stern of the dredging craft should be gradually fleeted along to widen the cleared area without deepening it unduly and so perhaps straining the wreck. It is important to maintain the flow of water completely under the ship and not to allow it to be deflected so that the gap closes and a fresh start has to be made.

If it is impossible to tunnel completely under the ship, the dredging craft must be stationed one on each side of her, and must work persistently from amidships to the bow and from amidships to the stern, while keeping themselves at an angle of 30–40 degrees to the ship, so drawing or sweeping the sand along. This will not only free the ship's bilges but will also scour the sand away on each side of her bottom, and so leave the ship resting throughout her length on a ridge of sand. The ship can then be freed by working her engines ahead with the rudder hard over first one way and then the other, and also by heaving in on either bow or quarter to haul her off the ridge. When thus dealt with, a ship usually begins to swing a degree or so, this arc increasing gradually until she frees herself. As a rule, the engines should not be driven astern, because this may bank up the sand around her and choke her inlets. Two dredging craft are not essential, but they do accelerate the work. With a vessel aground by the head on a steep bank one dredger may be used on each bow. Sometimes one craft may be moored to do the actual dredging while the other is used to fan away and disperse the silt.

Dredging a channel. When dredging a channel through which to haul out a stranded ship it is usual to start at the deep-water end with the dredging craft moored stern towards the ship and held in position by a dredging hawser (say 24-millimetre, 6 × 24 SWR) led from the ship. The dredging hawser should, if possible, be made fast in the dredging craft somewhere near her pivoting point, otherwise her stern will be girded and prevented from slewing. The strain is taken on the dredging hawser and the engines of the dredging craft are worked ahead, and as progress is made the cable of the dredging craft is veered and the dredging hawser hove in. If the dredging craft were kept on a dead straight course the channel would be only about 2 metres wide, so her stern is very slowly slewed from side to side by using her rudder, thus widening the channel and at the same time banking up the silt on each side. Frequent soundings are taken to check progress, and the course of the channel is well buoyed. When the dredging craft reaches the stranded ship she can be dredged free and swung into the channel in the manner already described.

HAULING OFF A STRANDED VESSEL

When a ship is fast aground it is better to rely on strong and well laid-out ground tackle than on tugs to haul her off. Powerful rescue tugs can exert a pull in excess of 200 tonnes on a towrope but, in general, greater forces can be exerted by strong ground tackle rigged with heavy purchases. Furthermore, in a swell a tug cannot keep the towrope sufficiently taut to take advantage of any extra force obtainable as the stranded ship rises and falls on the waves, whereas with strong ground tackle this extra force can be usefully employed to haul the ship seaward.

Before laying out the ground tackle it is necessary to consider and decide upon the best direction in which to heave the ship off, and whether she will refloat more readily bows or stern first. Broadly speaking, it is usually best to bring the ship off bows first, because most ships are usually deeper in draught aft and so the bows can be more readily moved.

Usually the most difficult part of any heaving-off operation is to slew the stranded ship's head or stern to the sea, but once this is done she can usually be refloated by perseverance and hard work. As soon as the ship is end-on to the sea the position is much improved, because she will be far less vulnerable to any subsequent bad weather, and by flooding-up and holding her securely by the ground tackle it should be possible to weather any but the worst of storms. Often it is found that a ship which has been driven ashore when lightly laden can be assisted off by gales once the preliminary work has been completed, because a heavy swell running in on a beach will help to lift her, and as she lifts a very great stress will be brought on the ground tackle and so cause her to surge seaward with each lift. In such cases it is most important to keep a heavy strain on the ground tackle, otherwise the seas will tend to swing the ship broadside-on to the beach again instead of working her slowly seaward.

Ground tackle (Fig. 7–6) is therefore usually rigged with strong purchases so that it can be subjected to heavy stresses and kept as taut as possible. There is much scope for improvisation in rigging these purchases, because usually only salvage vessels and bases have all the necessary gear. As very heavy stresses are set up during these operations, the normal deck fittings

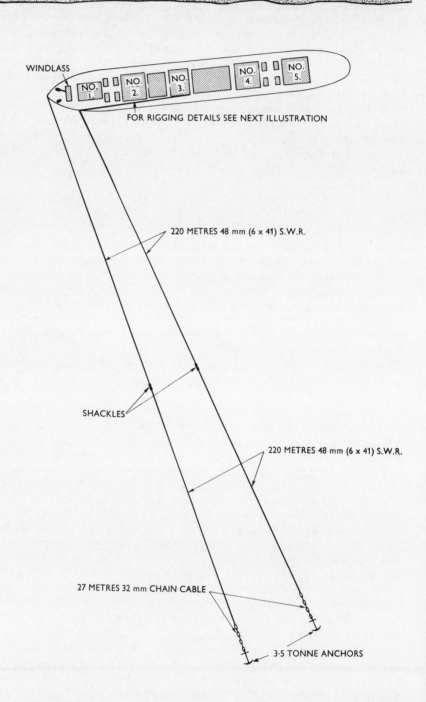

WINDLASS

FOR RIGGING DETAILS SEE NEXT ILLUSTRATION

220 METRES 48 mm (6 x 41) S.W.R.

SHACKLES

220 METRES 48 mm (6 x 41) S.W.R.

27 METRES 32 mm CHAIN CABLE

3·5 TONNE ANCHORS

FIG. 7–6. Example of the layout of ground tackle for hauling off a stranded vessel

are not sufficiently robust to use either as anchorages for the standing blocks of purchases, or for the stoppers used when fleeting the purchases. Suitable extempore anchorages (Fig. 7–7) must be improvised, for example by such means as passing several turns of steel wire rope around deck or cargo-hatch

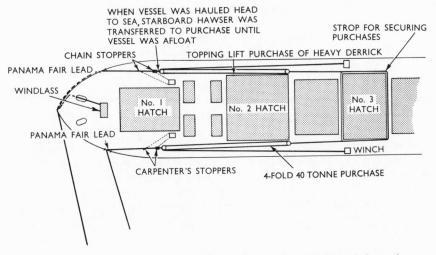

FIG. 7–7. Example of on-board rigging for hauling off a stranded vessel

coamings, deck structures, the bases of samson posts or the bedplates of winches.

EQUIPMENT AND VESSELS REQUIRED FOR MAJOR SALVAGE OPERATIONS

The salvage methods so far described only employ commonplace equipment with which all seamen are familiar. From a general-knowledge point of view, however, it is considered that brief descriptions of some of the methods used to raise sunken ships and of the special craft and equipment necessary for such major operations will be of interest and value to the seaman.

Cofferdams

When a vessel is sunk in shallow, sheltered water the usual method of raising her is to seal all except certain selected openings, repair the damage, and then build watertight, tower-like structures called *cofferdams* over the selected openings so that they extend from the hull of the ship to well above the surface of the sea. The necessary pumps can then be lowered down the cofferdams and installed inside them on the deck of the ship and the ship is then raised by pumping her clear of water.

With merchant vessels the cofferdams are usually built up on the hatch coamings of the cargo holds, and timber is generally used in their construction because it is more easily handled by divers than steel. The cofferdam is built up on the coaming, plank by plank, and secured to upright supports fitted all round. The whole structure is then well braced and shored on the inside to enable it to withstand the external water pressure.

For success this method needs sheltered water, because cofferdams which can be erected by divers are not very robust and will not stand up to a heavy sea. The depth of water from which a ship can be raised in this manner is limited by the strength of her decks, because they must withstand a considerable pressure when pumping begins.

Pontoons

Where sufficient buoyancy is unobtainable by pumping alone, additional buoyancy can be provided by the use of *pontoons*.

The salvage pontoon consists of a horizontal steel cylinder divided into watertight compartments which can be flooded and then emptied by compressed air, and it is fitted at one-third of its length from each end with a vertical mooring-pipe which extends through it from top to bottom (Figs. 7–8 and 7–9). For lifting work the pontoons are usually used in pairs, and the lifting capacity of each pair is about 160 tonnes.

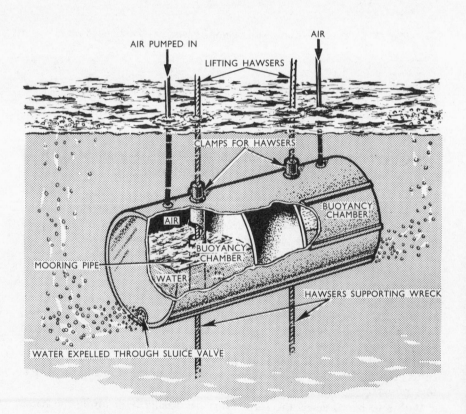

FIG. 7–8. Salvage pontoon

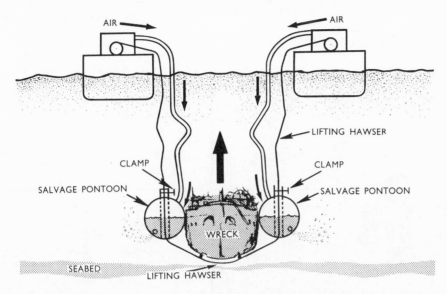

FIG. 7–9. A pair of buoyant salvage pontoons lifting a wreck from the sea bed

Having decided on the number of pontoons required to raise the vessel, an equivalent number of heavy lifting hawsers are passed in pairs beneath her, spaced at suitable intervals along her length, and the ends of each pair are then rove through the mooring pipes of the corresponding pair of pontoons. The pontoons are then flooded-up and sunk, and the lifting hawsers are hove taut and secured by divers on top of the pontoons by means of special clamps resembling Carpenter's stoppers. When all is ready the buoyancy chambers of the pontoons are blown clear of water by compressed air, and the vessel is raised by the lift exerted by the now buoyant pontoons. Care must be exercised at this stage to avoid damage to attendant vessels and craft, should the pontoons and casualty surface with a rush when the bottom suction breaks.

Pontoons are also used, secured firmly to the side of a vessel while she is being salvaged, to give her stability.

Portable air bags

Air bags can be used for lifting instead of pontoons. Two forms of bag are in general use; they are the *parachute* type and the *enclosed-box* type.

The *parachute-type* air bag (Fig 7–10) is supplied in a variety of sizes which give a buoyant lift of from one to 15 tonnes. It consists of a rubberised-fabric bag which has four lifting strops bonded to it. Air from the surface is admitted to the crown of the bag through an air control valve which is operated by a diver. The diver can thus regulate the rate of ascent, and greater control can be achieved by this method than can be obtained by regulation of the air supply at the surface. As the bag has an open base it cannot be canted from the vertical without spilling air, and its use is therefore restricted to vertical lifts as, for example, in aircraft salvage.

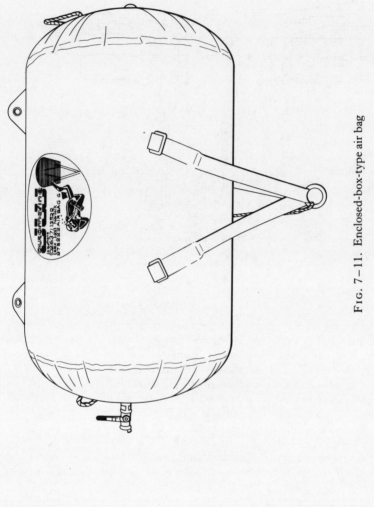

Fig. 7–11. Enclosed-box-type air bag

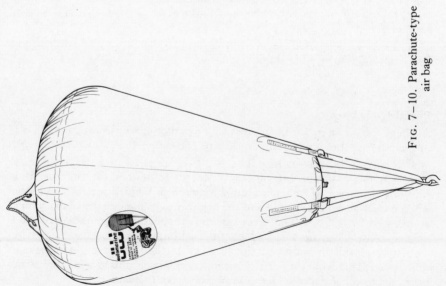

Fig. 7–10. Parachute-type
air bag

The *enclosed-box-type* air bag (Fig. 7–11) is constructed in a similar manner to the parachute type except that the bag is totally enclosed and is fitted with an air-release valve to permit deflation. It has a buoyant lift of from one to five tonnes and is more suitable for ship salvage because it can be canted from the vertical without spilling air. The valve assembly is built into the top of the bag and different air-pressure settings can be obtained by fitting the appropriate pressure switch into the assembly. The filling of the air bag and the rate of ascent are controlled by a diver in the same manner as for the parachute-type air bag.

Heavy sheer-legs lifting vessels (Fig. 7–12)

The heavy lifting vessels now used commercially depend for their lift on massive purchases hung from an A-frame stepped at one end of a large, shallow-draught barge. Their lifting capacities vary from 400 tonnes to 2000 tonnes but the majority of vessels fall within the lifting range of 800–1600 tonnes. Those having a lift in excess of 800 tonnes usually achieve it by the simultaneous use of A-frame and deck-mounted purchases, the lift being evenly distributed between them. None of these craft is in service with the Royal Navy and if such services are required they are obtained through charter action by the Ministry of Defence.

Capsized vessels

Vessels which have completely capsized are sometimes floated upside down by means of compressed air, but generally a ship so raised cannot be righted and is only fit for sale to shipbreakers. A vessel lying on her side can be righted by sealing and controlled pumping, water being left in selected compartments on the high side and buoyancy being employed on the low side as the righting moment. Alternatively, she can be parbuckled upright by means of strong hawsers, which are usually secured to levers built up on the ship's side and then hauled on by means of purchases anchored to fixed points ashore. If the vessel is large a combination of the two methods is used, and salvage pontoons may also be secured to the low side to provide additional righting moment with their buoyancy.

Salvage plant

Stocks of the necessary plant and equipment for salvage operations are maintained, ready for service, at all salvage bases and most naval dockyards. They consist of portable pumps, air compressors, electric generators, surface and underwater cutting and welding equipment, diving equipment, hawsers, blocks, underwater television equipment and many other items. Special items of submarine salvage equipment are held at the major salvage bases in southern England and in Scotland.

Portable air-compressors are supplied complete with air-driven tools which function under water, for use by divers. Such tools include hammers, drills, wood borers, rock drills, etc. The welding and cutting gear comprises oxy-hydrogen and oxy-arc equipment for underwater cutting, and electric equipment for underwater welding and above-water burning and welding. The necessary stocks of gases and portable electric generators are maintained together with this equipment.

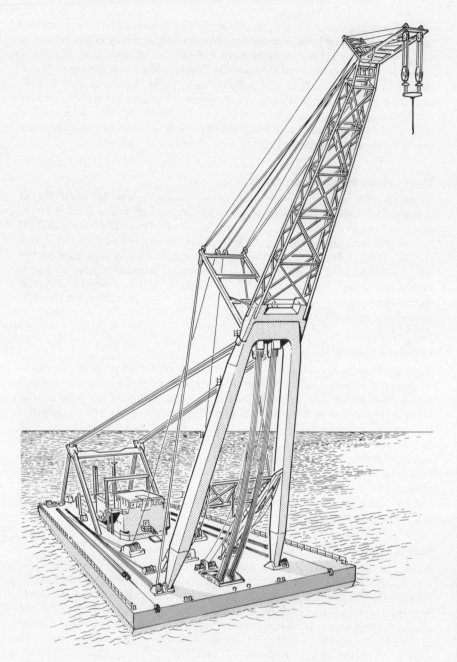

FIG. 7–12. Heavy sheer-legs lifting vessel

Salvage vessels

The salvage vessels operated by the Ministry of Defence serve a variety of purposes and are called *Mooring, Salvage and Boom Vessels* (MSBV). They fall into two classes:

1. CONVERTED COASTAL SALVAGE VESSELS which have been modernised. Each is fitted with a 470-kilowatt direct-reversing diesel engine which gives a speed of about 9 knots.
2. WILD DUCK Class (Fig. 7–13), fitted with either a 410-kilowatt or 560-kilowatt diesel engine driving a controllable-pitch propeller which gives a speed of about 10 knots.

Both classes displace about 1000 tonnes and they are designed to take the ground. Lifting arrangements comprise twin horns which overhang the stem. Each horn can take a working load of 25 tonnes on the point sheave and 50 tonnes on the inner sheave. Lifts of up to 200 tonnes can be taken over the bow apron by means of two six-fold purchases rigged on the foredeck. In two of the WILD DUCK Class, side lifts of up to 400 tonnes can also be taken. Each vessel has a foam/water firefighting monitor mounted on the mast or a kingpost, and carries 2730 litres of foam compound in an integral tank. All the vessels carry a small first-aid outfit of salvage pumps and gear together with a variety of diving equipment.

SALVAGE AND ASSISTANCE TO SHIPS CARRYING CHEMICAL CARGOES

The bulk carriage of dangerous cargoes at sea, particularly chemicals, is steadily increasing either in purpose-built ships or in specially converted tankers. Serious hazards could result from an accident involving one of these ships, and the following information regarding assistance in such cases should be read in conjunction with the current instructions published in BR 2170, *Ship NBCD Manual,* and BR 31, *The Queen's Regulations for the Royal Navy.*

A chemical cargo may not itself be dangerous but following an accident the mixing or release of chemicals in a marine environment could produce a serious local or general hazard because of the toxic, reactive, polluting or explosive characteristics of the mixture. Fires involving some chemicals cannot be fought by conventional methods because the introduction of water or carbon dioxide could aggravate the problem. Any ship offering assistance could also be faced, at the very least, with a severe downwind hazard resulting from the accident or any subsequent firefighting action.

Action by HM ships

If HM ships are called upon to assist chemical carriers in an emergency, the following precautions must be observed.

1. The ship should be positioned upwind of the casualty at all times.
2. The Gastight Condition Alfa should be assumed.
3. The number of hands on the upper deck should be restricted to those essential to the operation. If the cargo has been damaged these men should wear NBC respirators, but *on no account should respirators be worn on board the stricken vessel* as there may not be sufficient oxygen to support life.

The initial actions should be restricted to those necessary to save life. Hands involved in the rescue operation must be dressed in full NBC protective clothing and must use breathing apparatus. Any physical contact with chemicals should be avoided because the use of NBC clothing does not guarantee complete protection from some acids and concentrated vapours that may be encountered.

The Ministry of Defence (Navy) must be informed of the nature of the cargo by an IMMEDIATE signal bearing the prefix CHEMICAL CHECK. This signal should give the following information: name and nationality of the ship; geographical position of the ship; port of loading; details of dangerous cargo by technical name (trade names and manufacturers should be listed if technical names are not known); a situation report with particular reference to the state of the ship, the state of the cargo, the condition of the crew, any pollution, and salvage considerations.

Salvage action should only be commenced by authorisation and with advice from the Ministry of Defence, and in accordance with the instructions given in BR 31, *The Queen's Regulations for the Royal Navy* and BR 2170, *Ship NBCD Manual*. If practicable, a Salvage Officer should be present at the scene.

Action within the Ministry of Defence

On receipt of information that one of HM ships is involved in assistance to a chemical carrier every effort will be made to establish the type of cargo involved. Failing this, the receipt of the Chemical Check signal will be awaited and when the nature of the cargo is known the necessary procedures can be determined.

Information on chemicals is published by the Department of Trade in a pamphlet titled *SEACHEM* (Spillages Emergency Action for Chemicals). All the chemicals likely to be encountered in bulk are listed, together with the hazards they impose in the event of spillage or fire, the recommended procedures for dealing with an incident, and the approved antidotes and dispersants. This pamphlet is held by all Coastguard Area Headquarters and Rescue Co-ordination Centres from where advice may be requested. Additionally, the National Chemical Emergency Centre at Harwell will provide on request detailed information on most known chemicals, including their toxicity, flammability, explosiveness, the actions and precautions required in any emergency such as fire or spillage, and the first-aid treatment of casualties. The Centre can also provide similar details on many products which, although based on chemicals, can only be recognised by their trade names.

The necessary information thus elicited is passed to the ship by signal for advice of the officers engaged in the emergency. The Ministry decision to salvage will not normally be made until advice has been sought from interested parties, and will depend largely on the intactness of the cargo, the condition of the vessel and the opinion of the Commanding Officer at the scene.

Ships other than chemical carriers

With the increasing use of containerisation some hazardous cargoes may be shipped 'unseen' but the details should be included in the ship's cargo manifest, and an indication of the hazard and position of the container should be given in the loading plan or cargo stowage plan (see Chapter 4). It is

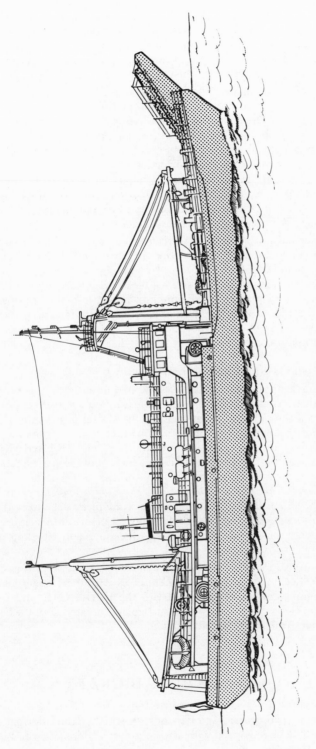

FIG. 7–13. MSBV of the WILD DUCK Class

possible that containers secured on deck could carry away because of heavy weather or some other disaster. Depending on their contents individual containers may sink or float, or may float in a state of negative buoyancy beneath the sea surface. Ships must therefore proceed with caution in the spillage area and the primary aim must be to minimise the danger to shipping.

Attempts should be made to gather the containers together to form a raft by passing securing lines through the corner castings. If possible a jury mast should be rigged on one container using the four corner castings as securing points, and the raft should be marked with a flag (flag Bravo) and a temporary light. The geographical position of the raft, or of the spillage area and its radius, and the estimated rate and direction of drift should be reported. If weather conditions are favourable it may be possible to tow the raft clear of shipping lanes. Within the limits of HM Dockyard ports the Royal Maritime Auxiliary Service can be called upon to assist. If a large number of containers are adrift it may be necessary to form several rafts.

It is not normally worth trying to recover containers which in any event may have become waterlogged and the contents spoiled. However, effort should be made to identify the contents by sighting the labels, provided they have not been washed off and are still legible. This is particularly important if the sinking of a container by demolition action is being considered; in addition to the risk of an uncontrolled explosion, the release of dangerous cargo into the water or the atmosphere may add to the existing hazards. Further information on containers is given in Chapter 4.

Dangerous Goods classification and marking

In most countries hazardous goods are shipped under strict packaging and stowage regulations and they can be identified by the *Dangerous Goods List* which is part of the *Cargo Manifest* held by the Master of the ship. For ships of British registration, and of other nationalities trading from the United Kingdom, it is a requirement that hazardous goods are listed with their technical name as well as their trade name, their stowage position and their classification according to the regulations of the *International Maritime Dangerous Goods Code* (IMDG Code) and *The Carriage of Dangerous Goods in Ships* (the Blue Book). Packages and containers are marked by an internationally recognised system of labelling. Further information on the carriage of dangerous goods including classifications and labelling is given on page 114.

When assisting in salvage operations, particularly where fire or flooding is involved, officers should acquaint themselves with the Dangerous Goods List or its equivalent, in conjunction with the IMDG Code and the Blue Book. If considered necessary, and particularly if any doubt exists, the Chemical Check procedure should be used.

SALVAGE OF AIRCRAFT

Occasions arise when it is necessary to search for, locate and salvage an aircraft. The decision to salvage depends on whether the information and material that may be recovered will justify the cost of ships, men and material expended on the operation.

Search

An aircraft that crashes at sea may manage to radio its position or be heard to transmit for a period sufficient for a ship or shore station to obtain a bearing. The crash may be seen by a ship, or the aircraft's position may be known through radar tracking at the moment of the crash. The best position derived from all the available information becomes the datum or starting point of the search.

A number of methods are available to locate an object on the sea bed. Most operational military aircraft are fitted with a sonar beacon which transmits automatically when submerged to a depth of more than one-and-a-half metres. The majority of warships are fitted with the means of locating these beacons and the Directorate of Marine Services (Naval) holds a stock of portable location equipments which can be used from most ships and light craft. Commercial trawlers can be chartered to trawl if the sea bed is suitable; side trawlers are preferable to stern trawlers because an aircraft so recovered will suffer less damage when being lifted by side derricks than by being lifted over the stern ramp. Pairs of ships using a wire sweep are effective but there is a risk of severe damage to the aircraft if or when it is fouled by the wire. If the underwater visibility is good, underwater television, observation-chamber diving and underwater-recovery vehicles may prove useful for identification.

Undoubtedly, the best method of location is by sonar equipment because it can also be used to direct a diver to the aircraft, or a salvage vessel to the exact position above the wreckage.

Recovery

After a suitable wire has been secured, the salvage vessel adjusts its position to plumb the aircraft and then heaves-in the wire at slow speed. Before the aircraft is hoisted clear of the water it must be allowed to drain in order to avoid unnecessary structural stresses. Additional wires are then passed around the aircraft to act as preventers or as bowsing-in lines.

SALVAGE OF HELICOPTERS

The work of a ship involved in helicopter salvage may be either of two operations: rescue of the aircrew, prevention of sinking, and securing the helicopter to the ship; or search, location and assistance in the recovery of a sunken helicopter.

The form and lightness of its construction, and the lack of suitable lifting points, make a helicopter particularly susceptible to damage by the lifting and securing lines. Thus the securing and recovery operation is complicated by the need to prevent further damage to the helicopter.

Helicopter construction

The most common design of helicopter has a single main rotor, the torque reaction of which is countered by a single tail rotor positioned to exert its thrust in the plane of the main rotor. The main rotor is driven through a gearbox which is supported from the relatively small area of the load floor by a few strong vertical frames. One of the frames also takes the main undercarriage attachments. The cabin roof or gearbox mounting, the frames

P

and the floor are covered with a skin, sufficiently thick to be stable. This forms a box strong enough to withstand all the flight and landing loads without the need of strong longitudinal members. The rear fuselage, of which the prime purpose is to support the tail rotor in its optimum position, is formed of a light skin with the minimum of internal bracing. In helicopter construction it is rare to find more than two layers of material (each no thicker than 2 millimetres) in any position except in the areas of the engine and gearbox mountings. Magnesium alloy was formerly used for the construction of the skin, because of its lightness, but unfortunately this material suffers from severe corrosion by salt water. This problem has now been overcome by the development of helicopter engines to the point where the extra weight of an aluminium alloy skin is acceptable. However, magnesium alloys are still used for the manufacture of gearbox castings.

Picketing attachments are usually fitted at various points on the airframe to secure the aircraft to the deck. Although these attachments may appear quite substantial they are unlikely to be able to take much load unless they are attached to the undercarriage. They are normally only intended for downwards loading; however, each picketing point should be capable of accepting the upwards loading from *one* Portable Salvage Equipment (see page 222).

SALVAGE OF DITCHED (FLOATING) HELICOPTERS

Helicopters which operate over the sea are usually fitted with flotation gear which inflates in the event of ditching. The primary purpose of the gear is to allow time for the escape or rescue of the aircrew; their rescue is the first priority for ships and helicopters arriving on the scene. However, rapid action by a ship or *search and rescue* (SAR) helicopter during this period may prevent the ditched helicopter sinking and will greatly facilitate its recovery. Helicopters are extremely expensive and even though one that has ditched may appear a complete write-off, an inspection will almost certainly reveal the cause of its ditching and may make its recovery worth while. Furthermore, if through good seamanship the helicopter suffers little salvage damage and repair is possible, it may even fly again.

Flotation gear and escape panels
The positions of the inflated flotation gear for various types of helicopter are shown in Figs. 7–14 to 7–17. The positions of escape panels are indicated by shaded areas.

Roles of ships
In addition to assisting the SAR helicopter, if one is present, ships should take the following actions in order of priority.
1. Rescue survivors.
2. Mark the ditched helicopter or the position of ditching, for future salvage operations where practicable.
3. Prevent the helicopter from sinking, by the attachment of additional buoyancy and/or securing to the ship.
4. Recover the helicopter, where possible.

Preparations

Crash boat. Whenever flying operations involving fixed-wing aircraft or helicopters are taking place a crash boat is kept at immediate notice, with all its equipment ready and the crew on call. The seaboat and/or the Gemini should be prepared, depending on the sea state, the weather conditions and the serviceability of boats. Ideally the seaboat should be used to recover survivors and the Gemini should be used for helicopter recovery work because this reduces the risk of puncturing the helicopter's own flotation gear.

Crash boat's crew comprises:

1. BOAT'S CREW.
2. MEDICAL RATING. If only one medical rating is borne in the ship, he should remain on board and another rating trained in first aid and proficient at mouth-to-mouth resuscitation should be substituted. This task could be undertaken by a suitably trained member of the boat's crew.
3. FLIGHT RATING. To provide advice on the attachment of supplementary flotation gear and on access into the helicopter for the rescue of casualties. The flight rating should be carried in the Gemini if it is used in addition to the seaboat.
4. TWO SHIP'S DIVERS OR SWIMMERS.

Crash boat equipment includes:

1. SUPPLEMENTARY FLOTATION GEAR comprising either the Portable Salvage Equipment for ditched helicopters or the MS 5 Dinghy provided by the Flight. The quantities of supplementary flotation gear required to support various helicopters are tabulated below:

TYPE OF HELICOPTER	NUMBER OF SETS
Wasp	3
Lynx	5
Wessex 1 or 5	6
Wessex 3	8
Sea King	8

2. PORTABLE RADIO for direct communication with both the parent ship and assisting helicopters.
3. FIRST-AID BAG.
4. BLANKETS sealed in a polythene bag.
5. A BAG OR BOX CLEARLY MARKED 'CRASH BOAT', containing the following items:

   Spherical float fitted with approximately 100 metres of line, to mark the helicopter should it sink. A buoyant marker-light should be used by night.

   Fireman's axe for breaking aircraft escape panels.

   Hand-operated wire cutters.

   Quick-release knife with sheath.

   Portable battery-operated floodlight or hand signalling lamp.

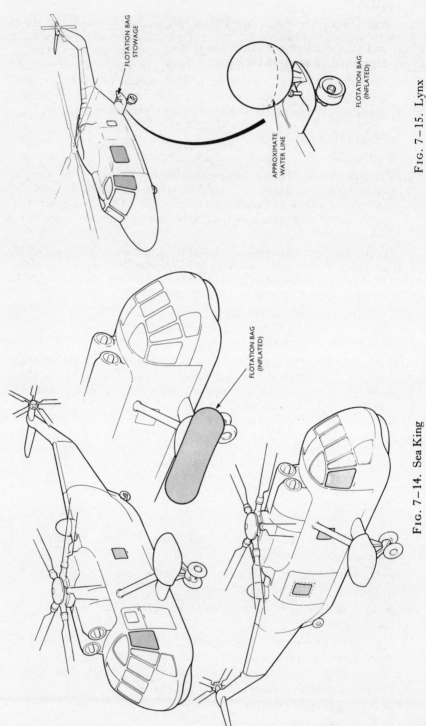

FLOTATION BAG
STOWAGE

APPROXIMATE
WATER LINE

FLOTATION BAG
(INFLATED)

FIG. 7–15. Lynx

FLOTATION BAG
(INFLATED)

FIG. 7–14. Sea King

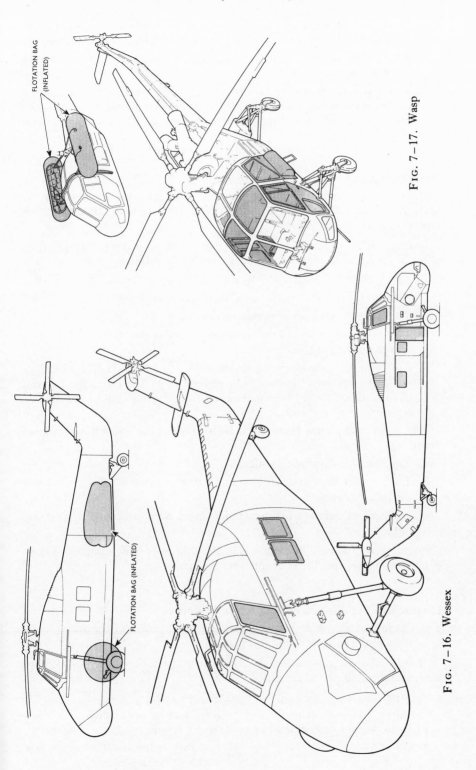

FLOTATION BAG
(INFLATED)

FIG. 7–17. Wasp

FLOTATION BAG (INFLATED)

FIG. 7–16. Wessex

      Salvage strop made up from 3 metres of 28-millimetre polyamide with a soft eye at each end, for attaching a ship's hawser to the helicopter.

6. RESCUE QUOIT fitted with approximately 100 metres of 10-millimetre polyethylene line.

7. TWO ADDITIONAL 9-LITRE FOAM FIRE-EXTINGUISHERS which should be provided from the hangar firefighting equipment allowance. The boat's crew should collect and return these extinguishers on their way to and from the boat.

Approach phase

During the approach to the ditched helicopter the men involved in the operation should be briefed and immediate preparations for securing or recovery should be made.

Briefing. After the crash boat has been called away, its crew and the crews of any assisting helicopters should be briefed on the following points.

1. The type of helicopter, and its escape arrangements and flotation gear.

2. The number of persons on board the ditched helicopter.

3. To report the number of persons rescued.

4. To return to the ship with survivors before commencing any attempt to recover the helicopter.

5. Any ordnance or underslung load known to be attached to the helicopter or any pyrotechnics known to be in the cabin. Advice on the removal of these items should be obtained from the ship's Flight or the ditched helicopter's parent unit.

The crash boat's crew should also be briefed on the following additional items.

1. The risk of fire from fuel spillage.

2. To keep the boat clear of the ditched helicopter to avoid puncturing the flotation gear.

3. Callsigns of assisting helicopters for direct communication by portable radio.

Recovery gear should be prepared in the ship to provide as many options of hoisting or securing the helicopter as are practicable.

Location of the ditched helicopter and its crew

The Operations Room and lookouts should be informed of the various aids to location of the helicopter and its crew.

Aircrew distress equipment. Aircrew carry the following equipment to assist searching ships and aircraft:

SARBE (Search and Rescue Beacon Equipment) *or* PLB (Personal Locator Beacon)	— Radio beacon and very-short-range voice facility on International Distress Frequency, 243.0 megahertz.
Miniflare	— Red flare rising to 60 metres which burns for 6 seconds.

Distress Signal (Night and Day) — Hand-held signal emitting red smoke by day or showing a red flare by night.

Sea light of lifejacket, operated by a sea-cell.

Heliograph.

Whistle.

Orange dinghy.

Helicopter Sonar Beacon. RN helicopters are fitted with a sonar beacon which automatically starts to transmit when submerged to a depth greater than one-and-a-half metres and can be heard on passive sonar or underwater telephone.

Reports and records

Reports. Generally an officer not directly involved in the rescue or recovery is detailed to prepare signalled reports on the ditching and the recovery operation. Ships carrying helicopters report in accordance with JSP 318, *Military Flying Regulations,* Part 2; other ships report in the format shown in ATP 10, *Search and Rescue,* British Supplement No. 1. Where diving and salvage assistance is required, signals in the formats of both JSP 318 and ATP 10 must be sent. If the helicopter has sunk, the depth of water must also be included in the signalled reports.

Photography. As many photographs as possible, taken from all angles, should be obtained of the whole recovery operation. These will not only assist in the assessment and improvement of recovery techniques but also assist in the separation of damage inflicted during the recovery from that associated with the ditching or the emergency which caused it.

Aircrew rescue

Aircrew close to or trapped in the helicopter should be assisted by a swimmer or ship's diver operating from the crash boat. Swimmers and divers working beneath the rotor disc are at considerable risk and must be warned of the hazards (see below).

Survivors clear of the helicopter. Survivors in the water should be recovered as quickly as possible, followed by those in dinghies.

Divers and swimmers

Clearance divers and SAR divers may dive without a lifeline; ship's divers and swimmers must wear a lifeline except when directly involved in the rescue of aircrew from inside the helicopter. The SAR diver is trained specifically for first-aid helicopter salvage and, when available, is the most suitable choice for this type of work.

Hazards to divers and swimmers. Even though ditched helicopters may float for a period of 20 minutes or more, experience shows that they are prone to sink or capsize suddenly. Divers and swimmers should not enter a helicopter except for the rescue of aircrew or for the placing of supplementary flotation gear, and they must be warned of the danger of being trapped inside the helicopter by flotation gear when it inflates. Work on the rotor head should be conducted from above and clear of the rotor blades. Divers and swimmers on lifelines are *not to work under the helicopter* on any account. Before they enter the water divers and swimmers must be thoroughly briefed on the procedure to be adopted.

The combination of a damaged helicopter and a high sea state may make it inadvisable to attempt either first-aid salvage or even to mark the helicopter.

Marking the helicopter

The line of the spherical float which is used as a marker buoy should be attached to the helicopter by a swimmer. A stick should be passed through the centre of the float and the line coiled round it in figure-of-eight turns. This ensures that the line has no loose bights to foul the swimmer or the helicopter and also that the line will run freely should the helicopter sink. Possible attachment points, in order of preference, are the undercarriage oleo legs, the sea-anchor/bow-towing bridle (Sea King only) and the helicopter picketing points. If none of these positions can be used the line will have to be secured to the rotor head. This position has the disadvantage that when the helicopter sinks, the rotation of the rotor winds up the line and submerges the float.

If the helicopter has sunk, the position of ditching should be marked with a quick reaction marker buoy (page 238) to serve as a datum for the subsequent search for the wreck.

Prevention of sinking

On completion of the initial urgent actions of recovering the aircrew and marking the helicopter, an attempt to prevent it from sinking must be made as quickly as possible. It must be decided whether to achieve this by the use of portable salvage equipment or by a hawser from the ship to the rotor head.

The Portable Salvage Equipment sets can be used by divers working away from the ship and will support the helicopter, a metre or so below the surface, until it can be recovered. However, if the ship can be kept close to the helicopter a hawser can probably be attached more quickly. Either operation should be carried out by two ship's divers or swimmers with the Diving Officer working from the crash boat — preferably the Gemini.

The Portable Salvage Equipment comprises an inflatable bag packed in a valise. It is provided with securing lines fitted with snap hooks for attachment to the helicopter and it is inflated by pulling the toggle of a lanyard which is stowed in a patch pocket at one end of the valise. Inflation takes about 25 seconds and, when fully inflated, the bag provides 450 kilograms of buoyancy. The scale of supply is such that a ship may not have sufficient sets of Portable Salvage Equipment to support the type of helicopter which has ditched (see page 217). In these circumstances additional sets will have to be obtained from ships in company.

It may be possible to insert and inflate a Portable Salvage Equipment, or a liferaft, inside the helicopter but there is a strong likelihood that it will be punctured by sharp projections. Such a measure can only be considered a temporary supplement to existing buoyancy while additional buoyancy is provided outside the helicopter. The bags should be attached to strong points around the outside of the helicopter such as picketing eyes, main undercarriage and the main rotor head. The positions of the bags should be disposed around the helicopter, and during inflation small adjustments may be made, to support the helicopter in a level plane.

If it is intended to secure the helicopter to the ship by a hawser, the salvage strop should be attached by passing one-and-a-half turns round the main rotor shaft below the rotor head. The strop should then be secured to a man-made fibre picking-up rope or berthing hawser. This initial line should be considered a preliminary securing arrangement to establish control over the helicopter; it should subsequently be replaced by the towing hawser, by which the helicopter can safely hang under the ship or be transferred to a salvage vessel.

If the helicopter has capsized, strops may be attached to the main undercarriage or fuselage securing points to prevent it sinking and to right it. Men engaged on salvage must remember, however, that the main rotor head is the only single point capable of supporting the whole weight of the helicopter.

Hoisting and securing facilities

The available fittings in the majority of warships are not ideal for lifting a ditched helicopter. However, the bullring, replenishment-at-sea (RAS) roller fairleads, ammunitioning davit and boat davits are suggested as possible means of lifting or securing a helicopter, depending on its weight.

Bullring. Capstan power will provide the quickest method of lifting a ditched helicopter clear of the water but heavy damage can be expected from contact with the ship's stem. The advantage of using the bullring is that a frigate may lie to the ditched helicopter while it still floats; if the helicopter sinks, it may be allowed to hang clear below the stem. This is the best method if a salvage vessel is known to be on the way because the helicopter can be suspended with minimum risk of further damage before transfer.

RAS roller fairleads. If the helicopter has to be lifted clear of the water and returned to harbour by a warship, considerable damage may be expected by the use of these fairleads; nevertheless, the damage will not be so severe as that caused by use of the bullring. When lifted by these means, the helicopter will need to be bowsed-in under the flare of the bow.

Ammunitioning davit. Although only suitable for a Wasp, the whip of an ammunitioning davit secured to the rotor head and backed up by berthing hawsers secured to the undercarriage legs has been used successfully to lift a ditched helicopter.

Boat davits also are only suitable for a Wasp. The davits fitted for the 7.44-metre motor boat, which have a SWL of 1.25 tonnes for each davit, have been used to recover this type of helicopter. Contact with the ship is inevitable and protection in the form of fenders and paunch mats, and bowsing-in of the helicopter, will be necessary. An unfair strain will be imposed on the davits if both falls are secured to the same point on the helicopter; one fall should be used for the main lift while the other supports the tail to keep the helicopter horizontal and assist drainage.

Helicopter weights

The maximum weights at which various helicopters can fly are shown overleaf.

After ditching, however, a considerable quantity of sea water may be contained within the helicopter thus increasing the lifting weight.

Helicopter Type	Maximum Weight (tonnes)
Gazelle	1.75
Wasp	2.5
Lynx	4.5
Wessex	6.5
Sea King	11.0

Hoisting precautions

Unless absolutely essential to the rescue or salvage operation, the helicopter's controls and switches should not be disturbed before they have been inspected by the officer investigating the ditching.

The salvage strop used to attach the ship's hawser to the helicopter is not strong enough to lift it out of the water. Even if available, the designed aircraft lifting sling may prove difficult to fit and so a strop of the appropriate strength (see helicopter weights above) should be made up. This lifting strop should be attached to the main rotor shaft below the rotor head and the lifting hawsers transferred to it before attempting to hoist the helicopter.

The stem or ship's side should be well fendered before the helicopter is hauled alongside. Steadying lines will be necessary but wires or hawsers should not be passed around the fuselage because they will easily cut through the light aluminium-alloy construction.

When the helicopter is alongside and secured, as many weighty items as possible should be removed and hoisted inboard, e.g. rotor blades, sonar ball, rescue hoist, etc.

A large amount of water may be trapped within the helicopter and frequent pauses must be made during hoisting to allow drainage. Where possible a second lift should be attached to the tail, by means of a wide padded strop or net, to keep the helicopter horizontal during hoisting. This will assist drainage and speed up the recovery but the tail should never be lifted beyond the horizontal.

Draining may be facilitated by cutting holes in the fuselage. Such cutting should be carefully considered, taking account of advice from the ship's Flight, because substantial damage may be inflicted for the sake of a relatively small gain in time. The under surface of the Sea King helicopter is marked to indicate suitable positions which may be cut to assist drainage (see page 226). Experience of recovering a Sea King indicates that draining can take up to two hours.

Action after recovery

When the helicopter has been hoisted clear of the water, action must be taken to reduce corrosion. The whole helicopter must be thoroughly washed, both inside and out, with fresh water. It should then be completely sprayed or wiped over with an approved water repellant (PX 24, Dewatering agent and temporary protective).

Special features of the Sea King helicopter

The Sea King is built with a boat-type hull and has two engines, which enables it to alight on the water in an emergency. In suitable weather, in the event of an engine failure the helicopter may, on the remaining serviceable engine, be able to take off again or taxi to a safe harbour or beach. If one engine fails the Captain of the helicopter will attempt to restart the engine; if this fails he will endeavour to lighten the helicopter enough for a single-engine take-off. Lightening of the helicopter includes jettisoning of fuel and pyrotechnics, with the attendant risk of fire, and possibly two aircrew may abandon the helicopter.

Ships approaching a Sea King on the water with its main rotor turning should take the following actions.

1. Attempt to communicate with the helicopter.

2. Ascertain whether any aircrew have abandoned the helicopter and are swimming clear of the main rotor disc.

3. Ascertain whether fuel or pyrotechnics have been jettisoned.

4. Take station at least 2½ cables clear, within the pilot's field of view, and in a sector of 90 degrees on either beam of the helicopter to avoid the path of take-off and any fuel that may have been dumped. The shaded areas of Fig. 7–18 indicate the suitable positions to take station.

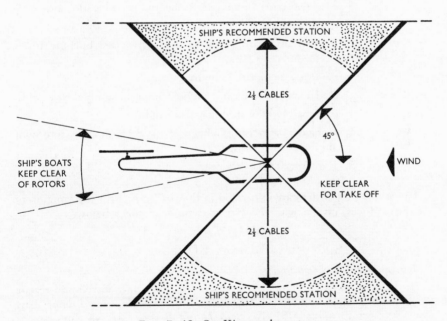

FIG. 7–18. Sea King on the water

5. Recover aircrew who have abandoned the helicopter, keeping rescue boats well clear of the main and tail rotors.

Should the take-off attempt fail, the flotation gear on the main undercarriage sponsons will be inflated by the aircrew, who will then shut down the engines, stop the rotors and stream the sea anchor.

Precautions. When the Sea King is floating the tail-rotor clearance is reduced to between a half and one metre. If the helicopter pitches or rolls the clearance between the main rotor disc and the wave tops may be greatly reduced without warning. Even in calm conditions, the Sea King is likely to capsize once the rotors have stopped. The Sea King is extremely stable when floating capsized, and righting it will require a very heavy lift.

Draining. Suitable positions which may be punctured to facilitate draining are marked on the hulls of Sea King helicopters, as already mentioned. These areas are outlined in white and bear the words 'CUT TO DRAIN' in yellow.

Bridge Emergency Orders and Bridge File

Orders for the Officer of the Watch are incorporated in the *Bridge Emergency Orders*. A typical example is shown below.

BRIDGE EMERGENCY ORDERS

Aircraft Ditching

PIPE: 'Helicopter ditched! Helicopter ditched! Away crash boat's crew'.

ACTIONS: 1. Turn towards and increase speed.

2. Mark the plot or fix the ship.

3. Detail and brief lookouts on the following location aids.

   a. Red smoke or flare.

   b. Red miniflare rising to 60 metres and burning for 6 seconds.

   c. Orange-coloured dinghy.

   d. Intermittent flash from helicopter on sunny day.

   e. Small light or flashing strobe light.

4. Consider launching helicopter for SAR duties, from own ship or ship in company.

5. Rig aircraft recovery gear.

The emergency orders are expanded in the *Bridge File* for information of the ship's officers on the bridge. A typical example is shown below.

BRIDGE FILE

Helicopter crash check-off list

1. Inform ships in company, area commander, and search-and-rescue co-ordination centre (see JSP 318, *Military Flying Regulations*, Part 2, Section 6, or ATP 10, *Search and Rescue*, British Supplement No. 1).

2. Activate search-and-rescue communications plan.

3. Commence narrative.

4. Close up lookouts and defence watch of Sonar Control Room crew.

5. Prepare crash boat and Gemini.

6. Prepare watertight buoyant marker light.

7. Dress at least four divers or swimmers.

8. Stop ditching gash.

9. Prepare medical reception for casualties.

10. Prepare lifting or securing arrangements for helicopter.

11. If helicopter has sunk commence search for sonar beacon using passive sonar.

On arrival at scene of ditching

1. Recover personnel from within the helicopter.

2. Recover personnel from the sea and then those in dinghies.

3. Boat or boats return to the ship with survivors.

4. Attach marker to the helicopter.

5. Attach line to main rotor shaft of helicopter.

6. Attach and inflate supplementary flotation gear.

7. *a. Wasp only.* Recover helicopter.

    b. Other helicopters. Decide on one of the following actions:

       (i) Hold helicopter up, and lash to the ship.

      (ii) Lie-to the helicopter.

     (iii) Allow helicopter to sink and hang under the ship.

    (iv) Lower helicopter to the sea bed and mark the position.

8. Take as many photographs as possible starting from the earliest opportunity.

9. Wash helicopter with fresh water and then spray or wipe with water repellant.

10. If helicopter has sunk, mark position accurately with a danbuoy. In strong tidal positions, bad weather, or when salvage may be delayed, two buoys should be laid.

11. Draw a plot showing position of the wreck relative to danbuoy(s) and forward it to the area commander.

SALVAGE OF SUNKEN HELICOPTERS

A sunken helicopter is a disorderly and unwieldy piece of wreckage. The helicopter usually settles in the inverted position with its heaviest and strongest part on the sea bed. In this position it is unstable and liable to move with the motion of the sea. The undercarriage will possibly be torn off or, at the least, loosened, the fuel tanks flooded and the sound-proofing saturated with sea water.

If the machine is complete its weight should be taken as the all-up weight at last take-off because the water inside the helicopter will compensate for loss of the main rotor blades and for the escape of the aircrew. These weights for various aircraft are listed on page 224.

Modern design does not permit a lifting ring to be built into the rotor head and so the designed lifting sling is usually attached to the top plate of the rotor head by self-locking pins. Although attachment of this arrangement is satisfactory under normal circumstances, it is generally considered beyond the capability of a diver with limited dive time, in poor light, with access obstructed by wreckage and without facilities to support the sling. Thus the usually-adopted method is to attach the lifting wire by a heavy strop passed round the rotor shaft below the rotor head. The rotor head has many sharp corners and the strongest strop a diver can handle has little margin to resist chafe and snatch without being overstressed when the helicopter leaves the water. Furthermore, this method of lifting is liable to damage a vital component of the helicopter but this penalty is more acceptable to the investigating officer than failure to recover the helicopter.

A net may appear suitable for bowsing-in or even for the main lift. The net must be capable of withstanding the abrasion of sharp edges as it will undoubtedly cut the helicopter structure to some extent. The material of the mesh should present as large an area as possible to the helicopter to minimise the cutting effect. The most suitable material for net construction appears to be plastic-covered aluminium wire which is the best compromise between the extremes of steel wire rope and polyamide webbing.

MSBVs are only just capable of lifting helicopters of Sea King size under the lifting horns in calm conditions. In less than ideal weather the helicopter will suffer damage from the sea during transport to harbour and any attempts to bowse-in are liable to inflict further damage by cutting the helicopter structure.

In the recovery of a sunken helicopter the Salvage Officer must select the most suitable method as dictated by the circumstances of the operation and use his experience to minimise any further damage to the aircraft.

CHAPTER 8

Moorings

Permanent moorings may be laid for the following purposes.

1. To make the most of the usually limited space of a harbour anchorage.
2. To berth ships as near as possible to the landing places so as to facilitate embarking and disembarking stores, cargo, crew or passengers.
3. To provide secure moorings for ships in crowded waters, especially for those laid up and others unable to move under their own power.
4. To ensure that ships are berthed precisely, and in the most suitable positions for each other's safety and for the preservation of lanes for harbour traffic.
5. To reduce the possibility of ships dragging in heavy weather. (A ship is usually more secure at a permanent swinging mooring than at anchor.)

The two main types of permanent moorings are the *swinging mooring,* where a ship secures head to buoy and is free to swing to the wind and tidal stream; and the *head-and-stern mooring,* where a ship secures head-and-stern between two buoys. Swinging moorings are always laid if space permits, because ships can make fast to them and slip from them with the minimum of help. Where space is limited, however, ships must be secured to head-and-stern moorings, which have the following disadvantages:

1. A ship usually requires tugs when securing to them and slipping from them.
2. When a ship is secured to them in a strong beam wind they are subjected to a very great load and so they have to be particularly strong and secure.
3. A mooring intended for a long ship is not suitable for a short ship.

Full information on all types of moorings is given in BR 8661, *Ministry of Defence Moorings Manual,* and remarks on shiphandling while securing to head buoys or between head-and-stern buoys appear in Chapter 13.

PARTS OF A MOORING

The three main parts of a mooring comprise the *ground tackle,* the *riser pendant* and the *buoy.* These parts are illustrated in Fig. 8–1 which shows a first-class four-leg swinging mooring. This mooring has a displacement rating of 50 800 tonnes and is used for ships with cable up to 95-millimetre Grade 1 steel, 78-millimetre Grade 2 steel or 66-millimetre Grade 3 steel. The total weight of the mooring is approximately 221 tonnes.

Ground tackle

Ground tackle consists of two or more mooring anchors, with a *ground arm* of mooring chain shackled to each and led to a *central mooring ring,* to which is shackled the *riser pendant.*

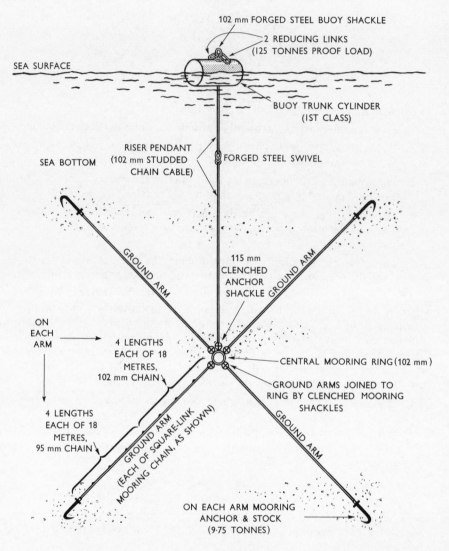

102 mm FORGED STEEL BUOY SHACKLE

2 REDUCING LINKS
(125 TONNES PROOF LOAD)

SEA SURFACE

BUOY TRUNK CYLINDER
(1ST CLASS)

RISER PENDANT
(102 mm STUDDED
CHAIN CABLE)

SEA BOTTOM

FORGED STEEL SWIVEL

115 mm
CLENCHED
ANCHOR
SHACKLE

GROUND ARM

GROUND ARM

ON
EACH
ARM

4 LENGTHS
EACH OF 18
METRES,
102 mm CHAIN

CENTRAL MOORING RING (102 mm)

GROUND ARMS JOINED TO
RING BY CLENCHED MOORING
SHACKLES

4 LENGTHS
EACH OF 18
METRES,
95 mm CHAIN

GROUND ARM
(EACH OF SQUARE-LINK
MOORING CHAIN, AS SHOWN)

GROUND ARM

ON EACH ARM MOORING
ANCHOR & STOCK
(9·75 TONNES)

Fig. 8–1. Diagrammatic sketch of a first-class four-leg swinging mooring showing the principal parts

Mooring anchors (Fig. 8–2). These are usually stocked, single-fluke anchors, and they are usually heavier than the bower anchors of the ships for which the mooring is designed. They are carefully placed and embedded to ensure that the mooring and its buoy are in the correct position. Because they are seldom dropped and embedded by dragging like a ship's anchor they have only one fluke, and a stock is incorporated to prevent the anchor from rolling out of its bed. Clumps are sometimes used instead of fluked anchors for small-craft and navigation-buoy moorings. A ship's stockless anchor is not usually suitable as a mooring anchor. Details of Admiralty mooring anchors are given in Table 8–4 on page 249.

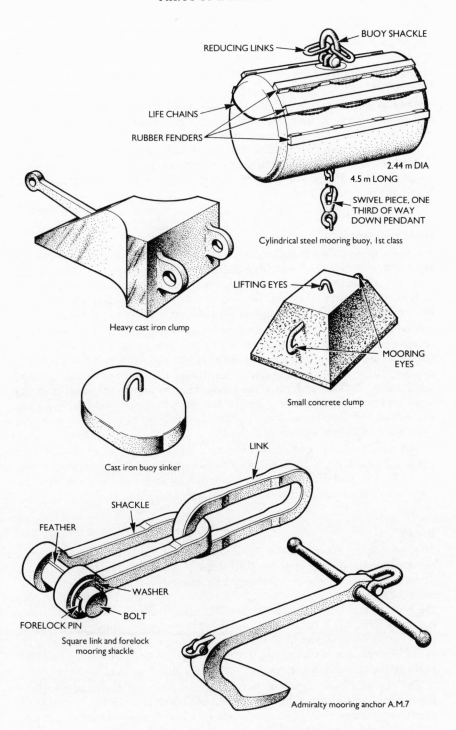

REDUCING LINKS

BUOY SHACKLE

LIFE CHAINS

RUBBER FENDERS

2.44 m DIA
4.5 m LONG

SWIVEL PIECE, ONE
THIRD OF WAY
DOWN PENDANT

Cylindrical steel mooring buoy, 1st class

Heavy cast iron clump

LIFTING EYES

MOORING
EYES

Small concrete clump

Cast iron buoy sinker

LINK

SHACKLE

FEATHER

WASHER

BOLT

FORELOCK PIN

Square link and forelock
mooring shackle

Admiralty mooring anchor A.M.7

FIG. 8–2. Mooring buoy and types of ground tackle for moorings

Ferro-concrete clumps or cast-iron sinkers are sometimes used in minor moorings instead of anchors (Fig. 8–2). These clumps and sinkers give a good hold in a soft muddy bottom, but it should be noted that concrete clumps lose about 40 per cent of their weight when submerged, because of their inherent buoyancy.

Arms of ground tackle. These are made up of 18-metre lengths of special square-link mooring chain, each link being approximately one metre long and of square section. The lengths are joined by special *forelock mooring shackles* (Fig. 8–2). *Clenched* or *welded mooring shackles* are used where the inner ends of the arms are shackled to the central *mooring ring* (Fig. 8–1), as most wear occurs in this position. These shackles have to be clenched or welded before the mooring is laid.

Riser pendants

Pendants are made up from lengths of Grade 2 steel studded-chain cable and are fitted with a swivel provided there is sufficient swinging room at the mooring. Pendants of head-and-stern moorings may be fitted with swivels so that, if necessary, they can be used as swinging moorings. The swivel is inserted at one-third of the length of the pendant from its upper end.

The lower end of the riser pendant is made of open end-link cable for a length equal to the maximum range of the tide. For any size of cable the open end links are made of the same grade steel but the diameter of the metal is approximately 20 per cent greater than that of the common studded links; see Table 8–3. This additional thickness compensates for the absence of the stud, and provides a greater margin for wear at the position where most movement and abrasion occurs. The pendant is secured to the mooring ring by a clenched anchor shackle (Fig. 8–1).

The length of the pendant of a standard mooring is equal to the depth of water at Mean High Water Springs plus two metres and the freeboard of the buoy. In exposed positions where heavy seas and swell are likely to be experienced the length is increased accordingly.

Buoys

Mooring buoys. Most modern Admiralty mooring buoys are built on the trunk principle and are cylindrical in shape (Fig. 8–2). The larger sizes are divided into watertight compartments by longitudinal and transverse bulkheads. The riser pendant is led up through a central trunk in the buoy, and the bolt of the buoy shackle is passed through the end link of the riser pendant. The ship's cables are shackled directly to the buoy shackle using the securing-to-buoy shackles. If this is not possible because the buoy shackle is too large for the securing-to-buoy shackles, then both cables are shackled to the reducing links, using one link for each cable.

The size of a buoy depends on the size and length of the pendant which it supports, and also on the reserve of buoyancy required for the buoy. A reserve of buoyancy of 35 per cent is usually allowed, but this may be reduced to 25 per cent if necessary. Table 8–2, at the end of this chapter, shows the various classes of mooring buoy and the size and maximum length of pendant with which each is designed to be used in normal circumstances. There are five classes of mooring buoy but in deep water a higher classification of buoy may be used because it has to support a longer riser pendant. Two further buoys, the *X-class* and the *Monster,* are provided to permit moorings to be laid at depths greater than those for which a first-class buoy is suitable.

Mark buoys. These are used to provide permanent navigational indications, e.g. to mark a safe channel or a particular hazard. There are five basic buoy shapes which are fitted to the buoy body, namely: can, conical, spherical, pillar and spar. Details are given in NP 735, *IALA Maritime Buoyage System 'A'.*

Temporary marks. Floating temporary marks are required for many purposes, for example:

1. To mark the position of a sunken object.
2. To mark shoals, rocks and channels when surveying.
3. To mark ranges for target practice.
4. To indicate the limits of a minefield when laying or clearing mines.
5. To mark the course for a regatta.

When possible, a temporary mark buoy should be moored to a clump or to a stockless anchor, and not to an Admiralty-pattern anchor, because when sweeping round with the wind or tide the riser pendant is likely to foul the upper fluke of an Admiralty-pattern anchor and possibly trip it so that both anchor and buoy will drift away.

Small casks, pieces of wood, or spars may be used as temporary mark buoys as they fit the purpose fairly well where there is little wind or tidal stream; but if the mark or its flag is to be seen from a distance when a fresh breeze is blowing or a strong current running, something more stable is required. In the Royal Navy three types of buoy are provided for laying temporary marks; the *quick-reaction marker buoy* (page 238), the *danbuoy* which is described in Volume I, and the *standard surveying beacon* (page 239) which can carry a taller and more conspicuous mark than the danbuoy.

TYPES OF MOORING FOR SHIPS

Single-clump mooring

The simplest form of mooring (Fig. 8–3) consists of a buoy, a riser pendant and a sinker or clump. It is generally used for small craft such as harbour launches.

Two-legged swinging mooring

The lighter swinging moorings in restricted waterways may be of the two-legged type (Fig. 8–4(i)), one anchor being laid on a leg of chain cable upstream, and the other on a similar leg downstream. The type illustrated is a *resilient mooring* in which the mooring ring is always suspended above the sea bottom, and the catenaries of the two legs are weighted with lengths of chain which act as dampers during surge loads.

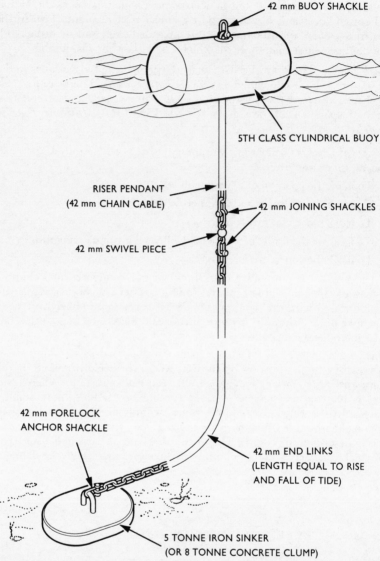

FIG. 8–3. Single mooring — a fifth-class swinging mooring for sheltered sites

Three-legged swinging mooring

The three-legged swinging mooring (Fig. 8–4(ii)) has greater holding power than the two-legged mooring, and is used generally for the heavier types of swinging mooring. Its resistance to dragging is nearly constant with the wind from any direction, but it occupies a wider area than the two-legged mooring.

Four-legged mooring

A four-legged swinging mooring (Figs. 8–1 and 8–4(iii)) is used for the heaviest types of ship. It has all the advantages of the three-legged mooring, and its four legs provide greater holding power.

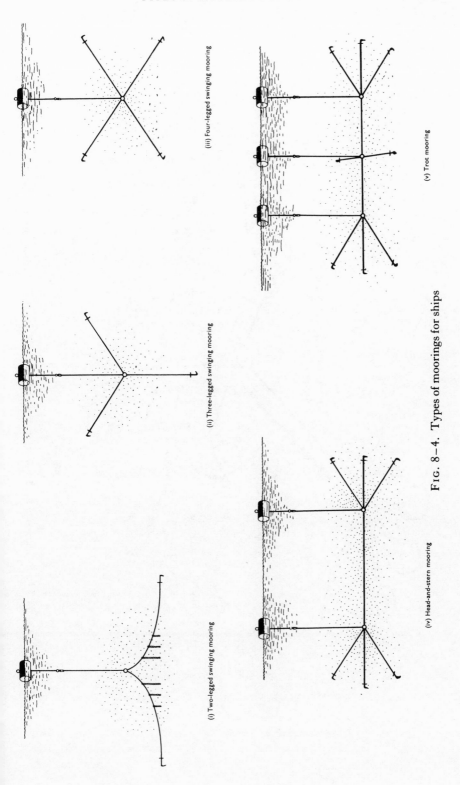

(i) Two-legged swinging mooring

(ii) Three-legged swinging mooring

(iii) Four-legged swinging mooring

(iv) Head-and-stern mooring

(v) Trot mooring

FIG. 8–4. Types of moorings for ships

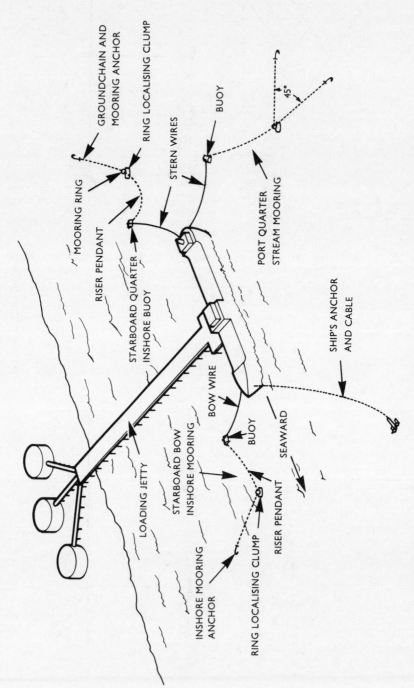

GROUNDCHAIN AND MOORING ANCHOR

RING LOCALISING CLUMP

BUOY

STERN WIRES

MOORING RING

RISER PENDANT

STARBOARD QUARTER INSHORE BUOY

PORT QUARTER STREAM MOORING

SHIP'S ANCHOR AND CABLE

BOW WIRE

BUOY

SEAWARD

LOADING JETTY

STARBOARD BOW INSHORE MOORING

INSHORE MOORING ANCHOR

RING LOCALISING CLUMP

RISER PENDANT

FIG. 8–5.   Typical alongside head-and-stern mooring with holding-on and hauling-off arrangements

Head-and-stern mooring

The type of mooring shown in Fig. 8–4(iv) is that generally used for mooring a ship head and stern. The mooring is usually laid along the direction of the tidal stream and the splayed legs are laid at an angle of 60 degrees to the fore-and-aft line of the mooring.

Trot mooring

A trot mooring is laid for securing a number of vessels in line, head to stern, and is economical in terms of space and material (Fig. 8–4(v)). As with the head-and-stern mooring, it is usually laid along the direction of the tidal stream and the splayed legs are laid at an angle of 60 degrees to the fore-and-aft line of the mooring.

Hauling-off moorings

Hauling-off moorings are usually provided in a harbour which is subject to swell conditions, for holding a ship clear of a jetty against her berthing hawsers. If the weather deteriorates and the ship is in danger of bumping heavily against the jetty or catamarans, the ship's officers should have her hauled off with the *off-fasts* (wires from the moorings) until the wind moderates.

In ports where a strong prevailing wind blows directly on to the alongside berths, hauling-off buoys, to which hawsers may be secured, are sometimes provided to enable ships to haul themselves well clear of the jetty against the wind when unberthing.

TELEPHONE CABLES AT MOORINGS

Certain mooring berths may be provided with telephone or teleprinter cables. For head-and-stern moorings the telephone cables are led from the shore along the bottom, clear of the ground tackle, to a separate buoy, sufficient scope being allowed in the cables for the tidal range. The ship's telephone cables are then joined to the shore telephone cables on this buoy.

Non-rotating telephone buoy mooring

The provision of telephone cables for a swinging mooring is complicated by the fact that the cables are liable to foul the riser pendant as the ship swings round the buoy. In some ports this difficulty is overcome by mooring the buoy with a three- or four-leg bridle to ground arms as shown in Fig. 8–6, thus preventing rotation of the buoy. The ship's cable is then shackled to links on a *spectacle-lug* which revolves around a collar fitted to the upper end of the buoy trunk. The shore telephone cable is led up through the buoy trunk and is thus clear of the mooring. The ship's telephone cable is tensioned, either as shown in Fig. 8–6 or by a patent tensioning reel fitted to the buoy, to avoid chafe by the anchor cables as the ship swings. The connection between ship and shore telephone cables is made at a connection box on the buoy which also incorporates a slip-ring unit to prevent twisting of the telephone cables. Where provision is not made at a swinging mooring to

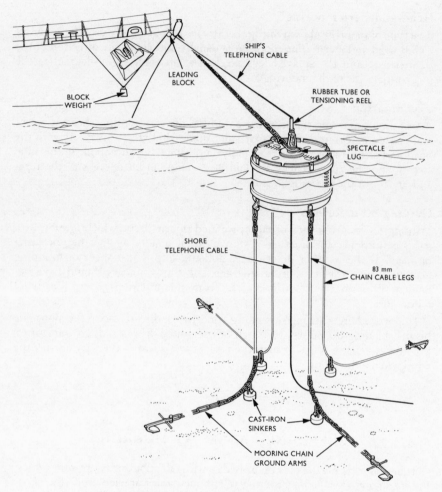

FIG. 8–6. Non-rotating telephone buoy mooring

prevent a telephone cable fouling the mooring, a watch must be set to keep it clear as the ship swings.

MISCELLANEOUS MOORINGS

Navigation mark buoy mooring

The mark buoy is moored as shown in Fig. 8–7 by means of an open-link chain bridle, a mooring ring, a swivel and an open-link chain riser pendant shackled directly to a cast-iron sinker.

Quick-reaction marker buoy

The quick-reaction marker buoy is provided to all HM ships and RFAs capable of operating helicopters, to enable them rapidly to lay a temporary mark. The buoy and its mooring are shown in Fig. 8–8.

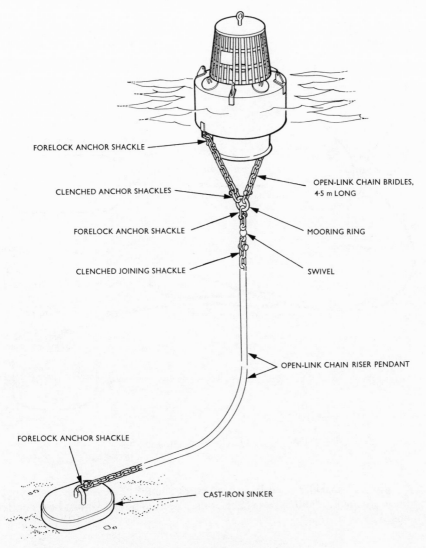

FORELOCK ANCHOR SHACKLE

CLENCHED ANCHOR SHACKLES

FORELOCK ANCHOR SHACKLE

CLENCHED JOINING SHACKLE

OPEN-LINK CHAIN BRIDLES, 4·5 m LONG

MOORING RING

SWIVEL

OPEN-LINK CHAIN RISER PENDANT

FORELOCK ANCHOR SHACKLE

CAST-IRON SINKER

FIG. 8–7. Mark buoy mooring

Standard surveying beacon and mooring

The standard surveying beacon together with a suitable mooring is shown in Figs. 8–9 and 8–10. The mooring wire should be adjusted so that its total length will be about one-third more than the greatest depth of water at the position in which it is proposed to lay the buoy, thus allowing for the effects of any tide, tidal stream or current. The buoy is designed to support (with 14 per cent reserve buoyancy) 220 kilograms, or 27.5 metres of 19-millimetre chain, and the pendant should not exceed this weight.

Modern survey ships are not able to lift beacons to a sufficient height for easy disconnection of the moorings at the lower ring. To permit separation at a low level, the 5-metre chain bridle is secured to the underside of the buoy

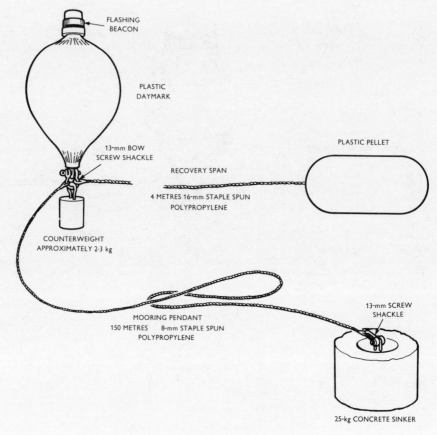

FLASHING
BEACON

PLASTIC
DAYMARK

13-mm BOW
SCREW SHACKLE

PLASTIC PELLET

RECOVERY SPAN

4 METRES 16-mm STAPLE SPUN
POLYPROPYLENE

COUNTERWEIGHT
APPROXIMATELY 2·3 kg

13-mm SCREW
SHACKLE

MOORING PENDANT
150 METRES   8-mm STAPLE SPUN
POLYPROPYLENE

25-kg CONCRETE SINKER

FIG. 8–8. Quick-reaction marker buoy

by a slip. All shackles used in beacon work should be of the forelock type; if these are not available screw shackles may be used but they must be securely moused.

CLASSIFICATION OF MOORINGS

Because of the great differences in length and displacement of ships several *classes* of moorings must be provided. Moorings are classified according to the proof load of the cable or the displacement tonnage of the ships which may safely use them. Generally speaking, *first-class* moorings are suitable for the largest vessels including large auxiliaries, *second-class* for vessels of cruiser size and small auxiliaries, *third-class* and *fourth-class* for destroyers or frigates, and *fifth-class* for other smaller ships and craft, such as mine countermeasures vessels. Classes of moorings for HM ships and auxiliary vessels are given in BR 8661, *Ministry of Defence Mooring Manual*.

A ship should not secure to a lighter class of mooring than that designed for her, but ships may use heavier swinging moorings than those specified for them, and also heavier head-and-stern moorings if the length between the

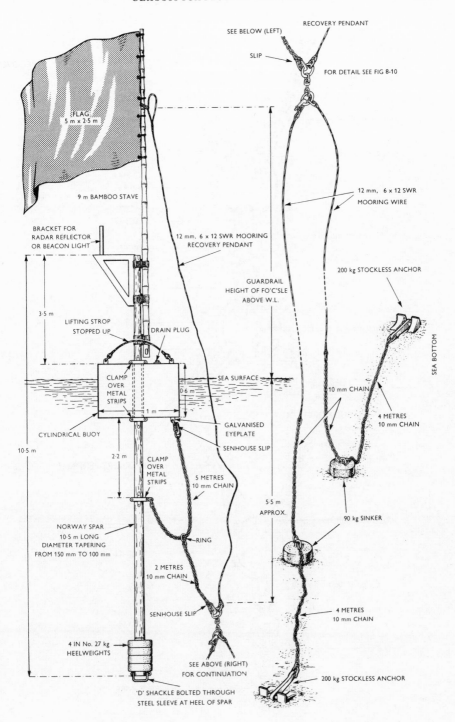

FLAG
5 m x 2·5 m

9 m BAMBOO STAVE

BRACKET FOR
RADAR REFLECTOR
OR BEACON LIGHT

3·5 m

LIFTING STROP
STOPPED UP

DRAIN PLUG

12 mm, 6 x 12 SWR MOORING
RECOVERY PENDANT

CLAMP
OVER
METAL
STRIPS

SEA SURFACE

0·6 m

1 m

CYLINDRICAL BUOY

GALVANISED
EYEPLATE

SENHOUSE SLIP

10·5 m

2·2 m

CLAMP
OVER
METAL
STRIPS

5 METRES
10 mm CHAIN

NORWAY SPAR
10·5 m LONG
DIAMETER TAPERING
FROM 150 mm TO 100 mm

RING

2 METRES
10 mm CHAIN

SENHOUSE SLIP

4 IN No. 27 kg
HEELWEIGHTS

SEE ABOVE (RIGHT)
FOR CONTINUATION

'D' SHACKLE BOLTED THROUGH
STEEL SLEEVE AT HEEL OF SPAR

RECOVERY PENDANT

SEE BELOW (LEFT)

SLIP

FOR DETAIL SEE FIG 8-10

12 mm, 6 x 12 SWR
MOORING WIRE

GUARDRAIL
HEIGHT OF FO'C'SLE
ABOVE W.L.

200 kg STOCKLESS ANCHOR

SEA BOTTOM

10 mm CHAIN

4 METRES
10 mm CHAIN

5·5 m
APPROX.

90 kg SINKER

4 METRES
10 mm CHAIN

200 kg STOCKLESS ANCHOR

FIG. 8–9. Standard surveying beacon (left) and its mooring (right)
The lengths of the mooring wires depend on the depth of water

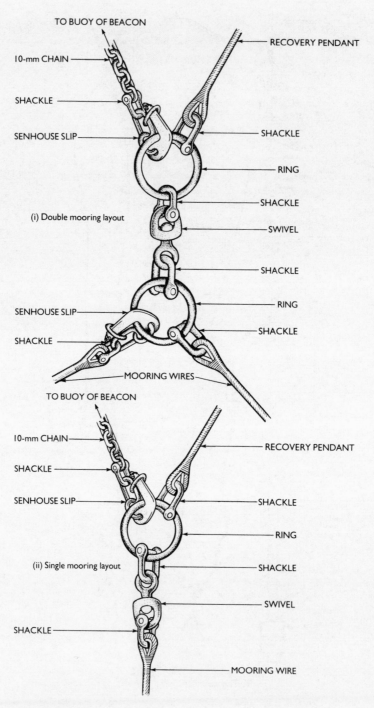

TO BUOY OF BEACON

RECOVERY PENDANT

10-mm CHAIN

SHACKLE

SENHOUSE SLIP

SHACKLE

RING

(i) Double mooring layout

SHACKLE

SWIVEL

SHACKLE

RING

SENHOUSE SLIP

SHACKLE

SHACKLE

MOORING WIRES

TO BUOY OF BEACON

10-mm CHAIN

SHACKLE

RECOVERY PENDANT

SENHOUSE SLIP

SHACKLE

RING

(ii) Single mooring layout

SHACKLE

SWIVEL

SHACKLE

MOORING WIRE

FIG. 8–10. Detail of method of securing standard surveying beacon and recovery
pendant to mooring wires of its anchors (see Fig. 8–9)

head and stern buoys is not too great. For this purpose one or two special *reducing links* are fitted to each buoy shackle of the heavier moorings to enable the securing-to-buoy shackle of a smaller ship to be joined to the buoy.

Table 8–1, at the end of this chapter, gives a list of the different classes of mooring, together with the size and material of ship's cable for which each class of mooring is suitable. The proof load of cable, which is related to its size and material, should always be the standard used when deciding whether a mooring is suitable for a particular ship, because it takes into account the maximum stresses involved at all states of loading, these usually being highest when the ship is at light-load draught owing to the large windage area she then presents.

In the last column of Table 8–1 is given the displacement of the largest ship for which each class of mooring is suitable. In determining the number of small craft which may lie abreast at any mooring, the aggregate proof load of the several cables should be the deciding factor. In sheltered waters, the number of ships permitted to lie abreast in a head-and-stern mooring may be calculated on a displacement basis, by adding to the displacement of the largest ship one-half the displacement of each of the other ships. This rule is to be applied at the discretion of local mooring officers, who should bear in mind that, at reduced displacements, ships present increased windage area. Proof load of cable is more reliable than displacement tonnage when determining the class of mooring because the proof load of a ship's cable is selected with due regard to her windage area.

HOLDING POWER OF MOORINGS

The forces acting on a ship riding at a mooring are:

1. A steady force caused by the tidal stream acting on the underwater part of the hull.
2. The wind force on the above-water surface of the hull, which may be steady or fluctuating dependent on whether the wind is steady or gusting.
3. The sudden snatch loading of the cable caused by the motion of the ship in the waves.

Some idea of the pull exerted on a mooring is given by the estimated forces developed on a destroyer, for example a head wind of 30 knots creates a pull of about 2·5 tonnes and an ahead tidal stream of 5 knots creates a pull of about 4 tonnes. The wind and tidal forces are approximately proportional to the square of the speed, i.e. if the speed is doubled the force increases by a factor of 4. In a wind of 60 knots gusting up to 85 knots the maximum transient force created would be of the order of 20 tonnes. To withstand these forces the class of ship quoted is fitted with 48-millimetre chain cable which is tested to a proof load of 92 tonnes.

The table overleaf gives estimates of the pulls which ships may be expected to exert on their moorings when acted upon by a 55-knot steady wind and a 4-knot tidal stream. It is assumed that the wind and tide act fore-and-aft along the ship.

It will be seen from the information in the table that when a ship is moored or anchored in an exceptionally strong current it is advisable to trail the propellers.

Type of Ship	Ahead Wind Resistance (Wind speed 55 knots)	Ahead Tide Resistance (Tidal speed 4 knots)	
		Hull	Locked Propellers
	tonnes	*tonnes*	*tonnes*
Aircraft carrier (16 500 tonnes)	30.0	2.9	6.0
Assault ship (12 000 tonnes)	24.0	2.3	3.2
Destroyer (5000 tonnes)	8.4	2.7	4.2
Frigate (3000 tonnes)	7.7	0.8	2.9

Mooring anchors must be well buried in the sea bed if they are to be effective, and the length of the ground arms must be sufficient to ensure that the pull on the anchor will be horizontal in all conditions of service, otherwise the mooring may drag. The most commonly used type of anchor is the Admiralty Mooring Type 7 (AM 7) anchor illustrated in Fig. 8–2.

The holding pull of an anchor depends, to a large extent, on its weight and the area of the flukes. It is only possible to obtain a high holding pull by forcing the anchor to penetrate deeply into the sea bed. The provision of an anchor of such capability has been the object of much research which resulted in the introduction of the Admiralty Mooring Type 12 (AM 12) anchor. This anchor will withstand a horizontal pull of 14.7 times its own weight, and the whole anchor will penetrate the sea bed after being pulled horizontally a distance of only one shank-length.

In the permanent mooring anchor with a fixed fluke and stabilising stock, it is possible to arrange the fluke below the shank, and separated from it by a certain optimum distance. In this way the fluke digs into the subsoil and develops sufficient pull to drag the shank in also. Consequently, the whole of the anchor contributes towards the holding pull, rather than just the fluke as in earlier designs. The provision of a stock prevents the anchor turning over under heavy load.

The larger the anchor the more strongly must it be constructed to withstand the stresses to which it may be subjected. The approximate holding powers, in reasonably good holding ground, of mooring anchors in terms of their weights are given in Table 8–4, on page 249. It should be realised that the weight of the mooring chain on the sea bed also contributes to the holding power of the mooring.

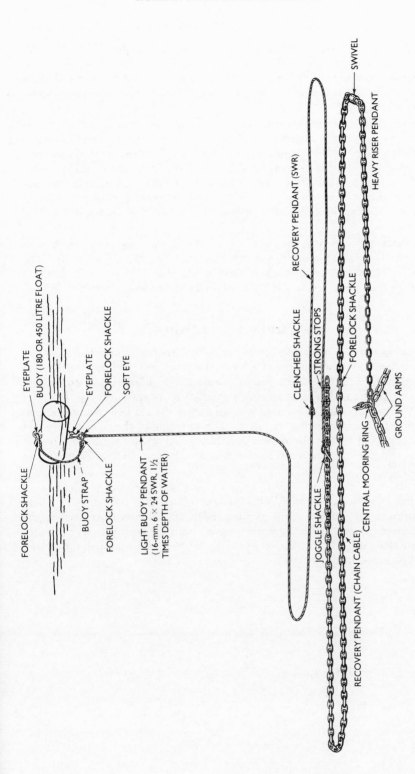

Fig. 8–11. Typical swinging mooring fitted for swamping

MAINTENANCE OF MOORINGS

Moorings exposed to strong tidal streams and rough weather naturally suffer more wear and tear than those in tideless waters. Corrosion, however, particularly in estuaries and in tropical harbours, can cause as much reduction in the weight of the cables as does the wear and tear caused by tidal streams and weather.

Ministry of Defence moorings are maintained by a sequence of *interim inspections* and *partial raisings*. An interim inspection consists of examination and maintenance of those components which can be lifted clear of the water without disturbing the ground tackle. A partial raising comprises the work necessary to gain access to the foot of the riser pendant and the mooring ring together with at least one of the anchors and its mooring chain. The other anchors and mooring chain are examined sequentially at subsequent partial raisings.

The intervals at which maintenance is carried out depend on the class of mooring; the lighter moorings being examined the more frequently. The sequence of maintenance work is shown in Table 8–5 on page 250 and further details are given in BR 8661, *Ministry of Defence Moorings Manual*.

SWAMPING A MOORING

A mooring which is used infrequently may be *swamped* to avoid unnecessary wear. Swamping of a mooring is achieved by removing the buoy shackle and the buoy. The riser pendant is then connected to a length of *swamp wire* (recovery pendant) which has a sinker shackled to its opposite end. The riser pendant, swamp wire and sinker are laid out on the sea bed in a convenient direction for recovery when required. The direction of the swamp wire and sinker are fixed accurately by bearings, horizontal sextant angles and transit marks, and this information is recorded in the Mooring History Sheet (Form D.233).

An alternative method of swamping is to fit a *swamp barrel* or float instead of a sinker to the swamp wire. This method is illustrated in Fig. 8–11 where a composite recovery pendant of wire and chain cable is connected to the heavy riser pendant. When the mooring is swamped both the riser pendant and the chain cable of the recovery pendant lie on the bottom with the swamp barrel watching over them.

TABLE 8-1.   CLASSES OF MOORINGS

CLASS OF MOORING	CABLE SIZE OF LARGEST ACCEPTABLE SHIP			MAXIMUM ACCEPTABLE FULLY-LOADED DISPLACEMENT
	GRADE 1	GRADE 2	GRADE 3	
	mm	*mm*	*mm*	*tonnes*
1st (4-leg) 1st (4-leg, telephone)	95	78	66	50 800
1st (3-leg) 1st (3-leg, resilient)	90	73	62	40 650
2nd (3-leg)	70	58	48	16 260
3rd (3-leg) 3rd (3-leg, resilient)	60	50	42	8 250
4th (3-leg) 4th (3-leg, resilient)	54	44	38	4 500
5th (3-leg) 5th (Sinker)	34	28	24	800

Notes:

(i) Particulars of anchor and chain cable outfits are given in BR 367(2), *Anchors, Chain Cable and Associated Equipment — Allowances.* For mooring purposes of HM ships and auxiliaries, forged steel cable is considered as Grade 2 and aluminium bronze cable as Grade 1.

(ii) First-class swinging moorings cannot accept any ship fitted with cable of size 28 millimetres and below, and the non-rotating telephone buoy mooring cannot accept any ship fitted with cable of size 38 millimetres and below, because the securing-to-buoy shackles are too small to pass over the reducing links or the links of the spectacle lug.

R

TABLE 8–2.   DIMENSIONS AND RESERVE BUOYANCY OF MOORING BUOYS

BUOY (CYLINDRICAL)			CLASS OF MOORING	CHAIN CABLE PENDANT		
CLASS (Note (i))	LENGTH	DIAMETER		SIZE	RESERVE BUOYANCY (Note (ii))	
					35%	25%
	m	m		mm	m	m
X-Class (4)	5.18	2.82	1st	102	61.87	72.24
			2nd	90	84.43	98.15
Monster (4)	4.88	2.44	1st	102	41.45	48.77
			2nd	90	57.61	67.06
First (4)	4.47	2.44	1st	102	37.49	43.89
			2nd	90	52.12	57.91
Second (4)	4.01	2.29	1st	102	28.04	32.92
			2nd	90	39.62	46.33
			3rd	76	56.08	65.53
Third (4)	3.51	1.98	3rd	76	31.03	36.58
			4th	66	48.77	56.69
Fourth (4)	2.90	1.68	4th	66	25.30	29.57
			5th (Exposed sites)	42	69.80	81.08
Fifth (2)	2.13	1.22	5th	42	21.03	24.38

Notes:

(i) The number of compartments in each class of cylindrical buoy is shown in brackets.

(ii) The reserve buoyancy includes 6.7 metres of equivalent-size end links and swivel.

TABLE 8–3.   FORGED STEEL RISER PENDANTS

Dimensions in millimetres

CLASS OF MOORING	NEW SIZE	WORN LIMITS		
		COMMON LINK	INTER-MEDIATE LINK	END LINK
1st (4-leg)	102	90	95	106
1st (3-leg)	102	83	90	95
2nd	90	70	75	84
1st (4-leg, telephone)	83	76	81	92
3rd	76	60	65	73
4th	66	52	57	64
5th	42	35	38	43

TABLE 8–4.   PERMANENT MOORING ANCHORS

TYPE OF ANCHOR	REMARKS	WEIGHT OF ANCHOR	MAXIMUM HOLDING PULL AS FACTOR OF ANCHOR WEIGHT
		tonnes	
Admiralty Mooring Type 7 (AM 7)	Needs more care in laying than the pick type. If practicable, it should be dragged into the bed after laying, to improve its hold	1.2 1.8 3.7 4.9 6.1 8.5 9.7	5.4
Admiralty Mooring Type 12 (AM 12)	Improved design, high efficiency anchor, permitting a reduction in weight. When dragged, it will bury itself in one shank-length	6.0	14.7

TABLE 8-5. MAINTENANCE OF MOORINGS

CLASS OF MOORING	INTERIM INSPECTION	PARTIAL RAISING
1st and 2nd	Biennial	7-year cycles
3rd	Biennial	5-year cycles
4th	18 months	3-year cycles
5th	No interim inspection	2-year cycles
1st (4-leg, telephone)	—	Individual legs are examined in sequence at annual intervals, when one leg of chain cable together with one length of mooring chain is raised. The remainder of the mooring chain and anchor are raised at alternate examinations of that leg (i.e. every 8 years).
Floating Dock	—	A sample leg is partially raised annually. When the dock is away for refit all legs are partially raised.
Navigation Buoy	Coincident with annual changing of the buoy	2 years

PART III

SHIP ORGANISATION

CHAPTER 9

Officer of the Watch in Harbour

'Every officer and other person, not being either the Commanding Officer or the Commanding Officer for the time being or the Executive Officer, is to be subordinate to the Officer of the Watch, whatever may be his rank, in regard to the performance of the duties with which the Officer of the Watch is charged.'

This declaration from BR 31, *The Queen's Regulations for the Royal Navy,* defines the status of the Officer of the Watch and signifies the importance of his position and responsibility to any officer undertaking this duty. In a large warship in harbour an officer is normally nominated for each watch, but on occasions when there are very few officers available — and generally in small ships — it is the custom to nominate an Officer of the Day who is on duty for 24 hours. An Officer of the Day has the same status and responsibilities generally as an Officer of the Watch.

RESPONSIBILITIES

Officers should be familiar with all the regulations concerning the Officer of the Watch and should have a thorough knowledge of the Captain's and the Ship's Standing Orders. In this chapter some elaboration and explanation of the regulations are given for the benefit of inexperienced watchkeepers in harbour. The responsibilities of the Officer of the Watch at sea are treated in a similar manner in Chapter 11.

In harbour the Officer of the Watch is responsible for the following:

The safety of the ship. This includes her safety from fire and collision; and her remaining safely at rest in her berth.

The safety of the ship's company. This refers mainly to the safety of all men in exposed positions and aloft; of all boats' crews, and passengers embarking in, disembarking from, or under way in, boats; and of men over the side or bathing.

Protection of certain parts of the ship's equipment, such as brows, ladders and awnings.

The outward appearance of the ship and her boats.

The ship's ceremonial and marks of respect to be paid and received.

The orderly conduct of all on board: a responsibility normally exercised through, or with the help of, the Regulating staff.

Supervision of the ship's routine and the organisation of all boat trips.

The safe embarkation of ammunition, fuel, stores and provisions.

Instruction of the gangway staff in their duties and the keeping of the prescribed records and books.

Since ships and circumstances differ so much, the notes given in this chapter must not be considered as complete. An Officer of the Watch must be prepared to act on his own initiative, keeping in view his overall responsibility for the safety of the ship. If in doubt, however, he should not hesitate to ask the advice of his seniors, such as the Duty Commanding Officer, the Executive Officer or, if necessary, the Captain.

GANGWAY STAFF

Composition

The watchkeepers who man the gangway, run the routine and assist the Officer of the Watch are collectively known as the *gangway staff*. The composition of the staff depends on the type of ship and the time of day. For example, in a large warship, the gangway staff would probably comprise a Midshipman, a Quartermaster and a Boatswain's Mate. Some large warships also have a Corporal of the Gangway if a Royal Marines detachment is borne.

In a small ship, such as a frigate, there will usually be only a Quartermaster and Boatswain's Mate, and they will keep watch both by night and by day.

Badges of office

The Officer of the Watch wears a sword belt and carries a telescope; the Midshipman of the Watch carries a telescope; and the Quartermaster and Boatswain's Mate each wear a boatswain's call and chain. In addition the Quartermaster wears a naval patrol armlet round the cuff of his left sleeve. The object of these tokens is to make the staff instantly recognisable wherever they may be.

Duties

The staff should be alert and smart at all times, and never be allowed to lounge or chat to bystanders. Their most important task is to keep watch, that is, constantly to observe what is going on in the ship and her vicinity so that they will be the first to see anything amiss or requiring attention. In addition each member has certain specific duties which can be summarised as follows.

The Midshipman of the Watch (or Second Officer of the Watch) should understudy the Officer of the Watch and deputise for him when necessary. It is usual to delegate to him the running of the ship's routine and the boat routine, and he should always write up the Ship's Log and generally supervise the remainder of the gangway staff. In small ships the routine is usually left to be worked by the ship's company on time without continual broadcast reminders. For example, a coxswain will get his boat ready and report at the correct time to the Officer of the Watch for a routine trip without his boat being called away.

The Quartermaster is deputy to the Midshipman of the Watch and Officer of the Watch. He assists them as necessary and acts as required when, for example, the Officer of the Day is not on deck, or when there is no Midshipman. He reads the barometer, the hygrometer and the sea temperature at the required times, strikes the ship's bell when necessary (usually only for the ceremony of Colours), and pipes any announcements over the broadcast system. He is in general charge of the gangways and their accommodation ladders or brows, and should supervise the Boatswain's Mate.

The Boatswain's Mate assists the Quartermaster with his duties, calls reliefs, and deputises for him if he is absent going the rounds. If a midship gangway is open as well as an after one he is usually placed in charge of the midship ladder or brow.

Corporal of the Gangway. The Corporal of the Gangway is normally a corporal in the Royal Marines. If none are borne, his duties are carried out partly by the Quartermaster and partly by the ship's Regulating staff. He keeps a security check on all incoming and outgoing parcels and packages to ensure that there is no illicit trafficking in dutiable goods or government property. He enters the names of all ratings proceeding on, or returning from, temporary duty ashore or in other ships in the *Gangway Duty Book*. He records in the *Gangway Wine Book* particulars of all wines, spirits, beer and tobacco received on board, for whatever mess or person, and also any disembarked. He takes charge of all correspondence other than Post Office mail and sees that it is delivered. He should go the rounds between decks at least once every hour in each watch during the night, and enter the results in the *Night Rounds Book*.

Equipment

The gangway staff have a clock and a desk that are situated normally in a small compartment under cover. In or near this place, called the Quartermaster's Lobby, the following gear should be kept and regularly mustered.

Binoculars
Large-scale chart of the harbour
Hand lead-and-line
Sea thermometer
Aldis lamp or portable damage-control lamp
One or two electric torches with spare batteries
Whistle
About 35 metres of 16-millimetre cordage
Cleaning gear
Small fender
Inflatable lifejacket (for rescue)
Lifebuoy and line (for rescue)

Daily Orders
A copy of the Daily Harbour Routine
Gangway Wine, Gangway Duty and Night Rounds Books
Watertight Integrity Log
Captain's Standing Orders
Ship's Standing Orders
Ship's Log
Any temporary orders concerning the OOW
Signal Log
Officers' Ashore/On-board Tally
Rough notebook

Dress

The dress regulations for dutymen are published in the *Appendix to the Navy List*. The details of dress to be worn on different occasions are, however, normally promulgated in the orders for the area.

Records — Ship's Log

In addition to the *Watertight Integrity Log* (see page 259) and the books kept by the Corporal of the Gangway (already mentioned), the Officer of the

Watch is responsible for the correct writing up of the Ship's Log. Instructions for the compilation of the log are given inside its front cover. At the end of his watch the Officer of the Watch inspects the log to make sure that it has been properly completed, and initials it when satisfied.

TAKING OVER A WATCH

The Officer of the Watch should come on deck in good time to receive the turn-over before his watch begins, and should obtain the following information from his predecessor.

Safety of the Ship

The scope of cable to which the ship is riding, whether she is at single anchor, moored or made fast to a buoy.

If at single anchor, the condition of the second anchor (i.e. if it is ready for letting go or not).

If the ship is at anchor or moored, the anchor bearings.

The state of the berthing hawsers if alongside, and any adjustment required because of wind or tide.

The NBCD State of Readiness and Watertight Condition of the ship.

The state of the Hazard Stateboard and the Important Keyboard.

Notice for power on the main propulsion machinery.

Any programme for embarkation or disembarkation of ammunition, fuel, stores or provisions; the times at which any auxiliaries or lighters are expected alongside; or, if alongside, when they are expected to leave.

Employment of Boats and Ship's Company

Which boats are lowered, and if at the ship, how made fast; if away from the ship, what orders they have been given, and whether they are under sail.

The employment of the hands, what routine is in force; what men, if any, are working over the side or aloft; and which watch, or part of the watch, is on duty.

Discipline

State of men under punishment and in cells; any men absent over leave, and any investigation pending.

Various

The state of ladders, brows and their safety nets if rigged, and any information about the outward appearance of the ship.

The whereabouts of the Captain and the Executive Officer or, if they are not on board, whoever is acting as Commanding Officer; any special instructions in force for the Officer of the Watch.

Any expected movements of ships in the harbour.

The berths of other warships in harbour, particularly flagships.

The state of the weather and a forecast, if available.

REPORTS TO CAPTAIN

As already remarked, the Officer of the Watch should not hesitate to consult his senior officers if in doubt; and if he considers the safety of the ship to be threatened he should inform the Captain, or in his absence the Duty Commanding Officer, immediately. Most Captains require in addition that the Officer of the Watch should report to them on the following occasions.

1. Five minutes before hoisting and lowering the colours.
2. On any marked deterioration in the visibility or the weather.
3. On the detection of any serious offences, for example violence, indecency or the misuse of drugs.
4. On the arrival or imminent departure of a warship.
5. On sighting a boat under way carrying a Flag officer with his flag flying.
6. On the approach of a boat carrying a Captain.
7. If anything else of particular interest occurs.

SAFETY OF THE SHIP

Emergencies

At sea the Emergency Stations procedure is used to initiate action to deal with emergencies, but in harbour this procedure is generally inappropriate because of the number of men who could be ashore. The duty part of the watch is used as the first line of defence against any harbour emergency. If this number of hands is insufficient a muster of all the non-duty personnel on board may be necessary to ensure they are accounted for and to provide further hands to deal with the emergency. This action is initiated by use of the main broadcast alarm followed by the pipe 'Emergency! Emergency! Clear lower deck' which is to be made by the Officer of the Watch or the senior officer on board. The pipe should state the position at which the hands are to muster and include any additional orders or information which will clarify the situation.

Ship's Standing Orders should specify the action to be taken, which includes:

1. Duty part of the watch to remain closed up to deal with the emergency.
2. Hands engaged in first-aid measures to combat the hazard are to continue their task until properly relieved.
3. Remainder of the hands to muster at the stated position. They should take warm clothing, especially at night, but they should not attempt to return to the messdecks to obtain extra clothing.
4. First-aid and damage-control personnel should be mustered apart from the remainder of the ship's company, ready to be detailed to support the duty part of the watch.

5. Mustering of the hands against the master list of the ship's company, taking account of the duty part of the watch and those shown to be ashore.

The allocation of extra hands is co-ordinated by the officer or senior rating in charge at the muster point and the Officer of the Watch remains in charge of the situation until relieved.

Fire

The organisation for firefighting is based on the hands available in the duty part of the watch. This is described in Volume II, Chapter 2, and further information is available in BR 2170, *Ship NBCD Manual*.

The duty part of the watch should be mustered and reported to the Officer of the Watch when they begin their turn of duty — usually at 1700, but on Saturdays and Sundays and make-and-mends usually at 1230. This is an important muster which enables the Officer of the Watch to ensure that all men are available, and at which the firefighting groups should be detailed and men nominated for specific tasks. Whenever a ship is in a dockyard a fire exercise should be conducted daily after the dockyard workmen have finished work for the day.

If a fire occurs when the ship is lying alongside, the local-authority fire brigade, the shore authorities and adjacent ships must be informed immediately, to ensure that assistance will be available should the fire spread or get out of hand.

Whenever dockyard workmen have been working between decks, the spaces in which they have been working should be inspected immediately after they have left the ship, and again half an hour afterwards.

The Officer of the Watch should be familiar with the regulations concerning the embarkation and disembarkation of dangerous materials and with the ship's organisation for putting them into effect. The following are the principal precautions against fire in these circumstances:

Whenever any vessel carrying explosives or flammable cargo berths alongside, any scuttles abreast her should be closed, the ship's company should be warned, and no smoking should be allowed on the upper deck on the side against which she is berthed. If a lighter is to remain alongside after work in her is finished for the day, she should be inspected and then her hatches or hatchboards should be replaced, covered and battened down.

Whenever oil fuel or explosives are being embarked or disembarked, sentries should be posted and certain radar and radio transmissions should be restricted. In the event of a thunderstorm the embarkation or disembarkation of explosives, oil fuel and gasoline must be stopped well before the storm reaches the ship and not be resumed until it has passed.

Collision

The most important precaution against damage resulting from collision is to keep strict control over the watertight integrity of the ship, and the responsibility for this in harbour is allotted normally to the Officer of the Watch. In certain large ships, however, control in harbour may be exercised from the NBCD headquarters, which in this case is kept manned permanently, both at sea and in harbour. The Officer of the Watch should exercise control in accordance with the NBCD State of Readiness and Watertight Condition in force. The system is described generally in Volume I, while details may be found in BR 2170, *Ship NBCD Manual*.

The *NBCD Door and Hatch Board* is used for recording the overall Watertight Condition of the ship. In large ships it is fixed in the NBCD headquarters, but in small ships it is portable, so that it can be placed where it can be supervised conveniently by the Officer of the Watch. A system of 'MAY BE LEFT OPEN' discs, of which a specified number are allocated to the forward and after sections of the ship, used in conjunction with the *Watertight Integrity Log* ensure that watertight integrity is maintained even if all the discs are issued. The Quartermaster is normally authorised to issue the discs, recording their movement in the Watertight Integrity Log. The Officer of the Watch should see that both the board and the log are kept scrupulously up to date.

If a collision appears imminent, the Officer of the Watch should pipe 'Emergency! Emergency! Clear lower deck', followed by 'Close all red openings'.

As a routine precaution at night, the watertight openings are usually brought to Condition Yankee when the messdecks and flats are cleared up for rounds, and revert to the normal day Condition when the hands turn to in the morning. If visibility deteriorates badly at any time, the same Condition (Y) should be ordered and the fog signal should be started.

Storm and tide

At anchor. In a storm or in an exceptionally strong tidal stream or current the chief danger is that of dragging the anchors and drifting on to a lee shore or into another ship. When a gale is imminent the normal precautions are: to put the main propulsion machinery at immediate notice; to clear away the anchors and cables ready for veering cable and for dropping a second anchor; and to set an anchor watch.

To check quickly if the ship's anchor is dragging, watch the compass bearing of any conspicuous object near the beam: if it draws forward this may indicate that the ship is dragging.

A more accurate method is as follows. Plot the anchor bearings (from the Ship's Log) on the largest-scale chart of the harbour. The fix obtained gives the position of the anchor when it was let go. From this point describe a circle of radius equal to the amount of cable veered plus the stem-to-standard distance. Fix the ship from the bridge and, if the position obtained lies outside the circle described, the ship must have dragged her anchor.

It is obvious that, if the anchor bearings were obtained from shore marks at short ranges, the actual bearings of these marks from the bridge when lying at the full scope of the cable will differ considerably from the original anchor bearings. This difference in itself does not necessarily mean that the ship has dragged but, if the shore marks are close, there may be little sea room in which to drag.

The first precaution to take is to veer more cable, so as to ensure that the cable is exerting a horizontal pull on the anchor. Further action is described on pages 466–467.

Alongside. When alongside, the possible dangers arise from the vertical movement caused by the tide and from the vertical and horizontal to-and-fro movements caused by large waves entering the harbour (a scend). In some ports it is essential to keep a continual watch on the berthing hawsers and to adjust them from time to time so as to ensure that each is bearing an even strain. Remember that the maximum rate of vertical movement occurs in the third and fourth hours for a tide of six-hour interval. If a scend builds up it may be necessary to double up some of the berthing hawsers, or to put out spring hawsers.

Watch the brows carefully also. You may have to adjust their securing arrangements at intervals. If the ship is moving in the berth she may cause the shore ends of the brows to roll about on the jetty. If this happens see that people approaching the brows from ashore are warned of, and protected against, possible danger.

Danger from radio and radar aerials

Dangers from radio and radar aerials are collectively known as *radio hazards*. They may affect men aloft, or arise from risk of fire when dangerous materials are being embarked, disembarked, or moved about on deck. The precautions needed are dealt with on pages 262–3.

SECURITY OF THE SHIP

Unauthorised entry and trafficking

The Officer of the Watch is responsible that no unauthorised person enters or leaves the ship, and that no dutiable goods enter or leave the ship by any method whatsoever except under the control of the Regulating staff, and that no illicit trafficking is carried on over the ship's side. In some foreign harbours the arrival of a warship may attract a considerable number of undesirable traders, and it may be necessary to keep unwanted boats clear of the ship and to prevent people clambering up the cable.

No gangway should ever be left unattended and no visitor should be allowed farther than the gangway until his credentials have been checked. If in doubt, and also for politeness, see that a visitor is escorted to the person whom he wishes to see on board.

It may be necessary at night to close one or more gangways. To close an accommodation ladder it is hoisted and the guardrails are set up; a brow can be closed by criss-crossing it with heaving lines.

Keys

Ship's keys are divided into four main categories: *Security Keys, Important/Attractive Keys, Armament Keys* and *General Keys*. All locks in a ship are provided with two keys, the control of which depends on their category and the size of ship. One key is for everyday use and the other is a duplicate for use in emergency.

Security Keys include those to containers used for the stowage of classified documents and to compartments in which classified equipment or stores are kept without the further protection of security containers within the compartments.

Important/Attractive Keys control the access to such compartments as the spirit store, Operations Room, certain store rooms, and to aircraft and boat fuelling arrangements.

Armament Keys include those to all compartments in which explosives, projectiles and weapons are stored or handled, together with their flooding, spraying, lighting and ventilation arrangements, and the keys to small-arms stowages and ready-use ammunition lockers.

General Keys comprise the remaining keys not covered in the above categories.

Custody, issue and records of keys

Security Keys are controlled by the same method in all ships. Those for containers of classified documents are kept in a combination-lock key box; those for compartments are kept in a security container provided for the Officer of the Watch. The duplicates are kept in secure containers separate from the originals. The issue of these keys is restricted and instructions for their handling are contained in the Captain's Standing Orders.

Important/Attractive, Armament and General Keys are kept in key cabinets or on keyboards, both of which are lockable and specially designed to suit the ship. Wherever possible General Keys are permanently issued to departments and held on departmental keyboards.

In large ships and those with a Ship Control Centre (SCC) the main key cabinet is sited in HQ1 or the SCC and is under the charge of the watchkeeper who issues the keys. The duplicate-key cabinet, which contains all duplicate keys in these categories, is sited in a widely separated position such as outside the Captain's cabin or in HQ2.

In smaller ships the Important/Attractive and Armament Keys are kept on a lockable *Important Keyboard,* and any General Keys not issued to departments are kept on a *General Keyboard.* These two keyboards are normally sited in a secure place such as the vicinity of the Wardroom or Captain's cabin but the Important Keyboard may be portable so that it can be secured in a more suitable position when the ship is at sea. The key to the Important Keyboard is held by the Officer of the Watch who issues the keys.

Issues and records. Important/Attractive Keys are issued only to authorised persons by signature in the *Important Key Book* or by a key tally system; similarly, Armament Keys are issued only to authorised persons against a signature in the *Explosives Log.* The persons authorised to draw Armament Keys are listed by name in the Explosives Log.

At the end of each watch the Officer of the Watch should examine the Explosives Log to ascertain whether:

1. The records of the issue of keys agree with the state of the keyboard.

2. The records of magazine rounds during his watch have been entered and signed for.

3. The records of magazine temperatures have been entered during his watch.

He should sign the log when he is satisfied that it has been correctly kept. If the log has been incorrectly kept he should inform his relief, who should take the necessary action to have the log completed correctly. In small ships the Officer of the Day examines and signs the Explosives Log when he is relieved of his duties.

Night rounds

In order to ensure the safety of the ship and to prevent irregularities and possible acts of sabotage, the Officer of the Watch or Day and one of his staff should go the rounds between decks, and also on the upper deck, from time to time during the night watches. Rounds should be carried out about once every hour but never at fixed times or over fixed routes. In a large warship it is customary for the Corporal of the Gangway to go the rounds; however, in some large ships rounds are carried out by damage-control patrols. The times of starting and finishing the rounds are entered in the *Night Rounds Book*; this book is signed by the Officer of the Watch on completion of his watch. It is important that, while rounds are in progress, one of the staff remains on deck to keep watch by the gangway.

SAFETY OF MEN

Safety of men working over the side

Whenever men are working over the ship's side — for example, the side party touching up the boot-topping or the hands painting ship — it may be necessary to hoist the International Code signal RY to give warning to approaching craft. Vessels and craft should proceed at slow speed when passing close to the ship.

Whenever divers are at work, either from the ship's side or from a nearby boat under the ship's control, the ship must display the appropriate lights and shapes prescribed by the International Regulations for Preventing Collisions at Sea (Rule 27(b)) and the International Code flag A must be hoisted by day. At night the ship must be prepared to signal the letter U (. . — in Morse code) when approached by other vessels, and by day and by night be prepared to make a warning signal by light or sound to any approaching vessel if it has not taken the appropriate action. The diving boat displays International Code flag A by day when approached by other vessels or craft, and at night displays an all-round white light. Additionally, any signals required by local orders must also be used.

In a strong tideway no man should be allowed over the ship's side without the Officer of the Watch's permission, and then only if he is wearing a lifejacket and has round him a strong lifeline (*not* a heaving line) which is tended inboard.

Radio hazards

Danger to men aloft, from radio transmissions or from the rotation of radar aerials, may arise from three causes.

1. Direct exposure at very close range to radar transmissions; this can produce internal heating of body tissues.

2. Although electric shock may not occur, sparks and slight burning may produce physical shock sufficient to cause a man to fall.

3. The unexpected rotation of a radar aerial that has previously been stationary.

There is also the risk of ignition of explosive or flammable substances by radio transmissions, such as when fuelling or arming aircraft.

A practical balance must be struck between real dangers and the operational need to transmit. In some cases work aloft may be quite safe while transmission is taking place, particularly for maintenance ratings who are aware of the dangers.

Radio transmissions and aerial rotation are normally restricted in the following circumstances:

1. When men are aloft.

2. When the ship is dressed overall.

3. When explosives are being embarked or disembarked, or handled on deck.

4. When flammable stores or fuels are being embarked or disembarked, or handled on deck.

Restriction is controlled by the Officer of the Watch by means of the ship's *Hazard Stateboard*. To prevent the occurrence of hazards, *safe-to-transmit* and *safe-to-rotate* keys or devices are incorporated in the circuits of the appropriate equipments; removal of a key or device renders that hazardous function inoperative. In practice, when the keys or devices are removed they are placed on the stateboard and the Officer of the Watch is thus aware that transmission and/or rotation is impossible. The Hazard Stateboard is of a standard design adapted to suit the ship's particular outfit of equipment. It shows which devices should be on the board to cater for any given condition — say, man aloft on the mainmast. The Officer of the Watch must see that no man goes aloft, or incurs a hazard, without first obtaining his permission and placing the appropriate safety devices on the stateboard. The particular procedure for the ship is stated on a *Procedural Guide* which is posted on the inside of the stateboard door. Also shown is a side elevation of the ship identifying the various potential sources of hazard. The Captain may authorise certain officers to relax precautions, in consultation with the Officer of the Watch, for essential operation or maintenance of equipment in special circumstances.

Where two or more ships are in close proximity, e.g. berthed alongside each other, the Officer of the Watch should not give permission for any operations requiring restrictions until he is sure that the necessary precautions have been taken in the ships close aboard.

Safety harness

Men working aloft or in any other similar hazardous position should wear safety harnesses properly secured as described in Volume I, Chapter 4.

S

Hands to bathe

Whenever hands are piped to bathe alongside the ship, a boat equipped with a lifebuoy attached to a lifeline should always be in attendance to go to the assistance of any bather in difficulty. The boat should be stationed about 50 metres from the ship to mark the outer limit of the bathing area. Any restrictions specified on the Hazard Stateboard should be imposed by the Officer of the Watch. Bathing should be under the supervision of an officer, and should be allowed only on one side of the ship; in tropical waters a good lookout should be kept for sharks.

Never allow bathers to get down-tide, or to leeward in a strong wind, or to swim outside the bathing area. If there is a swell, jumping ladders and scramble nets for bathers to climb on board should be rigged. The heads and gash chutes on the side on which bathing is to take place should be closed ten minutes before the hands are piped to bathe.

Libertymen

The Officer of the Watch should always supervise the embarkation and disembarkation of libertymen at the gangway, maintain strict silence among them both on board and in the boat while it is alongside, and, having regard to the state of the weather and the experience of the coxswain, should not allow any boat to be overloaded. It is the custom for senior ratings to enter or leave a boat before junior ratings. No one should be allowed to rest his arm or hand on the gunwale of an open boat, because of the danger of having it crushed. After sunset a light should be rigged at the gangway to illuminate the accommodation ladder and any boat alongside.

When many libertymen are landed an officer may be sent with a pier patrol to act as a piermaster at the landing place and ensure the safe embarkation of libertymen in their boats.

When a boat returns to the ship with libertymen, particularly after dark, one of the gangway staff should be stationed on the lower platform of the accommodation ladder to assist men getting out of the boat when necessary. A careful watch should be kept for men who appear incapable of getting out of the boat unaided; such men, and any who are utterly incapable, should be got out last of all and with lifelines round them.

Whenever a brow is rigged, either between ships or from ship to shore, it must have a safety net secured beneath it so that the centre of the net is slightly lower than the edges. When the ship is alongside, the approaches to the jetty end of the brows should be kept clear of obstacles, and at night they should be well illuminated. When the ship is in dock the dockside guardrails should always be in place, and at night the route to the brow should be kept clear and well lit.

BOATS

Boat routine

The Officer of the Watch is expected to see that boats are alongside the gangway by the times laid down in the boat routine, and that they leave the ship punctually. Coxswains of boats must report personally to him for orders before they man their boats. Libertymen should be piped in time to ensure that the boat can leave at the routine time.

Boats should be refuelled at the times laid down. If this is not possible, plenty of warning must be given to the Engineering department to provide the fuel when required. Batteries in boats should be checked daily.

The provision of extra boat trips for special purposes must not be allowed to disrupt the boat routine. Special trips should be combined with routine trips whenever possible. If in doubt on the advisability of providing a boat for an out-of-routine trip the matter should be referred to the Executive Officer or the Duty Commanding Officer. With a little tact and ingenuity the Officer of the Watch should be able to arrange all the various boat requirements so long as they are reasonable. He must know how long it takes the boats to go to different parts of the harbour.

Boats' crews should, as far as possible, be allowed the regulation periods for their meals. If a boat is likely to be away during a meal hour the galley staff should be warned in plenty of time so that the meal is not over-cooked, but is kept hot until the return of the crew.

If no boats are in the water, there must be some organisation in force to provide a boat and crew at night at short notice in the event of emergency.

Boats at booms

Whenever a boat is made fast to a boat-boom the coxswain should report the fact personally to the Officer of the Watch. All loose gear in the boat should be secured, the fenders should be placed (except on the outer side of a boat at the outer billet), no gear should be projecting or hanging outboard of the boat, and she should be riding comfortably with the correct amount of scope on her painter or boatrope. She should be clear of possible discharges from pumps etc. from the ship's side.

If there is any likelihood of bad weather it is advisable to hoist all boats except duty boats before dark, and at the same time to reeve boatropes and sternfasts for those boats which are to remain down overnight. Hoisting boats, even as a matter of routine, should always be regarded as an evolution and carried out smartly. Boatropes are normally unrove when the hands turn to in the morning, unless the weather is rough or there is a tidal stream running.

If the boats are bumping against each other or against the ship's side, or when the ship is swinging at the turn of the tide, the crews should be ordered to man their boats.

If a gale is imminent it is wise to hoist all boats. If a boat has to be left down it is best to send her inshore to shelter before the weather gets too rough, if there is a safe berth for her there. If this is impracticable she should be made fast astern, possibly on a hawser, because she will ride more easily there than at the lower boom. If the seas are breaking heavily a little oil dripped continuously from a bag slung over each bow of the ship will stop them breaking.

Boats alongside

A boat should never be allowed to lie alongside for longer than is strictly necessary; she should be ordered either to make fast to a boat-boom or to lie off.

When a boat comes alongside, except in calm weather, the gangway boatrope should be lowered to her and she should always make fast to it. It is unseamanlike to allow a boat to lie alongside unless secured to the boatrope. If ladies are arriving or leaving, the Midshipman of the Watch or one of the gangway staff should be sent to the foot of the ladder to help them disembark or embark.

In a strong tideway a tide spar should be rigged before the foot of the accommodation ladder to prevent boats from getting jammed under it.

If the ship is moored head-and-stern to buoys in a tideway, tide spars should be rigged abaft the foot of the accommodation ladder as well as before it, and an extra boatrope should always be rigged abaft the ladder for use by boats coming alongside head-to-stern.

Precautions before leaving the ship

Before a coxswain is ordered for the first time to go to a certain landing place he should be shown the plan of the harbour or anchorage, his course there and back, and any navigational dangers along his track. If the course is long and complicated he should be provided with a plan of the harbour or a tracing of it. He must have a watch or a clock in the boat.

All coxswains of boats should know the times of high and low water, the range of the tide and the time of sunset. It is a good plan to post these conspicuously above the gangway desk.

Although the coxswain is primarily responsible for the state of his boat and her crew, it is the duty of the Officer of the Watch to see that the crew are properly dressed and the boat is shipshape. When time allows, it is advisable occasionally to check various items of a boat's equipment, such as the lifebuoy in power boats, lifejackets for the boat's crew, the ground tackle, the boat's slings, and the boat's signal book. In rough weather each member of the crew should wear a lifejacket. Members of boats' crews must be able to swim. If a boat is to be away after sunset her navigation lights should be shipped and in working order. If a boat is to be sent on a long out-of-routine trip, make sure she has sufficient fuel for the trip there and back.

It has already been pointed out that the Officer of the Watch must see that no boat is overloaded when she leaves the ship. But if the weather seems likely to deteriorate he should also give the coxswain definite instructions as to what should be his maximum load in rough weather on the return trip, and about where to shelter if the weather is too rough to risk a return passage at all.

No one should be allowed to take away a boat under sail without supervision until he has proved himself to be a competent helmsman. It is customary for the Boat Officer to promulgate a list of those members of the ship's company who are allowed to take away boats under sail, and the Officer of the Watch should check that the name of any aspiring coxswain appears on this list.

Boats away from the ship

The Officer of the Watch must ensure that a good lookout is kept on the ship's boats and on all boat traffic near the ship; a lookout should also be kept from the signal deck if it is manned. Help should be sent at once to any boat in difficulties.

An occasional signal made to the ship's boats when they are away from the ship will prompt coxswains to keep an eye on their ship.

If a boat is going on a long trip out of sight of the ship the Officer of the Watch must satisfy himself that the coxswain and crew are fully prepared to look after themselves should the weather worsen, and that they know by what time they are expected back. It may be necessary to provide the crew with a portable radio with which to keep contact with the ship. If any doubt exists, recreational trips should be restricted to an area within sight of the ship.

It is by no means an uncommon event for a modern sailing dinghy to be capsized even in a moderate breeze by an experienced helmsman. To make certain that such an event is not a disaster, however, the following precautions must always be observed.

1. Helmsman and crew must wear lifejackets.

2. Dinghies must have adequate built-in or inflatable buoyancy to support both the boat and the crew in the water after a capsize.

3. Sailing in dinghies is to be carried on only under observation from the ship or in a place frequented by other boats.

4. A dinghy must never be overloaded either with crew or with stores, e.g. picnic gear.

Duty despatch boat

When in company with other ships the Senior Officer will detail one ship daily to provide a despatch boat to collect fleet correspondence from the Senior Officer's ship and distribute it among the other ships. The ship providing the boat also provides a mail orderly.

All fleet correspondence should be ready before the expected time of arrival of the boat on her collection trip. The mail orderly should report to the Officer of the Watch on deck and any correspondence should be handed over there. Handing over or receiving mail at the foot of the accommodation ladder is a bad practice; it may save a little time, but can easily result in the mail being dropped between the ship's side and the boat.

Appearance of boats

It is an old saying that a ship is known by her boats. The Officer of the Watch can do much to enhance the reputation of his ship by seeing that all boats under his orders are clean and shipshape, that their crews are smart in both appearance and drill, and that they are handled in a seamanlike way.

Boats' crews should be correctly and uniformly dressed in the rig ordered. They should wear clean white gym shoes, and when they are wearing caps the chin-stays should be down. In rough weather they may wear foul-weather clothing and lifejackets.

Do not hesitate to find fault with boats and let it be known that you expect a high standard. On the other hand, always remember to praise a coxswain if his boat looks specially smart, or if he handles her well in difficult circumstances.

PROTECTION OF SHIP'S EQUIPMENT

The protection from the weather and its effects on the ship's equipment situated on the upper deck, in the superstructures or outboard is generally the responsibility of the Officer of the Watch. Remarks on the handling and care of awnings are given in Volume II. The main need is to keep a lookout for the approach of squalls or rain, and to have the awnings sloped and if necessary frapped *before* the bad weather arrives at the ship. The same principle applies to the covering of the armament. If a flagship is in company it is customary to follow her actions over awnings, covering guns, etc.

The Officer of the Watch should remember that natural-fibre cordage shrinks when wet, and that after rain it is often necessary to check frapping lines, awning tackles, etc. to prevent distortion and damage to awnings and their stanchions.

In rough weather the accommodation ladders should be hoisted clear of the water if waves are breaking over their lower platforms, and a well-fendered jumping ladder should then be rigged well aft on each quarter (abaft the screws) where there will be the best lee for boats coming alongside. It may be necessary to rig a stern or a quarter boom for the boats.

APPEARANCE OF THE SHIP

In matters concerning the outward appearance of the ship, for which the Officer of the Watch is responsible, it is also customary to follow the movements of the Senior Officer. Examine the following points on taking over your watch, and see that your subordinates pay attention to them also throughout the watch.

Colours. The ensign, jack and masthead pennant or distinguishing flag should be hoisted close up with their halyards taut, and they should not be foul of or turned around staffs, mast or nearby rigging.

Armament and rotatable aerials. If not in use, these should be placed in their proper positions fore-and-aft or as laid down in the ship's orders.

Halyards, particularly signal halyards, and other parts of the rigging should be set up taut if not in use.

Boat-booms should be square with the ship's side, both in the horizontal and in the vertical plane. The bights of boatropes should not be allowed to trail in the water when they are not in use.

Ship's side should be clear, and there should be no ropes or fenders over it. Any shore boats should be kept well clear of the ship and such boats should never be allowed to make fast alongside, astern, or to the anchor cable.

Accommodation ladders should be rigged squarely, and the end of the gangway boatrope and its check line should be cheesed down on the upper platform. The supports of the lower platform should be kept clear of any flotsam.

Awnings should be taut and square. The hauling parts of the falls of awning tackles should be cheesed down.

Davits of boats which have been lowered should be turned inboard, and the lifelines should be recovered and squared off.

CEREMONIAL

The Officer of the Watch is responsible for ensuring that the necessary marks of respect are paid to passing ships or boats carrying senior officers, and to officers arriving on board or leaving the ship. Remarks on salutes and other marks of respect are given in Volumes I and II.

If a boat carrying a senior officer approaches and the Captain is out of the ship, the Officer of the Watch should, as a matter of courtesy, go to the foot of the accommodation ladder as the boat comes alongside and tell the senior officer that the Captain is away.

In a busy fleet anchorage it is advisable to detail a lookout to keep a watch for approaching ships and for boats flying distinguishing flags or pennants.

DISCIPLINE

Regulating staff

The Regulating branch includes the Master-at-Arms, Regulating Petty Officers and Leading Regulators. In small ships where no Master-at-Arms or Regulating branch ratings are borne their duties are carried out by the *Chief of the Boat* or the *Coxswain,* assisted by petty officers detailed as required. The Officer of the Watch, under the Executive Officer, is responsible that the Master-at-Arms, and any ratings employed on Regulating duties, carry out their duties in accordance with BR 31, *The Queen's Regulations for the Royal Navy.* These duties include the supervision of men under punishment, the control of libertymen, the conduct of patrols and escorts, the administration of Customs regulations, the conduct of rounds and the investigation of alleged offences. Some of these duties have already been discussed, and every Officer of the Watch should be familiar with the regulations concerning those not specifically mentioned in this chapter.

Investigation of disciplinary cases

Investigations were traditionally conducted on the quarterdeck but in modern ships this is generally unsuitable and the Regulating Office is now the normal venue. The Officer of the Watch is responsible for the primary investigation of all disciplinary matters. He should not, however, allow investigations to interfere with his other duties. If the investigation of a case appears likely to be long or complex he should ask for a relief to carry out his other duties or ask for another officer to investigate the case.

Charges. It is most important that any charge preferred against a man is worded correctly. Before the Officer of the Watch interviews the accused in serious cases which may lead to a court martial, he should read to him the prescribed warning about any evidence he may give. The various procedures for the investigation of offences are laid down in BR 31, *The Queen's Regulations for the Royal Navy,* and they are to be strictly observed. Charges against petty officers and serious charges against other ratings should be preferred by a Regulating Petty Officer, and charges against chief petty officers should, if possible, be preferred by the Master-at-Arms or the senior Regulating rating on board. Any charge against a senior rating should, whenever practicable, be investigated in a place clear of junior ratings.

Search. Fleet chief petty officers, chief petty officers and petty officers are exempt from personal search unless it is specifically ordered by the Executive Officer or the Captain. Leading ratings are exempt from personal search unless it is specifically ordered by the Officer of the Watch, the Executive Officer or the Captain, for a special reason in a particular case. If a man's kit is searched, the man and his divisional officer, or another officer, should be present at the search.

Drunkenness. The decision whether or not a man is drunk rests with the Commanding Officer who will base his finding on the evidence of witnesses, e.g. the Officer of the Watch or the Regulating staff. The definition of drunkenness is contained in BR 11, *Manual of Naval Law,* and every Officer of the Watch must be familiar with this definition. If, however, there is any doubt whether a man's condition is due to alcohol or to some other cause, the advice of a Medical Officer should be obtained. In cases of drunkenness which may lead to a trial by court martial, the opinion of a Medical Officer should always be obtained as soon as possible. Any altercation with a drunken man should be avoided and care must be taken to prevent him aggravating his offence.

A patrol is fully competent to state that a libertyman is drunk if he is apprehended ashore. Even if he has sobered by the time he has returned to the ship, the man is still answerable to the charge of being 'drunk on shore', and the Officer of the Watch *may not dismiss such a charge*.

A drunken man should be placed in confinement to prevent him aggravating his offence and from injuring either himself or his messmates. Before a man who is incapable is placed in confinement he should be examined by the Medical Officer, because when in such a condition he may require medical attention. Whenever a man is placed in confinement the Commanding Officer and the Executive Officer should be informed. A drunken man who has been placed under restraint should be released as soon as he is considered to be sober.

Fighting. When investigating cases of fighting or altercation the participants should be kept well apart from each other to prevent any further outbreak of violence.

Loss of stores. The loss of any stores or equipment, whether by accident or neglect, must be investigated by the Officer of the Watch.

EMBARKATION OF DANGEROUS MATERIALS

Before the arrival of a vessel or lighter alongside there should be nothing projecting outboard in her way and, where necessary, davits and boats should be turned in, boat-booms housed and accommodation ladders hoisted inboard.

Fenders and catamarans should be placed in position and a small berthing party detailed. Out of working hours the duty hands, assisted by members of the gangway staff, should be sufficient. It is important to be prepared for the arrival of a lighter and not to keep her waiting unnecessarily. She probably has several other ships to visit as well as your own. An officer should always be in charge when ammunition, stores or provisions are embarked or disembarked.

The precautions to be taken against fire when embarking or disembarking explosives, ship or aviation fuel have been mentioned on page 258, and precautions for radio and radar aerials on pages 262–3. When embarking or disembarking ammunition, only the authorised slinging and hoisting gear should be used.

When stores or provisions are to be embarked or disembarked the Supply Officer should be asked beforehand for details of their quantity and types so that the necessary number of men can be detailed for the job and the necessary gear prepared. When embarking or disembarking stores or provisions, a member of the Supply staff should be present, and a net should be slung between the ship's side and the gunwale of the vessel or lighter to catch anything which may fall from the hoists. When embarking or disembarking mails or kit, a member of the Regulating staff should be present.

RUNNING THE ROUTINE

In ships nowadays more emphasis is placed on each individual being responsible for going to his place of duty at the time ordered in the published routine or daily orders, and less emphasis on the continual piping of the routine and mustering of men before they start work. A time check is given early in the morning, and from then on the routine virtually runs itself. However, the Officer of the Watch must see that any routine announcements ordered for particular times are properly piped at precisely the right times; and he must make any routine reports to the Executive Officer at exactly the times required. No pipe should ever be made without the authority of the Officer of the Watch.

Piping and announcements generally should be kept to the minimum, and the number of words used in standard pipes should also be reduced to the minimum. For example, 'It is requested that Commander Brown may come to the shore telephone to speak to Major Smith' may be cut to 'Commander Brown — shore telephone'. Such abbreviations in the long run prevent the continual irritation and distraction caused by excessive broadcasting, especially to those not affected.

The Officer of the Watch must be quick to inform the Executive Officer or other Heads of Departments about any occurrences that will require a change in the routine, or which will entail some preparation or organisation for the next day or at some future time.

CHAPTER 10

Ship Upkeep, Fittings and Stores

This chapter is divided into three main sections: UPKEEP, NAVAL BASE ORGANISATION and FITTINGS AND STORES. The aim is to provide the Seaman officer with a guide to the principles and organisation for ship upkeep, an outline of Naval Base organisation and refit procedure, and a summary of the fittings and stores used in HM ships.

The reader is advised that the policy and practice of ship upkeep are under continuous review and that, as a consequence, the contents of this chapter may be subject to continuing change. The various subjects have been treated in a manner to provide an overall appreciation of the principles upon which ship upkeep is based. Precise details of practices and procedures should always be sought in the references quoted in this chapter.

UPKEEP

Upkeep is defined as 'The use of any or all the resources required to assure or restore a specified material condition or level of performance'. In the broadest terms, when applied to a ship, this means the whole range of activities required to maintain the designed performance of the ship and her equipment throughout her useful life. Every ship needs upkeep; the requirement can either be met in a planned and organised manner or it will be imposed as a result of breakdown — it cannot be escaped. The work involved in upkeep falls into four categories: preventive maintenance, corrective maintenance, modifications, and alterations and additions.

Categories of upkeep

Preventive maintenance involves work designed to minimise wear and deterioration, such as lubrication, cleaning and painting; adjustment to obtain optimum performance; and periodic examinations and tests of equipment to determine wear and reveal incipient defects. The work has to be planned and integrated into the ship's programme to ensure its timely completion. The interval after which a *maintenance operation* (item of maintenance work) has to be repeated is known as its *periodicity* which determines its method of planning. Planned maintenance operations having a periodicity of four months or more are co-ordinated by a central planning organisation in the ship, whereas operations having a periodicity of less than four months are known as *servicing* and are incorporated into the work programme at maintenance section level. Preventive maintenance is normally carried out continuously by ship's staff with occasional assistance from Fleet resources although some operations are scheduled to be undertaken by dockyards because of their complexity or need for specialised facilities.

Corrective maintenance is the work required to rectify defects which may be caused by damage, indicated by failure or poor performance, or discovered during preventive maintenance work. Corrective maintenance is undertaken by ship's staff, Fleet resources, dockyards or contractors and, depending on circumstances, it may require immediate attention or may be deferred to a more convenient time. Whenever practicable as much associated preventive maintenance as possible is undertaken simultaneously with the corrective maintenance.

Upkeep by Exchange (U × E) is a policy whereby particular items of equipment or complete units are removed and replaced by new or restored items. Exchange takes place when corrective maintenance is necessary, or when condition monitoring indicates a deterioration, or at a planned life interval for the original item. The unserviceable items are subsequently repaired or restored to acceptable performance standards by dockyards or commercial contract and are then returned to store for further use.

Modifications encompass any change to the design of an equipment or its constituent parts to rectify omissions or shortcomings in design, or to improve reliability or safety. Modifications can only be undertaken after they have been approved by the MOD(N) and are promulgated as changes to the relevant handbooks. Modifications are undertaken by ship's staff or dockyard, dependent upon their category which is determined by the cost, both financial and labour, incurred in their implementation. Modifications are also classified for degree of priority, to indicate the urgency with which they should be incorporated into the equipment.

Alterations and Additions (As & As) make a change of equipment fitted in a ship or a change of her structure to improve, for example, operational efficiency or habitability. As & As may involve more than one design authority, and they are always reflected as a change to 'As Fitted' drawings. As & As are promulgated by two methods:

1. A special series of *Defence Council Instructions* (DCIs) for approved As & As.
2. Predicted Refit Lists, which include proposed As & As.

Both documents indicate whether the work is to be undertaken by ship's staff or dockyard. Work by ship's staff on approved As & As may be progressed as convenient provided it does not prejudice routine maintenance, whereas dockyard work is normally undertaken, after agreement by relevant authorities, only when the ship is being refitted. Further information on As & As is given in *Fleet Engineering Orders*.

Ship husbandry

All departments in a warship, and not least the Seaman branch, are involved in her upkeep. Maintenance of the hull, structure, fittings, equipment and furnishings, where specialist engineering skills are not required, is collectively known as *ship husbandry*. The term is defined as 'the cleanliness, preservation and maintenance of a ship's structure, openings and systems, and the good appearance of the ship both outside and in'. Notes on the maintenance of seaman's gear are given in the relevant chapters throughout the volumes of this manual, and a chapter of Volume II is devoted to the practical aspects of ship husbandry. Further details are given in BR 2203, *Ship Husbandry Manual*.

MINISTRY OF DEFENCE (NAVY) ORGANISATION FOR FLEET SUPPORT

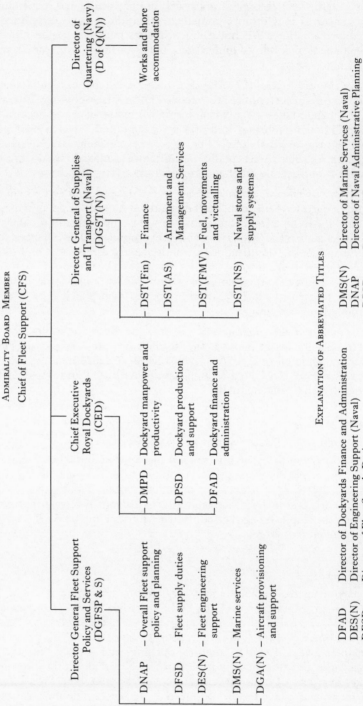

ADMIRALTY BOARD MEMBER
Chief of Fleet Support (CFS)

Director General Fleet Support Policy and Services (DGFSP & S)

DNAP – Overall Fleet support policy and planning

DFSD – Fleet supply duties

DES(N) – Fleet engineering support

DMS(N) – Marine services

DGA(N) – Aircraft provisioning and support

Chief Executive Royal Dockyards (CED)

DMPD – Dockyard manpower and productivity

DPSD – Dockyard production and support

DFAD – Dockyard finance and administration

Director General of Supplies and Transport (Naval) (DGST(N))

DST(Fin) – Finance

DST(AS) – Armament and Management Services

DST(FMV) – Fuel, movements and victualling

DST(NS) – Naval stores and supply systems

Director of Quartering (Navy) (D of Q(N))

Works and shore accommodation

EXPLANATION OF ABBREVIATED TITLES

DFAD   Director of Dockyards Finance and Administration
DES(N)   Director of Engineering Support (Naval)
DFSD   Director of Fleet Supply Duties
DGA(N)   Director General Aircraft (Naval)
DMPD   Director of Dockyard Manpower and Productivity

DMS(N)   Director of Marine Services (Naval)
DNAP   Director of Naval Administrative Planning
DPSD   Director of Dockyard Production and Support
DST   Director of Supplies and Transport

UPKEEP AND SEAMANSHIP ORGANISATIONS

Upkeep involves a definition of policy, an organisation for its implementation, the provision of dockyard and Fleet Maintenance Group (FMG) support, and the provision of the necessary stores and spare parts. The Royal Dockyards and the Naval Stores organisations are the responsibility of the Chief of Fleet Support, whereas FMGs are considered to be an extension of ships' staffs, and the allocation of their support for programmed maintenance is therefore undertaken by Commander-in-Chief Fleet. The policy and standards of upkeep within the Fleet, and the provision of specialist support, are the responsibilities of the Engineering Staff of C-in-C Fleet. It is also appropriate at this point to explain the organisation for seamanship in the Navy Department of the Ministry of Defence. This organisation determines seamanship policy which in turn is reflected in the design of seamanship material for the Fleet.

Navy Department upkeep organisation

The Chief of Fleet Support (CFS) is the Admiralty Board Member responsible for all matters concerning the material support of the Fleet. The table on page 274 shows the organisation of his department and the broad responsibilities of each directorate. The Directorate of Engineering Support (Naval) (DES(N)) is responsible for the engineering maintenance policy in the Fleet in conjunction with C-in-C Fleet; the injection of engineering support requirements into new-design ship and equipment projects; and the monitoring and sponsoring of base support policy and resource requirements.

Fleet upkeep organisation

The Fleet Engineering Staff is a central authority whose prime responsibilities are the development and implementation of engineering policy in ships administered by C-in-C Fleet. (Other authorities responsible for engineering administration of ships, e.g. Flag Officer Submarines, have similar responsibilities.) The Fleet Engineeering Staff includes some specialist support teams which are available to assist and advise ships on particular aspects of engineering practice which need specialised knowledge, experience or appliances, e.g. boiler inspection, vibration analysis, COGOG propulsion.

C-in-C Fleet's representatives in the Naval Bases are the Area Chief Staff Officers (Engineering) (CSO(E)s) who are responsible to their Area Flag Officers (who are in turn responsible to C-in-C Fleet) for all matters concerning the upkeep, repair and engineering support of the individual ships based on their ports. This includes:

1. Superintending all Fleet aspects of ships in dockyard hands for programmed maintenance, e.g. Refits or Docking and Essential Defect Periods (DEDs).

2. Arranging for the shore-based element of the upkeep of ships based on their ports, particularly the rectification of Operational Defects (OPDEFs) (see page 282).

3. Upholding the priorities established by C-in-C Fleet (and/or other authorities responsible for engineering administration) for the allocation of key resources.

Direct uniformed support to ships is provided by staff who work from the Fleet Maintenance Bases (FMBs) located at the main Naval Bases. Each FMB is under the charge of a Captain Fleet Maintenance (CFM) — who is also the Area CSO(E). The CFM is accountable to the Area Flag Officer for the following functions.

1. Administration of the FMB.

2. The provision of resources to undertake programmed upkeep in accordance with the programme promulgated by C-in-C Fleet.

3. The provision of resources to undertake unprogrammed work in accordance with the requirements and priorities of the Area CSO(E).

Instructions to ships on the procedures for dealing with equipment defects, for obtaining FMG and dockyard assistance, and on refit procedures are contained in *Fleet Engineering Orders.*

Navy Department organisation for seamanship

This section explains the arrangements within the Navy Department for the formulation of policy and for decisions on the material aspects of seamanship.

The Vice Chief of the Naval Staff is the Admiralty Board Member responsible for seamanship matters. The Assistant Chief of Naval Staff (Operations) is the Senior Co-ordinating Authority and is the final arbiter in all matters not requiring board approval. The Seamanship Policy Panel under the chairmanship of the Director of Naval Warfare consists of the Director of Naval Equipment and the Director of Naval Manning and Training (Seaman), and the secretary is an officer of the Directorate of Naval Warfare responsible for the Naval Staff aspects of seamanship affairs. The panel is empowered to co-opt additional members to facilitate its work, and is responsible to the Assistant Chief of Naval Staff (Operations). The business of the panel is conducted through the following subordinate committees, each under the chairmanship of the Director of Naval Equipment.

1. Replenishment-at-sea Committee.

2. Seamanship Materials and Techniques Committee.

3. Boat Committee.

4. Royal Navy Lifesaving Committee.

These committees normally meet at intervals of about six months and their composition is shown in the table on page 278. Their terms of reference and those of the Seamanship Policy Panel are set out below.

The Seamanship Policy Panel is responsible for the co-ordination and organisation of all policy matters relating to seamanship, replenishment at sea and lifesaving in the Royal Navy and for making recommendations. The panel co-ordinates seamanship policy within the Ministry of Defence (Navy); keeps under review the implementation of approved seamanship requirements and their effect on manpower; and keeps under review the exchange of ideas and information on seamanship both within the Ministry and with the Fleet.

The Replenishment-at-sea Committee keeps under review all aspects of replenishment of ships at sea and in harbour, and recommends improvements to related equipment and techniques.

The Seamanship Materials and Techniques Committee is sponsored jointly by DG Ships (DNE) and FOST to keep under review seamanship material and techniques other than those concerned solely with replenishment at sea.

The Boat Committee keeps in touch with developments in the boat-building industry and is empowered to appoint subordinate working parties for specific tasks in the discharge of the following responsibilities.

1. Reviewing proposals for new boats for all MOD departments.

2. Ensuring that all requirements for boats are adequately justified.

3. Recommending changes to the allocation of existing boats when this will result in a more economical use of resources.

4. Establishing requirements which cannot be met by the re-allocation of existing boats, and ensuring that agreed statements of requirements are formulated to meet tasks for which no existing design of boat is appropriate.

5. Monitoring the performance of new-design boats in service.

Note. For the purpose of the above responsibilities, a boat is defined as a vessel or craft not exceeding 15 metres in length, but excluding all specialised Army bridging and river assault craft.

The Royal Navy Lifesaving Committee keeps under review all aspects of lifesaving at sea and recommends improvements in related equipment and techniques.

UPKEEP PLANNING AND IMPLEMENTATION

The upkeep of modern warships has become more exacting as design has progressed. Suitable periods must be allowed for maintenance by the various departments of the ship in addition to the time allocated to docking and repair in dockyard hands. In short, it is essential that upkeep is incorporated into the planning of a ship's programme to attain the maximum seagoing use of the ship. Conversely, if upkeep is not given proper consideration, the condition of the ship will deteriorate leading eventually to breakdown and the inability of the ship to fulfil her role.

The detailed planning is integrated with the long-term plan whereby a ship undergoes a *Major Refit* about midway through her expected life, interspersed with *Normal Refits* which restore her condition for a further three to four years' service with the Fleet. Between refits a ship is planned to undergo one or two *Docking and* (repair of) *Essential Defect Periods* (DEDs). Further important periods which have to be planned are the *Assisted Maintenance Period* (AMP) when ship's staff are assisted with the maintenance task, and the *Self Maintenance Period* (SMP) when the ship's staff progress the work unaided or with limited assistance. For the AMP, assistance is provided to ships by additional manpower from *Fleet Maintenance Groups* (FMGs) which are administered from the Fleet Maintenance Bases. There are two other types of maintenance period in which dockyard assistance is involved: the *Dockyard Assisted Maintenance Period* (DAMP) which is planned for large ships at regular intervals so that defects beyond the capacity of a ship's staff can be repaired; and the *Pre-deployment* AMP which is a normal AMP

MINISTRY OF DEFENCE (NAVY) ORGANISATION FOR SEAMANSHIP

ADMIRALTY BOARD MEMBER
Vice Chief of the Naval Staff

SENIOR CO-ORDINATING AUTHORITY
Assistant Chief of Naval Staff (Operations)

SEAMANSHIP POLICY PANEL

Chairman: Director of Naval Warfare
Members: Director of Naval Equipment
Director of Naval Manning and Training (Seaman)
Secretary*: DNW

REPLENISHMENT-AT-SEA COMMITTEE

Chairman: Director of Naval Equipment
Members*: DG Ships (DNE)
DG Ships (DSDE)
DGW(N)
DNAP
DNW
DNOR
DST(AS)
DST(FMV)
DST(NS)
CINCFLEET
CINCNAVHOME
FOST
Secretary*: DST(FMV)

SEAMANSHIP MATERIAL AND TECHNIQUES COMMITTEE

Chairman: Director of Naval Equipment
Members*: DNW
DG Ships (DNE)
CINCFLEET
CINCNAVHOME
FOST
Secretary*: DNE

BOAT COMMITTEE

Chairman: Commodore Naval Ship Acceptance/Director of Naval Equipment
Members*: DG Ships
DNW
DNOR
DNMT(X)
CGRM
CINCFLEET
CINCNAVHOME
CED
DGST(N)
DMS(N)
H
DGTM (Army)
DMC (RAF)
CER
Secretary*: DNE

ROYAL NAVY LIFESAVING COMMITTEE

Chairman: Director of Naval Equipment
Members*: MDG(N)
DNW
RNSES
DGA(N)
DNMT(X)
DGST(N)
DG Ships
CED
CINCNAVHOME
RN Air Medical School
CINCFLEET
FOST
Secretary*: DNE

Note. Secretaries and members marked * are representatives of the nominated departments

MINISTRY OF DEFENCE (NAVY) ORGANISATION FOR SEAMANSHIP (*cont.*)

EXPLANATION OF ABBREVIATED TITLES

CED	Chief Executive Royal Dockyards	DNE	Director of Naval Equipment
CER	Controller, R & D Establishments and Research	DNMT(X)	Director of Naval Manning and Training (Seaman)
CGRM	Commandant General of the Royal Marines	DNOR	Director of Naval Operational Requirements
CINCFLEET	Commander-in-Chief, Fleet	DNW	Director of Naval Warfare
CINCNAVHOME	Commander-in-Chief, Naval Home Command	DSDE	Director of Ship Design and Engineering
DGA(N)	Director General Aircraft (Naval)	DST(AS)	Director of Supplies and Transport (Armament and Management Services)
DG Ships	Director General Ships	DST(FMV)	Director of Supplies and Transport (Fuel, Movements and Victualling)
DGST(N)	Director General of Supplies and Transport (Naval)	DST(NS)	Director of Supplies and Transport (Naval Stores and Supply Systems)
DGTM	Director General of Transport and Movements (Army)	FOST	Flag Officer Sea Training
DGW(N)	Director General Weapons (Naval)	H	Hydrographer of the Navy
DMC	Director of Marine Craft (RAF)	MDG(N)	Medical Director General (Naval)
DMS(N)	Director of Marine Services (Naval)	RNSES	Royal Naval Survival Equipment School
DNAP	Director of Naval Administrative Planning		

T

where, exceptionally, dockyard support is allocated and which all ships undergo as necessary when proceeding abroad.

To enable the task to be planned and to ensure a common standard throughout the Fleet and supporting organisations, the work involved in preventive maintenance is fully specified and presented to ships as part of the maintenance documentation.

Maintenance documentation

The practical implementation of preventive maintenance and planned upkeep through the agency of the Fleet Engineering Staff (Portsmouth) involves the provision to ships of a standard documentation system titled the *Maintenance Management System* (MMS). The system specifies the preventive maintenance work that ships are to undertake at prescribed intervals and provides methods of incorporating corrective maintenance and other work, e.g. modifications or ship's staff As & As. The essential features of the MMS are given below by a description of the documents and equipment involved, and full details are contained in BR 1313, *Maintenance Management in Ships*.

The *Ship Equipment List* is the basic document of the system and is compiled to indicate those equipments fitted in the ship which are subject to maintenance routines, where they are located and the number of the relevant maintenance schedule (see below). It is from this list that the MMS documentation package is compiled by the Fleet Engineering Staff for supply to the ship.

Maintenance Schedules are produced for individual equipments and systems. A schedule specifies as numbered maintenance operations all the recommended preventive maintenance for an equipment, and indicates the periodicity of each operation and who should carry it out. A brief job description is given for ship's staff operations, and dockyard operations are more fully described. The schedules are numbered in a common nine-figure system and the appropriate schedules are collated in loose-leaf binders for use by the departments.

Central Plan. Each Engineering department (ME and WE) is provided with a binder containing gridded sheets listing, for each equipment, all the ship's staff planned maintenance operations scheduled to be undertaken over a period of four years. Against each operation a diagonal line is marked in an appropriate square of the grid to indicate when maintenance is due according to the periodicity specified in the schedule. Completion of the operation is recorded by cross-ticking the original diagonal line. Additional forms in a separate binder are provided for recording the completion dates of operations scheduled to be undertaken at DEDs or refits. The Central Plan provides to the planner a ready reference to all scheduled planned maintenance operations, and the means of recording their completion.

Job Information Cards (JICs), which amplify the job descriptions of the maintenance schedules, are provided for all ship's staff maintenance operations except those indicated by 'None' in the JIC column of the schedule. A JIC contains the detailed instructions necessary to complete the work, including safety precautions, references to the relevant handbooks and the need for specialised tools or appliances. A card provides detailed guidance to the man carrying out the operation and is in a suitable form to be taken by him to the site.

Planning Cards and the *Central Planning Board.* For each ship's staff centrally planned maintenance operation a small planning card, commonly known as a *tram ticket,* is provided. The card gives brief details of the equipment and job description together with the location, schedule number and periodicity. Planning cards are used in conjunction with the Central Planning Board which is a louvre-type display with slots to accept the cards. A plain panel at the bottom of the board can be marked with dates and the ship's programme, and one at the side can be marked with the maintenance section responsible for the work being planned. The board is designed to cover a six-month period. At the beginning of a period, the planner takes all the planning cards for the ensuing six months, as indicated in the Central Plan, and arranges them in the board to suit the ship's programme and the manpower available. Reference to the cards in the board enables the planner to allocate the work to the maintenance sections. As the operations are completed the relevant cards are extracted from the board which thus provides an immediate display of outstanding, current and forthcoming work.

Maintenance Record Cards (MRCs) are provided for all ship's staff centrally planned maintenance operations. A card indicates the equipment, its location, schedule number and operation number, and is printed with a grid which has columns for recording the date and initials of the rating completing the operation. Individual cards are normally kept with their associated JICs and planning cards in transparent plastic envelopes which are stowed in standard filing arrangements at the planning centre. When indicated on the Central Planning Board, the planner extracts the appropriate envelopes from their stowage and allocates them to the various maintenance sections. On completion of an operation, the envelope is returned to the planner who extracts the Planning Card from the board and inserts it in the envelope which is then replaced in its stowage. At the same time the operation is cross-ticked in the Central Plan to indicate completion.

Equipment/Performance and Servicing Logs (PSLs). These logs are provided to cover the servicing operations (i.e. maintenance operations with periodicities of less than four months) for an equipment or group of equipments. The log indicates the schedule and operation numbers together with the means of graphically recording the performance of the equipment and of noting completion of the servicing operations. The logs are either kept together by the maintenance section or stowed individually at their equipments.

A *Section Planning Board* is supplied to each maintenance section to enable its work to be planned and controlled locally. The board is marked up with the names of the ratings in the section and the tasks they are required to complete for each day of the week. Two boxes are fitted at the bottom of the board: one to accommodate the envelopes of the work to be done, the other for those of work completed which are awaiting return to the planning centre.

Hull and Structure Record (Form S.338). This form, one copy of which is provided for each compartment, tank, etc. in the ship, is used to record the results of routine inspections and surveys. The forms are collated in a loose-leaf binder and constitute the ship's *Hull and Structure Log.*

Ship Equipment Files provide a readily accessible bank of information on machinery and equipment upkeep. Files are raised as the need arises for reports of a general nature, for reports of trials covering more than one equipment or system, and for any subject considered suitable by ship's officers. The files contain correspondence and signals; reports of defects and associated replies, together with a record of remedial action; and reports of trials, installation data, wear records, history sheets and other documents which relate to the equipment. The files are stowed in standard 2-drawer or 4-drawer cabinets located in suitable departmental offices.

Associated upkeep forms

The previous section dealt with the documents and equipment involved in the planning and implementation of preventive maintenance. Several associated forms are also used, the more important of which are explained below.

Defect Report (Form S.2018). This form is used for recording and reporting defects which cannot be repaired at the time of discovery and which need to be planned for future repair, or for defects which are considered to warrant an entry in the Ship Equipment File or reporting to the Fleet Engineering Staff or both, or for defects which are subject to special reporting procedures.

Defect Log (Form S.2019). This form is used for recording minor defects or other useful information on an equipment, and it is normally filed in the Equipment/Performance and Servicing Log.

Work Requisition (Form S.2020). This form is used for requisitioning work, other than defect repair, on other departments or base staffs. Such work includes modifications, ship's staff As & As, parts manufacture, special inspections, etc. The completed form may subsequently be used as a permanent record of work done or as a means of reporting it. The form is not used for defect repair; this is always requisitioned by use of the Defect Report.

Ship Report of Shortcoming in Material, Design or Support (Form S.2022). This form is the means whereby ships report shortcomings of any nature to the Fleet Engineering Staff. As well as the material aspects of equipment and its design, the form is used for all aspects of the support field such as documentation, training, manning, stores and spare gear, environment, tests, trials, management, etc. It is most important that shortcomings in any form are reported promptly and precisely because it is by the analysis of these reports that improvements can be recommended and effected.

Repair of defects

When minor defects arise, or are discovered, they are repaired by ship's staff. They are recorded on Defect Log forms but no reporting action is necessary unless the defect is unusual, or recurs frequently, or is subject to special reporting procedures, in which case it is reported to the Fleet Engineering Staff on Form S.2022.

More serious defects within the capacity of ship's staff are repaired immediately or, depending on circumstances, they are recorded by use of the

Defect Report and their repair is deferred to a more convenient time. It is important that as much preventive maintenance as possible is incorporated with the repair either by advancing the date of planned maintenance or by deferring the repair to coincide with the maintenance. Defects beyond the capacity of ship's staff, the repair of which may be deferred, are recorded on a Defect Report for subsequent repair by other resources. Both these categories of defect are further reported as required by the use of the Defect Report or Form S.2022.

Defects which affect the seagoing or operational efficiency of the ship are classified as *Operational Defects* (OPDEFs) and are reported by signal. When the repair is beyond the capacity of ship's staff, rectification is arranged by the staff of the Area CSO(E) using either Fleet Maintenance Base labour or dockyard resources.

Modifications

Ship's officers may propose modifications by the use of Form S.2022 but no modifications should be implemented until they have been officially approved and promulgated. Modifications fall into three categories: Category I — those which can be implemented by ship's staff, and Categories II and III — those which are beyond the capability of Fleet resources and are undertaken by dockyards; their categorisation depending on the cost of implementation. Modifications are also classified for priority, dependent upon the urgency with which they should be completed.

Approved modifications are promulgated in leaflets which are published as amendments to the relevant handbooks. A leaflet identifies the modification and gives the category and classification together with full instructions for implementation. In some cases where the priority classification requires early notification, the initial promulgation is made by signal. Ship's staff modifications, including those requiring Fleet assistance, are implemented together with preventive maintenance by incorporating their planning and control into the Maintenance Management System. Category II and III modifications are normally implemented during a refit or, exceptionally, some of a more urgent priority classification may be undertaken by dockyard defect procedure at an earlier date. Reports of completion are not normally required unless particularly stated in the promulgation leaflet or signal.

Alterations and additions

As & As may be proposed by ship's officers but are never progressed until they have been officially approved. Approved As & As are promulgated in *Defence Council Instructions* but this does not necessarily mean that the work can be initiated. Those classified for ship's staff implementation are integrated with preventive maintenance and progressed, provided the work does not prejudice that of maintenance. As & As classified for dockyard implementation are considered by a MOD(N) committee and, prior to a ship's refit, the appropriate authorities are informed of those As & As which are to be completed and those which are to be progressed in order of priority. At the end of the refit the As & As completed and progressed are reported to MOD(N) by signal.

DOCKYARD SUPPORT

The primary role of the Royal Dockyards is the repair and modernisation of ships of the Fleet. On occasions some of this work is undertaken at private yards under commercial contract.

The types of work and when it is undertaken have already been explained. Major and Normal Refits, DEDs and DAMPs are all programmed upkeep periods which have been agreed between the Chief Executive Royal Dockyards and the Naval Staff. As such these tasks are fully planned and budgeted, both financially and for their time and labour content. The work on OPDEFs and Pre-deployment AMPs is also an integral part of the dockyard task and, although not programmed, is allowed for on a contingency basis estimated on the experience of past requirements.

NAVAL BASE ORGANISATION

The facilities for support of the Fleet at a naval port are provided by various departments or establishments which are accountable to their headquarters directorates or administrative authorities. These departments also have certain responsibilities to the *Port Admiral* who is the co-ordinating authority for the Fleet support facilities within the organisation of a *Naval Base,* which is shown in the following table.

NAVAL BASE ORGANISATION

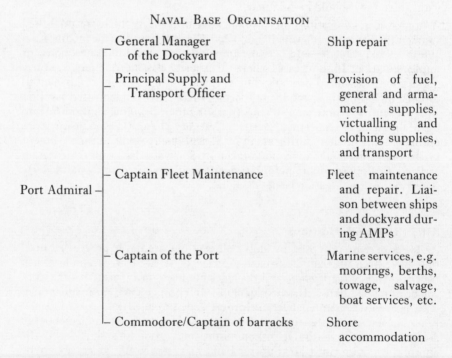

Port Admiral		
	General Manager of the Dockyard	Ship repair
	Principal Supply and Transport Officer	Provision of fuel, general and armament supplies, victualling and clothing supplies, and transport
	Captain Fleet Maintenance	Fleet maintenance and repair. Liaison between ships and dockyard during AMPs
	Captain of the Port	Marine services, e.g. moorings, berths, towage, salvage, boat services, etc.
	Commodore/Captain of barracks	Shore accommodation

The division of responsibility for the various services is sufficiently explained by the table, but the organisation of a dockyard requires further explanation for its ship repair function to be more fully understood.

DOCKYARD ORGANISATION

A Royal Dockyard is controlled by a General Manager who is accountable to the Chief Executive Royal Dockyards. The complete range of dockyard activities is divided between a number of functional departments, each under the control of a manager responsible to the General Manager. The work of these departments in a typical organisation is described below under the titles of the respective managers although minor variations may occur in some yards.

Planning Manager

The Planning Department is responsible for the broad planning of the dockyard programme and allocation of resources. The department operates through a number of sections which are collectively responsible for the arranging of ships into the dockyard programme, the planning of berthing and movements in non-tidal berths and docks, the costing of defect lists and As & As, the preparation of estimates and budgets, the advance ordering of material for planned work, and the design and drawing work associated with the dockyard programme. A *Design and Technical Information Section* provides support for these functions by the collection and provision of all the necessary data in the form of specifications, publications, drawings, etc.

Production Manager

The Production Department may appear to be the most important from a ship refit aspect because it is responsible for the execution of all the work, both *afloat* (on board ship) and in the workshops ashore, and for its presentation for acceptance. The department usually operates through a number of divisions. These are: a *Control and Administration Division* responsible for project planning and scheduling on a ship group basis, and for labour allocation; a *Weapons, Radio and Machine Shops Division* responsible for all weapons and radio work, and factory production; and a *General Trades Division* responsible for the work in the general trades, e.g. shipwrights, painters, boilermakers, joiners, smiths, sailmakers, etc.

Yard Services Manager

The Yard Services Department provides, maintains and operates all the services within the dockyard and at certain outstations. The services include craneage and dock machinery, electricity supply, steam and chilled-water supplies, telecommunication systems, and general cleanliness of the yard. The department also co-ordinates the planning for development of these services in the Naval Base and its outstations.

Personnel Manager

The Personnel Department is responsible for the recruitment and employment of staff; training, particularly of craft apprentices; fire prevention; management training; safety including training, inspections and accident investigation; and welfare.

Management Services and Productivity Manager

The Management Services and Productivity Department provides the management planning and method study services; operates the dockyard computer systems; provides dockyard overhead budgets; and administers the productivity bargaining arrangements.

Quality Assurance Manager

General quality assurance is achieved by ensuring that production conforms to the specifications and procedures determined by the Quality Assurance Department. This department specifies the standards to be met at each stage of the production process, and is responsible for audit of the control documentation during and on completion of the work to ensure that proper procedures have been followed and that the standards have been achieved.

Nuclear Power Manager

Certain Royal Dockyards have a Nuclear Power Department which provides support for the refit of nuclear-powered submarines, and is responsible for nuclear refuelling, health physics, and the trials of reactors and propulsion machinery.

Finance Manager

The Finance Department provides cost-accounting services to departmental managers, and is responsible for time recording, salaries and wages.

Dockyard Materiel Support Group

The Dockyard Materiel Support Group, under the administration of the Principal Supply and Transport Officer (Naval), provides a complete materiel support service to the General Manager.

REFIT PLANNING

To ensure the most economical use of resources and to give the best possible service to ships it is essential to gain the utmost advantage from modern planning methods. Dockyards use a three-tier planning system which is briefly described below.

Level 1 Planning, undertaken by the Planning Department, is the development of a broad-based plan for the general programming of all ships in hand and other work in the dockyard.

Level 2 Planning expands the work package accepted at Level 1 into individual projects on which detailed planning and scheduling is then undertaken. Separate *Project Control Offices* or *Project Control Groups* (PCOs or PCGs) are established, usually at a common location, for all the forthcoming and current projects.

Level 3 Planning, undertaken by the Production Department, is the detailed planning associated with each job. The planning comprises the allocation of individual jobs, raising demands for material, initiating quality-control procedures where applicable, requisitioning assistance when and where necessary, etc. Each workshop or trade category is controlled through a *Centre Trade Office* (CTO) located in the relevant workshop, or at the Project Control Office for the main afloat trades (the trades practised solely on board ship, e.g. shipwrights, welders, wiremen, etc.).

Thus the point of enquiry regarding the progress of a particular job is the appropriate Centre Trade Office whereas factors affecting the refit plan are the business of the Project Control Office and possibly the Planning Department.

Definitions of ship planning dates

It is important when planning ships' programmes that particular dates associated with dockyard work are clearly defined and understood. The following standard terms are always used.

DATE	DEFINITION
Non-operational Date	The date of the beginning of preparation for refit (i.e. de-ammunitioning, tank cleaning, etc.).
Start Date	Date on which ship is taken in hand by dockyard.
Terminal Date	The date by which refitting and installation work is complete, with the exception of certain trials, cleaning and painting work.
Completion Date	The date by which all work in a ship is complete, all yard trials including basin and specified harbour trials are complete; and all cleaning, painting, etc. is complete. The ship is ready for Sea Trials.
Operational Date	The date on which the ship is accepted as ready to join the Fleet or to start working up (i.e. after ammunitioning, storing, and ship's staff trials including Sea Trials).

REFIT PROCEDURE

The preparation for a successful refit commences at the start of the commission or on the completion of the previous refit. From this time the details of all defects and other work to be carried out must be fully and faithfully recorded. As the refit approaches, a standard programme is followed which enables the refit to be planned and undertaken by the dockyard. A typical programme for a Normal Refit is explained below but minor differences may occur for some ships or at some dockyards. The full details of refit, DED and DAMP procedures are contained in *Fleet Engineering Orders*, and for surface ships they are also given in BR 8593(12), *Ship Refit, Repair, Maintenance and Associated Procedures — Defect List Procedure for Surface Ships*.

The programme commences when the ship is informed by its administrative authority of the Start Date (SD) of the refit. This usually occurs 60 weeks prior to SD and at this time a ship's officer is nominated to be the *Refit Planning Officer*. He is responsible within the ship for the planning associated with the refit, which is required by *Fleet Engineering Orders* and described in *Practical Management in Ships*. Twelve months prior to SD the ship forwards a list of equipment requiring refit work for which special procurement action is necessary, and a list of approved As & As which the ship would prefer to be undertaken, together with the reasons supporting these preferences. Six months prior to SD the General Manager of the dockyard appoints a Project Manager who is the dockyard officer responsible for the overall planning and conduct of the refit.

Pre-refit Trials

During a period which extends from 30 weeks to between 16 and 13 weeks prior to SD the ship's staff carry out a comprehensive series of trials, tests and inspections of all machinery and equipment in accordance with the relevant handbooks, maintenance schedules and Pre-refit Trial documents forwarded by the ship's administrative authority (Area CSO(E) for ships administered by C-in-C Fleet). All defects, performance failures or out-of-tolerance readings discovered during the trials are recorded for subsequent action as dockyard defect items or for repair by ship's staff.

Defect lists

Defect lists are the method of informing the dockyard, the administrative authority and others, of the repair and maintenance work that needs to be undertaken. Ship's officers compile the lists which are divided into several parts and forwarded at various times.

Main Defect List. This list contains all the work which can be predicted early including scheduled preventive maintenance, all known defects and other authorised corrective maintenance, all authorised modifications, and mandatory calibration of test equipment. Approved As & As which it is planned to undertake are subsequently added to the list by the administrative authority.

Supplementary Defect List. This list contains any essential new corrective maintenance items and is despatched 4 weeks prior to SD.

Any further essential dockyard work arising after the Supplementary Defect List has been rendered is submitted individually on a Defect Report. The Project Manager will accept work within the contingency budget but when this is exhausted any further items are submitted through the Area CSO(E) who will negotiate with the dockyard.

Pre-refit visit

After completion of Pre-refit Trials the ship is visited by representatives of the staff of the CSO(E) of the refitting port (or the administrative authority, for ships not administered by C-in-C Fleet). The visit is planned to take place over five consecutive days in harbour between 16 and 13 weeks prior to SD, and during this period the Project Manager and other dockyard officers also attend. The purpose of the combined visit is to discuss and agree many topics which include Pre-refit Trials, the Main Defect List, As & As, refit preparations, assistance from the Fleet Maintenance Group, ship's staff refit work, etc.

Miscellaneous requirements

During the period approaching the Non-operational Date several miscellaneous requirements must be finalised and submitted at specified times by ship's officers. Examples and their timing in relation to the Start Date are shown below.

REQUIREMENT	WEEKS BEFORE SD
Application for refit offices	13
Report of completion of Pre-refit Trials	12
Application for shore accommodation	10
Application for tank-cleaning vessel	9
Estimate of Fleet Maintenance Group assistance required	8
Refit Preparation Letter containing the ship's proposed Refit Preparation Plan covering the period between the Non-operational Date and the Start Date	4

Four weeks prior to SD the dockyard issues a *Project Management Plan* for the complete refit, based on forward planning, information received from the ship at the Pre-refit Visit and by the Defect Lists, and on the A & A work to be undertaken.

Refit preparations

Three weeks prior to SD the dockyard issues an agreed plan for the refit preparation period based on the ship's proposals. The ship becomes non-operational 1 – 2 weeks prior to SD, and the programme of work in the agreed plan is undertaken, e.g. de-ammunitioning, de-fuelling and tank cleaning, de-storing, move to shore accommodation, establishment of refit offices, etc.

Refit Conference

One week prior to SD a Refit Conference is held which is chaired by the General Manager or his representative, and is attended by ship's officers, dockyard officers, and representatives of the administrative authority and Area Chief Staff Officer (Engineering). The function of this conference is to agree formally the work to be carried out, the time in hand, the general plan and responsibilities for presentation of equipment for trials.

Refit

On the Start Date the ship is taken in hand by the dockyard and the refit work is progressed in accordance with the Project Management Plan and as determined at the Refit Conference.

Two separate, mobile or portable, offices are normally established for the use of ship's staff during the refit. One is the *Refit Office*, in the charge of the Refit Planning Officer, which is used as the central point of contact between the ship and the dockyard, to contain all the data relevant to the progress of the refit and as the monitoring centre for all refit work. The other office is used as a general *Regulating, Routine and Stores Office*.

During the refit, ship's staff have many responsibilities in addition to those already described. Ship's officers' responsibilities are listed below and are fully explained in *Fleet Engineering Orders*.

DURING REFIT

1. The security and safety of the ship, and the safe operation and custody of its equipment.

2. Planning and co-ordinating work of ship's staff and ensuring that it is efficiently linked with dockyard work.

3. Carrying out trials and accepting dockyard work.

4. Liaising with other authorities concerned with the refit.

5. Maintaining proper care and preservation of idle machinery and equipment.

6. Ensuring that proper records are kept in Ship Equipment Files and other documentation.

7. Ensuring adequate security arrangements, including a comprehensive rounds routine and an organisation for posting sentries when necessary.

8. Ensuring the cleanliness of the ship.

9. Establishing a liaison with the Area Fire Prevention Officer and ensuring that there is an efficient organisation for firefighting and for providing welding sentries.

BEFORE ENTERING DOCK

1. Ensuring that propellers, rudders and stabilisers are in their docking positions, retractable hull outfits and bottom logs are fully housed, cranes and davits are properly stowed, bollards and fairleads are clear and ready for use, and that all guardrails are intact and properly rigged.

2. Ensuring that the heel, trim and ballasting of the ship are satisfactory to the repair authority.

3. Recording a statement of the amount of liquid retained in each tank.

WHILE THE SHIP IS IN DOCK

1. Proper observation of the regulations concerning explosives and fuel retained on board.

2. Ensuring that the ship is properly earthed.

3. Ensuring that no change is made to the distribution of weights, including liquids, without approval of the repair authority and that any such changes are properly recorded.

4. Ensuring that no machinery is run, or equipment or armament moved without specific approval from the repair authority.

5. Ensuring that adequate firefighting, pumping and flooding arrangements are available throughout the docking period.

6. Proper observation of the regulations concerning the cleanliness of the dock and the discharge of water into the dock.

7. Before undocking, that all underwater valves and fittings are in efficient working order, that all orifices in the ship's bottom are clear, and that all underwater valves and connections are shut.

8. When undocking, proper observation of the regulations concerning hull outfits.

Refit monitoring and reports

Ship's officers are required to monitor the progress of all work undertaken during the refit by means of a *Standard Refit Monitoring System*. The aims of monitoring are:

1. To enable the progress of the refit to be assessed with particular relation to the timely achievement of the stages of the refit plan.

2. To enable the work of ship's staff and the Fleet Maintenance Group to be planned to complement that of the dockyard.

3. To ensure that no agreed item of refit work is overlooked and that dockyard work is checked and accepted by ship's staff at the appropriate time.

Instructions for setting up the Standard Refit Monitoring System are sent to the ship 18 weeks prior to SD and further details are provided in *Practical Management in Ships* (published by C-in-C Fleet).

Weekly reports on the progress of the refit are forwarded by ship's officers to the Area Chief Staff Officer (Engineering). These reports reflect the ship's officers' opinions of refit progress as well as a factual summary of the progress achieved, and also report any changes that have occurred in the refit plan.

Formal inspections

Ships are formally inspected on certain dates towards the end of the refit period to demonstrate satisfactory achievement of the refit plan.

Terminal Date inspection. The ship is inspected by the Port Admiral who may delegate this responsibility to the General Manager unless the ship is proceeding to sea before Completion Date. The purpose is the presentation of the ship by the Project Manager and dockyard officers to demonstrate the completion of work required by the Terminal Date.

Completion Date inspection. The purpose of this inspection by the Port Admiral is the presentation of the ship jointly by the Commanding Officer and the Project Manager to demonstrate the completion of all programmed work by dockyard, ship's staff and the Fleet Maintenance Group, including trials, ship's staff training and agreed painting work, and that the ship is in all respects ready for Sea Trials.

Post-refit acceptance trials

On completion of the refit, comprehensive trials are carried out on all machinery, equipment and systems whether they have been refitted or not. The trials fall into two categories: *Harbour Acceptance Trials* (HATs) which comprise all those items of the trials schedule which can be completed in harbour, and *Sea Acceptance Trials* (SATs) to cover the scheduled items which can only be tested at sea. Certain items of HATs can be conducted as the refit progresses and should be finalised by Completion Date, e.g. electrical equipment and systems, whereas others such as the Basin Trial of propulsion machinery have to be integrated into a planned programme. External authorities are responsible for the conduct of some trials but in most cases ship's officers are responsible. Prepared schedules or check-off lists are provided for the trials of most equipment but if these are not available ship's officers should devise suitable trials seeking advice where necessary.

A *Post-refit Acceptance Trials Programme* to cover all the trials activities is drawn up by ship's officers in consultation with all associated authorities. An officer, usually the Navigating Officer, is nominated as the *Post-refit Acceptance Trials Co-ordinator* and he is responsible for arranging all trials and facilities throughout the trials period.

Operational Date Material Assessment (ODMA)

On completion of Post-refit Acceptance Trials each ship is assessed by its administrative authority to ensure that it is materially satisfactory for operational service. The assessment is planned into the Post-refit Acceptance Trials Programme and normally takes the following form.

1. Departmental assessments by the engineering staff of the administrative authority, taking into account results of trials conducted by independent authorities.

2. A whole-ship walk-round by the Area or Fleet Chief Staff Officer (Engineering) which usually takes place on the Operational Date.

Operational Sea Training

On becoming operational, ships undergo a period of operational sea training under the administration of the Flag Officer Sea Training (FOST).

The training comprises a comprehensive series of drills, exercises and inspections, designed to suit the type of ship, spread over a period of up to seven weeks. An initial shakedown period of one week is planned to test every piece of equipment in slow time under realistic conditions, to enable the officers and ship's company to work together and become familiar with the ship, and to test the organisation and ability of the ship to operate as a single unit. During the shakedown week a *Staff Sea Check* is conducted by officers and senior ratings on the staff of FOST to assess the state of the ship and her company, and their readiness for operational sea training. The shakedown week is followed by a Harbour Training and Defect Week in which various harbour exercises are conducted and any defects can be repaired. A Fleet Maintenance Group is available to provide assistance to ships' staffs if required. The remaining time is devoted to harbour and sea training, both as a single ship and in company, and includes a walk-round and formal inspections of the ship and divisions of the ship's company by FOST.

The form of training so far described is known as *Basic Operational Sea Training* (BOST). Facilities are also provided for ships to undergo *Consolidation Operational Sea Training* (COST) at suitable times throughout continuous commissions. COST is designed to assist in the maintenance and improvement of standards, taking into account the employment of the ship and changes in the ship's company imposed by the drafting system.

Prior to training, ship's officers should make liaison visits to meet the staff officers and discuss the programme of training. Full details of all training are given in the *Operational Sea Training Guide* which is issued to ships and authorities by the office of FOST. All other documentation is forwarded to ships three months prior to their arrival for training. It is most important that ship's officers make themselves conversant with the Guide and other documentation before arrival because there is little time for reading during the training period.

FITTINGS AND STORES

The definitions of *fittings* and *stores* can be easily confused because an item of stores may become a fitting by the method of its incorporation into the ship. A fitting consists of equipment or gear which is an integral part of the ship, may have been made expressly for her, and is fixed or kept in a more-or-less permanent position or stowage. Stores consist of items of a standard type which can be supplied to any ship for her general running and maintenance. The following notes are intended to give the Seaman officer an outline of the whole organisation for fittings and stores.

FITTINGS

Fittings can be subdivided into *ship's fittings* and *portable fittings*.

Ship's fittings comprise items which are built into a ship or are integral parts of her, examples being: the armament; pumps, fans and other machinery; propellers, rudders, capstans, winches, bollards, fairleads, etc. These items are all shown on ship's 'As Fitted' drawings but no accounts are kept for such equipment and it is not taken on charge by the ship's officers.

Portable fittings are either portable or can readily be made so, and they are divided into the following categories:

1. Fittings which are made for a particular ship and which, therefore, are not interchangeable with other ships and *are not* classified as *naval stores* (i.e. stores listed in BR 320D, *Catalogue of Naval Stores*), examples being: ship's badges, running rigging, awnings and other canvas gear, slings, and fitted furniture.

2. Fittings which may be interchangeable with other ships, but which, though of a standard nature, *are not* classified as *naval stores*, examples being: bread lockers, rifle racks, machine tools, portable pumps and anchor fittings.

3. Certain fittings which *are* classified as *naval stores* and which, though fitted in place, can be made portable. Examples are radio, radar and compass outfits, and weapon control equipments.

All these items are shown on various authorising lists, e.g. computer print-outs, lists of commercial fittings, Form D.6f, *Rigging Warrant*, etc. They are recorded in loose-leaf lists of portable fittings and are accounted for by the appropriate departmental officers. Portable fittings are not entered in the Main Store Account, neither are they accounted for by the Supply Officer.

STORES

Stores are classified under several main headings: *naval stores* which includes accommodation stores, general, electronic, weapon control and diving stores, musical stores and machinery spare parts; *air stores*; *victualling stores*; and *office machinery, stationery, books and forms*. All these categories of stores are the responsibility of the ship's Supply Officer and are handled by the Supply department. Other categories of stores, such as *armament stores, medical stores* and *hydrographic supplies*, are the responsibility of departmental officers, and *canteen stores* are the responsibility of the canteen staff.

NAVAL STORES

The term *naval stores* includes all standard items and materials of an established pattern which are in general use for the work or upkeep of a ship. The majority are catalogued in BR 320D, *Catalogue of Naval Stores* which is an authorised list and priced index of naval stores. Other naval stores are catalogued in *Illustrated Parts Catalogues* (IPCs) related to particular equipments or in *Joint Service Publications* (JSPs) appropriate to the categories of stores. The regulations governing their procurement, accounting, etc., are to be found in BR 96, *Stores Accounting and Storekeeping Manual*.

Identification

For cataloguing, accounting and indexing purposes each item of naval stores is identified by a *Naval Store Catalogue Number* (NS Cat No) or Part Number and a description, e.g. 0263/414–9831, *Slip, rigging*. The complete range of naval stores is divided into numerous *Management Code* groups. The first four digits of an allocated number indicate the code group to which that particular item is allocated. The last seven digits form the item identification number within the Management Code. To avoid ambiguity in any naval store transactions it is essential that the full NS Cat Nos and descriptions are always quoted. An abridged list of codes is shown below.

MANAGEMENT CODE	DESCRIPTION OF STORES
0091 and 0095	Accommodation stores
0100	Timber
0211–0299	Metal and metal articles
0310–0350	Textiles and cordage, and articles made from them
0411–0482	Miscellaneous articles, such as rubber, furniture, paint, etc.
0512–0699	Electrical and electronic stores including radio, radar and sonar equipment
0711–0726	Solid and liquid fuel, and lubricating oils
0831–0898	Weapon control stores.

Many items within the various stores ranges have been codified within the North Atlantic Treaty Organization and therefore have a NATO *Supply Classification* in addition to the Management Code. The NATO numbering consists of a four-digit Supply Classification and a two-digit *Nation Code* followed by the Item Identification Number, e.g. 4030–99–414–9771, *Hook, coaling purposes*. The whole number forms the *NATO Stock Number* (NSN) for the item. The item identification number remains the same in both systems of identification and, to show the relationship between NATO Supply Classification and naval Management Code, a *Cross Reference List* is given in BR 320G.

Accounting status

Stores are classified in BR 320 under three categories for accounting purposes: *Permanent, Consumable accountable* and *Consumable.*

Permanent stores are those which have a reasonably long life, are not consumed in use, may be repaired when unserviceable and then re-issued for use, and are sufficiently valuable to warrant continuous accounting throughout their life.

Consumable accountable stores are those which, although defined as *consumable*, either have intrinsic value or some other property which warrants control over their issue. Such stores are only issued to nominated persons when authorised by a responsible officer on Form S.156.

Consumable stores are those which are consumed or destroyed in use within a limited period, or are of such low value that they need not be accounted for after issue. These stores are usually issued at any time to nominated persons against a signature in the *Counter Book* (Form S.120).

Sea stores

Naval stores are issued to ships either as portable fittings or *sea stores*. The allowances of sea stores to the various classes of ship are shown on Form S.132, *Allowance List of General Stores*; Form D.1206, *Allowance List of Electronic, Weapon Control or Machinery Spare Parts*; and Depot Task List, *Allowance List of Air Stores*. The allowances of permanent stores are fixed in quantity and may only be exceeded by approval of the administrative authority whereas the allowances for consumable stores are given for a first outfit and stocks may be subsequently adjusted commensurate with usage.

Certain sea stores are sub-classified as *first-fitting* (FF), *fitted* (F), *navigational and trial* (N) or *hull equipment* (H) stores.

First-fitting stores comprise the anchors and cables, together with their associated gear; and boats and liferafts. These are usually sent to the ship when she is in an advanced stage of construction and fitted or placed in position by the shipbuilder.

Fitted stores are those which, though fitted in certain positions in the ship, are readily portable — firefighting appliances, for example — but they should not be confused with portable fittings. Fitted stores are usually sent to the ship and fitted in place during the final stages of building.

Navigational and trial stores, commonly known as *testing and tuning spares*, are those necessary to support the setting-to-work process of a ship's equipment and to enable her to put to sea before the main bulk of stores is embarked (e.g. for trials).

Hull equipment stores are the ship's machinery spares particular to the ship, which must be embarked and stowed in their proper positions before the ship proceeds to sea.

Accounting procedure

Particulars of all permanent and consumable stores are entered into an index card (*sagacard*) accounting system, known as the *Main Store Account*. The

U

account is divided by using different coloured cards for the three types of accounting status: permanent — pink; consumable accountable — blue; and consumable — white. On first commissioning, the account is handed to the Supply Officer as a record of all the stores on his charge. Permanent stores which are required for use in the ship are issued to the appropriate departments, and for this purpose the ship's Supply Officer prepares and issues lists of such stores (known as *Permanent Loan Records* (Form S.1099)) to the officers or senior ratings of the departments concerned. Transactions of these items are then recorded on the appropriate supply and return forms, the Permanent Loan Records and the Main Store Account.

Consumable items are issued from store on demand, as described on page 295, and noted in the Main Store Account so that timely replenishment can be made. The quantities of consumable stores initially embarked are shown in the Allowance Lists, Form S.132 or D.1206, but these quantities are adjusted by the ship's staff as experience of usage is gained and to satisfy expected requirements.

Stocktaking

Stocktaking in a ship is a continuous procedure, organised so that all sea stores in the charge of the Supply Officer are subject to stocktaking every eighteen months. Differences found are reported every six months.

Musters

Every six months the Supply Officer or his staff ensures that each custodian musters all the stores listed in his loan record. The stores on loan are also mustered, and signed for in the record, when initially issued and on change of custodian.

Replenishment

Stocks are maintained in ships by means of replenishment-at-sea (RAS) procedures or, when in harbour in the United Kingdom, by Dockyard Provider Services. Exceptionally, urgent stores are supplied by the most suitable means in response to signalled demands. Supply Officers are required to take maximum advantage of the first two methods.

AIR STORES

Air stores cover spare parts for aircraft and their engines, and items of equipment provided for their operation, maintenance and repair. The category includes compass and photographic equipment, and flying clothing, but not air radio stores which are dealt with as naval stores under Management Code 0624.

The majority of air stores are catalogued in AP 1086, *Catalogue of General RAF Equipment*. They are taken on charge by the Supply Officer in the Main Store Account and are handled in the same manner as naval stores.

VICTUALLING STORES

The term *victualling stores* covers a wide variety of items including some not normally associated with the word 'victuals' meaning food and drink. The different types of victualling stores for HM ships are listed below.

Provisions, which are subdivided into *fresh provisions*, e.g. fresh fruit, salad and fresh vegetables; *frozen provisions* which include meat, fish and quick-frozen vegetables; and *dry provisions* comprising a wide range of dried, packeted, tinned and bagged foodstuffs.

Clothing, which includes uniform articles of personal kit as well as protective clothing and bedding. It is classed generally as *loan clothing* which is issued on individual loan to the user, and as *cash clothing* (slops) which is sold to officers and ratings for the purpose of kit upkeep. Cash clothing is normally only carried in ships larger than frigates and is stowed in a special storeroom called the *cash clothing store* (slop room).

Tobacco comprising tinned pipe and cigarette tobacco and 'blue line' cigarettes drawn from Service sources.

Mess gear (Accommodation stores) comprising everything used for the preparation, serving and eating of food. The complete range is subdivided and classified as follows:

Officers' mess traps, for officers' messes and pantries;
Mess utensils for ratings' dining halls and messes;
Implements and galley gear, for all galleys.

Medical comforts, which include various special items of food and drink as prescribed for the sick by the Medical Officer; examples are soups, broths and consumable spirits.

The full range of items available is set out in BR 1246, *Rate Book and Vocabulary for Victualling Stores* and in JSP 307, *Joint Service Catalogue of Accommodation Stores*.

Stock levels

In seagoing ships stocks of *fresh provisions* are regulated according to the ship's requirements and to her facilities for keeping them in good condition. The maximum and minimum quantities of other provisions to be maintained in different classes of ship are laid down in BR 5, *The Naval Catering Manual*, which also gives instructions for the issue, inspection, stowage and return of provisions. Under normal conditions of service the stock of *cash clothing* held for sale should not exceed three months' average requirements. The stock of *loan clothing* items is specified in scales set out in an appendix to BR 96, *Stores Accounting and Storekeeping Manual*.

Stocktaking

As for naval stores, the stocktaking of victualling stores is intended to check the quantity and condition of each item remaining in store. The intervals between stocktaking vary according to the type of victualling stores and whether the ship is a tender to a base or parent ship, or is self-accounting. Full details are given in BR 96.

OFFICE MACHINERY, STATIONERY, BOOKS AND FORMS

Office machinery comprises typewriters, copying machines, calculators, etc. The allowances of such items, and the demand and supply procedures, are published in JSP 357, *Stationery, Publications, Typing, Printing, Binding and Office Machinery: Instructions and Procedures*. These items are taken on charge in the Main Store Account by the Supply Officer and then issued on permanent loan to departmental officers or senior ratings.

Stationery and Office Requisites comprise paper, writing books, rulers, stapling machines and staples, erasers, pencils, pens, etc. These goods are divided into the following two categories.

    Coded items which are common goods used in large quantities throughout the Service, and are listed in the *Stock Catalogue of Office Requisites for use in the Public Service* published by HMSO.

    Non-coded items which include special materials particular to some machines, security brief-cases, and articles which have to be manufactured or supplied to order (e.g. official stamps bearing ships' or department names).

On commissioning, ships are supplied on demand with an initial outfit in accordance with a scale of allowances dependent on the class of ship. Subsequent demands by ships, for replenishment and additional items, are forwarded at six-monthly intervals allowing for a two months' overlap of stock and for one month's delivery time. Full instructions on demanding procedures are given in JSP 357.

Forms. Standard printed forms used throughout the Service are known as Established Forms. Those particular to the Navy Department are numbered in the S-series and are listed in Form S.1, *Catalogue of Established S Forms*. An initial stock is supplied, without demand, to ships on commissioning, and demands for replenishment or additional forms may be raised at any time thereafter. Full instructions regarding S Forms are given in Form S1 and also in JSP 357.

Books of Reference (BRs) and other miscellaneous publications are listed in BR 1, *Catalogue of Books for the Royal Navy Classified Restricted and Below* which also contains instructions regarding their issue, custody and return. These publications are supplied to ships through RN Distribution Authorities (RNDAs) which are established at various suitable locations. HM ships generally are supplied to an authorised scale but, within certain allowances, the constitution of the initial outfit of books is negotiated between ship's officers and the appropriate RNDA. New books and amendments to existing books are distributed automatically and reasoned requirements of additional books may be demanded at any time through the ship's Supply Officer. Publications of a higher security classification are supplied either through an RNDA or the ship's administrative authority.

ARMAMENT STORES

Armament stores comprise guided weapons, torpedoes, ammunition, pyrotechnics, guns, small arms, mortar barrels, breech mechanisms, gun stores, special tools, etc. The descriptions and quantities embarked are shown in the *Warrant of Naval Armament Stores* which is an allowance list and charge document particular to the ship. The stores are in the charge of a ship's officer nominated as the *Explosives Responsible Officer* (ERO) and in some ships this responsibility may be shared by more than one officer. The routine accounting is carried out by a senior rating detailed to carry out the duties of *Explosives Accountant* (EA).

Explosives and ammunition are stowed in magazines or magazine lockers. In war conditions or during exercise periods small quantities may be kept in ready-use magazines or lockers. Pyrotechnics and smoke stores must always be kept in upper-deck stowages. Small arms, portable weapons and large spares for the fixed armament are stored in fitted stowages around the ship; other items are stowed in specially appointed storerooms. Special precautions are taken to ensure the safe custody of explosives, small arms and portable weapons. Tools, spares and items of equipment are issued on permanent loan to the officers or senior ratings most concerned with their use, and they are accounted for through the Explosives Accountant in a manner similar to that for naval stores issued on permanent loan.

The regulations, including organisation and responsibilities, for the handling and custody of explosives are laid down in BR 862, *Naval Magazine and Explosives Regulations*. Instructions for procurement and accounting of armament stores are given in BR 1032, *Naval Armament Stores Accounting Instructions for HM Ships and Fleet Establishments*.

MEDICAL STORES

The broad definition of *medical stores* includes medicines, drugs, surgical instruments, dressings, and equipment for medical and dental purposes which are catalogued in JSP 324, *British Joint Services Catalogue of Medical Equipment*. These items are held on board in the charge of the Medical or Dental Officer as appropriate. Where no Dental Officer is borne the Medical Officer has charge of such dental stores as are carried. Similarly the Squadron Medical Officer is responsible where no Medical Officer is borne, except that the Commanding Officer acts in that capacity when the ship is an independent command.

Information on medical stores is given in BR 1991, *Instructions for the RN Medical Service*, and the regulations governing procurement, accounting, etc. are contained in the RN Medical Service Standing Order No. 1, *Medical and Dental Storekeeping and Stores Accounting Regulations* which is published and distributed by the Medical Director General.

Scales and quantities

The scales of medical stores allowed to a ship depend mainly on the complement, deployment, and whether a Medical Officer and a Dental Officer are borne. Details are given in BR 1232, *Scales of Medical Stores for Service Afloat*.

The quantities laid down are based generally on six months' estimated requirements and represent the first outfit supplied to ships on commissioning. The scales are not inflexible, being amended as required by experience and according to changing practices and modern techniques. Consideration is given to reasoned demands for extra quantities or additional types of stores.

Sources of supply. Initial outfits and replenishments of medical stores are obtained from the nearest Royal Naval Hospital or RN Medical Store. Where no Dental Officer is borne, the initial outfit includes the necessary dental stores. When a Dental Officer is borne, the initial outfit of dental stores is obtained from the Defence Medical Equipment Depot, Ludgershall, Wiltshire; all replenishments of dental stores are also obtained from this source.

Accounting and stocktaking

A loose-leaf continuous ledger is used to account for all medical stores. Controlled drugs are mustered and surveyed every three months; other stores are mustered and surveyed every six months, on completion of which a report is rendered to the Medical Directorate General for audit purposes. Exceptionally, the stores are mustered on supersession of the responsible officer and on closing the account when the ship pays off.

HYDROGRAPHIC SUPPLIES

The term *hydrographic supplies* covers the charts, air charts, maps, books, publications and timepieces provided for the navigation of the Fleet.

Admiralty charts and navigational publications are produced by the Hydrographic Department, Ministry of Defence, Taunton, under the superintendence of the Hydrographer of the Navy. The distribution of these charts and publications, together with other navigational and meteorological publications, is arranged by the Hydrographic Department through Admiralty Chart and Chronometer Depots which are established at suitable locations.

Chronometers and navigational watches are normally supplied to ships through a Chart and Chronometer Depot, through which subsequent transactions should be made.

Scales of allowances and full details of the methods of supply of chart outfits, navigational timepieces and publications, and hydrographic forms, are published in NP 133, *Hydrographic Supplies Handbook*.

CANTEEN STORES

Canteen stores are the property of the Navy, Army and Air Force Institutes (NAAFI); their provision, custody and accounting are the responsibility of the Canteen Manager who is a member of the Naval Canteen Service. The stores are stowed in the canteen or in store rooms specially allocated to NAAFI. Ship's officers have no responsibilities with regard to canteen stores except for providing reasonable facilities for their issue, care and custody. In addition to the sale of canteen stores to individuals and messes, they may be purchased by the ship's Supply Officer to supplement Service supplies of food. Further information on canteen arrangements is published in BR 8508, *Navy, Army and Air Force Institutes (NAAFI) — Naval Canteen Service*.

PART IV

SHIPHANDLING AND NAVIGATION

CHAPTER 11

Officer of the Watch at Sea

AUTHORITY

The authority of the Officer of the Watch is defined in *The Queen's Regulations for the Royal Navy* as follows:

> '*Every officer and other person, not being either the Commanding Officer or the Commanding Officer for the time being or the Executive Officer, is to be subordinate to the Officer of the Watch, whatever may be his rank, in regard to the performance of the duties with which the Officer of the Watch is charged.*'

At sea the Officer of the Watch is thus the Captain's representative on the bridge. Furthermore, all his responsibilities remain with him whether the Captain is on the bridge or not, unless the Captain has specifically relieved him of them.

A junior officer carries no greater responsibility at any time than when Officer of the Watch. Just as a doctor may be expected to diagnose an emergency case and prescribe the correct treatment in a matter of moments, so an Officer of the Watch may be expected in an emergency to take the correct course of action (and there may be only one) to save the ship and her company from disaster. In both cases, only the most thorough training and full professional background knowledge, coupled with an alert mind, will ensure that the right action is taken at the time.

RESPONSIBILITIES

The chief responsibility of the Officer of the Watch at sea is the safety of the ship, and in particular her safety from collision. Whether or not a qualified Navigating Officer is borne, the Officer of the Watch has a certain responsibility for the ship's safety when approaching land, and in general for keeping himself informed of the position of the ship. He is responsible for keeping the ship in her station, for the steering, and for the safety of men on the upper deck and in exposed positions. He is expressly authorised to alter the course and speed of the ship to avoid immediate danger, but not otherwise without directions from the Captain. All these responsibilities are laid down in BR 31, *The Queen's Regulations for the Royal Navy*, Chapter 31, which every junior officer must have read and thoroughly understood, together with the *Captain's Standing Orders*, before assuming the duties of Officer of the Watch.

KNOWLEDGE REQUIRED

Rule of the Road

An Officer of the Watch cannot fulfil his most important obligation, that of the safety of the ship from collision, without having a *complete* knowledge of the *International Regulations for Preventing Collisions at Sea*. These regulations are published in Volume II; in BR 45(1), *Admiralty Manual of Navigation*, Volume I; in NP 100, *The Mariner's Handbook*; and in BR 453, *A Seaman's Guide to the Rule of the Road*. To know these rules thoroughly may entail learning the principal rules by heart, and every Officer of the Watch must not only put in some hard work at the beginning of his career on learning the Regulations, but must refresh his knowledge of them at frequent intervals. Captains should devise their own methods for testing the knowledge of their Officers of the Watch. It is an unfortunate fact that incomplete application of the Regulations is a contributory cause in most cases of collision. To put this in another way: if ships obey the rules implicitly they cannot collide with one another.

If yours is the giving-way vessel always remember that by taking action *boldly and early* you not only make clear your intentions to the other ship, but you prevent both ships from getting into proximity with each other. It is when ships are already at close quarters and danger is present that people may get flustered and make mistakes.

Bridge Emergency Orders and Bridge File

The *Bridge Emergency Orders* and *Bridge File* are kept available on the bridge for immediate use. The Officer of the Watch should be fully aware of the contents of each.

The *Bridge Emergency Orders* are presented in a tabbed file or an indexed card system or are displayed on boards. To enable quick and easy reference, colour coding is often used. The orders are written in the form of an aide-memoire to assist the Officer of the Watch in taking the correct action when confronted with an emergency or when information is needed quickly. The orders relate to such subjects as man overboard, steering gear or machinery breakdowns, helicopter operating, entering fog, etc.

The *Bridge File* contains orders and information of a less urgent nature to which the Officer of the Watch requires ready reference. Typical items included are: appropriate sections of the Captain's Standing Orders, Navigation Department Orders, extracts from the Navigational Data Book, switching arrangements for navigation lights, tables of masthead heights, list of maintainers of each radar and navigational aid, etc.

Knowledge of own ship

A professional knowledge of the capabilities of his own ship is essential to the Officer of the Watch. It is impossible to define precisely what is implicit in this, but the following are relevant.

Construction. The main features of the ship's construction, with particular reference to watertight compartmentation and vulnerability to collision. Her stability, and how it can be altered and controlled. The ship's organisation for control of damage.

Propulsion. The power and speeds obtainable with different arrangements of main propulsion machinery, and how these can be controlled from the bridge. Revolutions required for different speeds. Propeller and rudder arrangements.

Navigation. The navigational aids fitted in the ship, their capabilities and limitations (particularly their possible errors) and how each can be brought into play and used. These include compasses, sounding equipment, logs, high-definition warning surface radar, and radio aids to navigation. The ship-handling characteristics of the ship, and in particular the effect of wind on her handling qualities.

Steering and conning. The various methods available and how to change over to secondary from primary methods.

Communications. The ship's communications organisation and how it is linked with the bridge. Familiarity with all the tactical and manoeuvring signals and instructions appropriate to the ship's current task.

Armament and action. Those weapons which may be brought into action in an emergency by the Officer of the Watch and how to control them. The Action Information Organisation of the ship and how it works, particularly with regard to the surface and underwater situation.

Sources of information

Again, it is impossible to list all the possible sources of information, but the following give some indication of where or how to improve ship knowledge.

Construction. The fundamental need is for a knowledge of one's own ship, which can only be found by looking, and seeing for oneself. Chapters on warship construction, damage control and stability will be found elsewhere in this manual.

Propulsion. Information is contained in the *Ship Equipment Files,* the *Navigational Data Book* of the ship, and in BR 45(4), *Admiralty Manual of Navigation,* Volume IV. If in doubt, consult the Marine Engineering department of the ship.

Navigation. Consult BR 45, *Admiralty Manual of Navigation,* particularly Volumes I and IV, and ask the Navigating Officer to show you how to use any equipment on the bridge.

Steering and conning. Organisation and drills should be laid down in the Captain's Standing Orders.

Communications. The various tactical and other signal publications must be studied and, when on exercises or operations, the current orders.

Armament and action. Consult the appropriate group (Missile, Sonar or Radar) of the Operations department, and the user publications on weapons, sensors and the Action Information Organisation (AIO).

In addition to knowing his own ship, a capable Officer of the Watch draws on the fund of knowledge of many subjects, particularly seamanship, acquired throughout his training and career. In a warship the Officer of the Watch is part of the Command Team, of which each member plays an important part in the employment of the ship and her weapons to the best advantage. Besides the Captain and Officer of the Watch, the other members are the Principal Warfare Officer (PWO), the Navigating Officer and the various controllers of weapon systems.

How to con the ship

Orders for the wheel and engines should always be given clearly, decisively and in the correct terms, in order to avoid any misunderstanding. The correct orders to use are given in Volume I.

Layout of the bridge

Before keeping a sea watch for the first time in any ship an officer should acquaint himself with the layout of the bridge, the position of each instrument, communication system or electric switch, and the tone or noise of the buzzer or call-up on each communication system, so that in the dark he can immediately place his hand on the instrument he requires. Particularly important items are the telephones and intercom systems, the alarm pushes for the lifebuoys, the master switches for the navigation lights and the not-under-command lights, the position and controls of the bridge radar display and the controls for the sirens (or whistles).

LEAVING HARBOUR

The Officer of the Watch should be on the bridge in sufficient time to check that the special sea dutymen are at their stations and that the Ship's Log and other routine orders and papers have been transferred from the gangway to the bridge. He should have the communications numbers check their telephone communications with the forecastle and quarterdeck, and should personally check the readings of the gyro-compass repeaters in the primary and secondary steering positions, and on the wings of the bridge, with the Pelorus.

The Engineering department is responsible for testing the functioning of the main propulsion machinery, the engine-room telegraphs, the steering gear and the sirens; and also for testing the functioning of the gyro-compass repeaters and all electrical communications.

If the Officer of the Watch is provided with a *special-sea-dutymen check list* that enumerates all the items that must be checked before the ship gets under way, this should help him to make sure that there are no omissions.

Immediately before the ship gets under way the order 'Obey telegraphs' is passed from the bridge to the engine/control room, or control of the engines is passed to the bridge, *but only at the direct order of the Captain.* When the ship is clear of harbour the Captain will order the special sea dutymen to be relieved by sea dutymen of the watch.

TAKING OVER A WATCH

It is most important that a watch should be turned over thoroughly and conscientiously. When relieving, you should arrive on the bridge in good time to allow a full briefing, and if at night to allow also for your vision to become adapted. In warships under operational conditions it is customary to stagger the times of take-over for Officer of the Watch, Operations Room and armaments, etc., and not to use the traditional times of watch turn-over. Without such staggering there is an open invitation to a shadowing enemy to make his attack at, say, 0400 precisely, hoping to catch the entire ship in the throes of turning over the watches. Under operational conditions the Officer of the Watch will find it useful to visit the Operations Room on his way to the bridge. There he can obtain a quick briefing on the general situation and, in particular, the positions of all ships in the vicinity.

The relieving officer should insist on covering all the following items, in so far as they apply to the situation, before taking over.

COMMAND

The whereabouts of the Captain and any orders of his about the future conduct of the ship in his Night Order Book or elsewhere, and his orders for being called.

NAVIGATION

The whereabouts of the Navigating Officer and any orders of his about the navigation or about being called.

Position of the ship on the chart, her intended track, any set of current or tidal stream experienced, identification of any land or lights in sight and details of any expected to be sighted.

Course of the ship by gyro-compass and any compass errors. Any wheel being carried. Details of zigzag if in force.

Speed ordered and revolutions required for it, or to keep in station.

Propulsion machinery state in force and the notice for change. In steam-propelled ships, the engines or boilers connected and the maximum speed available.

Depth of water, and any orders about taking soundings.

Navigation lights. To be checked if lit; or, if not, any orders about when to switch them on.

OPERATIONAL SITUATION

Ships. Identity of ships in company, and any friendly forces expected to join or leave. The task and disposition of the force. Position, course and speed of any other ships detected or sighted and whether they are expected to pass clear.

Station. The ship's station, the identity and position of the guide and adjacent ships, and any necessary information about keeping in station. The tactical diameter in use, operational speed and stationing speed.

Communications. The organisation in force for manoeuvring signals, and any outstanding signals awaiting execution.

Action Information Organisation in force. Radar, sonar and other transmissions and the policy on their use. Lookouts closed up and their duties.

INTERNAL SITUATION

Ship's company work in progress; men working in exposed positions. State of seaboats, swimmer of the watch and the watch on deck. The situation of the helicopter if borne.

Organisation in force for damage control; the Watertight Condition and NBCD State of Readiness of the ship and who is in charge of it.

WEATHER

The state and forecast of the weather, and any likelihood of fog. If in fog, the organisation for making sound signals, the method of keeping station, any extra lookouts placed, fog lights in use, and any extraneous fog signals heard or radar contacts detected.

Taking over

Before finally taking over as Officer of the Watch you should check once again that the course ordered is actually being steered and that it is a safe one when laid-off on the chart, and that you are fully aware of the presence and movement of any approaching vessels that carry with them the slightest risk of collision. If considerably out of station you should not take over the watch until your predecessor has regained station. When fully satisfied that you can take charge, you should make it quite clear to your predecessor that you are doing so by saying, for example, 'I have the ship'. If you are not satisfied with the position of the ship, or her course relative to any dangers or to the guide, *you should not take over the watch* and the Captain should be informed.

ACTION DURING THE WATCH

Watching

While on watch never forget the significance of the word 'watch'. You should be constantly looking out ahead and astern, and should take pride in being the first to spot anything new that comes into view. If you are obliged to leave the place from which you can see out — in order, for example, to look at the chart — make sure that someone else is looking out on your behalf. If navigation lookouts are placed, ensure that they know the general situation and what especially to look for. The efficiency of lookouts can be greatly improved by encouragement from the Officer of the Watch and, conversely, they will become unreliable if ignored. This applies equally to the stern-lookout/lifebuoy-sentry, who should be kept in contact and aware of his responsibilities.

As soon as another ship is sighted for the first time *take a bearing* of her. Watch the movement of the bearing and continue to do so at intervals, even after avoiding action has been taken, until you are quite sure that the other ship is about to pass well clear.

It is a modern mistake to place faith implicitly in radar. The human eye can detect a change in the inclination of another ship more rapidly than radar; and radar sets and displays are not always adjusted to produce optimum results. The Officer of the Watch should depend on his own eyes, but should make sure that others extract information from radar and pass it to him — a point which will be referred to again later in this chapter.

Lookouts

In war the chief function of lookouts is to guard against surprise from either air or submarine attack. The Principal Warfare Officer is responsible for the duties and stationing of anti-aircraft and anti-submarine lookouts.

In peace the Officer of the Watch is responsible for any lookouts stationed to assist in the safe conduct of the ship. In a big ship, when the weather is clear, it is customary to place one lookout on each side of the bridge or pilotage position; but in a small ship the signalman on the bridge may be the only lookout by day, although it is customary to have lookouts placed at night. If the visibility is reduced the Officer of the Watch should immediately order additional lookouts. One is placed usually in the eyes of the ship and, if fog is low-lying and man-aloft restrictions permit, an additional lookout aloft is also valuable. As already remarked, the duties of the lifebuoy sentry should always be combined with those of astern lookout.

Lookouts usually do tricks of 20 minutes. It has been found that, even with the most conscientious men, results on average cannot be as good if the tricks are any longer. The Officer of the Watch should allocate the arcs which his lookouts are to scan.

Sometimes special lookouts are placed to watch and report to the Action Information Organisation on a particular item — for example, helicopters.

Lookouts should be encouraged to report *everything* which they sight, and should never be told to ignore anything.

Reports to the Captain

The Officer of the Watch is not expected to deal with every situation himself. His function rather is to be the first to become aware of a change developing in the situation and to summon up the people needed to deal with it. The most important person to call upon is the Captain, and the Officer of the Watch should never be afraid to do so. A wise Captain gives clear directions in his Standing Orders as to the circumstances in which he is to be called, and emphasises in them the importance of calling him *if in any doubt whatsoever.* He does not rebuke an inexperienced Officer of the Watch who occasionally calls him on some trivial matter. Neither the Captain nor the Navigating Officer can obtain any real rest at sea unless they are confident that they will be called (and thoroughly roused) in plenty of time when necessary.

The Captain is usually called on the following occasions.

Navigation

1. The detection or sighting of any ship likely to pass within, say, two miles. Failure to observe the Rule of the Road by any vessel that appears to carry the slightest risk of collision.

2. On any alteration of course being made to avoid danger (or for any other reason); and also whenever the Officer of the Watch thinks it likely that an alteration of course will be required for any reason.

3. If being set off track.

4. The detection or sighting of land or navigational marks, *or the failure to detect or sight them by the expected time.*

Operational situation

1. Any signal ordering or involving a change in speed, course or station; its receipt, execution and the action taken on it.

2. The sighting or detection of any warships other than those presently in company.

3. If own ship or a nearby ship is out of station, or if there is any difficulty in keeping station.

Weather. Any change in the weather. It is particularly important to call the Captain at night if the weather changes for the worse. The ship's course and speed may need to be adjusted in order to make a certain position on the following morning.

At sunset, with a report (see page 312).

Emergency. Any emergency situation — if possible, as soon as there are any signs that it may develop, rather than when it has already become critical. Various emergencies and the action appropriate to each are described later in this chapter.

Defects. On the occurrence of any defect which may affect the safety or operational capability of the ship.

Navigation and pilotage

The Officer of the Watch should keep himself informed of the ship's position and keep a check on her navigation or pilotage. Although an officer is borne for navigating duties, no one is infallible. No instrument is absolutely reliable. A conscientious check by the Officer of the Watch on the navigation and pilotage of the ship is one of the greatest safeguards against a stranding caused by human error or mechanical fault.

The compass should be checked for error at every opportunity, either by a transit of navigational marks or by a bearing of the sun or a star. The gyro-compasses should be compared with each other and with their repeaters hourly, and also with the standard compass in ships fitted with magnetic compasses.

A check should be kept on the actual course steered by the ship, and if she is yawing or carrying wheel the Officer of the Watch should see that the mean course steered agrees with the course ordered. The mean of the revolutions for each hour should be compared with the revolutions ordered, and the hourly log readings with the speed ordered.

The course laid off on the chart should be checked to ensure that it is a safe one. Every navigational mark should be identified as it comes in sight, and the position of the ship should be fixed at frequent intervals. The Officer of the Watch should know the approximate strength and trend of any current or tidal stream, and should report immediately if the ship is being set to one side or the other of her intended track. The Officer of the Watch should ensure that all chartwork is in accordance with the conventions shown in BR 45, *Admiralty Manual of Navigation*; all fixes should be clearly recorded on the chart, and they should also be recorded in the Navigational Record Book, Form S.3034 (see page 322). When approaching land the Captain should be asked for instructions about taking soundings and clearing away the anchors and cables.

When in formation with other ships in pilotage waters the Officer of the Watch should not follow the wake of his next ahead blindly, but should check the position, course and speed of his own ship and not hesitate to haul out of line if he thinks she is running into danger.

Action Information Organisation

All warships have an Action Information Organisation (AIO), which is designed to gather all the available information about ships, aircraft, submarines, etc., both near and far, and to present it quickly in an easily comprehensible form to the Command. The organisation is centred in a specially equipped compartment known as the Operations Room, and has a variety of plots, sensors and displays which are manned by trained personnel under the control of a Principal Warfare Officer (Officer in Charge of the Operations Room).

The Officer of the Watch has a duty at all times not only to feed information to the AIO, but also to see that it provides him with any information that can help him. He must ensure, for example, that the Operations Room is supplied from the bridge with up-to-date information about signalled courses, speeds and changes of formation; with visual sightings, and with visual confirmation or contradiction of radar contacts. At the same time, the Officer of the Watch should insist that the AIO tracks every ship as soon as detected, and reports to him her course and speed and whether she is expected to pass clear, and, if so, where and when will be her closest point of approach.

Responsibilities in relation to the Officer in Charge of the Operations Room. In discharging his responsibilities for the safety of the ship the Officer of the Watch is to take account of the advice of the Officer in Charge of the Operations Room, who may be better informed, and should not hesitate to seek information or clarification from him as necessary but should remember that he is also liable to be heavily involved in the tactical situation. Notwithstanding this, all the duties and responsibilities of the Officer of the Watch remain applicable irrespective of relative seniorities, and he may therefore accept or reject the advice or instructions of the Officer in Charge of the Operations Room. In any difference of opinion as to the action to be taken the Captain must be informed if time permits.

Responsibility when the ship is controlled from the Operations Room. In certain tactical situations the Captain, or Principal Warfare Officer, controls the ship by passing orders from the Operations Room to the Officer of the Watch. The Officer of the Watch has authority to query, modify or delay carrying out any instruction which appears likely to lead to a dangerous situation; he should always report circumstances that may not be appreciated by those in the Operations Room and should always be prepared to take any action that may be necessary. Should the Captain con the ship from the Operations Room the Officer of the Watch, if he sees a potentially dangerous situation arising, is responsible for informing the Captain.

Station keeping and changing

The Officer of the Watch is responsible for keeping the ship in her station. He must make it his business to keep *exactly* in station, realising that if he is lax he will not only inconvenience, but may endanger, other ships in company.

X

Remarks on keeping and changing station are in Chapter 14. In addition, the Officer of the Watch should be familiar with the relative-velocity problems involved in changing station, and how to use radar to help solve them, as described in BR 45(1), *Admiralty Manual of Navigation,* Volume I. He must also have a first-class knowledge of all the manoeuvring and tactical instructions in force in the Fleet.

The watch on deck

The relieving watch or part of the watch on deck should be mustered five or ten minutes before they are due to take over. The Petty Officer of the Watch should then detail them for their watch duties such as lookouts, messengers, lifebuoy sentry, swimmer of the watch and helmsmen. He should then detail the seaboat's crew. If lowerers are required they should be detailed from personnel closed-up as weapon crews or elsewhere.

Seaboats

Before he takes over his watch duty, the coxswain of the seaboat should inspect his boat and her gear, reporting on completion to the Officer of the Watch.

When the tactical and armament situation allows, the Officer of the Watch should exercise the manning of the seaboat from time to time and should always ensure that a qualified person is present at an actual lowering and hoisting.

Sunset

Half an hour before sunset the duty rating from the Marine Engineering department should test all electrically operated navigation lights, not-under-command lights and any other special lights, and report their state to the Officer of the Watch. The Officer of the Watch must see that the secondary navigation lights also are ready for immediate use if required.

At sunset the Officer of the Watch switches on the navigation lights (unless he has been ordered not to do so) and reports to the Captain in accordance with the Captain's Standing Orders. If the ship is darkened the Officer of the Watch is responsible that no lights show outboard, and he must send men round from time to time to check.

Signals

In the absence of the Signal Communications Officer, the Officer of the Watch should supervise the visual signalling watch.

Make sure that signals from other ships are promptly answered, that no unauthorised signals are made, and that important signals are immediately distributed to those concerned. The latter applies particularly to the reporting of manoeuvring signals to the Captain.

Take any opportunity that arises for ascertaining the names and destinations of any passing warships or merchant ships, and conduct signal communications exercises with any British or foreign merchant ships that are willing to co-operate. A merchant ship should not be called for exercise purposes, however, in pilotage waters, because this would distract her Officer of the Watch from looking after the safety of his ship. See that your ensign is dipped promptly in reply to the salute of a passing merchant ship; failure to do so is extremely discourteous.

Looking after the ship

Looking after the ship includes not only preventing damage to the ship and her equipment, but also ensuring the safety of men on deck and the comfort of those below, and the control of all matters which may affect the ship's routine.

When the ship is in a seaway, keep a careful watch on her behaviour, and if she appears to be labouring take appropriate action before she suffers damage. Advice on handling ships in rough weather is given in Chapter 15.

Keep an eye on the weather, particularly in the tropics where calm periods may suddenly be broken by heavy rain squalls. The Officer of the Watch should always be aware of the employment of the hands on deck and the state of the upper-deck equipment, so that when a squall approaches he can take the appropriate action.

In calm weather, and particularly at meal times, the ship's company should be warned, when possible, of any alteration of course which will heel the ship. In rough weather warning should be given, when possible, of any alteration of course which will increase the motion of the ship, as when turning broadside-on to the sea.

During the night watches, and particularly in rough weather, rounds must be conscientiously carried out both below and above decks every hour or half-hour. Men who carry out the rounds should look out for leaking hatches or scuttles, the securing of equipment (particularly on the weather decks) and any potential fire risks.

Attention must be paid to the ship's routine and good warning given of any change to it. It is most important to warn Heads of Departments as early as possible of any changes to the ship's programme, such as an alteration of the time of arrival in harbour.

ACTION IN EMERGENCY

Be prepared!

The Officer of the Watch must always be prepared to take immediate action to save the ship, or some member of her company, on his own initiative.

Think about the various emergencies that may occur during your watch, and run over in your mind the various actions to be taken, and their sequence, to cope with each situation. Exactly what would you do, for example, if you heard the cry 'Man overboard!'; or if the main engines of the ship ahead in column were suddenly stopped when steaming at 25 knots; or if your ship was surprised by an unseen enemy with, say, torpedo or some other kind of attack?

The Bridge Emergency Orders should cover all predictable emergencies but it is impossible to list all the actions required in differing circumstances. The appropriate action depends on the particular ship's organisation and on the tactical, operational or exercise orders in force. But unless you have rehearsed the actions in your mind, you will be powerless to act promptly. Some elaboration of certain contingencies is given later in this chapter.

Prevention is better than cure

Unfortunately many occasions requiring drastic and rapid action are allowed to arise quite unnecessarily, through the inattention or lack of foresight of the Officer of the Watch. This applies particularly to crises where danger of collision or grounding materialises apparently without warning. Early action to put the ship on a safe course, or to take the way off her, would have prevented a crisis from developing at all.

Most accidents at sea are caused by one or more of the following omissions or mistakes.

1. Failure to take the correct action because of incomplete knowledge of the Rule of the Road.
2. Failure to keep a good lookout.
3. Failure to take seamanlike precautions in potentially dangerous circumstances such as restricted visibility, or when under way without lights.
4. Failure to check the ship's position, course and speed frequently.
5. Failure to look ahead and realise that, unless some action is taken now, a dangerous situation will arise in the future.
6. Indecision and consequent delay until it is too late to save the situation.

If you have read this chapter so far you will know the remedies. Only the most important of these will be stressed once again: that is — if in doubt *call the Captain* and do so *in good time,* so that he can reach the bridge and take the necessary action *before* the situation has become dangerous.

Other information

Some remarks on emergency action when manoeuvring in a confined space or when faced with the inevitability of a stranding or a collision are included at the end of Chapter 13. Information about handling ships in heavy weather, such as how to heave-to, is given in Chapter 15.

Watertight integrity

A good insurance against a flooding accident is to maintain strict control over the opening of watertight doors and hatches in a warship at sea. Whenever a ship is afloat, a *Watertight Condition* is ordered which governs the number of watertight openings allowed to be open, i.e. the watertight integrity of the ship. Details of Watertight Conditions and their control are given in Volume I and in BR 2170, *Ship NBCD Manual,* but the main points are described below.

In NBCD State 1, which is the highest State of NBCD Readiness, watertight integrity is controlled from NBCD headquarters (HQ1). In NBCD States 2 and 3 control is exercised from HQ1 in large ships and from the Ship Control Centre (SCC) in small ships, or by the Officer of the Watch in those small ships which have no SCC.

The normal Watertight Condition of a ship in peacetime is Condition X-ray but Condition Yankee may be assumed at times of navigational hazard, e.g. while entering or leaving harbour, when in fog, during replenishment at sea, or when in narrow waters. Condition Zulu is rarely required in peacetime except for exercise. In time of war, Condition Yankee is the normal and Condition Zulu is assumed whenever necessary.

In an emergency, important watertight openings are closed on the order 'Close all red openings' passed on the main broadcast together with an alarm signal. This emergency order will probably be given in conjunction with the order 'Emergency Stations'.

When controlling the watertight integrity, the Officer of the Watch must ensure that he never allows more than the permitted number of watertight doors and hatches to be open in any part of the ship. The opening and closing of all watertight doors and hatches must be recorded in the *Watertight Integrity Log* and on the *NBCD Door and Hatch Board*.

Even when the control of watertight integrity does not rest with the Officer of the Watch, he must always be aware of the Watertight Condition in force, and he should not hesitate to order a higher Condition if he considers it necessary for the circumstances. However, it must be realised that a change from one Watertight Condition to another may require a change in the NBCD State of Readiness in order to obtain the hands necessary for the task.

Gastight integrity

Whenever there is a threat of nuclear, biological or chemical (NBC) attack, the Gastight Condition Alfa is superimposed on the Watertight Condition in force (usually Yankee or Zulu). In Condition Alfa, all openings (doors, hatches, ventilation flaps, valves, etc.) which, when open, are regarded as a threat to gastight integrity, are shut. To improve habitability when Condition Alfa is in force for lengthy periods, certain specified 'A' openings may be opened at the discretion of the Command, provided they satisfy only the immediate requirement, e.g. ventilation to the galley to allow the cooking of a main meal. The openings selected must be capable of being shut immediately on order, by sentries posted as necessary for this specific duty.

NBCD States of Readiness

There are three NBCD States of Readiness which govern the degree of NBCD manning, and the machinery and material arrangements of the ship other than the preservation of watertight and gastight integrity. The latter are controlled by the Watertight and Gastight Conditions. The responsibility for setting the State of Readiness rests with the Captain but the Officer of the Watch is responsible for ordering and controlling the State in force. This control is exercised through NBCD headquarters if it is manned.

Steering, conning and propulsion emergencies

Mistakes in passing orders. Clear and distinct intonation of orders greatly assists in obtaining the correct response. If the quartermaster or helmsman makes a mistake by setting the engines or wheel different from that ordered, you should become aware of this immediately by observation of the instruments on the bridge which indicate his actions. Do not rebuke him but concentrate on obtaining the correct wheel or engine settings. There are four cases of error which, together with the corrective action, are tabulated overleaf.

Error	Action
1. Wheel put the wrong way	Order 'Amidships' and then order the wheel required
2. Wheel put the correct way but by the wrong amount	Repeat the order
3. Engine telegraph put the wrong way, i.e. ahead for astern or vice versa	Order 'Stop'. Then order the required movement
4. Engine telegraph put the correct way but by the wrong amount, e.g. full ahead instead of slow ahead	Repeat the order

In any of the above cases call the quartermaster to the wheel if he is not already there. Later, when the situation is in hand, you may deal with the quartermaster or helmsman if the error was caused by their inattention. The best insurance against mistakes is to give your orders so decisively that there is no chance of misinterpretation.

Breakdowns in steering. A general description of the methods of conning and steering a ship is given in Volume I. In each ship the methods and drills for change-over of conning and steering positions are laid down in the Captain's or Ship's Standing Orders, and there is usually a summary available on the bridge. However, if a breakdown occurs the Officer of the Watch must know exactly what to do, and must start giving orders at once. He will only be able to do this if he has made himself familiar with the facilities available at each steering and conning position, and the action needed in each place to effect change-over.

Remember that while the steering control is being changed you will have to try to keep the ship on her course by the use of the engines. Warn the engine room what is going on and be prepared to make radical changes, such as, for example, stopping the engine on one side and increasing speed on the other; hoist the not-under-command signal by day, or switch on the lights by night; and remember your next astern, if in column.

Propulsion machinery breakdown. Certain breakdowns require immediate action to stop the propulsion unit concerned. For example, in the event of failure of lubricating-oil pressure the propeller shaft concerned must be stopped or its speed drastically reduced within seconds if serious damage is to be avoided; and this must be done without waiting for permission from the bridge. If this happens to your ship the first essential is to alert ships in company to the fact that something is wrong. The quickest way to do this is by making six short blasts on the siren. You must then show the not-under-command signal and hoist Flag 5, indicating 'breakdown'.

When in column, the most important initial action is to warn the ships astern by any suitable communications system. If a steering or engine failure occurs when in column, it is usually better to maintain heading if possible and to slow down gradually. If you have to leave your column, make an alteration of course sufficiently large to clear the line, but not so great that a broad inclination is presented to the ships astern. A turn of 20–30 degrees should be enough. Tell the ships astern exactly what you are doing.

If the ship ahead of you in column suffers such a breakdown you must be prepared to take instant and drastic avoiding action as necessary to prevent collision. It is impossible to lay down rules as to how ships should act, because the broken-down ship may be forced out of the line either one way or the other momentarily by the failure of the propulsion on one side of the ship only.

Compass breakdown. Only by being continuously alert, and by comparing the different gyro-compass repeaters frequently, will the Officer of the Watch detect quickly a compass failure. If the ship has gone off her course, he must immediately con her back by using a repeater that appears to be reliable. He must also bring into play the organisation for remedying the breakdown, which normally entails, amongst other things, summoning the maintenance rating and informing the Navigating Officer.

Existing gyro-compass alarm systems often cover only the master compass and are not designed to indicate failure of the compass transmission system. It is thus possible for the transmission system to fail without any alarm indication by light or bell. On the other hand, there may be occasions when the alarm operates even though the compass and its repeaters remain serviceable.

Man overboard

Precautions. The Queen's Regulations for the Royal Navy state that the Officer of the Watch:

'is responsible that orders are given to prevent any person going on to the weather decks when sea conditions or alterations of course or speed are likely to make it dangerous. Should it be necessary for men to go on the weather decks in dangerous conditions he is to ensure that orders are given to them to wear lifejackets which are to be inflated sufficiently to support the wearer in the water'.

Thus if a man is washed overboard it may be the fault of the Officer of the Watch. Always make it your business when in heavy weather to see that the ship's company is warned of any impending alteration of course, that lifelines are rigged where necessary and that some or all of the weather decks are placed out of bounds if any doubt exists regarding safety. If anyone needs to undertake urgent work on the weather decks the Officer of the Watch must also ensure that:

1. He has obtained permission.
2. He is accompanied by at least one other person.
3. They wear lifejackets which are inflated to at least two-thirds of their capacity.
4. They use safety harnesses.
5. The lifebuoy sentry has been briefed, is within hearing of the lifebuoy alarm and is wearing a lifejacket either belted on or fully donned as dictated by the conditions.

Action

1. Immediately on hearing the call or receiving the message 'Man overboard', ring the alarm for the lifebuoy sentry to throw his lifebuoys and markers,

and if in company make six short blasts on the siren to alert the other ships.

2. Tell the Action Information Organisation to mark the plot.

3. If safe to do so, start altering course round towards the man's position (see remarks below on Shiphandling).

4. Tell or send a message to the Captain, Executive Officer, Navigating Officer and sick-bay.

5. Set lookouts to search for the man in the water.

6. Call away the seaboat's crew or order the swimmer of the watch and attendants to stand by for rescue.

7. Make any appropriate signals to ships in company.

Picking up by boat. It is usual to pick up the man by lowering a boat. Traditionally the call 'Away lifeboat's crew!' in place of the usual 'Away seaboat's crew!' means that the boat is for saving life, and any officer or man nearby, whatever his rank or duty, should leap to the boat to man her. In fact, at sea the seaboat's crew is detailed and ready and should be in the boat before anybody else. However, it may well be preferable to use the traditional call in order to alert everybody, including the seaboat's crew, to the urgency of the situation.

The lowering and hoisting of seaboats, and hints to coxswains on how to pick up a man, are covered in Volume I.

Picking up by swimmer. If the weather or the tactical situation precludes lowering a boat it may be best, having placed the ship alongside the man overboard and to windward of him, to use a swimmer to recover him. The dress for the swimmer and the procedure for recovering the man overboard are described in Volume II, Chapter 3. The Officer of the Watch must ensure that the engine room, MCR or SCC is informed that a swimmer is in the water.

Shiphandling aspects. If a man falls overboard he will drop astern at 2.5 metres per second for every 5 knots of ship's speed. If, for example, a man falls overboard amidships from a frigate steaming at 20 knots he will be abreast the propellers in just under 5 seconds. Stopping the engines on the side from which the man fell, to prevent him from being drawn into the propeller race, will therefore be useless, unless the man falls from right forward in a long ship which is steaming at slow speed, because even at 10 knots it will take at least 10 seconds to stop the propellers from the time the order is received in the engine room.

Under most circumstances it will also be too late to put the wheel over towards the side from which the man fell in the hope of swinging the stern away from him. Besides, the side from which the man fell is often in doubt at first. Experience has shown that a man will probably float aft clear of the ship's propellers even if no action is taken to avoid him.

The best action to take is to increase speed and start turning with plenty of wheel as soon as it is safe to do so. During the latter stages of the turn the ship can be manoeuvred as necessary to bring her up to windward of the man and as nearly as possible beam-on to wind and sea so as to provide a lee for both the boat or the swimmer and the man. The inner screw should not be reversed at first, because then the ship will probably finish up well in advance of the man (see Chapter 12); and the seaboat should not be slipped until the ship is close to the man.

If it is required to retrace the ship's track to search for the man, the *Williamson* turn is an approximate method of doing so. Swing out with maximum wheel either to starboard or to port, and subsequently reverse the wheel so that the ship's head swings out to, but not beyond, 60 degrees from the original course; and then continue to swing back with full wheel, finally steadying on the reciprocal of the original course. In many vessels it will be found that the ship is now on or close to its original track.

The *Turning Guide* illustrated in Fig. 11–1 has been designed to assist the Officer of the Watch in deciding which way to turn on receiving the report of a man overboard. There are two principal factors which affect this decision.

1. Whether the seaboat or the swimmer of the watch is to be used. At all times during his watch the Officer of the Watch must be clear in his mind which method is to be employed.

2. The true direction of the wind in relation to the ship's head. The Officer of the Watch must work this out at frequent intervals.

In Fig. 11–1, the direction of the ship's head for all diagrams is towards the top of the illustration. The broad arrowhead pointing inwards for each diagram represents the true direction of the wind in relation to the ship's head; and the circle in each diagram represents the position of the man in the water. Knowing the true direction of the wind in relation to the ship's head and having decided which method to use, the Officer of the Watch can then select the appropriate diagram and, if using the swimmer, the best side for recovery.

It is emphasised that circumstances may preclude the use of the Turning Guide; it should only be regarded as a general guide. In particular, the bearing and altitude of the sun may, in smooth sea conditions, be a powerful factor in deciding the direction of the initial turn. If the sun is low and bright there will be a wide area of intense glare off the water which will make it difficult, or even impossible, to see a man's head. Therefore, in these conditions, the Officer of the Watch must consider whether his initial turn should be towards the sun to ensure that the man overboard is kept in view throughout the turn. During darkness or if the man overboard is not in sight the Williamson-turn method described above should be used.

Running into fog

When visibility closes down to within about a mile the precautions to be taken depend on whether the ship is alone or in company and whether in time of peace or war. As soon as the visibility starts to close down, or if a bank of fog is sighted ahead, the Captain should be informed. The following are the normal actions to be taken in peace.

When alone

1. Reduce to a safe speed having regard to the factors set out in the Rule of the Road.

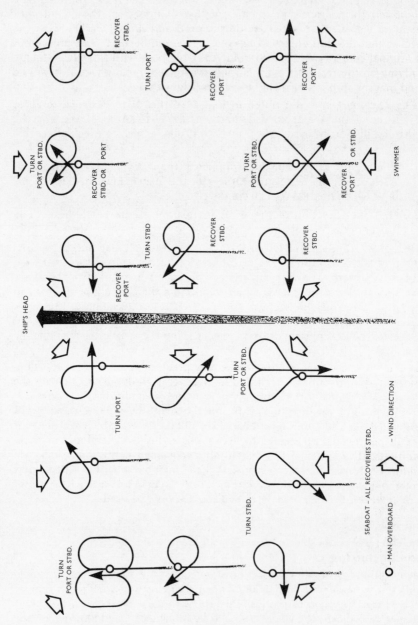

FIG. 11–1. Turning Guide for man overboard

2. Operate radar and make use of the AIO if these are not already in operation.

3. Station extra lookouts (see remarks earlier in this chapter).

4. Switch on navigation lights.

5. If in shallow water, start sounding.

6. If in the vicinity of land, have an anchor prepared for letting go and fix the position of the ship.

7. Review the NBCD State of Readiness and Watertight Condition (see remarks earlier in this chapter) and order changes if necessary.

8. Order silence on deck.

9. Start the prescribed fog signal and, if it is not an automatic device, ensure that the man who works it can time it accurately.

10. Warn the Engineering department and, if necessary, order a change in the machinery state.

11. If in any doubt about the ship's position, alter course to a safe course, parallel to or away from the coast (or danger), or stop the ship.

The remarks about passages in fog and thick weather given in BR 45(1), *Admiralty Manual of Navigation,* Volume I, should be carefully studied by every Officer of the Watch.

When in company

1. Station a lookout aft if there is not one already.

2. Switch on the fog light (if fitted).

3. Stream a fog-buoy or target to the prescribed distance as an aid to the ship astern to keep station, if ordered by the officer in tactical command (OTC).

The OTC may be expected also to signal orders about speed, the sounding of fog signals and the showing of navigation lights. Tactical instructions in force in the Fleet contain further orders about the conduct of ships in company in fog, and how these orders should be applied in war.

It is particularly important to know exactly what is laid down in the International Regulations for Preventing Collisions at Sea regarding the conduct of ships in fog.

Running into ice

The chief danger of drifting ice is that it is frequently accompanied by fog, and when navigating in regions where ice may be encountered a good watch should be kept for signs of the proximity of ice. The following signs indicate the presence of ice in the vicinity.

Ice blink, which is a reflection of light from large masses of ice. On a clear day or night, and particularly on a moonlit night, the sky along the horizon in the direction of the ice is markedly paler or lighter in colour than along the remainder of the horizon.

Absence of sea or swell in a fresh breeze, which in the absence of land indicates that ice is on the weather side.

Calf ice (small floes), which is a reliable sign of the close proximity of icebergs. When encountered in a curved line, the parent berg will be on the concave side of the line.

Herds of seals or flocks of razorbills far from land.

Loud noises akin to gunfire or heavy breakers, caused by large masses of ice breaking off icebergs which are disintegrating.

Echoes from the siren, which may be received from nearby and high icebergs.

When in the vicinity of icebergs, it should be remembered that about seven-tenths or more of their mass is below water and may project horizontally near the surface for a considerable distance from their sides. If, in restricted visibility, an iceberg is sighted a short distance ahead the best avoiding action is to go full speed astern, because if you turn to avoid it the submerged and projecting ledges of the berg may rip out the ship's bottom. The use of radar to detect ice is discussed on page 498.

RECORDS

Navigational Record Book (Form S.3034)

The Navigational Record Book is a small notebook provided on the bridge for the Officer of the Watch to record: alterations of course and speed with times; all fixes with associated observations; latitude and longitude when out of sight of land; depths of water when soundings are being used for navigation or when operating close to shoal water; and the bearings of transits and heavenly bodies, etc. and the compass errors found. Full instructions concerning the use, compilation and custody of the Book are given inside its front cover.

Ship's Log (Form S.322)

Instructions for writing up the Ship's Log are contained inside its front cover. At the end of his watch the Officer of the Watch completes his entries and initials the book before leaving the bridge. He should supervise and train his subordinates to take readings accurately and to make accurate estimates of the state of the sea and weather.

Wheel and Engine Order Record Book (Form S.580)

When entering or leaving harbour, when manoeuvring, or on any other occasion that seems to require it, the Officer of the Watch must see that a record of all wheel and engine orders is made. It is common practice in many ships nowadays to tape-record all conning orders instead of recording them in the *Wheel and Engine Order Record Book.*

Fishing Vessel Log (Form S.1176)

Full details of any encounters with fishing vessels in Home Waters are entered in the *Fishing Vessel Log.* The details are required in order to refute or substantiate claims for loss or damage of gear subsequently made by the fishing vessels concerned.

CONCLUSION

It may be thought that too cautious an attitude has been inculcated in this chapter. In fact the seaman's first need is an awareness of the dangers of the sea. A perpetual wariness and alertness forms the basis on which he can build wisdom and confidence, so that when suddenly faced with danger he remains calm and acts swiftly, because he is ready.

CHAPTER 12

Propulsion and Steering of Ships

The way in which a vessel behaves when being manoeuvred depends upon a number of variable factors. These include her means of propulsion, her steering, the shape of her hull, the disposition of her superstructures, her loading and trim, the weather, the depth and extent of the water surrounding her, and the presence of current or tidal stream. It is obvious that the handling of one ship may be very different from that of another. However, certain fundamental principles apply to all shiphandling situations. Experience naturally helps to increase the skill and competence of the shiphandler, but any officer who understands the principles of shiphandling, who has a good knowledge of seamanship and who prepares carefully for each manoeuvre, should be able to handle his ship successfully. In this and subsequent chapters the principles of shiphandling and how they should be applied in different circumstances are described.

PROPELLERS

When studying the handling qualities of any particular class of ship, the first considerations are the number, size and type of the propellers, and the type and power of the propulsion machinery. The handling of a single-screw ship fitted with steam-turbine machinery is very different, for example, from the handling of a twin-screw ship propelled by gas turbines.

Conventional propellers are of two main types, *fixed pitch* and *controllable pitch*, which are described below. When viewed from astern and when driving the ship ahead, a propeller is said to be *right-handed* if it revolves in a clockwise direction and, conversely, it is described as *left-handed* if it revolves in a counter-clockwise direction.

Fixed-pitch propellers

In the fixed-pitch propeller the blades are manufactured integral with the boss by which the propeller is secured to its shaft. The pitch of the blades (which cannot subsequently be altered) is a factor of design which is selected to suit the ship for which the propeller is intended. Thus the direction (ahead or astern) and the strength of the force developed by the propeller are determined respectively by the direction and speed of its rotation. In ships fitted with fixed-pitch propellers, means must be provided for reversing the direction of rotation of the propeller to develop astern power. In steam-turbine ships it is usual to fit a separate astern turbine whereas in other ships reversal is obtained either by direct reversal of the engine or by suitable reversible gearing.

Controllable-pitch propellers

All new-design RN frigates and larger warships are fitted with gas-turbine propulsion machinery. The majority of these ships are also fitted with controllable-pitch propellers to ensure efficient operation of the complete propulsion system. In twin-screw ships the propellers are usually in-turning and, as the shafts always revolve in the same direction, astern power is obtained by reversing the pitch of the propeller blades.

In the controllable-pitch propeller each blade is capable of limited rotation at its connection to the propeller boss, as indicated by the double arrowheads in Fig. 12–1. The blades can be set in unison at any desired angle within their limits of rotation on the boss by a mechanical or hydraulic system which operates through the centre of the propeller shaft. By this means the pitch can be varied smoothly from full ahead through zero pitch to full astern while the propeller and shaft rotate continuously in only one direction.

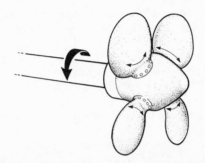

FIG. 12–1. Controllable-pitch propeller

These propellers enable the power of the propulsion machinery to be used at optimum efficiency throughout the full range and in varying conditions. Very low controlled speeds are made possible and, because the engines and shafts do not have to be reversed, great rapidity of manoeuvre is also obtainable.

Design of propellers
Broadly speaking, the larger the propeller the smaller is the loss of power through slip and the sternward velocity of the slipstream or race, and the greater is the efficiency. Both the diameter and the pitch of propellers react on the handling qualities of a ship. Five-bladed propellers are most common in HM ships and all new designs incorporate the largest size of propeller that can be fitted, the shaft speed being matched to the propulsion machinery by a gearbox to obtain optimum efficiency. In diesel-propelled ships the engines operate at the best economy and efficiency if they can be kept running steadily at a reasonably high speed. To achieve these conditions controllable-pitch propellers are fitted in conjunction with diesel engines.

Single-screw ships
In ships with a single fixed-pitch propeller, a right-handed propeller is almost invariably fitted. However, if a controllable-pitch propeller is fitted it may be left-handed, e.g. as in the ISLAND Class OPVs. Few warships have single screws but a large proportion of merchant ships are so fitted. It is more

efficient to drive a submarine under water by a single screw, and for this reason high-speed or nuclear-powered submarines are usually fitted with only one propeller.

Twin-screw ships

Most major warships, including some classes of submarine, have twin screws. In all cases twin fixed-pitch propellers are *out-turning* — that is, the starboard propeller is right-handed and the port propeller is left-handed. However, where two controllable-pitch propellers are fitted, the converse generally applies and the propellers are usually *in-turning*, i.e. right-handed to port and left-handed to starboard.

Quadruple-screw ships

Some large warships and merchant ships have been fitted with out-turning quadruple screws, two on each side. It is customary to work both the propellers on each side ahead or astern together, but the fitting of a separate telegraph for each shaft permits each screw to be operated individually. It is possible in this case also to work the two inner screws together and the outer screws separately, thus producing the effect of having three screws. In some quadruple-screw merchant ships the outer propellers of each pair are used when manoeuvring and the two inner propellers cannot be driven astern.

PROPULSION MACHINERY

Type of machinery

Steam-turbine machinery with single or double reduction gearing has been the most common form of prime mover but is now being superseded by the gas turbine for all medium to large warships. Various combinations of gas turbines, steam turbines and diesel engines are also commonly used to meet the differing requirements of high speed and cruising in various classes of warship.

Acceleration and deceleration

The acceleration and deceleration capability of the ship depends largely on two factors — the power available and the momentum of the ship. Momentum is the product of mass and velocity. To compare the ahead and astern powers of different classes of ship one can consider first the *full-ahead momentum* of each class. For example, a ship of 2000 tonnes displacement with a maximum speed of 30 knots would have a full-ahead momentum of 60 000 tonne knots. Then one can compare the ratio of ahead (or astern) power available to the full-ahead momentum in different classes.

In Fig. 12–2 six classes of vessel are compared. The areas of the arrowheads in the right-hand column indicate the relative *ahead power per unit of momentum* for each class of ship, and those in the left-hand column indicate the relative astern powers. It will be noted that the gas-turbine-powered destroyer and frigate, and the diesel-powered MCMV have high relative powers both ahead and astern, and this gives high acceleration in these ships; in turn this confers great advantages in manoeuvrability if the ships are wisely handled and the extra power is not misused. In a steam-turbine-propelled

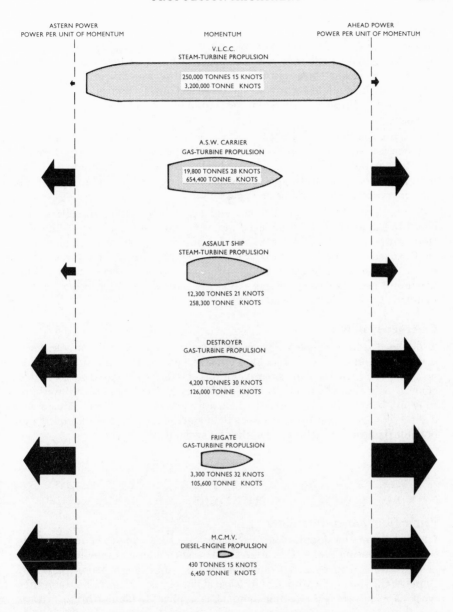

FIG. 12–2. Comparison of ahead and astern power in different classes of ship

ship the main turbines can drive the shafts ahead only and additional smaller turbines are fitted to drive the shafts astern; the effect of this is illustrated by the small relative astern powers of the assault ship and the VLCC. Furthermore, the example of the VLCC shows the very low ratio of power to momentum which severely restricts the manoeuvrability of large merchant ships. Factors affecting the acceleration and deceleration of ships are discussed in detail later in this chapter.

Y

Astern power

In naval ships fitted with steam turbines the astern power is usually about one-third of the ahead power. But because of the inefficiency of the astern turbines the steam consumption, or boiler power, at full power astern is similar to that required for full power ahead. In other words, slow astern will require three times the boiler power required for slow ahead for similar speeds.

One limiting factor is the temperature of the turbines. The rate at which it is possible to work up power without damage to the machinery depends on whether the machinery has been thoroughly warmed through. It is far more dangerous to work up fast while leaving harbour than when the machinery has been steaming for some time.

In ships fitted with gas turbines and controllable-pitch propellers, full ahead to full astern can be achieved in a very short time and these ships can stop and go astern quickly. Even though full power astern is available the ship's speed will not be as great as when going ahead because the resistance of the ship is much greater in the astern direction, and also because the maximum available power astern is usually limited for engineering reasons to much less than the full ahead power.

Emergency power

'Full ahead' and 'Full astern' are emergency orders and should only be used if the ship is in danger. If a sudden burst of power either ahead or astern is needed while manoeuvring, the revolutions should be increased by a sizeable amount with the telegraphs still at *half* speed. Even if these revolutions are rung off before the shafts attain them this procedure will indicate to the engine-room staff that prompt rather than emergency action is required, and possible damage to machinery can thus be avoided.

RUDDERS

Prime function of the rudder

Given that a model ship floating in a tank has a vertical rod projecting upwards from her pivoting point (*P* in Fig. 12–3). When a ship is moving ahead, *P* can be assumed to be about one-third of the ship's length from the bows. Suppose the ship to be propelled forward along a steady course. Now consider what happens when a twisting moment is applied suddenly to the vertical rod. The ship *yaws* or turns away from her original course by a certain angle. Owing to the ship's shape, the pressure of water on her hull now acts predominantly *abaft* the pivoting point and thus sets up a moment tending to swing the ship's bow back to the original course (Fig. 12–3(ii)). If a turn is to be maintained, this moment must be counteracted and the best way of doing this is to apply a force at the end of the ship where the lever will be a maximum. This is normally done by means of a rudder at the after end.

The prime functions of the rudder are therefore first to produce the moment to start the ship turning, and second to keep her turning (if desired) by resisting the tendency of the water pressure to push her back on to her original course.

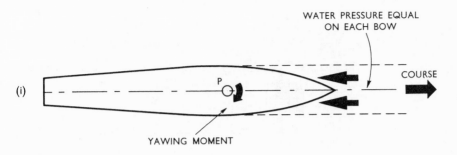

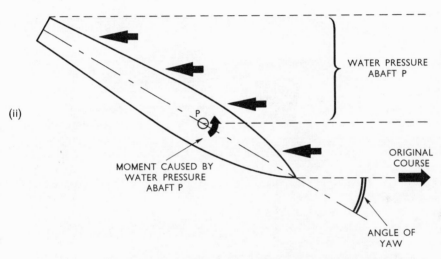

F IG. 12–3. Effect of water pressure on hull of ship moving forwards
(i) before a yaw; (ii) immediately after a yaw

Deadwood

The rudder can be used, however, for another important function. Most hull
forms need some flat vertical surfaces aft to maintain course stability and to
ensure easy course-keeping. The action of such vertical area, or *deadwood* (Fig.
12–4(i)), is to apply a sideways force, and hence a correcting moment, as
soon as the ship starts to yaw. The deadwood thus hinders turning, and must
be reduced in order to obtain good turning qualities. Therefore it appears
at first that good course-keeping is incompatible with good turning. However,
by judicious balance of hull shape and rudder area it can be arranged that
the rudder itself provides sufficient deadwood effect when held amidships
(or near it) to obtain good course-keeping stability, and then, when the
rudder is put over, the course stability is much reduced and the vessel turns
easily. This effect has been achieved successfully in recent designs of
destroyers and frigates for the Royal Navy.

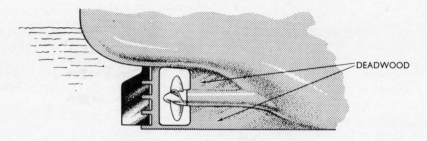

(i) Hinged unbalanced rudder

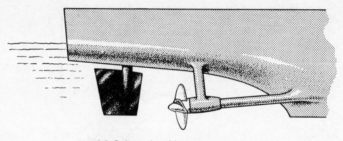

(ii) Balanced rudder

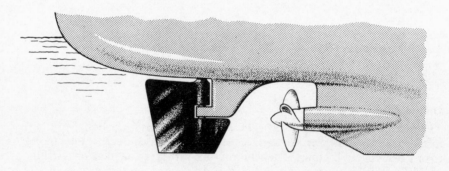

(iii) Balanced rudder, partially supported outboard

FIG. 12–4. Types of rudder

Types of rudder

The conventional hinged unbalanced rudder (Fig. 12–4(i)) is found in many merchant vessels, but warships are generally fitted with a balanced rudder (Fig. 12–4(ii)).

Hinged rudders

The unbalanced rudder is hung on pintles on a vertical stern-post and is therefore hinged at its forward end. This type of rudder requires more power to operate it than a balanced rudder and is generally less effective. It is of interest to note, however, that it is more effective than a balanced rudder at the start of a turn. This is because water pressure is increased against the deadwood on the side to which the rudder is moved. This pressure helps to start the ship turning (Fig. 12–5), but as soon as she does so the water pressure on the other side of the deadwood, caused by the ship swinging, cancels this effect, and the rate of turning is reduced.

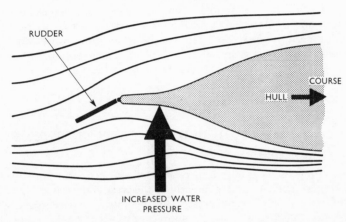

Fig. 12–5. Immediate effect of putting over a hinged unbalanced rudder

Balanced rudders

The balanced rudder as fitted in warships is usually supported entirely by the rudderhead within the hull. The ship's hull is cut away to a certain extent in the area before the rudder to improve her turning qualities, while the rudder itself acts partially as deadwood. About 25 to 30 per cent of the area of a balanced rudder lies before its axis. This has the effect of reducing the power required to turn the rudder with the ship moving ahead. Some ships have a balanced rudder that is partially supported outside the hull by an extension to the keel carrying a pintle (Fig. 12–4(iii)). This design suffers from the disadvantage that the flow of water on to the rudder is disturbed.

Rudder angle

Long experience has indicated that a maximum rudder angle of 35 degrees is satisfactory. An angle of 45 degrees will give a tighter turn but will reduce speed more. However, the additional turning capability is an overriding advantage in some classes of ship and a 45-degree rudder angle has been incorporated in some designs of warship. At high speeds, as the rudder angle is increased a situation may be reached where the turning force of the rudder suddenly reduces and the turn widens. This condition is known as *rudder stall*, and the possibility of its existence is investigated by experiments on models at the design stage. If present, action is taken to eliminate it so that it is most unlikely to occur in ships.

Modern rudder construction

The modern rudder has a thick section with a flat bottom and nearly parallel sides. This form has been found to delay the onset of rudder stall as compared with former designs, which were more rounded and tapered.

Unconventional rudders

Various new rudder designs have been tried including one incorporating a rotating cylinder to prevent stall and other more complicated arrangements. Generally the additional complexity cannot be justified for a normal destroyer or frigate, and balanced spade-shaped rudders are likely to be fitted as standard for many years to come. For special applications, for example where good manoeuvrability is required at low speed, unconventional rudders may be fitted. Further remarks on special types of rudder and propeller appear on page 357.

ARRANGEMENT OF PROPELLERS AND RUDDERS

Propeller slipstream

The positioning of the rudders in relation to the propeller slipstream is of primary importance. A rudder directly in the wake of a propeller is affected not only by the flow of water created by the ship's forward speed but also by the slipstream which is travelling appreciably faster, relative to the rudder, than the other water in the wake. This slipstream, or propeller race, is particularly advantageous when manoeuvring with little headway.

Single rudder

In the single-screw ship there is usually one rudder placed immediately abaft the propeller. This rudder is well placed to catch the greatest effect from the propeller race, and when going ahead from rest the rudder will have an immediate effect even before any headway is gathered.

In a twin-screw ship the single rudder is placed between the slipstreams from the propellers, as shown in Fig. 12–6, and therefore it cannot enter the slipstream until it has been given a large angle. This is a disadvantage both when there is little headway on the ship and also at the beginning of a turn.

Twin rudders

To improve the turning qualities of the twin-screw ship twin rudders can be placed so that each is in the slipstream of a propeller (Fig. 12–7). This is the arrangement in the majority of ships of the Royal Navy, and twin rudders have also been fitted to one class of single-screw ship. Twin rudders give better all-round manoeuvring qualities than those obtainable with a single rudder between the propellers and this advantage is marked at slow speeds and small rudder angles.

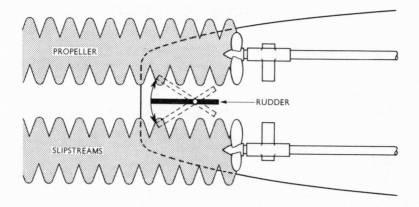

FIG. 12–6. Position of single rudder in relation to twin propellers, seen from below

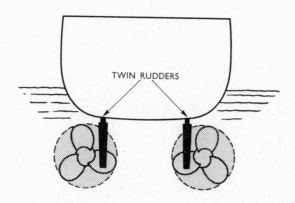

FIG. 12–7. Position of twin rudders in relation to twin propellers, seen from aft

Effects of hull form on rudder efficiency

The effect of a rudder of given design is dependent on the speed and turbulence of the water meeting it, so that in addition to the relative position of the propellers the form of the hull aft modifies the turning powers of a ship moving ahead.

In ships with bluff or rounded sterns the wake effect is large and the speed of the water passing the rudder may be as much as 35 per cent less than that of the ship. The eddying may cause part of the rudder to be in disturbed or dead water. This effect will be accentuated if the propeller is stopped and thus dragged through the water immediately ahead of the rudder. Conversely, in a ship with a fine run the reduced wake effect will result in greater rudder efficiency.

ACTION OF FIXED-PITCH PROPELLERS

For various reasons a ship's propeller does not usually produce a force acting exactly in the line of the shaft, and the net resultant force exerted by the propeller is usually at an angle to that line. It is convenient, however, to consider the net force of the propeller as consisting of two components, acting as follows.

1. Either directly ahead or directly astern (in the line of the propeller shaft).
2. Sideways, that is either to the right or to the left, when viewed from astern.

Sideways force

The sideways force of the propeller is caused by the shape of the hull and rudder, and the relation of the propeller to them. A certain amount of scientific investigation of these forces has been carried out at the Admiralty Marine Technology Establishment (AMTE) at Haslar. The description which follows is based on this work and on practical experience, and should enable the shiphandler to assess the sideways force and its effect on his particular ship. The wake caused by the hull shape is complex and can be shown to have several components. For example the *frictional wake* consists of water close to the hull being dragged along by skin friction. The flow of water past the propeller is not of uniform speed over the whole area traced out by the blades, so that a sideways component, caused by the wake, of the propeller force is almost always present. The shiphandler will find that the propeller behaves as though it gives rise to three effects which, when considered together, indicate the direction in which sideways force will act. These three effects can be called: *paddlewheel* effect, *pressure-and-suction* effect, and *lateral-wash* effect.

Paddlewheel effect

The propeller behaves *as if* it met with greater resistance at the bottom of the travel of the blades. Even if the whole propeller is immersed the effect is similar to that caused in a merchant ship in ballast when the blades come out of the water at the top of their travel. Remember that this is only an analogy which enables the shiphandler to determine the direction of the sideways force.

The force is considered to be caused in the following manner for a vessel with a single right-handed propeller. In the ahead direction the propeller produces a wash with a rotary motion which streams past the rudder. The upper part of this wash plays on the rudder and so exerts a force to starboard at the stern (Fig. 12−8(i)).

When the propeller rotates in the astern direction the upper part of the rotary wash plays on the A-bracket and deadwood, developing a sideways force to port at the stern (Fig. 12−8(ii)).

Thus, for the example given above and with the ship at rest, ahead revolutions will turn her to port and astern revolutions will turn her to starboard.

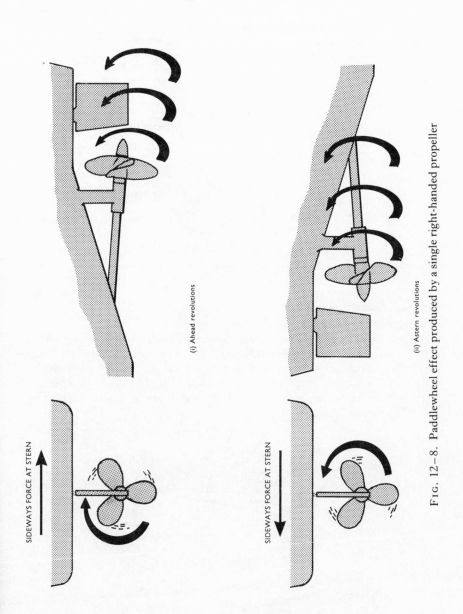

(i) Ahead revolutions

(ii) Astern revolutions

SIDEWAYS FORCE AT STERN

SIDEWAYS FORCE AT STERN

FIG. 12–8. Paddlewheel effect produced by a single right-handed propeller

Similar forces are believed to occur with twin-screw ships but the forces are much less marked and are also combined with the forces of other effects from which it is difficult to isolate the paddlewheel effect. Suppose it is desired to turn at rest to port in a twin-screw ship having out-turning screws. The shiphandler puts the starboard screw ahead and the port astern, and it can be seen that the paddlewheel effect from each screw helps to turn the ship in the required direction (Fig. 12–9). These effects are equally helpful when turning at rest to starboard.

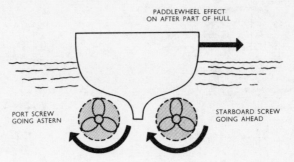

PADDLEWHEEL EFFECT
ON AFTER PART OF HULL

PORT SCREW
GOING ASTERN

STARBOARD SCREW
GOING AHEAD

FIG. 12–9. Paddlewheel effect (viewed from astern) in a ship with twin out-turning screws turning at rest to port

Pressure-and-suction effect

When going ahead the propeller is drawing water away from the hull, and when going astern it is throwing water on to the hull. In a single-screw ship this is unlikely to cause much sideways effect, but consider again a twin-screw ship (with out-turning propellers) turning at rest to port with the starboard screw going ahead and the port astern (Fig. 12–10). The starboard screw is drawing water away from the starboard quarter, so causing a loss

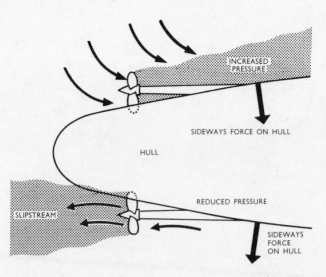

INCREASED
PRESSURE

SIDEWAYS FORCE ON HULL

HULL

REDUCED PRESSURE

SLIPSTREAM

SIDEWAYS
FORCE
ON HULL

FIG. 12–10. Pressure-and-suction effects in a twin-screw ship with out-turning propellers turning at rest to port, viewed from above

of water pressure against the hull there; while the port screw is throwing water against the port quarter and increasing the pressure there. The combined effect is to produce a sideways force pushing the stern to starboard, so helping the ship to turn to port. Similarly, when the directions of the propellers are reversed, this effect assists a twin-screw ship turning at rest to starboard. The extent to which this effect is felt depends on the shape of the hull and the positions of the propellers in relation to it.

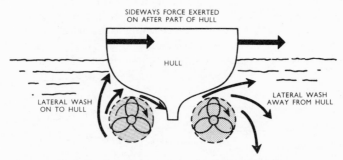

FIG. 12–11. Lateral-wash effects (viewed from astern) in a twin-screw ship with out-turning screws turning at rest to port

Lateral-wash effect

If the ship is moving ahead or astern the rotating propellers throw the water directly astern or ahead. When the ship is turning at rest, however, the supply of water to each propeller is restricted and slip develops, so that some of the water, instead of being pushed forward or aft, is thrown out laterally. Consider again the twin-screw ship with out-turning screws turning at rest to port. It can be seen from Fig. 12–11 that the blades of the port screw during the upper part of their rotation are throwing water out laterally against the hull and so helping to turn the ship to port, while the blades of the starboard screw are pushing water away from the hull and also assisting the turn. Similarly this lateral-wash effect helps to turn the twin-screw ship at rest to starboard. Again, it must be realised that the extent to which this effect is felt depends on the position of the propellers in relation to the hull.

Thrust

Each of the three components of the sideways force of the propellers in a twin-screw ship with out-turning propellers helps to turn her at rest in the direction intended. If he wishes to turn at rest to port the shiphandler puts the starboard engine ahead and the port astern, because common sense tells him that the thrust in the fore-and-aft line by the propeller shafts on to the thrust blocks will pull the ship in the required direction. However, the distance between the shafts is small in relation to the length of the ship and hence the couple exerted may not be very great (Fig. 12–12). The relationship between differential thrust and the individual sideways forces of propellers is extremely difficult to assess and has not yet been fully explored experimentally. Nevertheless, the sideways forces generated by fixed-pitch out-turning propellers always assist the differential thrust when turning a twin-screw ship at rest or nearly at rest.

A little reflection will reveal that if a ship has fixed-pitch in-turning propellers, paddlewheel effect and lateral wash will act in opposition to pressure-and-suction effect and to the fore-and-aft thrust when she is turning at rest. The first two effects are opposing the turn and thus the behaviour of the ship is not so easily predictable as for a ship fitted with out-turning screws. In such a vessel the shiphandler should carefully study all the available information and take the earliest opportunity to gain experience of the ship's manoeuvring characteristics.

The shiphandler will gain a better understanding of how his ship will manoeuvre if he keeps in mind the existence of the sideways propeller forces as well as the fore-and-aft thrusts. It will probably be helpful for him to have a good look at the after part of the hull and at the relative positions of propellers and rudders, when the ship is in dock or by studying her drawings.

FIG. 12–12. Disposition of propellers and thrust blocks in relation to length of ship

The ship's manoeuvrability depends, however, upon many other external factors, which have already been mentioned and which will be discussed later in this chapter. Shallow water in particular may modify greatly the effects already described.

Single-screw ship

If a ship with a single right-handed screw proceeds ahead from rest the paddle-wheel effect carries her stern to starboard, and hence tends to turn the ship to port initially. As headway is gained this effect is progressively reduced. Thus it is usually necessary at first to apply starboard wheel to keep the ship on a steady course, but the amount of wheel can be gradually reduced as the ship gathers speed. When the screw is put astern the effect is to swing the stern to port and this effect is noticeable even after sternway has been gained. Often this swing is so strong when going astern that it cannot be counteracted even by full opposite rudder. The question of how best to turn a single-screw ship at rest is discussed in Chapter 13.

ACTION OF CONTROLLABLE-PITCH PROPELLERS

Forces are developed by controllable-pitch propellers in exactly the same manner as by fixed-pitch propellers. However, the direction and effect of these forces differ because regardless of the selected pitch (i.e. whether developing ahead or astern thrust) the propeller continues to rotate in the same direction. It is important to understand how these effects differ in ships fitted with controllable-pitch propellers because certain handling characteristics, which might otherwise be considered inexplicable or unpredictable behaviour, can then generally be resolved.

The action of these forces is illustrated below by two examples: firstly, the behaviour of a ship fitted with a single left-handed (i.e. rotating counter-clockwise when viewed from astern) controllable-pitch propeller and a single rudder, such as an ISLAND Class OPV which is diesel propelled; and secondly, the behaviour of a ship fitted with twin inward-turning controllable-pitch propellers and twin rudders, such as the *Amazon* and *Broadsword* Class frigates or *Sheffield* Class destroyers which are propelled by gas turbines.

Single controllable-pitch propeller (Fig. 12–13)

In a single-screw ship fitted with a single rudder, no turning forces are developed by pressure-and-suction effect or by differential thrust. Paddlewheel

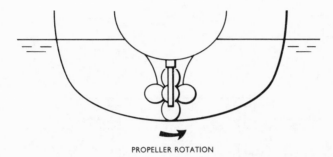

PROPELLER ROTATION

FIG. 12–13. Arrangement of single controllable-pitch propeller and single rudder

effect will always tend to throw the stern to port, increased by a certain amount of lateral wash impinging on the starboard side of the deadwood. The total effect of these two forces is dependent on:

1. The selected pitch of the propeller.

2. The revolutions (speed) of the propeller.

With the propeller rotating at zero pitch and at minimum revolutions the sideways forces at the stern will be minimal, and they will progressively increase with the power applied to the propeller.

   Thus, when going ahead from rest, there will be a tendency for the bow to pay off to starboard, but the major turning effect is achieved by the propeller wash acting on the rudder which is positioned immediately abaft the screw. Furthermore, it can be expected that the turning circle to starboard will be smaller than that to port.

   Reversing the pitch. The stern will be thrown to port under the action of the propeller, and putting the rudder over to counteract this is not likely to be effective until the ship has gathered sternway. If it is desired to swing the stern in the opposite direction — for example, when berthing starboard-side to — the swing must be started in the required direction *before* the pitch is reversed. Therefore, disregarding the effect of wind, the arrangement of a single left-handed controllable-pitch propeller and a single rudder makes it simpler to berth alongside port-side to.

   Turning short. The ship will turn much more easily to starboard with slight headway using short bursts of ahead and astern power combined with full rudder action (starboard when going ahead and port when moving astern) to assist the turn.

Twin controllable-pitch propellers (Fig. 12–14)

In ships fitted with twin controllable-pitch propellers and twin rudders the propellers are generally inwards-turning (i.e. port propeller clockwise and starboard propeller counter-clockwise when viewed from astern) regardless of whether ahead or astern pitch is selected.

The action of the propellers is illustrated by considering the forces developed in a ship turning at rest to port with ahead pitch set on the starboard propeller and astern pitch on the port propeller.

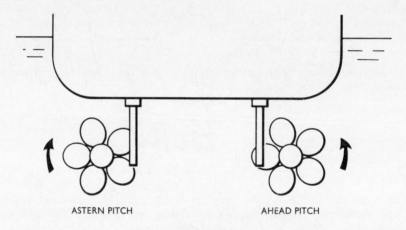

ASTERN PITCH   AHEAD PITCH

INWARDS-TURNING PROPELLERS

FIG. 12–14. Arrangement of twin controllable-pitch propellers and twin rudders

If the two propellers are set to the same pitch (port astern and starboard ahead) and to the same revolutions, the following effects will appear.

Paddlewheel effect. The forces created by the two screws will be equal and opposite. They will cancel each other and there will be no sideways force.

Pressure-and-suction effect. Pressure from the port screw against the port stern section and suction from the starboard screw on the starboard side will *assist* the turn to port by moving the stern to starboard.

Lateral-wash effect. The forces from this effect cancel each other and there will be no resultant sideways force.

Thrust. The effect of ahead pitch on the starboard screw and astern pitch on the port screw is to *assist* the turn to port.

In the circumstances described above only two of the propeller forces assist in turning the ship. However, because the forces developed by paddlewheel and lateral-wash effects are dependent on the selected pitch and revolutions, they could oppose the turn of the ship in certain circumstances. For example in the manoeuvre described above, if the starboard screw were set to a greater pitch and higher revolutions than the port screw then the paddlewheel and lateral-wash effects of the starboard screw would be greater. Thus the overall effect of these two forces would be to turn the stern to *port*, i.e. against the turn.

This counter-productive nature of two of the propeller forces may be particularly noticeable when only one screw is used with ahead pitch and the other is set to zero pitch. If, for example, ahead pitch on the starboard screw and zero pitch on the port screw were selected to turn the ship to port, then paddlewheel and lateral-wash effects would directly oppose thrust and pressure-and-suction effect. The ship may not turn at all unless the rudder is put over to take advantage of the flow of water past the starboard rudder. On the other hand, going astern on one screw with the other set to zero pitch allows all four forces to act in unison. In the example of turning to port at rest, if astern pitch on the port screw and zero pitch on the starboard screw were selected the propeller forces would be as follows.

Paddlewheel effect is greater on the port screw than the starboard screw, which moves the stern to starboard.

Pressure-and-suction effect of the port screw exerts pressure on the port side of the stern, which moves the stern to starboard.

Lateral-wash effect is greater on the port than the starboard side, which moves the stern to starboard.

Thrust of the port screw in the astern direction turns the ship to port.

Provided there is sufficient headroom the ship may more easily be turned in either direction by going ahead on both screws and using the excellent turning moment provided by the twin rudders which are ideally situated in the wash of each propeller. However, because of the rapid acceleration of gas-turbine propelled ships, care must be taken not to gather too much headway.

TURNING

Forces acting on a turning ship

When anything moves in a circular or curved path there is an acceleration towards the centre of the path. This acceleration is caused by a force called *centripetal* force. In a ship the centripetal force is the resultant of all the lateral forces acting on the hull and rudder. The centripetal force on the hull alone acts through the pressure of sea water on one side of the hull, and it can be assumed that it acts through a point called the centre of pressure (S in Fig. 12-15). When the rudder is first put over, and before the ship has begun to turn, the ship will probably heel inwards, because the rudder force acts below the centre of gravity G (Fig. 12-16(i)). In addition there is a tendency for the ship to be pushed bodily outwards from her original line of advance. As the ship begins to turn, she heels outwards because the centripetal force on the hull (which is greater than the rudder force) normally acts at a point below her centre of gravity (Fig. 12-16(ii)). The ship now travels along a path of gradually increasing curvature until, after turning through about 90 degrees, the path becomes approximately circular.

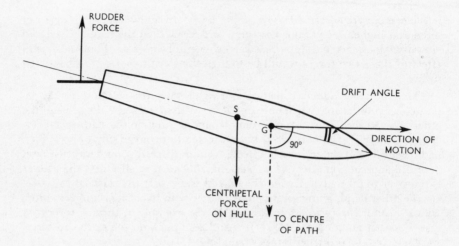

FIG. 12–15. Forces acting on a ship while turning. *S* is the centre of pressure

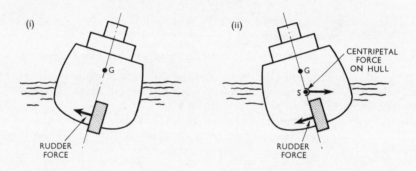

FIG. 12–16. Forces acting on a ship
(i) immediately rudder is put over; (ii) when ship begins to turn

Drift angle

Consider the paths described by various parts of a ship turning under rudder when steaming ahead (Fig. 12–17). Each point in the ship must follow a path approximately concentric with that described by the centre of gravity. The angle made by the tangent to the curved path of any point with the fore-and-aft line is known as the *drift angle* at that point at any given instant.

The drift angle has its highest value at the stern and it diminishes gradually along the fore-and-aft line in the forward direction until a point is reached, usually nearer the bow than the stern, where it is zero. Forward from this point the drift angle gradually increases in the opposite direction. When drift angle is quoted the value given is normally that measured at the centre of gravity.

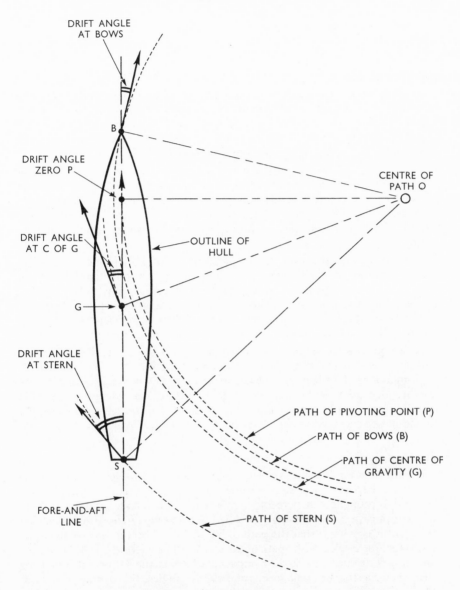

FIG. 12–17. Paths described by various parts of a ship turning under rudder when
moving ahead
(The radius of the turning circle shown is much smaller than normal.)

The value of drift angle is dependent on a number of factors such as the
ship's underwater form and design of rudder, her displacement and speed,
and the direction and force of the wind; but in any particular ship it is
principally dependent on the angle of rudder in use. As angular momentum
increases during the early stages of a turn, so drift angle rapidly increases.
In a turn using steady rudder angle the drift angle at the centre of gravity

z

eventually settles down to a figure in the region of 10 degrees after the ship has turned through about 90 degrees.

Pivoting point

The point where drift angle is zero is called the *pivoting point* of the ship (*P* in Fig. 12–17). At any instant during the turn the direction of movement of the pivoting point is along the fore-and-aft line of the ship, and to an observer there the bow will appear to be swinging towards the centre of curvature at the same rate as the stern is swinging away from it.

The position of the pivoting point is not fixed but moves along the fore-and-aft line, being influenced by the same factors that determine the value of the drift angle. It is dependent more on the ship's speed than on the angle of rudder in use. For a large ship it may oscillate between the bows and the centre of gravity. For practical purposes an average position must be established.

It can be taken that in large ships of orthodox hull shape the average position of the pivoting point when going ahead is about one-third of the ship's length from the bows. In destroyers or frigates it may well be farther forward, while in fast patrol boats or similar fast light craft it may be ahead of the boat when she is turning at speed. When a ship has sternway the pivoting point usually moves to a position nearer the stern than the bows.

It can be seen from Fig. 12–17 that the radius of curvature of the ship's path is greater at the stern than at the pivoting point; the more so as drift angle increases. This fact must be taken into account when plotting in advance the intended track of the ship in restricted waters, e.g. when it is intended to turn into harbour between two breakwaters. Clearly such a manoeuvre should not be executed under a large angle of rudder, if avoidable.

Turning circle

The path of a ship's compass platform as she turns through 360 degrees at a certain speed (i.e. at a steady value of either revolutions per minute for fixed-pitch propellers or percentage power for controllable-pitch propellers) and with a certain rudder angle is called her *turning circle*. From what has been said it is evident that the path of her stem will be very nearly the same as this turning circle but the path of her stern will be well outside it. However, since it is convenient to use the compass platform as the datum when plotting turning circles for different speeds and rudder angles, this definition is used. Thus the turning circles given in the ship's data may not coincide with the turning circles traced out by her pivoting point, although in most ships they will not be dissimilar, because the compass platform is usually not far from the pivoting point when moving ahead.

A typical turning circle is shown in Fig. 12–18. It illustrates that after a turn through 360 degrees the ship's compass platform *H* is usually slightly ahead of, and slightly inside, the point at which the wheel was originally put over.

In Fig. 12–18, *A* is the position of the compass platform at the moment of starting to put the rudder over. *B* is the position at which the ship begins to turn. *C, D, E, F, G* and *H,* are the positions where the ship has turned through 45, 90, 120, 180, 270 and 360 degrees respectively. The distance *AB*

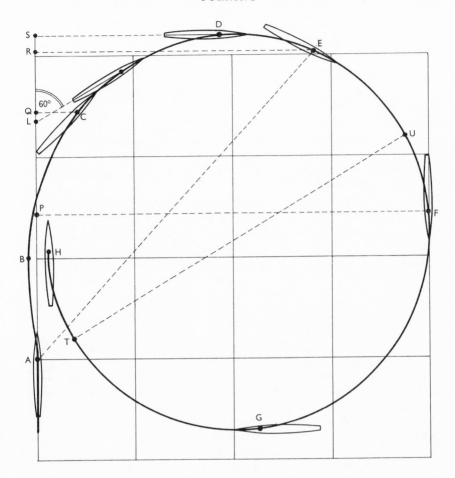

FIG. 12–18. Typical ship's turning circle

is dependent on the speed of the ship, the rate at which the rudder is applied and various other influences such as the wind. On completion of a 360-degree turn, as already stated, most ships are inside their original track, as at *H,* but some are outside it.

The following definitions are used in connection with turning circles and with the accurate plotting of the ship's track on a large scale.

The *advance* of a ship for a given alteration of course is the distance that her compass platform moves in the direction of her original line of advance, measured from the point where the rudder is put over. In Fig. 12–18, *AQ* is the advance for a turn of 45 degrees and *AR* is the advance for 120 degrees.

The *transfer* of a ship for a given alteration of course is the distance that her compass platform moves at right-angles to her original line of advance, measured from the point where the rudder is put over. In Fig. 12–18, *SD* is the transfer for a turn of 90 degrees.

The *tactical diameter* is the amount that the compass platform has moved at right-angles to the ship's original line of advance when she has turned through 180 degrees. In other words, it is the transfer for an alteration of course of 180 degrees, e.g. *PF* in Fig. 12–18.

The *final diameter* (also called the *steady turning diameter,* particularly in turning trials data) is the diameter of the turning circle when the ship's path has finally become approximately circular, e.g. *TU* in Fig. 12–18.

The *distance to new course* is the distance, measured along the original line of advance, from the position of the compass platform when the rudder is put over to the point of intersection between the old and new courses. In Fig. 12–18, *AL* is the distance to new course for a turn of 60 degrees. For turns of over 120 degrees the distance to new course becomes too large to use as an accurate means of plotting the track.

The *intermediate course and distance* gives the direction and length of the line joining the position of the compass platform when the wheel is put over and the position when the ship has turned through any particular angle. In Fig. 12–18, the angle *SAE* is the intermediate course for a turn of 120 degrees. The intermediate distance for this turn is the length *AE*.

Effect of hull form on turning circle

A ship of fine underwater form will turn in a larger circle than a ship of similar length and draught but of fuller form. Modern warships are generally of great length in proportion to beam and thus tend to have large turning circles, but great improvements in turning capability have been achieved in recent classes through fitting rudders of improved design, and through fitting twin rather than single rudders. The shape of the underwater part of the hull aft, particularly the *cut-up* area, as shown in Fig. 12–19, has a most important effect on the size of the turning circle. Certain external effects, such as that of wind, on the size of the turning circle are discussed later in this chapter.

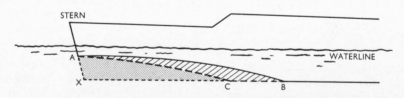

FIG. 12–19. Effect of cut-up area on turning qualities
The ship with the larger cut-up area *ABX* will have a smaller turning circle than the one with the smaller cut-up area *ACX*

Effect of single screw on turning circle

In a ship fitted with a single right-handed fixed-pitch screw the sideways force exerted by the propeller creates a tendency for the ship to turn to port when going ahead. With a left-handed controllable-pitch propeller the effect is reversed, the ship turning more easily to starboard, hence the turning circle with this type of propeller is usually of smaller diameter when turning to starboard than when turning to port.

Effect of a turn on speed

The effect of the drag of the rudder and the sideways drift of the ship will result in a progressive loss of speed while turning, even though the shaft revolutions or percentage power are maintained at a constant figure. For alterations of course of up to 20 degrees the reduction of speed may not be very great, but for those between 20 degrees and 90 degrees the speed usually falls off rapidly. For alterations exceeding 90 degrees the speed may continue to fall slightly, but it usually remains more or less steady. The rate of deceleration depends upon the initial speed of the ship and the angle of rudder applied, and it varies greatly between different types of ship.

Very roughly, most warships when under full wheel will have lost about one-third of their original speed after turning through 90 degrees, and their speed will then remain steady as the turn continues. The figures for an average cargo ship are similar to those for a heavy warship.

An accurate estimate of the deceleration caused by a turn is helpful when manoeuvring in company, particularly when the ship has to turn through a large angle to take station in a column.

The time taken to turn through a given angle depends on the initial speed and the angle of rudder applied; usually the faster the speed and the greater the rudder angle the sooner will the turn be completed.

Turning trials

To obtain data on a ship's turning performance at different speeds and angles of rudder, comprehensive turning trials are carried out by the Admiralty Marine Technology Establishment in the first ship of each new class. One method that can be used by the ship's officers to obtain the data is quite simple. A floating mark, or a boat carrying observers, is placed in sheltered water with plenty of sea-room all round. The ship then approaches at a certain speed and applies a certain angle of rudder so that she will turn through 360 degrees round the mark. At certain angles of turn (e.g. at 30, 60, 90 degrees, etc.) a bearing and range of the mark is taken from the compass platform, and the exact time is noted. If observers are in the boat they take reciprocal bearings and ranges at the same instant. The process is repeated for different speeds and rudder angles. Further guidance is given in BR 45(4), *Admiralty Manual of Navigation*, Volume IV. The method generally adopted by AMTE is to use special observation stations on shore, or accurate radio-fixing aids, in selected areas.

Occasionally the ship's officers carry out turning trials in a new ship shortly after commissioning for the first time, but it is customary to accept the figures for the first of the class. From the data so obtained the ship's track under wheel can be plotted accurately on the largest desired scale, either when it is required to plan the intended track in advance (for example, when entering a harbour) or to establish the track accurately after an alteration of course. Methods of plotting the ship's track accurately on a large scale are described in BR 45(1), *Admiralty Manual of Navigation*, Volume I. These methods allow for the fact that after the ship is steady on her new course an appreciable time will elapse before she regains the speed she was making before the alteration of course.

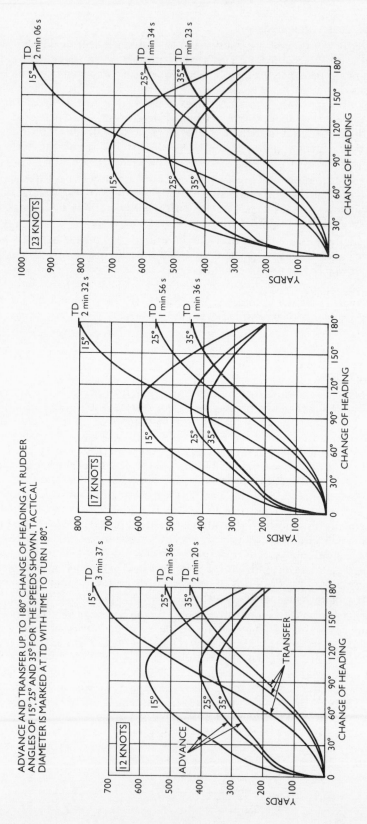

ADVANCE AND TRANSFER UP TO 180° CHANGE OF HEADING AT RUDDER
ANGLES OF 15°, 25° AND 35° FOR THE SPEEDS SHOWN. TACTICAL
DIAMETER IS MARKED AT TD WITH TIME TO TURN 180°.

Fig. 12-20. Alternative method of graphical presentation of turning data

Conditions for turning trials

Calm weather is necessary for the conduct of turning trials. The effect of wind and sea on turning performance is so marked that results obtained in rough weather will probably show confusing variations from the normal. If the method of plotting involves the use of a datum point that is either on shore or moored, there should be no tidal stream or current in the area. The trials should be carried out in a depth of at least 35 metres, or preferably in a depth of at least ten times the ship's draught, in order to avoid shallow-water effects. Special trials may be carried out in shallower depths to determine their effects on the turning performance.

Presentation of manoeuvring data

Nowadays turning trials and manoeuvring data are frequently measured in metric units. However, for shiphandling and navigation purposes it is Navy Department policy that distance continues to be expressed in Imperial units. Hence the *yard* may still be found in use for this purpose in the appropriate chapters of the *Admiralty Manual of Seamanship* and other publications.

The results of turning trials are issued to each ship of the class and should be placed in the ship's Navigational Data Book. The report contains the full turning data, in both tabular and graphic form, and other manoeuvring information such as acceleration, deceleration and the behaviour of the ship after centring the rudder during turns of various rates.

Abridged turning data for all HM ships are also published in BR 45(4), *Admiralty Manual of Navigation,* Volume IV. Full information for each ship would be too voluminous for inclusion, so the condensed details are shown as a series of curves of advance and transfer for various speeds and rudder angles. Fig. 12–20 shows a typical example of a frigate's turning data presented in this manner.

Determination of the speed at any point in a turn

The speed remaining at a certain point in a turn can be calculated in the following way. From the turning trials data the ship's turning circle, for a given speed and rudder angle, can be plotted accurately. In the trials the time on completion of each 30-degree change of heading is noted during each turn. If the length of arc between two adjacent 30-degree points on the turning circle is measured, and divided by the time taken to alter course through that 30-degree arc, this will give the mean speed half-way between the two points. These mean speeds can then be plotted as a graph, against change of heading (P, Q, R, S in Fig. 12–21). From the graph the speed remaining at any point in the turn can be read off. These graphs, or tables of speed remaining, usually appear in the turning-trials reports.

Heel when turning

As explained earlier in this chapter, the initial heel when the wheel is put over is inwards, because the rudder force is acting at a point below the centre of gravity of the ship. As the ship begins to turn, the centripetal force on the hull (which is greater than the rudder force), acting through water pressure at a point below the centre of gravity, overcomes the tendency to heel inwards

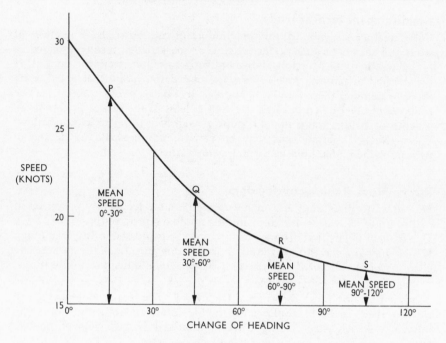

FIG. 12–21. Graph constructed to show the speed remaining at any point in a turn

The figure shows the curve of a ship having an approach speed of 30 knots and turning with a rudder angle of 35 degrees

and causes her to heel outwards. This outward heel is very noticeable in most warships turning at high speed. If the wheel is eased quickly the angle of outward heel will increase, because the counteractive rudder force is removed while the centripetal force remains, until the rate of turning decreases (see Fig. 12–16(ii)). If a power boat is carrying a heavy deck-load the outward heel during a turn could be aggravated dangerously by quickly easing or reversing the wheel. Should an alarming heel develop, speed should be reduced instantly. In fast, shallow-draught craft, whose resistance to lateral movement is relatively small, there is considerable side-slip rather than outward heel, because the centripetal force on the hull is lessened. Therefore when turning at speed the rudder pressure causes such boats to heel inwards. In a fast motor-boat the initial inward heel caused by multiple rudders at high speed may be violent.

Effect of reversing the inner screw when turning

A Captain should know the circumstances in which reversal of the inner screw or use of astern pitch will be advantageous in his ship. Where reduction in the turning circle is required and loss of speed is acceptable or desirable, for example when negotiating a sharp turn after passing through breakwaters, the inner screw can often be reversed with good effect. When avoiding a danger ahead, however, the reduction in advance with the inner screw reversed is usually so small when the ship is proceeding at any speed that no advantage would be gained, other than loss of headway. If a turn under full rudder appears unlikely to take the ship clear of the danger it may be preferable not to risk a broadside encounter, but instead to take as much way off the ship as possible by going full speed astern on both engines.

Steaming with one engine stopped

The amount of rudder required to enable the course to be maintained with one engine stopped will vary with individual ships and in different weather conditions. A large ship may require 10 degrees of opposing rudder, and a destroyer considerably less. A smaller rudder-angle will be required if the shaft can be trailed, but if machinery repairs are being carried out this will not normally be possible.

Steaming with one screw trailing may lead to a significant saving of fuel in some gas-turbine ships at about the cruising speed. Although there is extra drag from the trailing screw, the other engine is able to operate at a higher efficiency resulting in a net reduction of fuel consumption over twin-shaft operation.

Steering by main engines

The procedure for steering by main engines will vary according to circumstances and with the opinions of individual commanding officers. Some prefer a standard procedure whereby the same set of engines is always maintained at constant revolutions and the other set varied so as to maintain the course. When it is required to make good the best possible speed in a ship which normally carries weather helm it will be preferable to keep the weather engines at constant maximum revolutions for the given machinery state and to decrease the revolutions of the lee engines as necessary to maintain the course, and vice versa for a ship which normally carries lee helm.

ACCELERATION AND DECELERATION

Factors affecting gain and loss of speed

The following factors determine the acceleration powers of a ship.

1. INERTIA. A heavy ship is slower both to gain and to lose speed than a smaller ship with comparable engine power (see Fig. 12–2).

2. SHAPE OF HULL. Of two ships of similar displacement the one with finer lines accelerates more rapidly and carries her way farther than the one of fuller form.

3. RESPONSE OF PROPULSION MACHINERY. A ship propelled by gas turbines or diesel engines responds more rapidly to engine orders than a ship driven by steam turbines. This shows particularly in the longer time taken to run-down steam turbines from a high ahead speed, even if maximum astern power is applied. Some diesel-engined ships have non-reversing engines, so that to go astern the shafts must be reversed through gearing. Such ships cannot stop engines when manoeuvring but merely put the gears in neutral, so that the shaft trails and any braking effect of the propeller is lost.

4. DESIGN OF PROPELLERS. The size and design of the propellers must be considered in conjunction with the propulsion machinery. The effect of large slow-turning propellers of coarse pitch is felt more rapidly than that of smaller faster-turning propellers. A large propeller acts as a considerable drag when slowed or stopped and thus improves the deceleration of the ship; when reversed, the effect of its astern revolutions is felt immediately. In ships fitted with controllable-pitch propellers, astern power can be applied rapidly by reversing the pitch: so rapidly in fact, that safeguards have to be designed into the machinery control system to prevent excessive torques and thrusts developing in the shafts during an ahead – astern manoeuvre.

5. STATE OF SHIP'S BOTTOM. The drag of a foul bottom has more effect when decelerating than when accelerating from rest.

6. DEPTH OF WATER. The effect of shallow water will be to reduce the ship's acceleration and, in general, the indications are that deceleration will also be reduced, i.e. the ship will take longer to stop.

Rates of gaining and losing speed

A knowledge of the rate at which a ship gains or loses speed in different circumstances is invaluable when manoeuvring in company. These rates depend chiefly on the displacement of the ship, her condition of loading, her draught, the power of her engines, the size of her propellers and the depth of water. The corresponding rates for one ship will differ largely from those of another, and the rates for a particular ship may change considerably with her condition of loading. It is customary to give the rate in the form *yards per knot;* this value is used as a factor when taking up or changing station (page 433).

When turning trials are carried out some data on acceleration and deceleration are also usually obtained. These additional data come under the heading of acceleration and deceleration trials. Further data are usually subsequently obtained by ship's officers so that acceleration and deceleration throughout the speed range and with differing applications of power are known. From this information suitable figures are deduced which will satisfy the majority of manoeuvring requirements.

Typical figures are shown below to illustrate the approximate rates of gain or loss of speed for various warships.

SHIP DISPLACEMENT	ACCELERATING	DECELERATING
tonnes	*yards/knot*	*yards/knot*
25 000	100	100
12 000	80	80 – 200
6 000	50 – 60	50 – 60
3 500	15 – 25	15 – 25

Although shown in relation to displacement, it must be remembered that the rates are not necessarily proportional, being affected by many other factors such as hull form, engine power, wind resistance, etc.

When increasing or decreasing speed by changing the ahead revolutions, the rate of acceleration or deceleration is affected by so many factors and varies so much in different parts of the total speed range that it is difficult to recommend any practical method of allowing for it accurately when manoeuvring. It is common practice to use a standard figure for the ship under all conditions (e.g. 100 yards per knot for a heavy ship, 25 yards per knot for a frigate or destroyer). It must be realised that this method may prove extremely inaccurate in certain circumstances, and the shiphandler should be prepared to make bold and rapid adjustments of speed during a manoeuvre if it appears that the estimate is wrong. An example of the practical application of the method when taking up station is given in Chapter 14.

FACTORS AFFECTING SPEED

Foul bottom

If a ship lies for long in harbour, particularly in a tropical harbour, her bottom becomes fouled by weeds, barnacles and other marine parasites or growths, and the speed attainable with a given number of revolutions is reduced. The extent of fouling depends largely on the locality of the harbour, being much worse in some harbours than in others even within the same area. The amount of fouling can be reduced by proceeding at high speeds or by lying at anchor in a fresh-water river.

The loss of speed caused by fouling can be given roughly as a fixed percentage of the clean-bottom speed, over the whole speed range. The effect is approximately the same for all classes of ship. For example, the growth accumulated during 6 months in average tropical waters would cause a reduction of about 10 per cent. Under these conditions a 30-knot ship would have her maximum speed cut to about 27 knots, while normal revolutions for 15 knots would give only $13\frac{1}{2}$ knots through the water.

If docking is impossible, a considerable improvement in speed can be obtained by listing the ship and scraping the exposed hull, because the greater part of the growth is near the waterline. The actual speed obtained at different revolutions should be checked frequently, especially in tropical waters, because any estimate of loss due to fouling can only be a rough guess.

Shallow water

When a ship is moving in shallow water the gap between the ship's hull and the bottom is restricted, the streamline flow of water past the hull is altered and the result is seen as a greatly increased transverse wave formation at the bows and again at the stern. In fact, the increased size of the stern wave is a sure indication of the presence of shallow water. The energy expended in the waves formed by the ship is a loss from the power available to drive her, and therefore in shallow water her speed is reduced. Furthermore, the restricted flow of water past the stern reduces propeller efficiency, which also tends to reduce her speed. Usually, the higher the speed the more pronounced is the reduction of speed. In extreme cases, and particularly in ships of low freeboard aft, the quarterdeck may be flooded by the stern wave.

The effect of shallow water on handling the ship is discussed further on page 356.

GOING ASTERN

When a ship is moving astern the pivoting point moves well aft. Thus the turning moment of the rudder is greatly reduced as compared with the situation when moving ahead. Also, the propeller slipstream no longer plays upon the rudder. For these reasons a ship does not steer nearly so well astern as ahead, particularly at lower speeds. In a twin-screw or multiple-screw ship this defect can be overcome to a certain extent by using the propellers on either side. However, in a single-screw ship the difficulty is accentuated, because in going astern the screw kicks the stern to port, and in some cases the use of full starboard rudder fails to counteract this. In calm weather a single-screw ship is best manoeuvred astern by pointing the stern to starboard of the desired direction, gathering plenty of sternway and stopping the engines. The rudder should then steer the ship.

In general, the rudder cannot be relied on to control the steering when the ship is making a stern board. Even when there is ample sea-room and when handling a ship that is known to steer well astern, it must be remembered that a heavy strain is brought on the steering gear and that there may be difficulty in righting the rudder.

The size of the turning circle when moving astern is generally much greater than at the same speed ahead.

FACTORS AFFECTING A SHIP'S HANDLING QUALITIES

Draught, trim and loading

A moderate reduction in the draught of a warship, as occurs when her fuel is low, usually causes a slight increase in her tactical diameter. In a merchant ship such as a general cargo ship or tanker the difference between her turning qualities when lightly laden and when fully laden is very marked. When deeply laden a cargo ship has a much larger turning circle than when lightly laden, and she is more sluggish in answering her rudder.

Trim by the stern usually increases the tactical diameter, but helps a ship to keep her course more easily when on a steady course. When trimmed by the bows her turning circle is likely to be decreased; she does not answer her wheel as readily as usual, and once she has started to swing it is more difficult to check her. The effect of trimming is to move the ship's pivoting point towards the deeper end.

List

The effect of a list is to hinder a turn in the direction of the list and assist a turn away from it. A list to port decreases the tactical diameter of a ship turning to starboard, and vice versa.

Speed

The effect of speed on tactical diameter will vary from one type of ship to another. Often higher speed may lead to a greater tactical diameter because the rudder may stall. Modern rudders, however, are able to operate satisfactorily at higher water speeds and greater angles, and hence the tactical diameter may not vary much with speed. Indeed, in one particular class of ship it has been found that there is a best speed giving the minimum tactical diameter and at higher or lower speeds the tactical diameter is greater. Watchkeeping officers should be fully aware of the effect of speed on the turning qualities of their ship.

Wind

General effects. In most ships the pivoting point is well forward when moving ahead, so that the pressure on the greater exposed area abaft this point tends to turn the ship into the wind. When going astern, the pivoting point moves aft and the stern tends to fly into the wind. The degree to which these effects are felt depends largely on the shape and disposition of the ship's superstructure. For example, a ship with a very high forecastle and much of her top-hamper forward is not affected a great deal when going ahead, but her stern seeks the eye of the wind rapidly as soon as she gathers sternway. The effect on the ship's turning circle usually is to expand the curve in the two quadrants in which her bows are turning away from the wind, and to contract it elsewhere. When turning away from the wind the ship is sluggish in answering her rudder. She may be carrying lee rudder already to keep her on her course, so that in order to start the turn more wheel than usual must be applied. When avoiding a danger ahead remember that the advance will be greater when turning away from the wind.

Wind effects are felt more strongly when speed is slow, and in a merchant ship when she is lightly laden. As ahead speed is reduced the bow usually falls off the wind more and more rapidly until, when the ship has lost all way, she lies approximately beam-on to the wind.

Effect when turning at rest. When turning at rest in calm weather a ship pivots about a point somewhere between her centre of gravity and the centre of area of her underwater profile. This point is normally somewhat forward of amidships, but it moves forward or aft with trim by the bow or stern respectively. Under the influence of wind the attitude of a ship when stopped depends on the relation between the area exposed to the wind before and abaft the at-rest pivoting point. Usually a warship lies with the wind within 20 degrees of the beam, and when settled there she requires a greater turning moment than normal to start her turning at rest.

Drift. Any ship drifts to leeward under the influence of wind, the rate increasing progressively with loss of headway or sternway and with an increase in the angle of wind from the fore-and-aft line. When stopped and beam-on to the wind, the ship, as she drifts to leeward, begins to transmit her motion to the water surrounding her. The rate of drift increases up to a point at which both the ship and a body of surrounding water are moving bodily to leeward. Immediately the ship moves ahead or astern she will then enter water that is not drifting and so will reduce her own rate of drift to leeward.

Effect of sea. In the open sea a strong wind is, of course, accompanied by heavy seas or swell. Their effects on the handling of the ship are discussed in Chapter 15.

Current and tidal stream

Clearly the ship's handling qualities are not affected in any way if the whole body of water covering the area in which she is manoeuvring is moving at a constant speed. In narrow waters, allowance must be made for the distance the ship will be moved by the stream during a manoeuvre. But it frequently occurs in confined waters that the stream differs considerably within a small area, so that the bows and stern may be exposed to quite different currents. The effects of current and tidal stream when handling a ship in narrow waters in various situations are discussed more fully in Chapter 13.

Shallow water

The effects of shallow water on the speed of the ship and on the flow of water past the hull when moving ahead have already been described. These effects may become excessive if the depth of water is less than one-and-a-half times the draught, particularly if the ship enters such water at high speed. She may become directionally unstable and fail to answer her rudder at all, and the draught aft may increase so greatly as to cause the propellers to touch bottom.

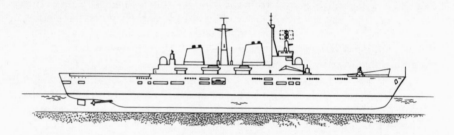

F IG. 12–22. Clearance between keel and sea bottom — an aircraft carrier in a shallow harbour

The effects are likely to be particularly pronounced in ships where the propeller slipstream does not play directly on to the rudder. The effects of shallow water on steering in restricted waters such as canals or rivers are usually worse than in the open sea, and are more likely to have dangerous results. The only way to regain control is to reduce speed drastically at once.

When manoeuvring at slow speed or turning at rest in a confined space in shallow water, the expected effects from the rudder and the propellers may not appear. Water cannot flow easily from one side of the ship to the other, so that the sideways force from the propellers may in fact be opposite to what usually occurs. Eddies may build up that counteract the propeller forces and the expected action of the rudder. If the attempt to turn at rest in shallow water with ahead revolutions on one shaft and astern on the other fails, or the turn is very sluggish, the situation will almost certainly become worse if the revolutions are increased. Stopping the engines to allow the eddies to subside, and then starting again with reduced revolutions, is more likely to be successful. The extremely small clearance between keel and bottom in many harbours becomes obvious if a heavy ship in shallow water is drawn out to scale, as in Fig. 12–22, which shows a carrier drawing 7.3 metres in a depth of 10 metres.

SPECIAL TYPES OF RUDDER AND PROPELLER

To conclude this chapter a brief description of a number of unorthodox types of propeller and rudder is given. Some of these have been fitted to HM ships or boats, as mentioned below.

Kitchen rudder

The Kitchen rudder consists of a pair of vertical plates that can be moved around the propeller of a boat so as to control the flow of water from it. The rudder is described in Volume II. The advantage of the gear is that it enables the boat to go astern without reversing the propeller. This is done by closing the plates so as to form a semicircle abaft the propeller. In addition, the two plates, both when closed abaft the propeller and when open, can be moved round the propeller from starboard to port, so controlling the direction of the stream from it and enabling the boat to manoeuvre well in confined spaces. A number of ships' power-boats have been fitted with Kitchen rudders.

Active rudder

The active rudder (Fig. 12–23) is constructed with a small propeller built into the trailing edge. The propeller axis turns with the rudder and the propeller can be rotated in the forward or reverse direction to create a stream in the plane of the rudder. The propeller of the rudder is in addition to the ship's main propellers. The active rudder is used for accurate manoeuvring and can also be employed to propel the ship at slow speeds. The propeller can be driven by either electrical or mechanical means. In the electric type the propeller is driven directly by a reversible electric motor incorporated into the construction of the rudder. The mechanical type employs a shaft which passes through the rudder stock, and bevel gearing, to drive the propeller, the power being provided by an electric motor or diesel engine located in the steering gear compartment. Active rudders are fitted in some mine countermeasures vessels.

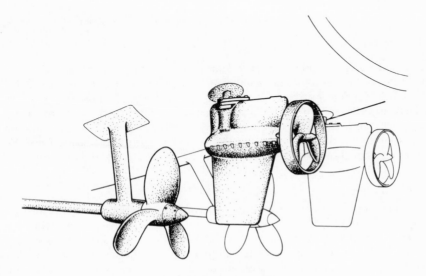

FIG. 12–23. Active rudder

Bow rudder

In some ships a conventional rudder is fitted at the stem in addition to the normal stern-rudder arrangement. The bow rudder improves the steering performance when going astern but is centred and unused when moving ahead normally. This type of rudder is fitted to specialised vessels requiring good astern manoeuvring in restricted waterways, e.g. ferries frequently using ports with difficult access to berths.

Bow thruster

The bow thruster (Fig. 12–24) consists of a reversible propeller mounted in a transverse tunnel which passes through the hull low down in the fore

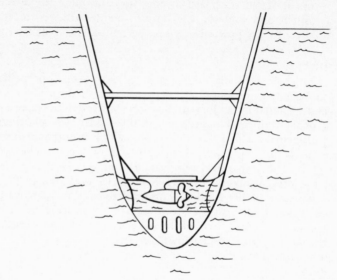

FIG. 12–24. Cross-section at bow of ship to show arrangement of bow thruster

end of the ship. A force to port or starboard can thus be exerted at the bow to assist in the turning of large ships or the accurate manoeuvring of smaller vessels. To reduce hull resistance when the thruster is not in use the openings of the tunnel can usually be closed by faired doors which conform to the shape of the hull. The propeller can be driven either by an electric motor incorporated in the housing or mechanically by shafts and gearing from the compartment above. Some HM ships and RFAs are fitted with bow thrusters.

Jet propeller

The first application of mechanical power to ships consisted of an installation by means of which water was drawn by a steam-driven pump through openings in the bows and ejected through nozzles in the stern. This system proved far less efficient than the paddlewheel and the screw propeller, and is now only used in certain specialised craft. One such modern application is the propulsion system of the Boeing 'Jetfoil' hydrofoil where water is drawn up from the level of the foils and discharged through manoeuvrable jets at the stern. The pumps are driven by gas turbines. These craft are used as ferries over quite long distances in various parts of the world.

Paddlewheels

The term 'paddlewheel' is applied to a form of propeller which rotates about a horizontal transverse axis above the vessel's waterline, and consists of a wheel having paddles or *floats* attached to its periphery. The paddles may be fixed or *feathering,* the latter giving better performance but involving high initial costs and requiring more maintenance. The paddlewheel held undisputed sway during the first half of the nineteenth century, but was superseded for ocean work by the more convenient screw propeller. Paddle tugs remained in service at some dockyard ports until about 1981. These were invariably *side-wheelers,* and were fitted with feathering floats.

Vertical-axis or cycloidal propellers

Vertical-axis or cycloidal propellers are virtually feathering paddle-wheels set on a vertical axis in the bottom of a vessel. The degree of feathering can be controlled so that the resultant of the blade forces acts in any desired direction and thus the vessel is both propelled and steered by its propeller. One example is the Voith-Schneider propeller which is fitted to some classes of Ministry of Defence tug. Fig. 12–25 shows the side elevation of an *Irene* Class tug in which the propeller is fitted forward and driven by a 250-kilowatt diesel engine, and Fig. 12–26 shows an underside view of the propeller. One great advantage of this arrangement is that it is virtually impossible to gird the tug because the towing point is well aft and the towing strain will haul the tug into the line of the tow.

Fig. 12–27 shows the operation of this type of propeller. The vertical blades are mounted in an assembly which rotates continuously in only one direction about the fixed centre R. Each blade is capable of oscillating about its vertical axis and all the blades are controlled in unison by a mechanical linkage centred at O. The centre of the linkage can be offset from the centre of rotation by a control system which is operated remotely from the bridge. Consider, for example, a vessel fitted with a single propeller: if the centres of rotation and of oscillation are coincident the blades have no pitch and so no thrust is created (Fig. 12–27(i)). If the centre of oscillation is moved aft then during the course of rotation the blades will assume the pitch shown in Fig. 12–27(ii) and create a force towards the stern which will propel the vessel ahead. If the centre of oscillation is moved forward and to port the force developed will drive the vessel astern at the same time as turning it to starboard (Fig. 12–27(iii)). Fig. 12–27(iv) illustrates the case in which the vessel turns to starboard at rest.

Delicate and rapid control is achieved because the power developed by the propeller, which is proportional to the offset of the centre of oscillation, is smoothly variable throughout its full range. Where greater control of manoeuvring is required — for example the dynamic positioning of offshore supply vessels — it is common to fit two cycloidal propellers, one forward and the other aft. With such an arrangement it is possible to propel the ship in any desired direction without turning her.

2A

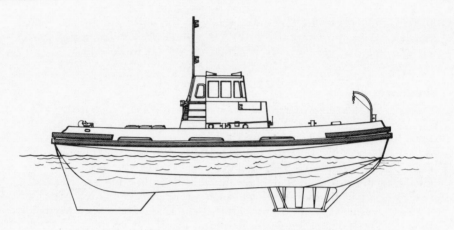

FIG. 12–25. *Irene* Class tug fitted with Voith-Schneider propeller

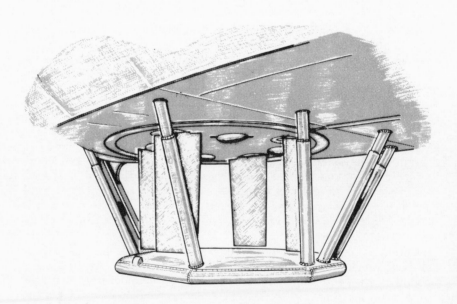

FIG. 12–26. Underside view of Voith-Schneider propeller looking forward from
port side

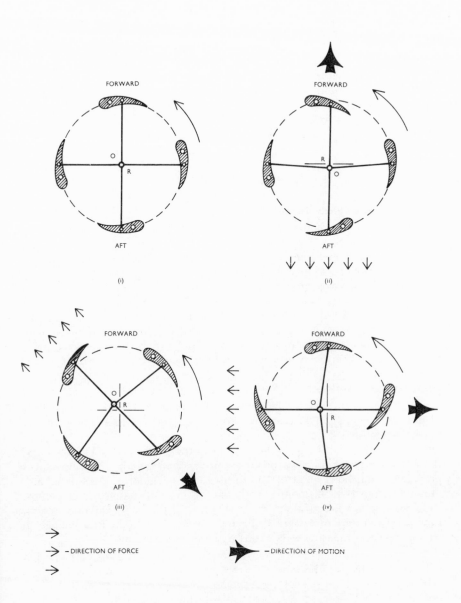

Fɪɢ. 12–27. Action of the cycloidal propeller

CHAPTER 13

Handling Ships in Narrow Waters

In the previous chapter we have seen how a ship should react to her rudders and propulsion system in different circumstances. The practical application of this knowledge, to the problems of manoeuvring the ship in narrow waters and of berthing her in harbour, is described in this chapter.

PREPARATION

A ship's handling qualities

On assuming a new command an officer should study all the information available, in the Ship Equipment Files, the Navigational Data Book and elsewhere, about her steering and propulsion systems, about previous experience of the ship's handling qualities and about any peculiarities of her construction, such as projecting screws, sponsons or overhanging superstructures. All this information will help him to form a complete idea of the ship's character that will improve his judgement as he handles her. He should take the opportunity as soon as possible of practising various manoeuvres in open waters, such as dropping and picking up a lifebuoy, turning into and away from the wind, steering at slow speed and with sternway, and turning at rest.

Importance of a plan

A sound plan is the essence of all successful pilotage. Having decided on a plan, the Captain should discuss it with his Navigating Officer and with any other officers concerned, e.g. the Executive Officer and the Marine Engineer Officer, so that it is clearly in their minds as the manoeuvre is executed and the Captain's intention at each stage is understood by all. If circumstances prove different, however, from those envisaged in the plan, the shiphandler must be prepared to modify his plan or even abandon it altogether. Shiphandling is a practical art which, because of the many variable factors, cannot be reduced to a rigid drill, and quick adaptability to a change in circumstances is thus an essential quality in the shiphandler.

An essential feature of the plan for any manoeuvre is a forecast of what will be the effect of the wind, current or tidal stream. Clearing bearings should be worked out so that the Navigating Officer can ensure that the ship does not drift unobserved into shoal water during the manoeuvre.

Judgement of speed and distance

When there is no wind or tidal stream, speed can be judged by watching some object floating alongside, provided it is not affected by the wash of the propellers or the movement of the ship. In a wind or tidal stream, however, the movement of the ship must be observed by watching transits on shore, because it is the speed *over the ground* that is important. In an open anchorage, particularly at night, small pieces of wood thrown into the water near the bridge can be used to show when the ship has lost her way through the water (known as a Dutchman's log — see also Volume II).

Judgement of distance is much affected by the observer's height above the water; from a high bridge objects appear much nearer than from a low one.

When approaching a berth the direction of the ship's head in relation to anything ahead (a jetty, for example) is best estimated by standing amidships on the bridge so that the stem marks the fore-and-aft line. When conning from the wing of the bridge (or from the island of an aircraft carrier), some object lying directly ahead in the ship should be used as a mark instead of the stem.

Precautions

Critical situations may arise very suddenly when manoeuvring in narrow waters, and to cope with them quick action is necessary. Such situations may be caused by an error of judgement, an unexpected manoeuvre by a nearby ship, failure of propulsion machinery or steering gear, misinterpretation of an engine or wheel order, a squall or shift of wind, or a wrong forecast of the strength or direction of the tidal stream.

To guard against failure of steering gear, pitch and power control levers, engine-order telegraphs and the siren, these items are always tested as a routine before the ship gets under way; with the exception of steering gear they should also be tested before a ship approaches pilotage waters after an ocean passage.

If a wheel or engine order has been misinterpreted it is best to order the wheel amidships, or stop the engine, before again giving the correct order. Experience has proved that the mistake will be corrected more quickly in this way than by reiterating the original order.

Generally speaking, ships should always be handled in narrow waters at slow or moderate speed; excessive speed is unseamanlike and may well lead to confusion and accident. This does not mean that the engines should always be confined to slow speed; in single-screw ships particularly, some manoeuvres necessitate the propeller being driven at high speeds; it is the speed of the ship through the water that must not be excessive.

When manoeuvring in a harbour both anchors should always be ready for letting go immediately. If the way of a ship has to be checked by her ground tackle in an emergency, both anchors should be let go rather than one, because it is better to lose both anchors, if this will avert a collision, than to save one and suffer a collision.

When berthing alongside or leaving a jetty the inshore anchor, while ready for letting go, should be kept stowed in the hawsepipe and not eased out or hung a'cockbill. This should greatly reduce the risk of damage to the anchor or hull should the flare of the forecastle foul the jetty, bollards or fittings.

Astern power in some warships is relatively low. Although the design of engines and propellers is the governing factor, in the case of a steamship it is possible to vary the power available by the number of boilers connected but it is customary to manoeuvre with maximum power available. Gas-turbine powered warships have much greater astern power, and this is dependent on the number of gas turbines available for use. Before manoeuvring in harbour it is seamanlike to ensure that an adequate reserve of power is available.

Accidents can often be prevented by the quick and intelligent use of hawsers. Men should be trained in the expert use of hawsers and heaving lines, and these should always be ready at hand. The hawsers should be faked down on deck, and the dangers of extension of man-made fibre ropes should always be borne in mind.

CONTROL AT SLOW SPEED

A ship's handling qualities at slow speed should be fairly evident from the description, given in the preceding chapter, of propeller and rudder effects and of how these effects are influenced by outside factors such as the wind.

Generally, a ship continues to steer well so long as her propellers are turning ahead, however slowly. Thus it is best, particularly in a heavy ship, to take most of the way off the ship early, so that the propellers can be kept turning slowly ahead in the final stages of the approach to the berth. If he fails to do this, the shiphandler may be obliged to use astern power — and hence lose control of the steering — just at the most delicate stage of the manoeuvre. This point underlines the advantage of controllable-pitch propellers, which can be kept going at very slow ahead or astern pitch, so providing good control at slow speed. Occasionally a relatively high approach speed may have to be maintained in order to overcome the effect of a cross current or wind during the approach to a berth.

A stern wind causes a ship to carry her way farther than normal, and a head wind slows her down more quickly. This factor will affect the shallow-draught ship with a high superstructure far more than a heavy deep-draught ship. For all ships the effect of a current or tidal stream is usually much more noticeable than that of the wind; a very strong wind indeed would be needed to counteract the effect of quite a moderate current (the effect of 20 knots wind is approximately equal to that of 1 knot tidal stream).

When reducing speed, the possible effects of shallow water (as described in the previous chapter) must be kept in mind. When entering solid-walled pens, for instance, most of the way should be taken off the ship before the propellers reach the line of the entrance, for their effects may be nullified by the restricted and shallow water inside the pens.

TURNING IN A CONFINED SPACE

The most important points to remember when turning in a confined space are how the pivoting point of the ship changes position when moving ahead or astern, and the resultant effect if there is any wind. Provided there is a little room in which to gain headway or sternway, the shiphandler should be able to take advantage of the wind and use it to help turn the ship. In a single-screw ship, in certain circumstances, it may be said in advance that she will turn readily one way — that is, either to port or to starboard — and that it will be difficult or practically impossible to turn her the other way.

Single-screw ship in calm weather

When there is no wind the best way to turn a ship with a single left-handed controllable-pitch propeller, in a confined space, is to starboard.

First put on full starboard wheel and go ahead at high power. The wash from the propeller, acting on the rudder, will then swing the stern to port even before any appreciable headway is gathered. As the ship moves ahead the rate of swing will increase more and more swiftly. This movement should be continued until the sea room available dictates that way must be checked. Now apply high astern power and, as soon as the way is almost checked, reverse the wheel to hard a'port. The sideways force from the propeller will immediately act to pull the stern to port and so help to continue the swing. As soon as sternway is gathered the effect of the rudder will enhance this tendency. Continue the movement astern as far as possible. Then apply ahead power and put the wheel immediately to hard a'starboard. Continue to 'back and fill' in this way until the turn is completed (Fig. 13–1).

FIG. 13–1. Turning short in a right-handed single-screw ship, with no wind

Even in calm weather it is difficult to turn a single-screw ship short round to port.

Single-screw ship in a wind

Much depends on the direction of the wind relative to the ship throughout the manoeuvre, and in single-screw ships the following points should be borne in mind.

1. The stern seeks the wind when the ship is moving astern.
2. When stopped, or nearly so, the ship tends to turn broadside-on to the wind.
3. When making a stern board the rudder has little effect until the ship has gathered considerable sternway.
4. The sideways force from the propeller is felt most when the ship is stopped or moving slowly and is proportional to the rate at which the propeller is revolving and the pitch.

It follows that in a strong wind it may be easier to turn a single-screw ship short round to port than to starboard. Suppose that initially there is a strong wind from the starboard beam, and the shiphandler attempts to turn to starboard in a confined space (Fig. 13–2). Consider what will happen if he loses headway *before* the wind has been brought round on to the port bow (position 2). Now when he goes astern the tendency of the stern to seek the wind counteracts the sideways force of the propeller and he soon finds himself

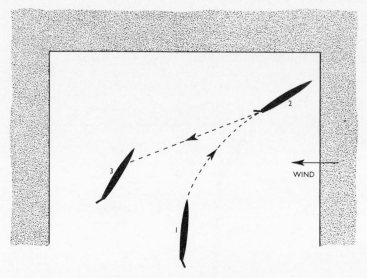

FIG. 13–2. Turning short in a right-handed single-screw ship, with wind initially from the starboard beam — *wrong method*

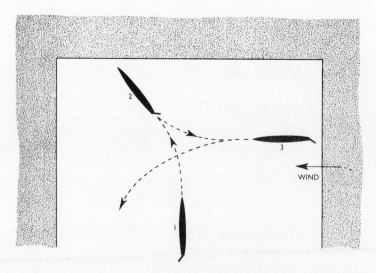

FIG. 13–3. Turning short in a right-handed single-screw ship, with wind initially from the starboard beam — *right method*

almost back where he started (position *3*), except that by this time he will probably be farther down-wind.

If, instead, he starts the manoeuvre by going ahead with full port rudder to position 2 (Fig. 13–3), when he goes astern the sideways force of the propeller will be overcome more and more as the ship gathers sternway and the stern seeks the wind, so that the ship reaches position *3*. From here it is simple to go ahead with wheel hard a'port and complete the turn.

It would be tedious to consider various directions of wind and how they would each influence the problem of turning a single-screw ship round short. Considering the facts already mentioned, the officer in command of a single-screw ship will be able to work out the best course of action under the prevailing circumstances. In general it will be found that the single-screw ship can be turned short *away from the wind*, either to port or to starboard; but she can be turned *into the wind* only if space permits headway to be maintained until the wind has been brought across on to the opposite bow.

Twin-screw ship

The forces acting on a twin-screw ship (and how these forces are modified in shallow water) when the screws are put ahead on one side of the ship and astern on the other are described in the previous chapter.

When turning in a confined space in a twin-screw ship, it is usually advantageous to gather slight headway or sternway if space allows, as in a single-screw ship. This applies especially if the ship starts from the natural attitude of lying stopped with the wind on the beam. It is often found that the maximum rate of swing is achieved if the ship is kept moving ahead slowly while she is turning into the wind, and astern when turning away from it. The most effective position for the rudder is normally hard over in the direction of the turn, so long as at least one screw is going ahead.

Aids to turning in a confined space

The most usual way of assisting a ship to turn in a confined space is to employ tugs (see page 407). A simple method that is always available is to use an anchor. A description of how to turn short on an anchor is given on page 377.

ANCHORING AND MOORING

If she is to anchor or moor, the ship will in most ports be allocated a particular berth by the shore authority. In unfrequented havens she may select one for herself, in which case the Captain must consider such points as the depth of water, range of tide, holding ground, prevailing weather conditions and proximity of landing places. A full discussion of these points is given in BR 45(1), *Admiralty Manual of Navigation*, Volume I, as also is the method of piloting the ship so as to anchor her in a predetermined position.

Swinging room when at anchor

A ship at single anchor requires more room than one moored, as explained in Volume I. In deciding the radius of the swinging circle there are two considerations: the proximity of fixed dangers such as shoal water and other charted objects such as rocks or piers; and the proximity of nearby ships at anchor that are themselves swinging round in their berths.

Distance from charted dangers

The safe radius for a ship at single anchor should be established initially by considering only the proximity of charted dangers, and not other ships at anchor whose nearness varies according to how they are swung. This radius may be obtained by adding the following three items.

1. The length of the ship.
2. The maximum amount of cable which can be veered on the selected anchor.
3. A *safety margin*. It is impossible to lay down a precise rule as to how near danger a ship may be anchored, but an ample margin of safety should be allowed in expectation of bad weather and the ship dragging her anchor. At single anchor it is usual to allow a safety margin of at least one cable increased as necessary to allow for:

    the accuracy of the anchorage fix;

    the time for the anchor to reach the bottom after letting go;

    the likelihood of bad weather; and

    the likelihood of dragging (i.e. the nature of the bottom, holding power of the anchor, etc.).

It should be appreciated that in certain circumstances, rigid application of these considerations could preclude some anchorages which would be quite safe in good weather, or in sheltered conditions, or for a short duration. In these circumstances it would be appropriate to accept a smaller margin of safety consistent with prudence.

Suppose a ship of length 155 metres, with 10 shackles of cable available on each bower anchor, comes to single anchor. Allowing an appropriate safety margin, her safety swinging circle might be:

	metres	*yards*
Length of ship	155	170
Maximum usable cable, 10 shackles	275	300
Safety margin	230	250
Safety swinging circle radius	660	720 *or* 3.6 cables.

Her berth must not be less than 3.6 cables clear of all charted dangers.

Distance from other ships

When choosing an anchorage it is important that the position selected is sufficiently far from other ships to ensure that there is no danger of the ships fouling each other as they swing round their anchors. The *minimum* swinging radius to allow against such an event is the length of the ship plus the length of cable veered. Thus the distance apart of adjacent ships should be twice the minimum radius, which allows for the following events to take place without danger or difficulty.

1. A ship may approach and anchor in the line without finding an adjacent ship swung over the point where her anchor is to go.

2. A ship anchored in the line may weigh anchor alone without fouling the others.

3. Two adjacent ships may swing towards each other and at the same time have their cables drawn out to their fullest extent. This is, however, most unlikely to occur, since if there is a strong wind or stream the ships will be lying parallel and drawing out their cables in the same direction; and if the ships swing in opposite directions it is probably because the tidal stream is on the turn and almost slack, and the wind at the same time is light, so that their cables are not laid out towards one another.

In the case quoted above the distance apart of two similar ships may be calculated as follows:

	metres	yards
Length of ship	155	170
Length of cable veered (say, 6 shackles)	165	180
Minimum swinging radius	320	350 *or* 1¾ cables;
Distance of ships apart	640	700 *or* 3½ cables.

Space in harbours is often scarce and therefore it is seldom that the distance apart of two radii, to allow for the third event above, can be allowed. If the berths of adjacent ships are placed at one radius apart, however, both of the other two events can occur without difficulty. It is customary therefore to place the berths of similar ships at one radius apart. Ships must be on their guard against swinging towards one another, but the risk is small. However, if two ships of dissimilar classes are berthed next to one another the distance between their berths should be at least that of the radius required for the larger of the two ships.

Reduced swinging radius

If space is particularly restricted, the distance apart of ships may be reduced by allowing a *minimum* radius equal to the length of the ship plus 45 metres (50 yards). In the case quoted above, the minimum swinging radius would be:

	metres	yards
Length of ship	155	170
Anchoring margin	45	50
Minimum radius	200	220 *or* 1.1 cables.

Care must of course be taken to ensure that anchor cables of adjacent ships do not foul each other, and the anchoring margin may have to be increased accordingly. Regardless of this reduced distance from adjacent ships, it must be noted that the safety swinging circle (see page 368) of any particular ship does not change.

Swinging room when moored

The object of mooring ships is to conserve space, and the *minimum* swinging radius may be taken as the ship's length plus a mooring margin of at least 18 metres (20 yards). For the ship mentioned above this would give:

	metres	yards	
Length of ship	155	170	
Mooring margin	18	20	
Minimum swinging radius	173	190	*or* 0.95 cables.

Care must be taken that anchor cables of adjacent ships do not foul each other, and the mooring margin may have to be increased accordingly, dependent on the amount of cable veered on each anchor. When planning mooring berths, it must be remembered that ships may have to moor or unmoor independently of each other whatever the direction of the wind or tidal stream. Thus the berths may have to be planned at an even greater distance apart (see also page 448). Furthermore, a safety margin of at least one cable from any charted danger must be added to the radius of each berth.

Amount of cable to be veered

The amount of cable to be veered depends upon a number of factors, e.g. the swinging room, the type of cable and anchor in use, the strength of the wind, tidal stream or current, and the holding ground. Perhaps the most important point to emphasise is that the anchor — and particularly the present Service type AC 14 anchor — is most efficient when subjected to a horizontal pull by the cable on the seabed. The aim should be to ensure that enough cable is veered to permit this condition to be met.

The majority of HM ships are fitted with either forged steel or aluminium bronze cable. For a given strength (proof load) aluminium bronze cable is larger and heavier than forged steel cable. Thus for two ships anchoring in similar circumstances, one with aluminium bronze cable and the other with forged steel cable, the curves formed by the two cables in the vertical plane will be different. In the case of the heavier, aluminium bronze, cable the bight or catenary will be quite steep whereas the lighter, forged steel, cable will form a shallower catenary. It can thus be seen that, for a given depth, it is necessary to veer more forged steel cable than aluminium bronze cable to ensure a horizontal pull at the anchor, because of the shape of the catenary. This point is illustrated by the graph shown in Fig. 13–4. The curves show the minimum amount of the two common types of cable which should be laid out in various depths of water to ensure a horizontal pull at the anchor. The curves are based on the requirement in calm weather and a tidal stream or current of 5 knots. In strong winds, or in exceptionally strong streams, more cable will be required.

The amount of forged steel cable required for various depths can also be calculated by the following rule:

Amount of cable to veer in shackles is one-and-a-half times the square root of the depth of water in metres.

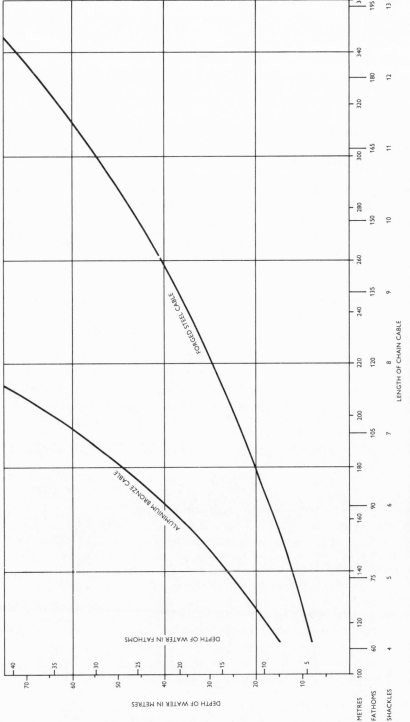

FIG. 13–4. Graph showing the *minimum* length of cable to be veered in relation to depth of water

For example:

Depth of Water	Cable to Veer
metres	shackles
9	$4\frac{1}{2}$
16	6
25	$7\frac{1}{2}$
49	$10\frac{1}{2}$

The holding pull of the anchor is normally expressed as a factor of its own weight. For example, the AC 14 anchor will hold up to 10 times its own weight if the ground is good. In particularly good ground consisting of a mixture of sand, shingle and clay, the holding pull of the anchor can rise to approximately $12\frac{1}{2}$ times its own weight; while in poor ground of soft, silty mud it will drop to about 6 times. Some idea of the force likely to be exerted on the ship can be obtained from the table on page 244. Knowing his ship, the Captain can estimate the pull likely to be exerted on his anchor in the prevailing circumstances. He must then take note that if there is not sufficient cable out to exert a horizontal pull at the anchor, its holding pull will drop in accordance with the following scale:

Angle of Inclination of Cable at Anchor	Percentage of Maximum Holding Pull of Anchor
5 degrees	80
10 degrees	60
15 degrees	40

The exact conditions which give rise to these angles are not of much practical significance to the seaman. It is, however, important to realise how the holding pull decreases if for some reason insufficient cable can be laid out to ensure a horizontal pull at the anchor.

Advice on the action to take when anchored in harbour in a gale or tropical storm is given in Chapter 15.

Approach to an anchor berth — reduction of speed

It is easier to anchor in the exact berth if steerage way can be maintained up to the moment of anchoring. If ships are anchoring in company it is essential to keep steerage way to permit ships to maintain station. For these reasons HM ships usually anchor with headway and lay out the cable under the ship. This method is known as the *running anchorage*.

When anchoring with headway the speed when letting go should not be more than two to three knots over the ground. Too high a speed may strain or even part the cable while too low a speed will prolong the operation unduly.

The alternative to anchoring with headway is to stop in the berth or just beyond it and then, having let go the anchor, go astern laying out the cable. This is known as the *dropping anchorage*; it is usually adopted by merchant vessels, and for any HM ship anchoring independently this method may well be more seamanlike than the running anchorage. HM ships with underwater fittings near the forefoot are obliged to use the dropping anchorage to prevent the cable being laid out under the ship and damaging these fittings. For the same reason these ships are not permitted to moor.

The *advantages* of the dropping anchorage over the running anchorage are:

1. The cable is laid out down-wind and/or down-stream (the running method being into the wind and/or stream). This is the best direction for modern anchors and cables, and there is less risk of damage to the protective bottom composition and underwater fittings.

2. There is less risk of tumbling or slewing the anchor as the ship lays back on the wind and/or stream after letting go. (When carrying out a running anchorage this risk is reduced if the wind and/or stream are well on the bow when letting go, since the result will be to widen the bight of cable.)

3. There is less wear on the hawsepipe and cable, and less chance of damage, since the cable does not turn so sharply at the bottom of the hawsepipe while it is being laid out.

4. The ship usually gets her cable more quickly.

The *disadvantages* of the dropping anchorage as compared to the running anchorage are:

1. Shiphandling is less precise in the final stages because way is taken off the ship in the last part of the approach.

2. The cable is not laid out in a bight up-wind and/or up-stream as it is with a running anchorage and so cannot absorb the strain gradually as the ship falls back on her cable. This was more important with the old Admiralty Standard Stockless anchor, where the heavier cable provided a larger share of the holding power.

3. The final moments of anchoring take longer and the operation may not look so smart as a briskly executed running anchorage.

A rough guide to the reduction of speed on approach to an anchor berth for various classes of ship is given in the table on page 374. Modifying factors such as wind and current must always be taken into account.

Approaching an anchor berth in deep water

When anchoring in very deep water it is customary to veer some cable (perhaps one shackle or even more depending on the depth of water) during the approach. This is to prevent the cable attaining a dangerous speed while running out after the anchor has been let go. There is also a danger that the anchor and cable may fracture on striking the bottom at high speed. *The speed of the ship must be reduced to 4 knots or less* before starting to veer cable otherwise damage may be inflicted on the hull by the anchor and then by the cable.

The results of investigation to establish maximum safe speeds at which different classes of ship may proceed without causing damage *after cable has been veered* are summarised in the table on page 375. Classes of ship precluded from veering cable when under way, e.g. *Sheffield* Class destroyer, are omitted from the table; these ships should veer cable when in the anchorage with way off the ship and prior to letting go in the final position.

Guide to Reduction of Speed on Approach to an Anchor Berth

Distance from Berth	Speed and Engine Orders							
	HMS Hermes	Invincible Class Carriers*	Assault Ships	County Class Destroyer	Sheffield Class Destroyer*	Broadsword Class Frigate*	Amazon Class Frigate*	Leander Class Frigate
cables								
10	8 knots	10 knots	8 knots	10 knots	10 knots	10 knots	10 knots	12 knots
8								
6		Slow ahead	Slow ahead					
5								
4	Stop	Stop	Stop					
3						Slow ahead		
2¼								
2		Half astern		Stop	Slow ahead		Slow ahead	Stop
1½	Slow astern							
1					Half astern			
¾						Half astern	Half astern	
½								
In berth			Half astern	Half astern				Astern power as necessary

*For these classes of ship, information is for a dropping anchorage

LENGTH OF CABLE VEERED	MAXIMUM SAFE SPEED	
	COUNTY CLASS DESTROYER	ROTHESAY AND LEANDER CLASS FRIGATE
shackles	knots	knots
$\frac{1}{2}$	4	5
$\frac{3}{4}$	7	7
1	9	8

Approaching an anchor berth in a wind

If, during the approach to an anchor berth, the wind is not dead ahead, allowance for leeway must be made by adjusting the course so as to keep the ship on her head bearing or transit. The officer who is conning must be prepared to make bold alterations of course because the ship rapidly loses her way just before letting go, especially if the wind is on the beam. The weather anchor should normally be used so that the cable cannot foul the stem as the ship drifts to leeward after anchoring. If the approach has been made head-to-wind, the ship's head is cast about 10 degrees towards the side opposite the anchor just before it is let go, to ensure that the cable runs out clear on the windward side.

In a gale it is advisable to approach head-to-wind. After anchoring, the ship's head will pay off rapidly, so it is essential to cast her head slightly in the right direction before letting go. To give the anchor a chance of embedding itself and holding, a length of cable more than twice the depth of the water should be allowed at first to run out freely, and the cable should then be braked carefully to bring the ship's head back towards the wind without dragging the anchor.

Approaching an anchor berth in a stream

A high contrary wind is necessary to overcome the effect of a moderate stream, and it is therefore customary to anchor head-to-stream rather than head-to-wind. Anchoring with a following tidal stream (or current) of more than half a knot is not recommended, because a heavy strain is imposed on the cable, particularly when the ship is swung athwart the stream. In a heavy ship of deep draught it may be found that at this stage the cable-holder brakes cannot hold the cable, while there is not time to turn the ship head-to-stream with the engines before the cable has run out to the clench and parted.

If wind and stream are from opposite directions and it is impossible to approach so as to stem either, the shiphandler must estimate in advance (allowing for a 1-knot tidal stream to be approximately equivalent to a 20-knot wind) how the ship will move after she has let go her anchor and how the bight of cable will be laid out on the sea bed, and must then drop whichever anchor he considers will have the best chance of holding.

In a strong current or tidal stream the anchor should be let go with the ship stopped, and as the ship drifts downstream the cable should be paid out gradually in such a way as to keep her head-to-stream. Violent yawing in a strong river current can be checked by letting go both anchors spanned across the stream, but this procedure is obviously unsuitable for tidal waters, where each change of stream would put half a turn in the cables.

Action after letting go an anchor

When anchoring in less than 30 metres of water an amount of cable equal to twice the depth of water should first be allowed to run out freely to enable the anchor to embed itself. Thereafter the brake of the cable-holder or windlass should be applied so that the cable is kept growing at an angle of about 30 degrees with the vertical. The brake should not be applied fiercely and the cable should not be snubbed; only sufficient brake should be applied to permit it to render if the cable becomes taut. When a stationary cable tautens and then slackens it is a sign that the ship has come to rest.

When anchoring with headway in company, ships should lay out their cables in a straight line from their anchors, way being reduced by the engines and not by the cable-holder brakes. A heavy strain on the cable not only tends to weaken or part it but may also drag the anchor away from the correct berth. Anchoring with too much way on gradually weakens the cable, leading eventually to the risk of parting the cable and possibly causing dangerous accidents. When anchoring, if care is taken both on the bridge and on the forecastle the life of the cable will be increased and the ship's safety assured.

Approach to a mooring berth

The following remarks refer to *mooring* as understood in HM Service, i.e. with two anchors down and cables middled at a mooring swivel. This method of anchoring the ship, although giving reduced holding power when the ship is riding in any direction other than in the line of the anchors, is sometimes necessitated by restricted swinging room.

It is important that the cable should be laid out from the first anchor in a straight line to the planned position of the second anchor, and that the ship's stem should be held as near as possible to this line when middling (Fig. 13–5). The first anchor (normally the weather one) should therefore be let

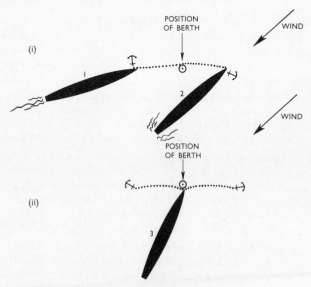

FIG. 13–5. Running moor
In (i) the ship lets go the first (weather) anchor in position *1* and the second (lee) anchor in position *2*. In (ii) the ship is middled in position *3*

go with good steerage way on the ship, and the course steered should be such as to make good along the intended line of the anchors, up to the time of letting go the second anchor. In the approach the engines are stopped about one cable farther on than would be the case in coming to a single anchor.

The work of middling should not be left entirely to the cable holders. If there is a cross wind or current, the engines should be worked so that the bows are kept on the line of the anchors. In calm weather, with no cross current, the engines should be used to gather slight sternway to assist the middling process.

Normally the line of anchors is selected such that they stem the current or prevailing wind. It is inadvisable to moor a heavy ship with a stream of more than half a knot under her. When mooring against a strong current it is sometimes preferable to execute a dropping moor (Fig. 13–6). The

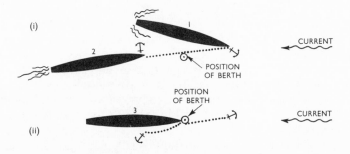

FIG. 13–6. Dropping moor
The ship lets go the first anchor in position _1_ and then drops astern to let go the second in position _2_. From there she makes headway, to middle in position _3_

upstream anchor is let go first. After letting go the second anchor (position 2), the engines can be used to bring the ship back towards the upstream anchor, thus reducing the strain on it when middling.

Turning short round an anchor

A very useful method of turning a ship where manoeuvring room is limited is to let go an anchor and, holding it at short stay, make headway round it on a taut cable. When doing this, however, two points must be borne in mind: first, that the anchor should not be let go where it may foul the ground tackle of other ships and moorings, or the cables of telegraph and telephone services; and second, that the manoeuvre must be made at slow speed and the cable tautened very gradually. The cable will be growing aft throughout the turn and so may be given a bad nip by the after edge of the hawsepipe, and any sudden stress might then part the cable.

The wheel is first put over in the required direction, with the ship moving slowly ahead, then the anchor on the side towards which she is turning is let go. The engines are stopped and sufficient cable to hold the bows is allowed to run out on the brake (say, a length equal to about twice the depth of water), while the way of the ship is reduced and the cable gradually tautened. When the cable is taut, slow ahead power is applied until, with the wheel over, the ship makes headway round her anchor to the required direction.

Remember that when a wind is blowing the ship will always swing head-to-wind when finally the anchor is weighed, and that this may cause her to swing back towards her original heading.

Dredging an anchor

Towing an anchor at short stay in order to improve manoeuvrability is sometimes called *dredging an anchor*. For example, when going alongside in an offshore wind, or when passing through a narrow entrance where there is a strong cross-stream, the ship lets go the anchor at slow speed as she approaches, and drags it along the bottom. This has the dual effect of enhancing the control of the bow and of holding it upwind or upstream. Care must be taken to ensure that no underwater cables or submerged equipment are in the vicinity.

Weighing anchor

As the cable is hove in, the ship will gather a certain amount of way towards her anchor which will help to break the anchor out of its bed. A single-screw ship usually requires considerable room to turn, and in confined anchorages in calm conditions it is often best first to heave in cable to short stay, until there is just sufficient scope of cable out to prevent the anchor coming home, and then to make headway round the cable to the required direction as described earlier.

When weighing in company, warships usually first heave in to short stay before weighing, to ensure that their anchors are broken out simultaneously when the order to weigh is given.

It is important to ensure that when the anchor is aweigh the bows will not pay off in the opposite direction to that in which you wish to turn. This can be done by first allowing the bows to pay off slightly in the wrong direction while shortening-in the cable, so that in the final stage of weighing the bows are given a very decided cast in the required direction.

When heaving in cable to weigh anchor, the cable may grow athwart the stem and so be subjected to a bad nip. When this occurs 'Avast heaving' should be ordered until the bows swing towards the anchor and the cable grows clear again. If this is not done a heavy stress will be imposed on the links and joining shackles of the cable as they pass across the stem, which may result in the cable parting or being severely strained.

Unmooring

Although the cables may give the impression of being clear, there may be turns some distance below the swivel. Before unmooring, it is sometimes advisable to bring a strain on the cables by using gentle astern power, when any turns may clear. In order to bring a strain on both cables it may be found necessary to turn the ship cautiously in the direction of open hawse.

The lee, or downstream, anchor is invariably weighed first. With wind or stream across the line of anchors, start weighing the weather anchor immediately the lee anchor is off the ground, because the ship may swing into danger if she remains riding to eleven or twelve shackles of cable. (See also page 448).

BUOY BERTHS

The methods of sending the picking-up rope to a mooring buoy and of securing the bridles to the buoy are described in Volume II. This section is concerned with the handling of the ship while approaching and while securing in buoy berths. A description of the buoys and their moorings is given in Chapter 8. A ship can either secure head to a single buoy or head-and-stern between a pair of buoys.

Approach to a single buoy

In calm weather with no appreciable wind or stream the ship is headed for the buoy at slow speed and brought to rest with the hawsepipe over the buoy so that the end of the bridle can be lowered through it directly to the buoy jumpers. A plan must be prepared beforehand to enable speed to be reduced and astern power applied at the appropriate distances from the buoy. It is advisable to take the way off the ship a little short of the buoy, while the picking-up rope is being passed, and then edge up to the buoy slowly. If there is any stream or current the ship should be headed into it, if possible. If this is not done great difficulty will be experienced in holding the ship's bows near the buoy for a reasonable time while the picking-up rope is being secured. If there is a wind from one side or the other in addition to the stream, the ship should be headed upstream but slightly to windward of the direction of the stream, when it will be found that by applying occasional power ahead and by the use of the wheel, the pressure of the stream can be made to balance the leeway and the ship can be held stationary close by the buoy (Fig. 13–7). Thus the presence of tidal stream or current can help by enabling steerage way to be kept during the process of securing.

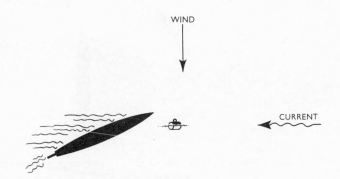

FIG. 13–7. Where to hold the ship while passing the picking-up rope if wind and stream are from different directions

If there is a wind but no stream the ship should preferably be headed into the wind if possible; but if the wind is strong, difficulty will be experienced in preventing the bows falling off the wind when way has been lost. An approach directly down wind may be easier, particularly if the ship has a high forecastle or upperworks forward, because the stern seeks the wind whenever astern power is applied. However, it is impossible to maintain this attitude once the picking-up rope has been secured, and it is difficult to shackle on the bridle until the ship has swung right round head-to-wind.

If there is no stream but it is impossible to head into the wind while approaching the buoy, because of lack of sea room, the ship should be stopped not only to windward of, but short of, the berth (Fig. 13–8). From such a position it should be possible to keep the ship turning slowly into the wind with slight headway during the process of hooking on, while the boat carrying the picking-up rope will have a down-wind passage to the buoy. An alternative plan would be to turn short on an anchor into the wind from a point immediately to leeward of the buoy, but this would involve the risk of dropping the anchor foul of the buoy moorings.

When securing to a single buoy the handling of the ship should not be assumed to have ceased as soon as the picking-up rope has been hooked on. Engines may have to be used, particularly in a large ship, in order to keep the hawsepipe over the buoy while shackling on the first bridle.

Do not hesitate to use a tug when securing to a buoy if difficulty is foreseen either because of poor handling qualities of the ship or because of the environment of the berth. This applies particularly to single-screw ships.

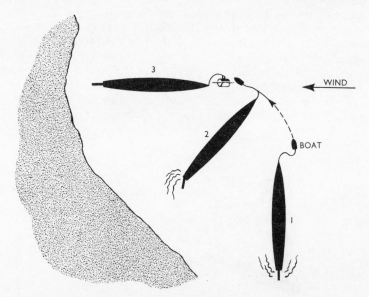

FIG. 13–8. Approach to a single buoy when there is insufficient room to approach upwind

In position *1*, stop and lower boat; in position *2*, turn into wind with slight headway; in position *3*, picking-up rope secured

Slipping from a single buoy

If there is no wind, current or tidal stream when the buoy is slipped, astern power should be applied until the ship is well clear of the buoy before any attempt is made to turn in the required direction. Nothing is gained by turning with the buoy close under the bows, because not only is the ship's freedom of movement then restricted but the buoy may easily foul her propellers when she goes ahead.

If there is a wind the buoy will spring well clear of the ship when it is slipped and the ship's bows will start to pay off from the wind, so that it will then be possible to go ahead without first moving astern, the rudder being used to swing the stern clear of the buoy if necessary. In a tideway, the ship can be cast in the required direction by her rudder before slipping.

Unless unavoidable, the sliprope should not be slipped when there is a heavy strain on it, because the slip may jump up and injure the man who knocks it off. The hauling end of the sliprope should be surged until there is little strain on it and then the slip should be knocked off.

In a small ship a sliprope may be rove from a point well aft in the ship if there is a stream running and it is necessary to turn on slipping. On letting go the bridle the ship will swing right round, bows downstream, provided that the point in the ship where the sliprope is secured is abaft the centre of underwater pressure. It may be advisable to reeve a sliprope forward as well, in order to keep the bows under control until it is time to turn the ship.

Securing between two buoys

Trots of mooring buoys for securing a number of ships head-and-stern are usually laid along the line of the tidal stream or prevailing current; so that, when securing a ship between two buoys, difficulty is more likely to be caused by the wind than by the stream.

If it is possible to approach the head buoy directly in calm weather the manoeuvre is simple. The ship is stopped as close as convenient to the head buoy and as nearly as possible along the line of the buoys, and boats can then be sent simultaneously with picking-up ropes to the head and stern buoys.

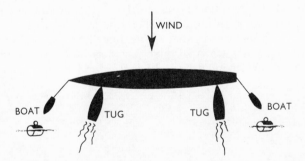

FIG. 13–9. Securing a heavy ship between two buoys when the wind is from the beam

If there is a wind from the beam (Fig. 13–9) the ship must be stopped to windward of the berth to allow for the drift to leeward while the picking-up ropes are made fast. In a large ship a tug is necessary both forward and aft to control the rate of drift and to hold the ship in her berth while the bridles are secured. A small handy ship may approach the head buoy down wind, if there is sea room, secure to the head buoy and then allow the wind to carry the stern round to the stern buoy (Fig. 13–10). At first she must place the head buoy under her lee bow and must then control the rate of swing by working the engines.

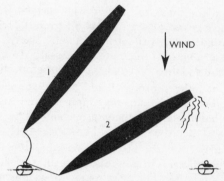

FIG. 13–10. Securing a small ship between two buoys when the wind is from the beam

Turning the ship when securing between two buoys

A common requirement in securing between two buoys is that, after entering the harbour and before securing to the buoys, the ship must be turned end-for-end so that she will be secured heading out of harbour (Fig. 13–11). If there is room to complete the turn before approaching the buoys, this may be done and the buoys may then be approached making a stern board, with allowance for the effect of the wind after the ship has been stopped beside the berth. It is better either to complete the turn before approaching the berth, or to bring the ship up dead between the buoys and then turn at rest there. An attempt to start the swing in the final stage of the approach will require the most delicate judgement if the ship is finally to finish up in the correct position between the two buoys.

When it is intended to turn at rest in the berth, the bridge must first be placed in exactly the right position. Therefore it is essential to work out in advance the transits or bearings that will facilitate this. In doing so, remember that the pivoting point when turning at rest is not so far forward as the bridge but more nearly amidships. In Fig. 13–11 is shown an approach,

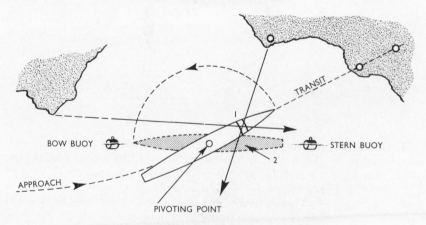

FIG. 13–11. Turning at rest between two buoys
Position *1*, initial position of the bridge marked by cross bearings and a transit;
position *2*, final position of the ship

uncomplicated by wind, in which the bridge is first placed correctly, in position *1*, so that after turning at rest the ship finishes up between the two buoys (position *2*). It is advisable almost to complete the turn before sending away the boat from aft, to avoid the risk of fouling the screws with the stern picking-up rope.

It is important to realise that if the ship is not placed initially in the right position, one or other of the buoys will be fouled during the turn. If there is a wind blowing across the line of the buoys, allowance must be made for the bodily drift of the ship to leeward during the period of the turn. In Fig. 13–12 the ship has been stopped in position *1* too close to the bow buoy.

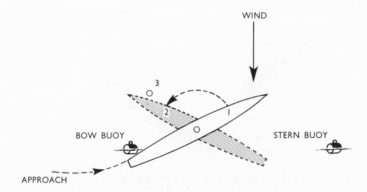

FIG. 13–12. Approach too close to bow buoy before turning at rest to secure between two buoys

If the turn is continued beyond position *2* the bow buoy will be fouled. The only solution then would be to move the ship ahead until her pivoting point was in position *3*, complete the turn there and then make a stern board to a point abreast of and to windward of the berth. Had the wind been from the opposite direction, it would have been necessary to start making amends by going astern from position *2*.

A worse situation is likely to arise if the ship is placed initially too near the stern buoy. Fig. 13–13 shows a situation similar to that in Fig. 13–12, but

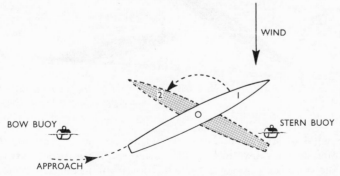

FIG. 13–13. Approach too close to stern buoy before turning at rest to secure between two buoys

with the ship initially too close to the stern buoy. From position *2* it may well
be more difficult to get ahead and complete the turn without fouling the stern
buoy which, in any case, is difficult so see from the bridge. Again, if the wind
had been from the opposite direction it would have been trickier for the ship
to extricate herself astern from position *2*.

Turning a small ship between two buoys

A single-screw ship should normally be secured between two buoys with the
help of tugs, but a reasonably handy single-screw ship, or a small ship of any
kind, may be turned and secured between two buoys by the following method

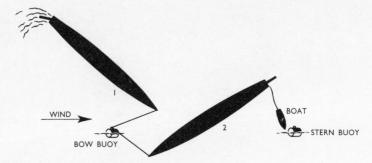

FIG. 13–14. Securing a small ship between two buoys by turning on the bow buoy

in fair weather. If there is no wind or stream, the ship uses the bow buoy
to turn on. The ship should approach and stop so that the stem lies about
one-third of the length of the berth from the bow buoy (Fig. 13–14, position
1). Having secured the picking-up rope to the bow buoy, the ship is turned
by applying power slow ahead, with full rudder, and at the same time the
picking-up rope is hove in. The ship having turned about, as far as position
2, the stern rope can be made fast and then both head and stern ropes hove
in. This method can be used also if it is necessary to approach before the
wind.

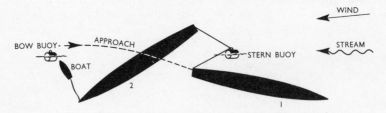

FIG. 13–15. Securing a small ship between two buoys by turning on the stern
buoy

If the wind or stream, or both, are setting out of the harbour the ship
should approach as shown in Fig. 13–15 and stop with the stern reasonably
close to the stern buoy, keeping the wind or stream on the bow (position *1*).
The picking-up rope is secured aft to the stern buoy (care being taken not
to foul the picking-up rope while manoeuvring to maintain position) and then

the wind and stream will swing the ship round stern-to-wind while a boat is being sent away with the picking-up rope for the bow buoy (position 2).

Slipping from head-and-stern buoys

When slipping from head-and-stern buoys it is preferable and more seamanlike to let go the stern rope and recover it safely before letting go forward—this obviates the danger of fouling a propeller. The forward and after slipropes can be let go together and the ship can be turned by her engines to get the bow and stern clear; with a single-screw ship it may be necessary to use a tug if the space is very limited.

In a wind, if it is directly along the line of the buoys, the lee buoy should be slipped first. When the weather sliprope is surged and let go the buoy will spring clear and the ship will tend to swing beam-on to the wind. She can then go either ahead or astern, as necessary, to clear the berth.

If it is required to leave by going either directly ahead or directly astern when the wind is on one side or the other, both slipropes should be surged until the ship lies well to leeward of the berth; both slipropes should then be slipped together and the ship moved off in the required direction. If it is necessary to leave the berth at an angle to the line of the buoys, the ship can be cast in the required direction by slipping one buoy first and allowing the wind to blow her round before slipping the other.

USE OF BERTHING HAWSERS

Intelligent handling of berthing hawsers can add greatly to the ease and speed with which a ship is berthed alongside, and the effect of heaving in any particular hawser under any given circumstances must be known. The standard nomenclature of berthing hawsers used in the Royal Navy is given in Volume I, together with other information on the handling of hawsers.

Effect of hawsers on movement of ship

It is assumed in the first place that the ship is stopped and lying square with the jetty. If a fore breastrope is then made fast and hove in, the bows will obviously be moved in towards the jetty; but, because the ship will also turn about her pivoting point, her stern will move away from the jetty at the same time. This movement of the stern will not be as great as that of the bows, because the pivoting point is not rigidly held, and so the ship will also move bodily towards the jetty. If, on the other hand, an after breastrope had also been made fast and held taut, the ship would have pivoted about her stern as the fore breastrope was hove in, and she would have been swung in towards the jetty by the bows. If both fore and after breastropes are hove in together, the ship will be breasted in squarely with the jetty. If either of these hawsers is led ahead or astern it will act as a spring, and as it is hove in the ship will be moved ahead or astern at the same time as she is moved towards the jetty.

It is now assumed that the ship has a certain amount of headway when the fore breastrope is made fast. As the ship moves ahead this hawser will grow aft and, as it tautens, her head will be bowsed in towards the jetty. The momentum of the ship acting through her centre of gravity will increase this swing, because the ship will then pivot about her bows and her stern will swing out. If, instead of the fore breastrope, an after breastrope had been made fast the result would have been very different. The pivoting of the ship would then have been well abaft her centre of gravity, and her forward momentum, acting through her centre of gravity, combined with the pull of the hawser on her quarter, would have resulted in the ship being moved in bodily towards the jetty and very nearly parallel with it.

Summarised, the difference is that with a ship moving ahead a fore headspring bowses the bows in sharply and swings the stern out, whereas an after headspring will scarcely turn the ship; in both cases, however, the ship is moved bodily in towards the jetty. With the ship moving astern, these effects are, of course, reversed.

Should the spring be led from the ship abreast her centre of gravity, she will move in bodily without being cast in either direction, and her alignment with the jetty can then be altered by using rudder.

BERTHING ALONGSIDE A JETTY

Berthing marks at naval bases

In naval bases where berths are normally marked a common system of berth marking has been adopted for the guidance of ships' officers. The marks are tabulated below but it must be noted that the bow and stern marks are optional and that night marking is provided only if the lighting at the berth is insufficient for the day marking to be identified.

BERTHING MARKS AT NAVAL BASES

	BOW	COMPASS	STERN
Day	Red flag*	Green flag	Blue flag*
Night	Fixed red light*	Fixed green light	Fixed blue light*

* These marks are optional

Twin-screw ship berthing alongside in calm weather

In calm weather with no stream a twin-screw ship should be steered towards the middle of the berth in the final approach to an alongside berth, at an angle of between 15 and 20 degrees to the line of the berth (Fig. 13–16). The offshore screw should be put to slow or half astern so as to bring up the ship parallel to the berth, the wheel being used as necessary. If possible the inshore screw should not be used to check the way of the ship, because its wash will tend at first to throw the stern out and then, as a mass of water is propelled forward between the ship and jetty, it will cause the whole ship to be moved bodily outward. With controllable-pitch propellers the best combination of power and pitch is found from experience; a finer angle of approach is often appropriate.

Adequate catamarans must be provided for ships whose propellers project beyond the maximum beam of the ship. Suitable types of catamaran and fendering are described in Volume II. Even with 3-metre catamarans amidships, propellers projecting about three-quarters of a metre will touch

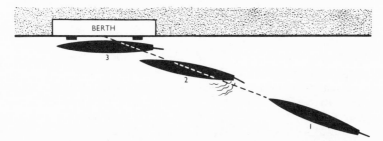

FIG. 13–16. Approach alongside in a twin-screw ship in calm weather
Position *1*, engines stopped, wheel amidships, heading for centre of berth; position
2, offshore engine slow astern, wheel as required; position *3*, ship stopped about
5 metres from fenders

the wall if the ship lies stern-in at an angle of only about 5 degrees. In such
ships the greatest care must be taken that the after part does not touch first.

Twin-screw ship with wind blowing on

If the wind is blowing on to the berth a twin-screw ship should make her
approach at the same angle as in calm weather but from a point farther out,
so that she is heading for the far end of the berth or for a point even farther
up the jetty (Fig. 13–17). If the wind is blowing strongly onshore, in a ship

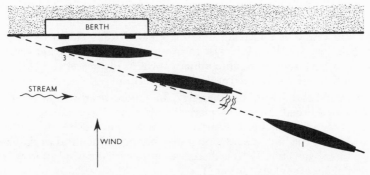

FIG. 13–17. Approach alongside in a twin-screw ship upstream with wind
blowing on
Position *1*, engines stopped, heading for far end of berth; position *2*, offshore
engine slow astern; position *3*, ship about 10 metres from fenders

greater than about 5000 tonnes displacement the aim should be to stop her,
preferably by going astern on the offshore screw only, parallel to the berth
and about 10 metres off the fenders. If she is brought up much farther out
she will gather excessive leeway before touching. The effect of going astern
on the inshore screw may be used to advantage if the stern develops too fast
a swing in, or if the wind is setting the ship too rapidly towards the quay.
In assessing this effect, the nature of the jetty (i.e. whether solid or built on
piles) and of the contours of the sea-bed in the vicinity must be considered
in advance.

In a stiff onshore wind (or stream), during the approach it may be necessary to use an anchor, letting it go when stopped some distance off the jetty and parallel to the berth (see also page 394).

A ship of shallow draught with high forecastle and superstructure forward tends to pay off the wind rapidly as soon as way is lost. In such a ship, if the anchor has not been used initially, there is a danger that the bows may be blown down heavily on to the jetty. To avoid this, throughout the manoeuvre the bows must be kept swinging slowly outwards. A stream from ahead combined with the use of the wheel will help.

However, if the bows take charge and start to swing rapidly towards the quay there are three possible remedies. One is to go astern on the inner screw, as described above; but some time will elapse before the pressure of water between ship and quay has built up, and meanwhile the swing will be accentuated. A second is to give a burst of ahead power with the wheel hard over away from the berth. This will probably check the swing but will only be an effective remedy if there is still room to gain the inevitable headway. The third possible remedy is to drop an anchor. The inshore anchor will probably give the more immediate check to the swing, but may be difficult to weigh on leaving the berth; hence it is more usual to let go the offshore anchor. The application of astern power on the offshore screw is not likely to help, partly because it will cause more water pressure towards the berth and partly because the stern tends to seek the wind once sternway is gathered.

Twin-screw ship with wind blowing off

If the wind is blowing off the berth a twin-screw ship must keep her bows well up to the jetty until a hawser has been passed. Once the stem has drifted outside the throw of a heaving line the situation can seldom be recovered except by a tug. It is therefore wise to approach at a rather greater angle than in calm weather, to head the ship initially towards the nearer end of the berth and to get the bow wire passed at the first opportunity.

If the wind is blowing off the jetty, but more nearly from astern, the approach at a broad angle may place the ship in an awkward predicament after the bow wire has been secured. The wind now pushes the entire hull outwards while the bow is held, and it may be very difficult to work the stern in (Fig. 13–18, position *1*). It is therefore better with the wind aft to approach at a fairly shallow angle (position 2).

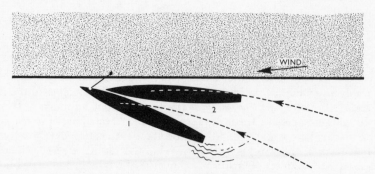

FIG. 13–18. With wind along the jetty, the broad approach *1* may make it more difficult to swing the stern in than with a finer approach 2

Effects of current or tidal stream

If the stream is running parallel (or nearly so) to the jetty, either from ahead or astern, and provided the wind is not too strong, the shiphandler can use the stream to control the lateral movement of the ship. First he should stop the ship, off the berth and heading directly into the line of the stream. If the stream is from ahead he can now use the wheel so as to bring the pressure of the stream on to the desired bow and so move the ship laterally either to starboard or to port as required, using slight ahead or astern revolutions as necessary to keep the ship stationary relative to the berth. If the stream is from astern the same principle can be applied, the stern being canted so as to bring the stream on to the appropriate quarter.

Not infrequently it is found that berths have strong eddies running in the opposite direction to the main stream, and at pile jetties there are sometimes eddies running at an angle to the jetties. The presence of such eddies can usually be discovered in advance by studying the *Sailing Directions,* local tidal-stream diagrams or atlases, or by making local inquiries; the plan for approaching the berth can then be modified accordingly.

Checking the way

It is important in approaching alongside berths to make a plan in advance to show when and where to reduce speed and stop engines, in order to avoid making the final approach with too much headway. This applies particularly if the wind or stream is from astern.

If the wind is blowing the ship down laterally on to the berth it is essential to check all headway or sternway before she touches. The damage done by scraping along a wall or another ship will almost certainly be far more extensive than that caused by a sideways bump, whose worst effects can usually be prevented by fenders.

Berthing alongside in a single-screw ship

The foregoing remarks apply generally also to the berthing alongside of a single controllable-pitch screw ship but the marked sideways force of the propeller must be taken into account. Remember that when power is reversed to take the way off the ship the sideways force from the left-handed propeller will swing the stern to port and the bow to starboard; but also that when going slow ahead the propeller slipstream will impinge directly on to the rudder and so have an immediate effect. Thus when going alongside port-side-to in fairly calm weather the approach should be made at an angle of about 15 to 20 degrees with the jetty, and the ship headed for a point a little ahead of the centre of the berth. When the engine is put astern, the stern will swing in towards the jetty and the bows away from it. The rate of swing can be checked if necessary by the headrope.

When going alongside starboard-side-to in a single controllable-pitch screw ship the angle of approach should be rather finer, say from 10 to 15 degrees with the jetty, and the ship headed for the centre of the berth. As her bows approach the jetty the wheel should be put hard over to port to swing her bows away from the jetty and her stern towards it. Just before the ship is parallel to the jetty astern power should then counter the ship's swing so that she is stopped parallel with the jetty abreast her berth. As before, if the rate of swing is too great it can be checked by a headrope. Dredging the anchor (see page 378) may be a help if there is a strong off-shore wind.

Use of a spring to bowse-in the ship

If there are ships berthed ahead and astern of the berth it may sometimes be advantageous to get the bows in first, secure a headspring in the manner shown in Fig. 13–19 and then swing the stern in by going ahead on the spring with the wheel over away from the jetty, surging the spring if need be.

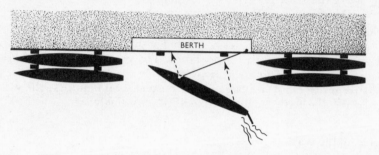

FIG. 13–19. Bowsing-in by going ahead on a headspring

LEAVING AN ALONGSIDE BERTH

Use of a spring to swing the stern out

When leaving an alongside berth unaided by tugs it is usually preferable to leave stern first, after swinging the stern clear by going ahead against a fore headspring. Before starting, it is helpful to investigate the mechanics of the manoeuvre, to ensure that the spring is rove in the most advantageous way.

In Fig. 13–20(i) the line of the entire spring is forward of the point P at which the ship bears initially on the catamaran or fender. As soon as the engine is put ahead there is a good turning moment tending to swing the stern out, and this situation continues until the stem bears against the jetty (Q in Fig. 13–20(ii)). After this the engine and rudder will be the sole agents available for swinging the ship farther out, if this is required.

If the catamaran or fender against which the ship is to bear is placed farther aft, as shown in Fig. 13–20(iii), the turning moment arising from the spring will be lost much earlier. If the spring is rove from farther aft in the ship, as shown in Fig. 13–20(iv), the turning moment disappears as soon as the bow bears on the jetty, and beyond this point the spring actually tends to stop the outward swing of the stern. So it is clearly an advantage to reeve the spring from well forward in the bows and to place the fender or catamaran up forward, so long as it is not forward of the point on the jetty where the spring is secured.

A good supply of fenders must be provided to take the push where the bows rest on the jetty, and because of the flare it is easier to tend these fenders on the quay. Even so the shiphandler must proceed with the utmost care to

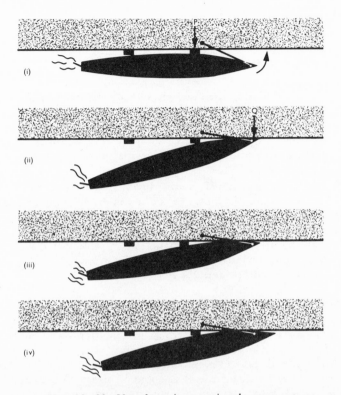

FIG. 13–20. Use of a spring to swing the stern out
(i) Correct position for spring and fender to obtain optimum turning moment.
(ii) Limit of turning moment from spring and fender; ship now pivots on stem.
(iii) Fender too far aft; turning moment from spring soon lost.
(iv) Spring too far aft in ship; hinders turn as soon as bow touches jetty.

avoid damaging the plating on the inner bow. If the catamaran and spring
have been correctly placed, sufficient outward swing should, in many cases,
be obtainable without the stem having to touch at all. This is particularly so
in a twin-screw ship. The initial movement against the spring should be made
by applying slow ahead power to the outer screw, with the wheel over towards
the wall. If slow astern power is applied as soon as the stern is clear, it will
assist the swing by forcing a stream of water ahead between the wall and the
hull, tending to move the entire ship outwards. If astern power on the inshore
screw is continued, however, the stream of water working forward will
eventually push the bows out and cause the stern to swing in again as stern
way is gathered. This possibility must be foreseen when deciding how far
out to swing the stern initially.

Effects of wind and stream on leaving an alongside berth

If a stream is setting along the jetty from aft it will force the stern out as soon
as the after wires are let go, and there may be no need to go ahead against
a headspring.

If the wind is blowing onshore, although it may be possible to swing the
stern out by the use of the engines, wheel and headspring, there is a danger

that when making a stern board out of the berth the bows will be scraped along the wall. If the wind is of any strength it is essential to use tugs, unless to warp out the ship is a practicable alternative. The problems of getting away from a quay in strong onshore winds are discussed further in Chapter 15.

The difficulty of getting the bows clear also presents itself if the stern is sprung out when the stream is running from ahead. An alternative plan is to go astern on a backspring rove well aft and swing the bows out, but this procedure involves the risk of fouling the jetty with a propeller and is not usually advisable in multiple-screw ships, particularly those with proud propellers.

An offshore wind is obviously a great boon. By letting go the forward or after wires first, either the bows or stern can be allowed to swing out. Alternatively, if all hawsers are let go together the ship will drift bodily away from the quay. But if the ship has some high mass of superstructure either forward or aft, the effect of the wind on this must be anticipated. For example, in a ship having much windage forward it is best to let go the after wires first and hold on to the headrope until the stern is well out.

Single-screw ship leaving an alongside berth

As always, the sideways force of the propeller must be taken into account. When leaving a starboard-side-to berth astern, the stern need not be sprung out very far, because it will swing rapidly away from the jetty as soon as astern power is used. Do not allow the bows to scrape along the berth, and be prepared to use starboard wheel when going astern. Adequate fendering must be provided. When swinging the stern out from a port-side-to berth the swing must be continued to a much greater angle to allow for the fact that when going astern the stern will swing rapidly back towards the jetty.

If there is a wind, or tidal stream or river current, from ahead, it is usually most suitable in a single-screw ship to go astern on a backspring in order to swing the bows out. There is usually little danger of fouling the propeller, but adequate fendering must be placed to take the push of the ship's quarter on the wall. The mechanics of the spring must be arranged on similar lines to those required for a headspring, as already described.

BERTHING ALONGSIDE ANOTHER SHIP

Going alongside a ship at anchor

Going alongside a ship at anchor in calm weather is very similar to going alongside a jetty, except that the anchored ship is free to swing and will pivot round her stem, and the water pressure from your bows as you close the anchored ship will tend to swing her stern away if the approach is made too fast and at too fine an angle.

The approach in a twin-screw ship should therefore be made at an angle of about 15 degrees with the other ship, at slow speed and with the approaching ship headed for the bows of the other. The approaching ship is then stopped by reversing power to the outer propeller, and the berthing hawsers, particularly the after ones, are passed and secured as quickly as possible. When alongside each other, the ships should be kept apart by catamarans (usually provided by the anchored ship), and each should be well fendered at the break of the forecastle or just before amidships where first contact between the two ships is most likely to occur.

In a wind, particularly one of any strength, the anchored ship will probably be yawing, which will make the manoeuvre more difficult. The stem of a ship yawing at anchor traces a path like a figure of eight, as shown in Fig. 13–21.

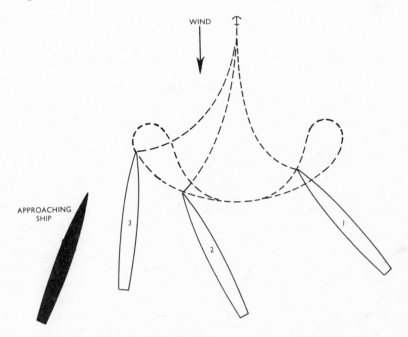

FIG. 13–21. Going alongside a ship yawing at anchor

As the ship reaches the limit of her yaw to one side, in addition to her broadside movement she will come up into the wind and surge ahead. She will then drop back as she yaws to the other side. Before going alongside a ship which is yawing at anchor the approaching shiphandler should watch her carefully to determine the extent of her yaw. The approaching ship should then be stopped just outside the limit of the other ship's yaw to one side, heading a little off the wind and pointing towards the anchored ship as in Fig. 13–21. Then, as the anchored ship again approaches the limit of her yaw to that side, the approaching ship can be edged in towards her and placed alongside her as she begins to yaw in the opposite direction. The manoeuvre requires good judgement and smart handling of the berthing hawsers. When there is risk of damage to either ship, the yawing ship should let go a second anchor.

Slipping from alongside another ship

When slipping from alongside a ship at anchor or secured to a buoy in calm weather it is useless to try to cast the bows or stern out on a spring, because both ships will pivot together round the cable of the anchored ship. If all the hawsers are let go the ships will soon drift apart, and in a small ship this drift can be helped by bearing off the other ship.

In a wind it is best to let go the forward hawsers and hold on to the after ones until the bows of the two ships have swung sufficiently far apart, and then let go the after hawsers and go ahead when the sterns of the two ships are clear. The inner propellers of the two ships must not be allowed to foul each other.

USE OF AN ANCHOR AT AN ALONGSIDE BERTH

Letting go an anchor before going alongside

In some harbours it may be necessary to let go an anchor before going alongside, so that, when the ship subsequently casts off, her bows can be hauled clear of the berth by her cable. She can then weigh her anchor and go ahead into the fairway. The anchor should be let go in such a position that, when the ship is secured alongside, the cable grows abeam and with sufficient scope to ensure the anchor holding when the bows of the ship are subsequently hauled off; the shallower the water the closer to the jetty can the anchor be let go. If, for some reason it is only possible to allow a very short scope of cable it is best to use the inshore anchor so that the cable leads under the ship's bottom to the anchor; there will then be a better chance of the anchor holding as the bows are hauled off. In HM ships the offshore anchor is often preferred, in order to avoid damage to the hull plating or underwater fittings. If, after clearing the berth, the ship has to turn by steaming round her anchor, it should be let go some distance away from the jetty.

In calm weather the ship approaches at right-angles to the jetty and pointing to the head of her berth; and as the anchor is let go at the required distance from the jetty the rudder is put over to swing the bows in the required direction. As the way of the ship is reduced the cable is braked to assist the swing of the bows, and a headrope is passed ashore and used to prevent the bows swinging out too far. The ship is eventually stopped a little more than half a ship's length ahead of her berth, when a stern rope is passed ashore and the ship is backed stern first into her berth. The use of an anchor may also be dictated by a stiff onshore wind (or stream) when berthing (see page 388).

Slipping from alongside with an anchor down

When slipping from alongside with an anchor down, the stern must be cast out on a spring or hauled out by a tug before the bows are hove out by the cable, otherwise the stern will foul the jetty and possibly damage the rudder or propeller. As the bows are hove out the stern must be held in position, either by the tug or by working the engines against the cable, otherwise the stern may swing in again and foul the jetty. The heaving-out of the bows should be controlled by a fore breastrope to prevent the ship from overriding her anchor.

In an onshore wind the help of a tug to haul the stern out, and to keep it from swinging in while the cable is hove in, is essential unless the wind is light and the ship particularly manoeuvrable.

STERN-TO BERTHS

In some harbours where there is insufficient room to berth many ships alongside, some ships are obliged to berth at right-angles to a jetty, with their sterns secured to it by hawsers and with their anchors laid out ahead. This type of moor can only be employed where there is a negligible range of tide, and it is commonly used in Mediterranean ports; for this reason it is often called the *Mediterranean* (or *Med*) *moor*.

The major considerations are to veer sufficient cable so that the ship can swing clear of other ships at the berth when leaving, to lay the anchors sufficiently far apart to make the ship secure in a wind, and to ensure that the anchors do not foul those of other ships. In a shallow harbour it is recommended that a frigate veers about 4 shackles of cable on each anchor, and that the cables are spanned with an included angle of about 50 degrees, so as to make the ship more secure in a wind. It is obvious, however, that the berth will not be safe if a gale blows from abeam. If such weather is forecast it may be advisable to leave the berth and put to sea or seek a sheltered anchor berth.

Approach to a stern-to berth

The ideal approach to a stern-to berth, showing the distances involved, is illustrated in Fig. 13 – 22. Initially it must be decided how far out from the jetty to lay the anchors; it is advantageous when leaving to have them as far out as possible. For a vessel with 7 shackles of cable to each anchor, 4 shackles would be a reasonable scope allowing for one shackle on deck and a margin for error of 2 shackles. Thus with a span of 50 degrees the anchors should be laid 45 metres (50 yards) each side of the centre-line of the berth at a distance of 216 metres (236 yards) from the jetty.

In a twin-screw ship in calm weather the approach is made parallel to the jetty towards the position where the first anchor is to be let go. Having let go the first anchor (Fig. 13 – 22, position *1*), the bow should be cast to port to prevent the cable running under the ship and to bring the starboard hawsepipe to the correct position for letting go the second anchor (position *2*).

When both anchors are down the ship is manoeuvred into her berth, veering cable as necessary during the process, and the hawsers are passed from the quarterdeck to the jetty as soon as practicable. As the stern approaches the jetty it is advisable to shift the con to the quarterdeck where the situation can be observed. If the starboard anchor has dug in firmly the ship is manoeuvred into its berth by slowly veering the starboard cable while going astern steadily at low power. The stern is secured to the jetty by two hawsers which provide more security if they are crossed under the stern, but in some ships this may not be practicable. After the stern has been secured the moor is tautened by heaving in and equalising the strain on the anchor cables. When secured, both cables should be taking a moderate strain and standing well out of the water. It must be remembered that no margin has been allowed for safety astern in the case of a wind from ahead and so there must be no slack in the cables.

An alternative method of approaching the berth is shown in Fig. 13 – 23. Having let go the first anchor (Fig. 13 – 23, position *1*), the ship is turned

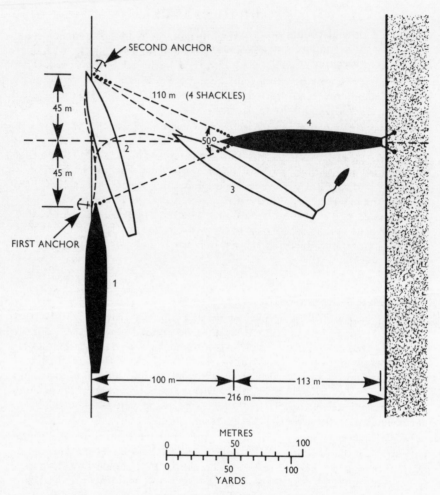

FIG. 13–22. Approach to a stern-to berth in calm weather

by the engines, nearly at rest but with a little headway, until she is lying parallel to the berth but slightly beyond it (position 2). She then goes astern into the berth, letting go the second anchor somewhat inshore of the first so that it is almost underfoot. Cables are veered, and the stern hawsers are passed as soon as the stern is close enough to the jetty. Note that if the stern way is checked by braking the cables their weight will tend to spring the ship forward and, to prevent this, they may have to be veered again roundly or the engines kept moving very slowly astern until the stern hawsers are secured.

In a single-screw ship (Fig. 13–24), having let go the first anchor the ship goes ahead letting the cable run until she reaches the position for letting go the second. The second anchor is now let go and its cable allowed to run, while the cable of the first anchor is held and the ship turned on it. The sideways force of the propeller while the ship gathers way astern into the berth must be allowed for in the amount of the initial turn. Before going astern the ship must be heading to port of the line of the berth.

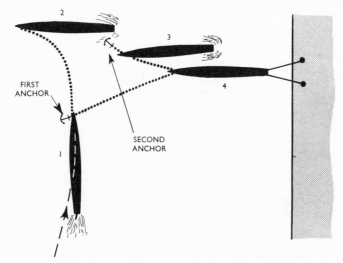

FIG. 13–23. Alternative approach to a stern-to berth

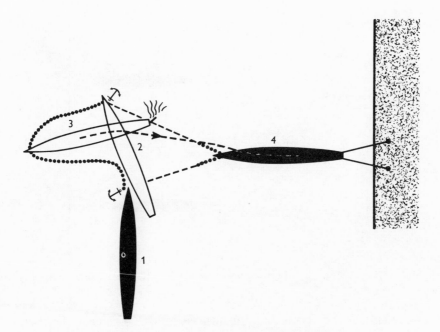

FIG. 13–24. Going astern into a stern-to berth in a single-screw ship

Effect of the wind in the approach to a stern-to berth

A wind blowing directly on to the jetty obviously makes the whole manoeuvre easier, because it assists the initial turn and then helps the ship astern into the berth. However, if the wind is blowing more-or-less parallel to the jetty it can be put to good use if the approach is made down-wind. The ship will

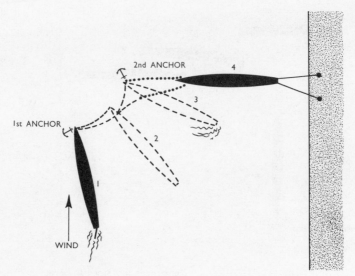

FIG. 13–25. Approach to a stern-to berth down-wind

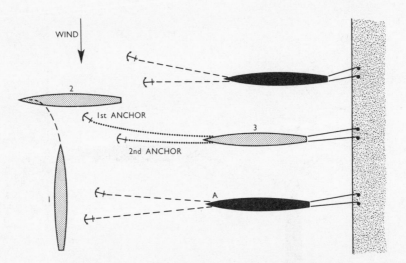

FIG. 13–26. Berthing a twin-screw ship stern-to in a tier

turn readily on the first anchor provided she is given a swing at the start to make sure the wind blows on to the offshore quarter (Fig. 13–25). The movement astern into the berth is easily controlled because if sternway is made the stern will work up into the wind, but if the way is checked the stern will drift down towards the line of the berth. The ship should finally be brought to rest to windward of the berth to allow for drift while the stern hawsers are being secured.

If the wind is parallel to the jetty but from ahead, or if there is not much room around the berth because of other ships already moored either side of it, the approach can be made in a twin-screw ship as in Fig. 13–26. The ship is first turned at rest so as to finish up broadside to the wind in a position to windward of, and offshore of, the intended positions of the anchors. She then goes astern, letting go first the windward and then the leeward anchor. It is not possible to obtain much span between the anchors, but the movement astern should be easy to control, as explained in the previous paragraph.

A wind blowing directly off the jetty is a hindrance, but in a reasonably manoeuvrable twin-screw ship the berthing should be feasible without assistance. In a single-screw ship, however, it is difficult to turn stern to wind with anchors down, and even more so to back into the berth under control; the help of a tug is therefore strongly recommended. Furthermore, in any type of ship, when berthing stern-to with one anchor inshore of the other, the shorter cable should be ideally to windward and nearly underfoot to restrain the wind-induced movement of the bows. Should there be a prevailing wind parallel to the jetty it may therefore be advisable to employ a tug so that the anchors can be laid out in this manner.

Use of ground tackle

In some Mediterranean ports permanent moorings are laid for stern-to berths. When the ship has completed berthing using her own anchors and cable she is transferred to the ground tackle by divers, with the use of a crane, provided by the local port authority. The anchors and cable are then stowed, and this considerably eases the problem of leaving the berth.

Leaving a stern-to berth

Opinion is divided, when slipping from a stern-to berth, on the advisability of keeping a stern rope rove while the cables are hove in. The ship does not have to move very far forward before a stern rope loses its effect in checking a swing of the stern, and it might foul a propeller or hamper the use of the engines when they are needed. Nevertheless, some shiphandlers prefer to retain the windward hawser rove as a slip rope until the ship has moved forward sufficiently for the stern rope to be of no further use in manoeuvring.

The positions of the anchors should be plotted and considered in relation to the direction in which the ship will swing as she leaves the berth. For example in Fig. 13–26 the centre ship will swing to starboard, because of the wind, as soon as the stern ropes are slipped. If she attempts to weigh the leeward anchor her stern will foul the adjacent ship at A. She must obviously use the engines to move ahead until her stern can swing clear, thus overriding the port anchor before it is weighed. But if she moves well clear ahead and swings head to wind before weighing there is considerable danger of a foul anchor, because in this case the starboard cable will have been dragged across the port cable (Fig. 13–27). Her best method in these circumstances would be to move well clear ahead of the berth with the assistance of the engines until over the position of the starboard (windward) anchor and then weigh it, keeping the ship as nearly as possible on the heading of the berth by using the engines while this is done. She may then be allowed to swing head to wind, and to drop astern over the port anchor and weigh it. Clearly it is an advantage to drop one of the anchors initially sufficiently far out to enable the stern to be hauled clear of adjacent ships when unberthing.

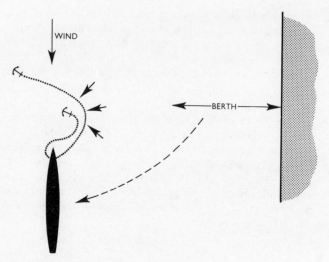

FIG. 13–27. Danger of foul anchor when leaving a stern-to berth in a beam wind

EMPLOYMENT OF HARBOUR PILOTS

The relations between Captain and pilot, and the ultimate responsibility of the Captain for the safety of his ship, are laid down in BR 31, *The Queen's Regulations for the Royal Navy*. The pilot should be regarded as the expert on local conditions, and in certain circumstances the Captain may have to rely entirely on his knowledge, but this does not necessarily mean that the actual handling of the ship should be undertaken by the pilot. While it is normally desirable for the Captain to handle the ship, with the pilot offering the necessary information, there may be occasions — where tugs are employed or where expert local knowledge is necessary, e.g. canal transits — when it will be preferable for the pilot to order the precise movements of the engines and rudder, in order to avoid the controversial procedure of dual control. It is always advisable to pass the pilot's orders via the Officer of the Watch, particularly if the pilot's knowledge of English is not fluent. Nevertheless, whatever procedure is adopted, the Captain's responsibility remains.

The procedure in British naval ports is also laid down in *The Queen's Regulations for the Royal Navy*.

There are occasions when the employment of a commercial pilot is compulsory. In foreign ports, particularly in traversing rivers or inland waterways where local traffic regulations or speed limits may be in force, it is advisable to use a pilot on the first occasion of entry and leaving, at the least. On other occasions the services of a pilot to control tugs may be necessary because of his knowledge of the language or of the signals to be used. However, as a Captain acquires experience of a port he should dispense with the services of local pilots as soon as practicable. It is essential to develop pilotage skill in HM ships so that they will be able to cope with intricate pilotage tasks in active operations or war, when no local assistance may be available.

MANOEUVRING WITH THE HELP OF TUGS

While it is good training to manoeuvre without tugs, especially in ships with reserves of power and excellent handling qualities, there are occasions when the use of tugs is necessary, even by quite small ships. For example, the finest shiphandler in the world could not hold his ship stopped between buoys in a strong beam wind without external aid. If conditions are doubtful it is better seamanship to employ tugs at the outset rather than to call them in to extricate the ship from a difficult position at a late stage, when it may be much more difficult to get the tug secured and exerting her force in time to save the situation. It is unwise not to use tugs on occasions, and it should not become a matter of pride to refuse the help of tugs in all circumstances.

Types of tug and their capabilities

Particulars of the principal types of tug used in dockyard ports and naval bases are shown in the table below.

Class	Bollard Pull	Overall Length	Draught	Power	Speed	Type of Propulsion
	tonnes	metres	metres	kW	knots	
Adept	27.3	38.1	4.6	3350	13	Twin cycloidal propulsion units
Confiance	24.5	47.2	4.3	2400	13	Twin controllable-pitch propellers
Director	18.0	47.9	3.65	2600	13	Two paddle wheels
Dog	16.0	28.7	3.8	1770	12	Twin propellers
Girl	6.5	19.2	2.4	660	10	Single propeller
Modified Girl	6.5	21.3	2.74	660	10	Single propeller
Felicity	5.5	23.8	3.35	825	8	Cycloidal propulsion unit
Trident	3.0	17.7	2.4	440	8	Cycloidal propulsion unit

Paddle tugs are included in the table only for the purpose of comparison as they are now being withdrawn from service and their places are being taken by tugs fitted with cycloidal propulsion units (see page 359).

Tugs fitted with cycloidal propulsion units, known as water tractors, are most manoeuvrable and have the ability to exert full thrust in any direction. If the tow is secured to the towing hook which is right astern it is unlikely that they will be girded because the strain will always align the tug with the tow. These tugs can rapidly alter the direction of tow and they excel in a push–pull configuration because of their ability to 'walk sideways'. A water tractor usually secures with its stern against the tow so that the propulsion unit which is forward of the bridge is clear of the tow and the ability to steer is maintained.

Single-screw, medium-powered tugs are the best to use with a rope from their towing hook. They steer well at slow speed, and are thus suitable for towing ahead; and they can also maintain their position easily and without loss of power when pushing.

High-powered twin-screw tugs have considerably less control when towing ahead, but can maintain their position well when pushing or when pulling astern with a rope out over the bow.

Girding

Ships should avoid gathering headway or sternway when a tug's hawser is growing at a broad angle to the ship's fore-and-aft line, e.g. when hauling off a wharf. Lack of judgement in such circumstances may manoeuvre a tug into a helpless position, possibly capsizing her (Fig. 13–28).

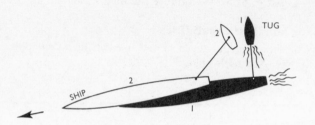

Fig. 13–28. Girding
Position 1. Ship goes ahead while stern is being hauled out. *Position 2*. Tug girded and in danger of being capsized

Modern tugs have great engine power in relation to their size, and the strength of their towing hawsers is in proportion to their engine power. Consequently if a tug is *girded* — that is to say, pulled laterally through the water, with the towing hawser growing out on her beam — there is no certainty that the hawser will part before she is capsized; moreover, in these circumstances there is a possibility of the slipping arrangements in the tug failing to function. As already described, it is unlikely that a water tractor will be girded. Slipping arrangements must also be provided in the ship being towed, but it should be remembered that when a hawser under strain is slipped from a high-freeboard ship it is liable to endanger the crew of the tug. Methods of securing tows and slipping arrangements are described in Volume II, Chapter 10, and they must be fully understood by all concerned.

Control of tugs

Quite often the Captain need not use a pilot to control the tugs: he may control them himself, in which case he must use either the local code of whistle or flag signals or, if in a dockyard port or naval base, the standard orders listed below. It is important that tugmasters should be briefed about intentions in advance of the movement, either at a conference on board or by radio, and they should be kept fully informed while the movement is in progress. Tugmasters are experts at their work and can be expected to know the quickest and most efficient way of applying the force required, and they will often be able to offer advice, particularly about local conditions. The minimum instructions should be passed to tugs — that is, what to do rather than how to do it — and *all orders should be prefixed with the tug's name*.

Standard Orders for Control of Tugs

1. Main Control Order	Push/Pull/Stop
2. Main Control Order (Tug alongside as engine tug)	Ahead/Astern/Stop
3. Qualifying Control Order	Dead slow/Slow/Half/Full
4. Qualifying Direction Order	Take me ahead/astern; Take my bow to port/starboard; Take my stern to port/starboard.
5. Securing	Secure: Your bow to my port/ starboard bow/quarter (abreast turret, bridge, etc); Your hawser to my port/ starboard bow/quarter; Your hawser to my stern/bullring.
6. Completion	Stand by to be let go; *Tug reports* 'Ready for letting go'; Letting go now; Finished. Thank you.
7. Emergency	Stand by to be slipped; *Tug reports* 'Ready for slipping'; Slipping now *or* Stand by to slip; *Tug reports* 'Ready for slipping'; Slip; *Tug reports* 'Slipping now'

Examples of the use of these orders are given for two of the manoeuvres which are described below.

Securing alongside or to buoys with the help of tugs

The most usual occasion when tugs are needed in berthing alongside is when there is an offshore wind, and the obvious way to use the tugs is to have them push on the leeward side (Fig. 13–29). This applies also to berthing between two buoys in a beam wind.

Typical Orders for Control of Tugs — Berthing

Fig. No.	Orders
13–29(i)	'Jack. Secure your bow to my port bow' 'Jill. Secure your bow to my port quarter' 'Jack and Jill. Stand by to push'

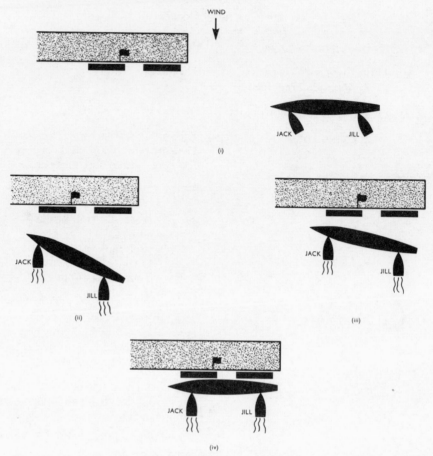

FIG. 13–29. Ship assisted by two tugs going alongside with wind blowing off the berth

Fig. No.	Orders
13–29(ii)	'Jack. Push slow' 'Jill. Push full'
13–29(iii)	'Jack. Push dead slow' 'Jill. Push slow'
13–29(iv)	'Jack and Jill. Push dead slow while I secure' 'Jack and Jill. Stand by to be let go' 'Jack and Jill. Letting go now' 'Jack and Jill. Finished. Thank you'.

If only one tug is available, the best place for her to push may be difficult to judge, but it will obviously be somewhere near the centre of gravity.

When employing tugs to push, the thinness of the plating used in parts of the structure of some modern warships should be borne in mind. It should be realised also that the tug experiences great difficulty in maintaining her position if the ship acquires any appreciable headway or sternway, or if there is a strong stream running.

Slipping from alongside with the help of tugs

If two tugs are available, one should secure to the ship's bow and the other to her stern, each by a short towrope led from the towing hook, and then both tow the ship off the jetty broadside-on (Fig. 13–30). When well clear of the

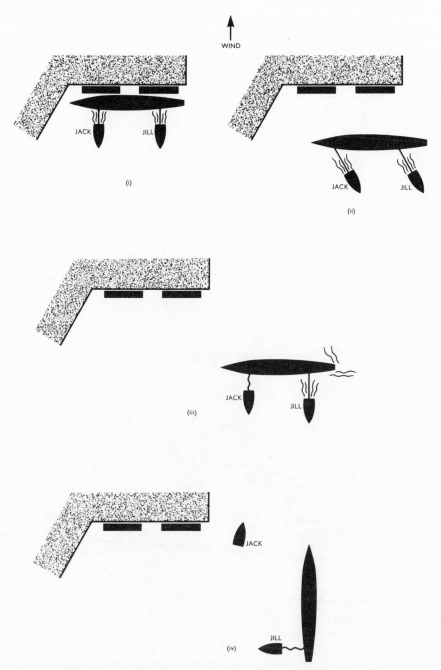

FIG. 13–30. Ship assisted by two tugs leaving a berth with the wind blowing on

jetty the tugs can be slipped if no longer required but they are often kept in attendance to assist the ship out of harbour.

TYPICAL ORDERS FOR CONTROL OF TUGS — SLIPPING

Fig. No.	*Orders*
13 – 30(i)	*As appropriate:* 'Jack and Jill. Pull slow' *or* 'Jack and Jill. Pull half' *or* 'Jack and Jill. Pull full' *or* 'Jack and Jill. Stop'
13 – 30(ii)	'Jack and Jill. Take me astern'
13 – 30(iii)	'I am checking my stern way by going slow ahead'
	'Jack. Stop. Stand by to be let go'
	'Jack. Letting go now'
	'Jill. Pull my stern to port'
	'I am going slow ahead port, slow astern starboard'
13 – 30(iv)	'Jill. Stop. Stand by to be let go'
	'Jill. Letting go now'
	or in emergency
	'Jill. Stop. Stand by to slip'
	'Jill. Slip'.

If only one tug is available to get a ship away from a jetty in an onshore wind, she should tow outwards from a point fairly well forward, between the stem and amidships. As the tug begins to haul off, the ship should work her engines and wheel as necessary to swing the stern out (Fig. 13 – 31). The ship

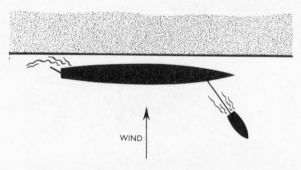

FIG. 13–31. Using a tug to assist in leaving an alongside berth in an offshore wind

then moves bodily outwards. In a single-screw ship some headway will be gained by the need to go ahead with the wheel hard over towards the jetty; the direction of tow of the tug should therefore be forward of the beam to prevent her being girded.

Moving about in harbour with the help of tugs

Having got away from a jetty with the aid of a tug hauling off forward, the ship sometimes has to continue using this tug to help her round some sharp bend. The ship should not go ahead until the tug has moved round ahead of her, and it may be necessary also to move the tug's wire to the ship's stem before starting.

If a tug is secured from her own bows to the ship's stern, she is able to work her engines so as to assist the action of the ship's rudder and engines when negotiating sharp bends.

When a tug is towing ahead the ship's speed must not be allowed to rise above a point about 3 knots below the tug's maximum speed (see table on page 401), because when the tug is required to slip the tow she will have to reduce speed, and having done so the drag of the towing hawser will reduce her speed still further. In practice a large ship can usually proceed at about 7 knots with a dockyard screw-tug towing ahead. During a turn, the reduction of ship's speed allows the tug to recover position ahead, but the tug must work over to the inner bow of the ship before the turn is started. If she does not do so, she will not only hinder the turn but also run the risk of being girded.

Turning in a confined space with the help of tugs

If a twin-screw ship has power on her main engines she should not secure tugs alongside if it can be avoided. The ship's own engines provide a considerable turning moment, and the presence of the tug alongside will probably not expedite a turn and may cause damage to the ship's side if there is a swell. A better method of using tugs to help a turn is to use a small tug ahead pulling, and to secure a large tug by a hawser close in to the quarter in the manner shown in Fig. 13–32. This large tug not only pushes the stern round but holds it in position when required, e.g. to secure to a buoy. She can either push by going ahead or pull by going astern on the hawser, as need be. A third tug may stand by to push or pull from the beam as required.

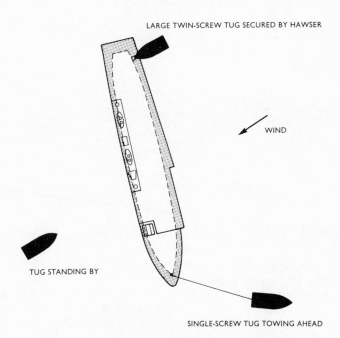

FIG. 13–32. Turning a large ship at rest with the aid of tugs

2D

Large ships such as aircraft carriers and amphibious warfare ships should normally use this method of turning at rest. Smaller ships may prefer to modify the method depending on the weather and the power they have available. A frigate, for example, may not secure a tug at all but merely have one standing by forward and another aft to push if required. If, however, this plan is adopted the shiphandler must accept that a tug may not be able to maintain correct position all the time, ready to push the instant she is required.

PASSING THROUGH A NARROW ENTRANCE

The difficulties in passing through a narrow entrance when entering or leaving harbour arise from the desirability of approaching on a steady course at right-angles to the line joining the two piers, or from the presence of a cross wind or stream. If there is no room to approach at right-angles the use of tugs or warps is essential. For example, in leaving the berth shown in Fig. 13–33 a good method would be to secure the warp in the manner shown, and then to go ahead on it with full port wheel in order to bring the ship

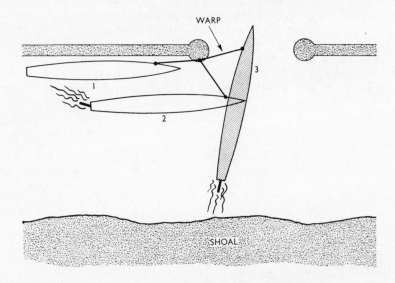

FIG. 13–33. Warping a ship through a narrow entrance

round to head through the entrance. As soon as she has reached position *3* the warp is cast off and the ship goes ahead.

If there is a cross wind or stream (Fig. 13–34) the approach should be made from a point up stream or up wind to allow for leeway during the approach. If the approach is made crabwise to allow for the cross current, a sharp swing using full wheel may be necessary as the ship reaches the entrance, to keep her stern and bows clear of the piers. This need will almost certainly be reinforced by the fact that the bows, on reaching the point between the pierheads, will probably enter slack water, or be sheltered from

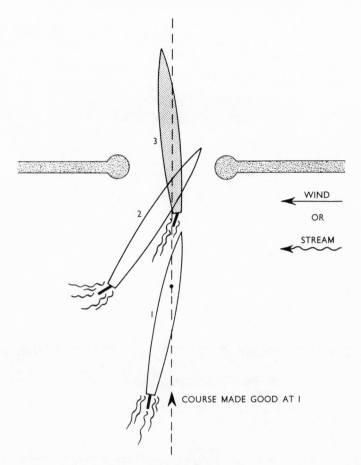

WIND

OR

STREAM

COURSE MADE GOOD AT I

Fɪɢ. 13–34. Passing through a narrow entrance with a cross wind or stream, or both

the wind, so that the stern will be carried rapidly down stream or down wind if no remedial action is taken (Fig. 13–34, position 2). The advantage of keeping up a reasonable speed if possible during the manoeuvre is obvious.

Dredging an anchor, as described earlier in this chapter, may be a helpful expedient when passing through a narrow entrance (see page 378).

PASSAGE THROUGH CANALS, RIVERS AND NARROW CHANNELS

The effects of shallow water on the speed and steering of a ship, described in Chapter 12, are intensified in a canal or similar narrow shallow passage, because the movement of water around the ship is confined. A ship moving along a canal pushes ahead of her a volume of water proportionate to her size and speed. A lateral wave is formed just ahead of the ship, constituting a zone of increased pressure (Fig. 13–35). Just astern a similar but smaller wave travels along with the ship. Between these two waves there is a trough along

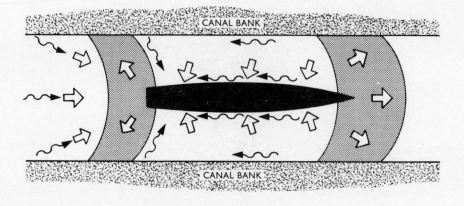

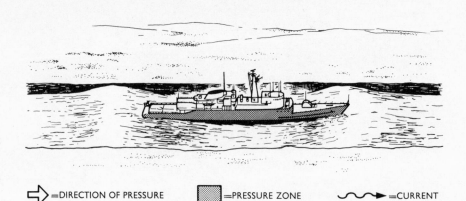

▷ =DIRECTION OF PRESSURE   ▢ =PRESSURE ZONE   ∿▶ =CURRENT

FIG. 13–35. Zones of pressure and suction caused by passage of a ship through a canal

the length of the ship constituting a suction zone. Anything floating is repelled by the wave at the bows, and similarly the bows of the ship itself are repelled from anything solid such as the canal bank. The suction zone tends to attract any floating thing towards the sides and quarters of the ship, and also to cause the after part of the ship to be attracted towards the bank. The water level in the canal ahead of the ship is raised, while astern of her it is lowered. If speed is increased and the depth and width of the canal are little more than the draught and beam of the ship, the effects are noticeable a long way ahead and astern of the ship. It is on record that a ship proceeding at excessive speed in the Manchester Ship Canal parted the hawsers of a ship moored three miles ahead.

Effect of canal on ship's speed

To maintain the level of water in the canal an opposing current is set up that flows rapidly past the sides of the ship (Fig. 13–35). This current is strongest close to the ship and near the surface, and weakest at the bottom of the canal and near its sides. Combined with the shallow-water effect, this opposing stream retards the ship's progress. For example, a heavy ship passing through the narrow sections of the Suez Canal may make good only 5 knots at revolutions for 7 knots, while passage through the Gaillard Pass of the Panama Canal may reduce the ship's speed by as much as 40 per cent.

To prevent damage to the banks and to craft moored, a speed limit is imposed in canals and in many rivers, and this must be rigidly obeyed. If the draught is such that there is only a little water under the keel, the ship's speed should be kept well down, and a careful watch kept on the state of the wave formation caused by the ship's passage. An increase in the bow and stern waves indicates that the ship is going too fast. She tends to settle deeper in the trough, and her speed may drop suddenly, causing the stern wave to overtake the ship and render the steering uncontrollable. The same effect may occur when the revolutions are reduced rapidly, so it is all the more important not to go too fast, and if obliged to reduce speed, to do so gradually if possible.

To sum up, a ship when in a canal has a critical speed above which her steering becomes increasingly erratic because of the shallow-water effects. This is known as the *canal speed,* which cannot be exceeded with safety.

Effect of canal on ship's steering

So long as the ship remains in the centre of the canal the pressure distribution is equal on either side of the ship; the steering will not be affected and little wheel should be required to keep her on course, provided that the canal is of symmetrical cross-section. The fact that little wheel is being used indicates that the ship is following the best track in a canal or narrow passage. Conversely, the need to apply a large amount of wheel to keep on course shows clearly that the pressure distribution is unequal. This may occur either because of the configuration of the bottom, or simply because the ship has approached too close to one bank. The danger is that the pressure from this bank against the bows, combined with the attraction of the after part of the ship to that bank, will throw the bows off this near bank and cause the ship to sheer violently over towards the opposite bank (Fig. 13–36).

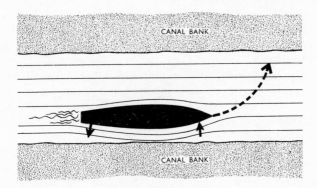

FIG. 13–36. Start of a sheer caused by a ship approaching too close to a canal bank

Correction of a sheer in a canal

In a canal the use of the wheel alone may be quite insufficient to correct a sheer, hence the shiphandler should be ready to use the engines on the instant, or to let go an anchor immediately, if the need arises. In a twin-screw ship it has been shown by practical experience that the best method of breaking a sheer is to increase the speed (or pitch) of the screw on the side towards which the ship is sheering and to reduce the speed of the screw on the other side or even to stop it (Fig. 13–37). But unless the initial speed of the ship is low, even drastic alterations of revolutions may have little effect.

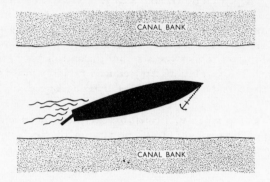

FIG. 13–37. Action required in a twin-screw ship to check a sheer to port in a canal

Experiments have further shown that it may be less effective to reverse the engine (or propeller pitch) on the side away from the sheer than merely to stop it. There is also the danger of damaging the propellers by swinging the stern too close to the bank. Meanwhile the rudder may be entirely ineffective in checking the sheer, and, if so, the anchor opposite the direction of sheer should be let go and dragged at short stay (Fig. 13–37).

In a large ship, if prompt action with the engines and rudder as described has failed to have any effect on the sheer, it is probably best to apply full astern power in order to take the way off the ship, and if necessary also to let go both anchors. If this is not done by the time the sheer has carried the bows past the centre of the channel it is unlikely that the ship can be prevented from striking the opposite bank.

In smaller single-screw ships a sheer is best checked by full ahead revolutions (or full pitch) and full rudder, but on occasions the sideways force of the propeller when going astern may be used to prevent the stern swinging on to the starboard bank.

In any ship quick judgement is necessary when correcting a sheer, to ensure that the correcting action is removed and possibly countered as soon as it begins to take effect; otherwise it is quite easy to produce a sheer in the opposite direction and ground the ship on the bank from which she was originally swinging away.

Smelling the ground

The effect of water pressure against the bows from the presence of shelving water on one side, causing the bows to swing away into deeper water, is the phenomenon known as *smelling the ground*. In a narrow passage or canal it can produce a dangerous sheer towards the opposite shore or bank, but it can be beneficial if the water opposite the shoal is deep and safe. The effect is most marked if the bottom shelves steeply, as shown in Fig. 13–38.

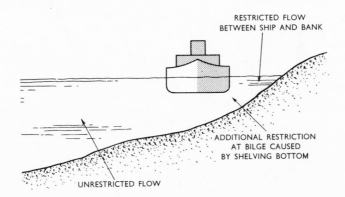

FIG. 13–38. The phenomenon of 'smelling the ground' is accentuated by a shelving bottom

Rounding a bend where there is little current

As the ship approaches a bend in a canal or river there will be a tendency for the bows to smell the ground on the outer bank and so to be swung round the bend. In negotiating a bend it may be found that it is unnecessary to use any wheel towards the direction of the bend, because the water pressure on the outer bow will be just sufficient to carry the ship round. In fact, if the ship approaches the bend on the outer side of the channel it may be necessary to use opposite wheel to keep her safely in the channel as she rounds the bend. If she approaches the bend too close to the inner bank there is a danger that she may take an uncontrollable sheer towards the outer bank. Nice judgement is therefore required in selecting the best course to follow and if there is little current it is generally advisable to keep to the centre of the channel, but inclining slightly to the outside of the bend, when it will often be found that very little rudder is required to negotiate the bend.

Negotiating a bend in a strong current

If there is a strong current or tidal stream running round a bend, as is often the case in rivers and estuaries, its effects may be quite opposite to those caused by smelling the ground. On the straight reaches in a river the current usually runs more strongly in mid-channel than at the sides; but on bends the current normally runs strongest and deepest along the outer bank of the bend, and there may be slack water, or even a reverse current, along the inner bank.

When a ship is moving upstream round a bend the current may tend to throw the bows outwards, as shown in Fig. 13–39, thus counteracting any tendency of the water pressure to push the bows off the outer bank. The shiphandler must be prepared in such a case to use wheel boldly in the direction of the bend and must avoid approaching too close to the inner bank.

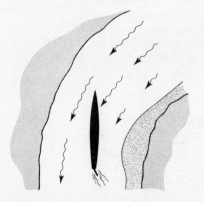 

FIG. 13–39. Passage round a bend
— upstream

FIG. 13–40. Passage round a bend
— downstream

When the ship is moving downstream, particularly if the approach has been made somewhat on the inner side of the bend, there may come a time when the current is tending to push the stern strongly towards the outer bank (Fig. 13–40). It may therefore be necessary to use opposite wheel to forestall this, or at least to apply early the opposite wheel needed for steadying the ship on the next straight reach. Again any tendency to 'smell' the inner bank may be overcome by the outward pressure of the current on the stern. The degree to which these effects of current are felt depends on the length of the ship in relation to the width of the navigable channel.

A pilot's knowledge of local effects in rivers and canals is often invaluable. As a fairly general rule, ships should not pass each other on sharp and narrow bends.

Effect of wind when rounding a bend

The swing of a ship as she turns round a bend tends to be increased or decreased by a wind, depending on the direction in which it is blowing. Probably the most difficult situation is that of a lightly laden single-screw ship proceeding down river and before the wind, when negotiating a sharp bend to starboard. As the ship turns round the bend both the current and the wind tend to swing her stern towards the outer bank; if this swing gets beyond control, to reverse the screw (or pitch) will be useless because the sideways force of the propeller will only accentuate the swing. But all should be well if the rate of swing is kept firmly under control at the start.

Two ships meeting in restricted channels and canals

When two ships meet in a restricted channel, rather than incline much towards their respective sides they should steer to pass close to each other. With care there is little possibility of accident because, as they close, the water pressure between them will force their bows apart; on passing they will tend to parallel each other; and when separating, their sterns will be drawn together. These influences will thus counteract the effect of the nearer bank, and the two ships should have no difficulty in regaining the centre of the channel.

In broad and deep canals ships going in opposite directions may be able to pass each other while both are under way, but usually one of the ships must make fast to the bank to allow the other to pass her. In some canals — the Suez Canal, for example — the bank is cut away at intervals to form sidings in which a ship can make fast.

Making fast to the bank. A ship is made fast to a canal bank in much the same way as she is secured alongside a jetty, except that the way of the ship is reduced very gradually to stop her abreast the berth with as little astern movement of the engines as possible. Plenty of time should be allowed for the manoeuvre, and it is usual to begin reducing speed when the ship is about a mile from the berth. An unhandy ship is usually stopped in the centre of the canal and then warped alongside the bank by means of her hawsers. Easily handled ships can be manoeuvred closer to the bank before the hawsers are sent ashore; but great care must be taken, particularly in twin-screw ships, to avoid getting the stern too near the bank and so endangering the rudder and inshore propeller. Except in a current or strong head wind, two breastropes should be sufficient to hold the ship in her berth.

Effect on the berthed ship when another ship passes. A berthed ship will surge considerably in the wash of a passing ship, and no hawsers will be able to hold her steady. The berthed ship should therefore be free to move as the other passes her, and her hawsers should accordingly be slackened right off as the passing ship approaches. Given that the berthed ship lies with her bows towards the approaching one, the effects of the passing ship's bow wave, trough and stern wave on the berthed ship as they reach and pass her are as follows. First, the berthed ship's bows are repelled towards the bank as the bow wave reaches her; she then surges ahead in the current of the trough and her bows are drawn away from the bank by its suction while her stern is pushed towards the bank by the bow wave; as the stern wave reaches her bows her movement ahead is stopped, and at the same time her stern is sucked out from the bank by the trough; finally, as the stern wave passes her stern, the ship surges astern and tries to follow in the wake of the passing ship (see Fig. 13–35).

This surging must be controlled by the engines and rudder to prevent the stern from being drawn too far out from the bank and colliding with the quarter of the passing ship, and also to prevent the berthed ship from surging too far astern. The surging can be controlled quite easily by a kick astern and then a kick ahead on the engines, with the wheel put over away from the bank. In twin-screw ships only the offshore propeller should be used.

Course of the passing ship. The passing ship should approach along the centre of the canal at slow speed, and should endeavour to keep along the centre of the canal as she passes the other ship, even though it entails passing close aboard of her. Even if the course of the passing ship would appear to take her too near the berthed ship, the ships will in fact sheer away from each other; whereas if the passing ship attempts to give the other a wide berth, she may then come under the influence of the far bank of the canal and take a sheer towards the berthed ship, with dangerous results.

MOVEMENT OF SHIPS IN DOCKYARD BASINS

Two methods are available to place a ship in a berth, or shift her berth, in a dockyard basin. Previously this was always done by *roping,* i.e. warping the ship to its berth by means of hawsers brought to capstans situated at suitable points around the basin. Roping is still used to a limited extent in some yards, but nowadays it is generally easier, quicker and cheaper to use the more handy and powerful tugs which have become available to move ships in dockyard basins.

DOCKING AND UNDOCKING

The operations of docking and undocking ships described here are those carried out in the Royal Dockyards; the methods used by other yards are, in general, very similar.

Conditions required

In tideless waters, or in a basin, a ship can be docked or undocked at most times. In tidal waters, however, the docking and undocking of a ship depend upon the depth of water over the sill of the dock and upon the state of the tide, and the operations are usually begun three to four hours before high water, so that the ship can be docked or undocked and the dock gates be closed at, or just before, the time of high water.

At some ports the neap rise may give insufficient depth of water over the sill of the dock for certain ships to be docked at that tidal period.

Preparation in the ship

All fairleads and bollards should be clear and ready for taking the docking hawsers, and bollard strops and slips should be provided forward and aft. Each part-of-ship should provide at least four heaving lines, two on each side; and though it is customary for the dockyard to provide the docking hawsers, the ship's berthing hawsers should be ready for use. The ship's side should be clear of obstructions which might interfere with the handling of hawsers; all side-scuttles and ports should be closed, accommodation ladders hoisted inboard, davits and boats turned in, and all cranes, derricks and boat-booms should be housed. Awnings should be furled, the anchors should be hove home but otherwise ready for letting go.

It is essential that the ship should have no list before docking. She should be trimmed either level or slightly by the stern, as directed by the dockyard officers. Retractable underwater fittings, such as sonar domes and bottom logs, should be housed, the propellers and stabilisers brought to their correct docking positions, and the rudder secured amidships. The Commanding Officer, and the Weapon and Marine Engineer Officers are required to certify that the ship is in the correct condition, on the *Docking Certificate* (Form S. 1238) which is forwarded to the Production Manager of the dockyard prior to docking.

A berthing party may be required by the dockyard to assist in handling the hawsers; if so, it should be sent to the dock before the ship leaves her berth.

Docking hawsers

The hawsers usually required for docking a ship are listed below. They are passed in pairs, one on each side (the weather one first), in the following order.

1. FIRST FORE-GUYS, which are led through the foremost bow fairleads.
2. DOCKING-SPRINGS, which are led from ahead through the fairleads abreast the break of the forecastle or just before the bridge; in small ships such as frigates, however, one docking-spring only is passed, and it is led from right ahead through the bullring or stem hawsepipe.
3. SECOND FORE-GUYS, which are led through the fairleads abreast the bridge.
4. FIRST AFTER-GUYS, which are led through the fairleads abreast the after superstructure or near the after gangways.
5. SECOND AFTER-GUYS, which are led through the aftermost quarter fairleads.

The springs are used to warp the ship ahead, and the guys to square the ship so that she lies along the centre-line of the dock. The after-guys are also used to take the way off the ship, and it is important that when these are passed they should be secured as quickly as possible, because this is a critical stage of the operation.

Preparation in the dock

Flat-bottomed vessels are sometimes built with side docking-keels, and for such vessels three lines of keel blocks are provided, but no bilge or breast shores except when they are placed in a floating dock. For vessels with rising bilges one line of keel blocks and bilge and breast shores are provided. The keel blocks are laid along the bottom of the dock and the shores are laid on the dockside within reach of a dockside crane. Breast shores are provided with lanyards at each end to enable them to be manhandled into place.

Marks, each with the name of the ship, are painted on each side of the dock, two forward and two aft, to indicate the exact position in which the stem and the stern of the ship should be. Other marks may also be painted on the dockside to indicate such positions as those of the 'cut-up' (the after end of the keel), the propellers, the sonar dome, etc.

Catamarans are provided for use in connecting services to the ship when she is in position in the dock. The docking hawsers are provided, and light tripping-lines are rove across the dock at intervals to keep the bights of the fore-guys and springs clear of the blocks on the bottom of the dock as the ship is warped in; they are tripped and hauled clear as the ship approaches them. Other gear provided includes: lanyards and slings for the shores; docking purchases — heavy mechanical SWR purchases which are clapped on to the guys and used to square the ship in her correct position as the dock is pumped out — and plumb-bobs and docking-bobs, which are used to ensure that the ship is upright and in her correct position.

When preparations are complete, the dock is flooded to the same level as the water outside, and the caisson is then removed or the dock gates opened. A diver is usually in attendance while docking, and ship's officers must ensure that no hazard to him is created by the ship.

Entering the dock

The ship is towed from her berth to the dock, the number of tugs varying with the size of the ship. For a large ship three tugs are usually employed, one ahead, one astern and one secured alongside amidships. A pilot is usually in charge and the ship is manoeuvred by the tugs alone because her engines are not available for use and her propellers have been set to their docking positions.

The ship is headed for the dock entrance and then placed by the tugs with her bows just inside the entrance and pointing directly up the centre-line of the dock. The fore-guys are then passed and secured, and the ship is warped into the dock while the tugs at her quarters help to keep her stern in the correct line.

If the fairway opposite the dock is narrow and a tidal stream is running across the dock entrance, the ship may be placed alongside the dock wall just upstream of the entrance and heading downstream, with a tug secured to her inshore quarter (Fig. 13–41). A hawser is then passed from the tug to a bollard upstream of her, and the first fore-guys and springs are passed to the ship and secured. The tug then surges her hawser, thus allowing the stream to swing the stern of the ship out from the wall, and at the same time the bows of the ship are warped round the knuckle of the dock while the tugs help to keep her correctly positioned.

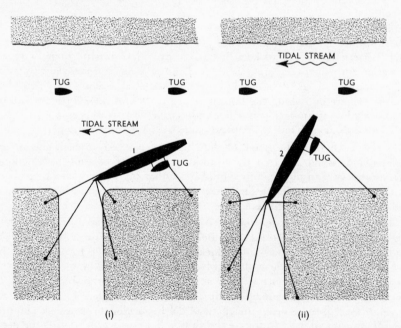

FIG. 13–41. Warping a ship into a dock entrance when a tidal stream is running across it

Docking

From the moment the first fore-guys are secured in the ship the representative of the Captain of the Port (normally the Master Rigger) is responsible for positioning her in the dock to the satisfaction of the officer in charge (normally a Constructive Officer). The docking-springs are taken to capstans at the head of the dock, and the guys, which are passed successively in pairs as the ship is warped through the entrance, are taken to bollards on each dockside. The Master Rigger signals his requirements by radio (or by whistle and handflags, which are seldom used nowadays) to the men working the hawsers and capstans and to the pilot in charge of the tugs. As the ship is warped up the dock by the springs the guys are taken forward from bollard to bollard and worked as required to breast the ship squarely in the dock, and just before the stern passes over the sill the tugs are cast off.

When the stem of the ship is a short distance off the stem-marks this fact is signalled to the officer in charge of docking, who then orders the ship to be brought up on the guys. Finally, the ship is squared off in her correct position by the guys and springs, and then secured by two fore-guys (one on each bow) and two after-guys (one on each quarter). One or two brows are then placed by a dockside crane.

Docking-down

When the officer in charge is satisfied that the ship is correctly placed in the dock, he takes over charge of the operations and orders the docking purchases to be rigged. The docking purchases are hooked to the middle of the spans of the two fore-guys and the two after-guys, and are then led at right-angles with the guys to bollards on the dockside and set up. The ship's position in dock can be very accurately adjusted in this manner and she can be securely held there by keeping the docking purchases taut.

A diver is sent down to ensure that the grooves in the sill of the dock are clear, and the caisson is then replaced. *Sewing marks* are then chalked on the stern and on each side of the stem: one on the waterline and one 15 centimetres above it; these indicate the fall of water after the ship has been *sewed* (grounded) on the keel blocks. Other methods used to indicate sewing are a pole painted with distinctive coloured bands suspended from the ship, or a wooden wedge floating in the water and secured to the ship by a taut lanyard. Docking-bobs are rigged over the centre-line of the dock to check that the ship is lying along the centre-line as she is docked. It is usual to rig one docking-bob just before the stem with another farther forward to avoid errors due to parallax, and a third bob is rigged just abaft the stern. (The docking-bob is a light wire, with a ring at its mid-point, rigged across the dock; the plumb-line is rove through the ring and tended at the dockside, and its length is adjusted so that the bob is kept immersed to reduce oscillation.)

All brows, except one which is slung on a crane, are now removed and the officer in charge then gives the order to start pumping. He usually stations himself on the caisson where he can keep in touch with the ship's officers, see the after sewing and draught marks and the dock water-level marks, and note the general progress of the operation.

If breast shores are to be used they will have been cut to the required length, marked, and ranged in the correct sequence on the dockside. The positions on the ship's sides where the heads of the shores are to bear are marked by chalk.

When the keel of the ship is about half a metre or so off the blocks, pumping may be stopped and a diver sent down to ensure that all is clear. Pumping is then resumed and, if breast shores are to be used, the after shores (*pinning shores*) are hoisted in when the water is seen to leave the after sewing mark, indicating that the keel is sewed aft. The shores are set up to the positions marked on the ship's sides, with their outer ends resting on the dock *altars* (steps) and secured by wedges. After the keel is sewed along its full length, pumping is again stopped and the remaining shores are hoisted in and set up in sequence from aft to forward. At the same time catamarans may be used by ship's staff to connect services (e.g. sewage outlet pipes, water supply to the salt-water main, etc.) to the ship. Pumping is then resumed and as the openings for flooding arrangements become exposed flooding bonnets are fitted over them, and hoses are connected from the bonnets to dockside hydrants. Pumping may be temporarily stopped to enable these operations to be completed. As the water level falls the catamarans must be continuously tended to ensure that they do not damage the propellers or propeller shafts, and that they do not ground on the dock altars or dock services because a catamaran so grounded may entail reflooding the dock and so waste time.

When the dock is pumped out, any bilge or bottom shores that may be required are cut to length and set up. The docking purchases are then unrigged, and if breast shores are used their wire preventers are set up taut and their wedges checked.

The brows are then placed in position and secured. Any remaining services (e.g. fresh water, electricity, etc.) are connected and the ship is earthed by means of the approved arrangements. (For glass-reinforced plastic vessels special earthing arrangements are fitted adjacent to the keel.)

During the period that the ship remains in dock, the securing of shores is checked at regular intervals, particular attention being paid during periods of dry sunny weather when the shores are liable to shrink and also just prior to week-ends.

Flooding-up

A few days before the ship is due to be undocked, and well before any flooding operations are begun, the *Undocking Certificate* and *Certificate of Changes of Weight in Dock* (Form S.1238b) must be completed and forwarded by the Commanding Officer of the ship to the Production Manager's department of the Dockyard.

The *Undocking Certificate*, which is signed by the Commanding Officer, contains statements to the effect that the various underwater fittings of the ship, such as seacocks, bottom logs, sonar domes, submerged torpedo-tubes and their sea connections are shut and in good working order, these statements being signed by the officers responsible for the fittings.

The *Certificate of Changes of Weight in Dock* is also signed by the Commanding Officer, and contains details of all changes of weight which have been made in the ship while she has been in dock. If any changes are made after the certificate has been forwarded, full details must be forwarded immediately to the Planning Manager's department. The changes must be approved, and any necessary adjustments calculated and passed to the Production Manager's department before flooding of the dock is begun.

Before flooding is begun, bottom and bilge shores and any staging are removed, and any arisings are cleared from the dock. Chicken-netting covers are rigged around retractable domes to prevent flotsam entering the openings. (These covers are subsequently removed when the vessel is afloat.) Catamarans are secured to prevent them damaging the ship or themselves when the floodwater enters the dock. Hoses and cables carrying shore supplies are either disconnected or slacked off to allow for the rise of the ship in the dock; all brows, except one which is slung on a crane, are removed, the docking purchases are rigged on the fore-guys and after-guys, and the docking hawsers are passed and rove.

When all is ready the Constructive Officer who is in charge of this stage of the operation gives the order to flood the dock, and the penstocks are opened and water enters the dock. Flooding is usually stopped as the water level approaches the sewing marks (i.e. just before the ship becomes waterborne) so that a comprehensive check for leakage at all underwater fittings may be made. If no leaks are discovered, flooding is continued and as the ship lifts off the keel blocks the docking purchases are worked to keep her in the correct position. Any breast shores used will float clear and they are tended to prevent them fouling obstructions before they are recovered by the dockside cranes. When the level of water inside the dock is the same as that outside, the caisson is removed and the docking purchases are unrigged, and charge of the operation is handed over to the representative of the Captain of the Port.

Undocking

The ship is warped to the entrance by the docking springs, which are led aft from the ship to the dockside capstans, while the guys are worked to keep her in the middle of the dock. As her stern reaches the entrance, tugs are secured and then tow her clear, the guys being cast off as ordered by the officer in charge of the move. As soon as the last guy is cast off, the manoeuvring of the ship is under the charge of the pilot, and he gives the necessary orders to the tugs to tow her to her berth.

Floating docks

When a ship is docked in a floating dock the disposition of her weight in the dock must be very carefully considered, both to avoid straining the structure of the dock and to preserve its stability. The displacement and trim of the ship, and the distribution of weight in her, must therefore be adjusted beforehand to the requirements of the Planning Manager's and Production Manager's departments.

The ship is placed in the dock so that her centre of gravity lies directly over the centre of buoyancy of the dock. The position of the ship's centre of gravity is obtained from the ship's docking plans and then indicated by a mark painted on each of her sides, and the position of the dock's centre of buoyancy is marked on each side of the dock. Although breast shores may not be necessary to support the vessel in dock, they are generally used in a floating dock to ensure that the sides of the dock do not deflect inwards under the strain of supporting the ship on the keel blocks.

In other respects the operations of docking and undocking are very similar to those for a dry dock.

Docking small vessels with considerable trim

Vessels, such as some tugs, whose draught forward differs considerably from their draught aft, require extra care when being docked-down. When the after end of the keel touches the keel blocks the vessel is *pinned* in position by breast shores placed immediately above the point where the keel touches the blocks. Due allowance must be made, when positioning the shores on the ship's sides, for their forward movement as the vessel continues to settle on the keel blocks. The pinning shores are not set up, but held lightly in position to steady the ship until the keel is sewed for its full length; then the remainder of the breast shores are placed, and all are set up together.

Docking destroyers and frigates

Particular care is necessary when docking-down a destroyer or frigate to ensure that her rudders and propellers are not damaged. The ship should be trimmed only slightly by the stern and, if necessary, the propellers must be set to their correct docking positions.

Frigates whose fuel and ammunition have been disembarked are liable to be rather tender. To ensure a safe docking a Constructive Officer is nominated to check the stability and ensure that the minimum ballast is retained on board. Particular care must be taken to ensure that no weights are moved on board when docking or undocking, and that the *Certificate of Changes of Weight in Dock* has been accurately compiled in every detail.

Docking submarines

The Commanding Officer of a submarine must first inform the officer in charge of docking-down or flooding-up that his ship is in the required state of trim, and during these operations he should not alter the trim without consulting the officer in charge. Before entering the dock it is usual to blow all main tanks and leave the main tank Kingston valves open until the ship is docked-down; before flooding-up, however, the main tank Kingston valves are closed.

A submarine is supported in dock either in a cradle or on keel blocks with breast shores. However, when breast shores are used, they have to be placed where the vessel is broadest and these positions are usually under water when the vessel is sewed. Thus steadying shores are initially placed against the casing to keep the vessel upright until the breast shores can be put in position and set up. On completion of docking the steadying shores can be removed.

When undocking, the steadying shores are again placed in position before the dock is flooded, and they remain until the vessel is fully afloat.

ACTION IN EMERGENCY

In the various manoeuvres covered in this chapter it has been shown how, in order to keep the ship under the control of her Captain rather than under the dominance of wind or current, it is necessary to plan fully in advance, to use moderate speed, to employ warps and anchors when necessary, and not to despise the assistance of pilots and tugs. In short, when manoeuvring in narrow waters prevention is better than cure. If, however, the shiphandler starts to lose control there is often some emergency action that will enable him to reimpose it. If it is to be effective this action must be applied quickly and resolutely. The action usually available is the use of full rudder, or the use of full power ahead or astern, or letting go an anchor.

The quick effect of a burst of power ahead with the wheel hard over must be appreciated. To start a ship swinging in the desired direction, or to stop her swinging in an undesirable direction, this action is usually far quicker in its effect in a twin-screw ship than to go astern on one side and ahead on the other, particularly in shallow water. The headway gained at first is not very great. But, of course, if full power ahead or astern is used, the shiphandler must watch the ship like a hawk and take off the power almost before it has begun to have effect. Otherwise he will soon find that the ship is shooting ahead or astern and getting into worse difficulties than she was in before.

Finally, even when an accident appears inevitable there is usually some action that can be taken to minimise the damage. This is one reason why every seaman should have a good knowledge of the construction of his ship, and hence of how she can best withstand an impact. Consider the following:

1. If the choice lies between colliding with another ship and running aground, it may be preferable to go aground and thus confine the damage to one ship. This applies particularly to ships carrying dangerous cargoes.

2. The most vulnerable parts of a ship's hull, and those where extensive damage is most difficult to repair, are the bilges, the propeller shafts with their 'A' brackets, the propellers and the rudders. If grounding is inevitable it is therefore preferable to ground head-on than to attempt to turn and so risk ripping open the bottom of the ship.

3. If collision with another ship is inevitable the damage can be minimised by striking her a glancing blow, preferably bow-to-bow, quarter-to-quarter, or bow-to-quarter. Striking the other ship head-on amidships or turning athwart her bows and so allowing the other ship to strike yours amidships must, if possible, be avoided. A ship is very vulnerable amidships, because any serious underwater damage there will flood her largest compartments, i.e. the machinery compartments, and when these are flooded the ship may founder.

4. There should be no hesitation in using anchors in an emergency to check a ship's headway, or to turn her, or to prevent her from drifting on to a lee shore.

5. If collision with a jetty is unavoidable, it is better to turn and strike it a glancing blow than to strike it head-on, and also to try and position the ship so that at the moment of impact she is parallel to the jetty and has no fore or aft movement. The resulting damage will probably be above the waterline and not so extensive as that caused by a head-on collision.

CHAPTER 14

Handling Ships in Company

Warships often operate in groups rather than singly. The arrangement of ships in a group may be such that ships are spaced several miles apart: or they may be only a few cables apart; or — when replenishing at sea, for example — they may be as little as 15 metres apart when steaming close aboard.

Definitions

A single ship, or a small number of ships operating as an entity for manoeuvring purposes, is called a *unit*. An ordered arrangement of two or more ships or units proceeding together is called a *formation,* while an ordered arrangement of two or more formations is called a *disposition.* The ship on which other ships take station when forming up, or keep station when formed up, is called the *guide.* Thus there will be a guide for each disposition, but there will be also *formation guides* in each formation.

When ships are formed along a straight line in any direction they are said to be in a *line,* and at one end of the line will be the *line guide.* If the ships in the line are formed directly ahead or astern of the line guide, they are said to be in *column,* if directly abeam of the line guide they are in *line abreast* and if on some line other than directly ahead, astern or abeam of the line guide they are said to be on a *line of bearing*.

Fundamentals of manoeuvring

Close formation may be required when entering or leaving harbour, on ceremonial occasions, or for certain operations in war. But it is also frequently exercised because it is an excellent means of training in shiphandling and provides an opportunity for officers to develop initiative, good judgement, confidence and comradeship.

To be successful at handling your ship in company you must cultivate a trained eye so that you can judge accurately relative distances, courses, speeds and rates of turning. You must have a thorough knowledge of the manoeuvring capabilities of your ship and of all the instructions about the conduct of formations, so that you will be able to act with rapidity and certainty. Above all, you must always consider your obligations to adjacent ships, particularly to ships astern of you. In the days when heavy ships almost always steamed in column it was the custom to place a large notice in the forepart of the bridge, bearing the words: REMEMBER YOUR NEXT ASTERN. You will learn undoubtedly from the mistakes of your next ahead how best you can help your next astern. If your ship is the guide, particular attention should be paid to the steering and to keeping the speed ordered both accurate and steady.

Measurement of distance. The practice of expressing distance at sea in miles, cables and yards will continue in the Royal Navy because the mile, which is logically based on latitude, subdivides more conveniently into cables and yards than into metric units. Miles, cables and yards are used in this chapter but in some instances equivalent metric values are also used.

The fact that ships astern of you appear to be steering badly or are out of station may be the fault of your own ship.

STATION-KEEPING

Station-keeping when in line or column

Ships in line keep station on the line guide, that is, each ship should maintain the correct bearing and distance from the guide. But in endeavouring to do so a ship is bound to be influenced by the behaviour of the other ships in the line between her and the guide. Bearing and distance are always measured from the foremast of the guide to the foremast of the ship keeping station, or, in the case of ships without foremasts, between the navigating bridges of the two ships. A ship at the end of a line of bearing may find difficulty in observing bearings and distances of the guide, because the guide is obscured by intervening ships. Obviously, in keeping her correct station the end ship will be influenced by her bearing and the distance from the ship next to her. If all ships in the line were, for example, slightly outside distance, it might be impossible for the end ship to keep correct distance from the guide without getting dangerously close to her adjacent ship.

Thus it is clear that one or two ships who are lax in keeping station will not only destroy mutual confidence in the line, but may positively endanger other ships.

The ship should always be conned by the Officer of the Watch, and station is best kept in column by ordering the quartermaster to steer a course that will maintain the correct compass bearing of the foremast of the column guide.

Accuracy in keeping station

It is evident that accuracy in station-keeping is essential, not only for smartness but also for the safety of ships concerned. In certain cases it is directly related to operational efficiency.

As Officer of the Watch you should try to keep station with the smallest possible alterations of speed and course, but this can be done only if such alterations are applied very promptly, as soon as the ship begins to get out of station. Alterations in speed of from one-third to half a knot and of from 2 to 5 degrees in course should suffice in calm weather. But do not shrink from taking much more resolute action if you appear to be getting rapidly out of station. If you are as much as one cable out of station you will not be justified in taking ten minutes to creep back. Remember that to change the station of a ship by one cable in six minutes her speed must be altered by one knot from that of the column.

Large ships steaming at slow speed — and all ships steaming into steep head seas — will require larger alterations of speed and course than are adequate to keep station normally. Small ships are more affected than heavier ships by the wind, the sea and the wash of the next ahead, and in them it is better to use larger but briefer alterations of speed.

Methods of keeping station

The bearing is normally measured from the azimuth circle on the Pelorus, which is the central gyro-compass repeater on the compass platform. The

Officer of the Watch should know if there is any error at the Pelorus and must apply it as necessary when keeping station. Since distance when stationed is measured between foremasts, allowance must be made for the position of the measuring instrument in the observer's own ship and the position of the object being ranged on in the other ship. Information about ranging instruments used for station-keeping is given in BR 45, *Admiralty Manual of Navigation*. When using a vertical angle from some high object, such as the masthead to the waterline, it is necessary to observe the waterline at a point immediately below the high object. When in column this point cannot be seen, but some equivalent level can be selected by eye. Alternatively, the waterline may be neglected and any two well-defined marks, such as the masthead and the deck level at the stern, can be used.

Radar is frequently employed for keeping station, particularly when steaming at night without lights. At times sonar may also prove helpful. But on occasions the operation of either may be prohibited, and officers must be capable of keeping station in column at night by other means. One method is to observe the size of the ship ahead in the field of your binoculars, and act as necessary as soon as it begins to increase or decrease. Provided you keep in the same place on the bridge, you can in calm weather get an early indication of opening or closing by watching for any movement of your own forecastle up or down relative to the wake of the next ahead.

Keeping station in column in a narrow channel

When proceeding along a narrow channel in a strong beam wind or cross current, you should steer so as to make good a course down the centre of the channel. If ships follow in the wake of their next ahead the line will sag to leeward and the rear ships may be in danger of grounding or, in a swept channel, of striking mines. Ships in column may be ordered to pass over the same ground as the guide, but the senior officer is not obliged to make such an order, because captains are always individually responsible for the safe navigation of their own ships.

It is of interest to note that if there is a cross current or tidal stream the wakes of the ships in a column do not give a true indication of the tracks made good over the ground. On the other hand, if there is only a cross wind the wakes do lie along the ground tracks of the ships (Fig. 14–1).

Keeping station on a line of bearing

When in column the bearing of the guide tends not to change rapidly, and the chief problem is how to maintain correct distance. When stationed on a line of bearing, a small discrepancy in course or speed from that of the guide may result in a fairly rapid change of bearing, as well as a change of distance. If you plot your own position relative to that of the guide, on a manoeuvring form (Form S.376) or on the Battenberg Course Indicator, you will see much more easily what action is necessary to regain station. In Fig. 14–2 the correct station of a ship relative to the guide is shown at *A*. If observations show that the ship has gained bearing and is inside distance it might be assumed, without plotting, that the correct action is to reduce speed and alter course *outward*; but if the actual position, *B*, of the ship is plotted it will be

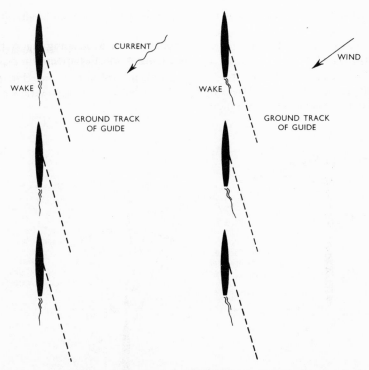

(i) Effect of cross current on track and wake   (ii) Effect of cross wind on track and wake

FIG. 14–1. Effect of cross current and cross wind on ships in column

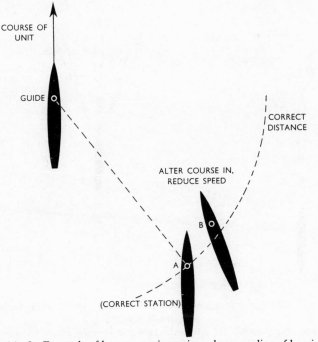

FIG. 14–2. Example of how to regain station when on a line of bearing

seen that the correct action is a reduction of speed and a slight alteration of course *inward*.

A better understanding of the problem of keeping station on a line of bearing can be gained by working out what will happen if the ship stationed keeps a steady speed, but alters course either inward or outward. The effects of such alterations are shown in Fig. 14–3 both for a ship stationed abaft and before the beam of the guide.

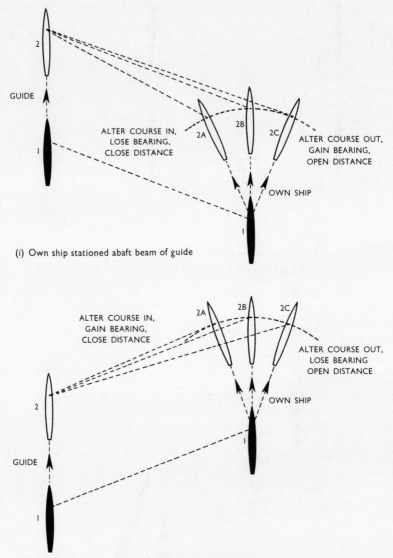

(i) Own ship stationed abaft beam of guide

(ii) Own ship stationed before beam of guide

F IG. 14–3. Effect of alterations of course at steady speed when keeping station on a line of bearing.
In each case the position *2B* shows the result of keeping steady course, *2A* that of altering course inwards and *2C* outwards

A common fault when keeping station on a bearing is to use excessive alterations of course. Once the ship is on the correct track it should be possible to keep her there with alterations no greater than 2 degrees either way.

Open formation

Modern tactics frequently require the adoption of circular and similar formations rather than standard distance and manoeuvring interval. Although ships may not be in line, the maintenance of accurate station remains important if the purposes for which the formation is designed are to be fulfilled.

It is essential that the position of own ship, guide and other units should be kept plotted on a manoeuvring form or the Fleet Formation Board, not only for reference and convenience in maintaining or changing station, but also in order that alterations of course, and changes in the direction of the axis, may be executed correctly and at short notice. For many open formations it is often convenient to plot on the face of the radar display the positions of the guide and other vessels in company.

ALTERING COURSE

Definitions

A *turn-together* is a manoeuvre in which all ships turn simultaneously, thus maintaining their true bearings and distances from the guide. On the other hand, to *wheel* is to alter course in such a manner that on completion of the manoeuvre all ships will be in their former relative positions. When wheeling, the *pivot ship* of a line is the wing ship in that line on the side toward which a wheel is being made.

Wheeling when in column

The correct execution of a wheel by a single column depends largely on the station-keeping of ships in column at the time the guide starts to turn. If ships of similar type are in correct line, and put their rudders over at the same point and on the same heading as did the guide, little difficulty should be experienced in turning in her wake. Ships in column should be steadied by compass on the bearing of the guide at the moment she starts to turn, and each ship should try to get perfectly steady as the turning point is approached. A swing, or large rudder angle either way, upsets the estimation of the right moment to start the turn, and alters the normal turning path of the ship.

The exact moment to put the rudder over may be judged by the position of the *kick* or swirl in the wake made by the rudder of the next ahead, if she is turning correctly in the guide's wake. If the ship ahead is turning badly, one must try to turn in the wake of the guide, provided this can be done without closing the next ahead unduly. The correct position of the kick of the next ahead, relative to own ship's compass platform at the time the order is given to put the rudder over, may be calculated for various speeds of ship.

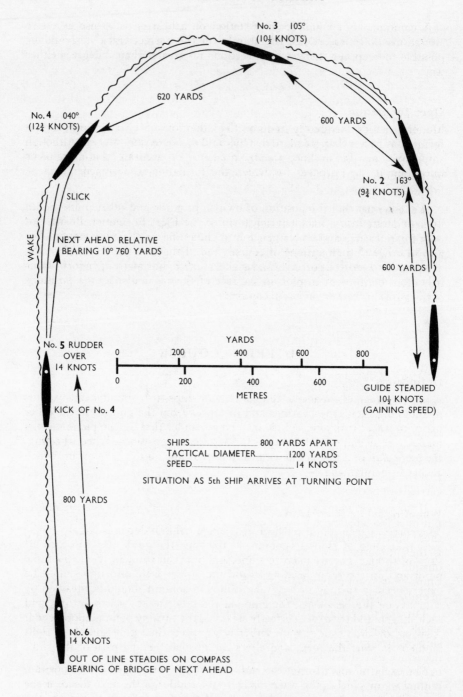

FIG. 14–4. Column of ships altering course 180 degrees by wheeling

For example, at 15 knots, if the distance from bridge to rudder is 115 metres (125 yards) and the time taken to put the rudder over is 15 seconds, the next ahead's kick should be just abreast the compass platform. (Own ship will travel 115 metres in 15 seconds.) At 30 knots the kick should be 115 metres (125 yards) *before* the compass platform because own ship will travel 230 metres in 15 seconds at this speed. This method presupposes that the kick does not develop until after the rudder has been put over, which is not strictly the case. It is only by constant practice that the correct moment can be judged under varying conditions.

Another method is by relative bearing of the bridge of the next ahead, or of the guide, calculated for various speeds and positions in the line. These methods are illustrated in Fig. 14–4.

A common mistake before the start of a turn when wheeling is to steady by compass outside the true turning-point. This can be overcome by taking a bearing of the foremast of the guide at the moment of the order to execute the wheel, and then steering that course until the turning-point is reached. The outward swing of the next ahead's stern, combined with her loss of speed when turning, gives the impression that she is falling across own ship's bows. The natural temptation to steer outside her at this stage must be resisted, as she will soon draw clear, and will remain so during the completion of the turn. The bows must, however, be kept well inside the *wake* of the next ahead, i.e. inside the path traced out by her stern. The bows should, in fact, be kept somewhat inside the middle of her slick.

When completing the turn, especially when ships ahead are turning badly, watch the bearing of the guide and bring the ship on to the correct bearing as she arrives on the signalled course.

No column of ships can wheel satisfactorily unless the leading ship steadies accurately on the new course. She should habitually ease the rudder at the same moment and apply the same amount of opposing rudder to steady on the new course, so that other ships may learn what to expect. It is imperative that she should not swing past her course and thus ruin a manoeuvre otherwise carried out perfectly by the remainder of the column.

If the correct moment to start the turn has been misjudged and the rudder put over too late, more wheel must be used and speed increased. If, despite these measures, the ship turns outside, she will fall astern of station, and it is then important to remember the instruction that the ship must steady outside the track until she can edge into her place at the correct distance. Ships which cannot be relied upon to observe this instruction will be a source of embarrassment to those astern.

Turning too early, and inside, is a fault which can be rectified in the early stages. The rudder should be eased promptly, otherwise in a large turn the ship will soon find herself in an uncomfortable position. It may not be necessary to reduce speed if the rudder is eased as soon as the bow is seen to be drawing across the stern of the next ahead, for the ship will subsequently require to turn in a smaller circle with increased rudder and will lose distance in the process. An unnecessary reduction of speed must inevitably hamper the next astern. When a large vessel is being followed by a smaller vessel of, say, frigate size, it must be remembered that the large vessel will lose more speed in the turn and thus it may be necessary for the frigate to reduce speed in order to avoid closing up.

Altering course together

When ships in line turn together, any differences in advance and transfer between the ships will make station-keeping difficult during and immediately after the turn. For example, the Officer in Tactical Command (OTC) may indicate that the tactical diameter to be used is 1200 yards. At the speed of the Fleet the guide's advance for a 90-degree turn may be 1000 yards whereas the remaining ships in the line, using wheel to produce a tactical diameter of 1200 yards, may advance only 900 yards (Fig. 14–5). They must therefore

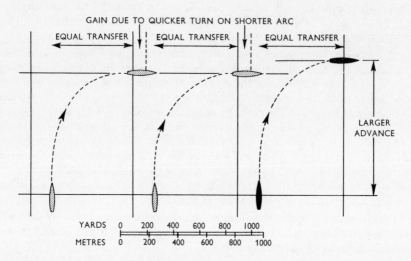

FIG. 14–5. Turning 90 degrees together — effect of variations in advance

vary their rudder angles as necessary during the turn. Even when executing a 180-degree turn together it is undesirable to use the same wheel throughout the turn if the advance of the guide differs greatly from that of the remainder, for although ships may complete the turn either in correct line *or* at correct distance, they will not achieve *both* (Figs. 14–6 and 14–7).

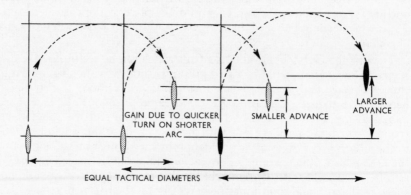

FIG. 14–6. Turning 180 degrees (line abreast)

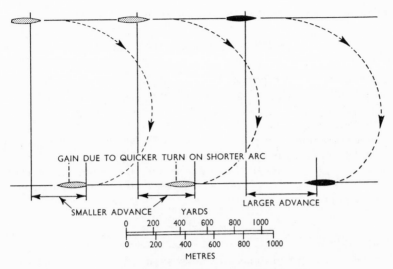

GAIN DUE TO QUICKER TURN ON SHORTER ARC

SMALLER ADVANCE   YARDS   LARGER ADVANCE

0   200   400   600   800   1000
YARDS

0   200   400   600   800   1000
METRES

FIG. 14–7. Turning 180 degrees (line ahead)

The remedy in the above cases is to start the turns under a small amount of wheel and later increase the rudder angle considerably, though the estimation of the rate at which the guide is turning is by no means easy. Thus, in addition to maintaining the correct bearing and distance throughout the turn, the shiphandler must judge the inclination of the guide and compare it with the heading of his own ship.

TAKING UP AND CHANGING STATION

Speed to be used

The speed to be used in a force by ships changing station is indicated in tactical publications. However, a new station should always be taken up promptly unless the OTC indicates to the contrary by giving a definite time at which the ship is to be in station, or otherwise controls the action to be taken.

Gaining ground

In Chapter 12 it was mentioned (page 352) that an allowance of a number of yards per knot is used when accelerating or decelerating, but the shiphandler was warned not to expect great accuracy from the method. Common practice is to allow between 100 yards per knot for a heavy ship and about 25 yards per knot for a small ship. The particular figures for any ship are determined from the results of acceleration and deceleration trials, and by experience.

EXAMPLE

Suppose a frigate is approaching a formation from astern at 20 knots and is ordered to take station 3 cables astern of another ship proceeding at 12 knots. At what distance astern of the other ship should the frigate reduce speed to 12 knots?

Allowing 35 yards per knot, the frigate should reduce speed to 12 knots at:

$$35(20 - 12) + 600 = 880 \text{ yards.}$$

Acceleration and deceleration tables

Instead of allowing ships to accelerate and decelerate at rates governed by their individual characteristics, the OTC may order standard rates for his force and promulgate these in tables. In practice, however, it is unlikely that in a force consisting of large and small ships the latter will be able to achieve the standard rate by the usual orders for the change of speed, and it will be necessary for the Officer of the Watch to vary his revolutions/percentage-power orders during changes of speed in order to keep station accurately on the heavy ships.

Losing ground

When a ship is required to take up a new station that is practically astern of her, there are three possible ways of doing so, given that the guide continues on her present course.

1. If there is only a short distance to drop, she may reduce speed and then increase again, using any available data on deceleration and acceleration.

2. If time permits she may turn through 180 degrees, and then continue the turn right round through a further 180 degrees at the appropriate moment. The time taken to turn through 360 degrees at various speeds can be obtained from Turning Trials results. To find how far the ship will drop distance on the guide by a 360-degree turn it is necessary to consider:

   a. the advance for this turn,

   b. the time required to regain the speed lost during the turn, and

   c. the distance travelled by the guide during the manoeuvre.

   It is helpful to construct a table or graph showing how much ground will be lost by a 360-degree turn at various speeds and rudder angles. When the new station is ordered one can see at a glance if there is time to complete a 360-degree turn without finishing astern of the new station. A typical table appears below and a graph constructed from these figures is shown in Fig. 14–8.

GROUND LOST DURING 360-DEGREE TURN AT VARIOUS
SPEEDS AND RUDDER ANGLES

	DISTANCE LOST BY 360° TURN AT:			
RUDDER ANGLE	15 KNOTS	20 KNOTS	25 KNOTS	30 KNOTS
degrees	*yards*			
10	3800	4000	4400	4800
15	2800	3000	3200	3600
25	2000	2100	2400	2600
35	1800	1900	2200	2200

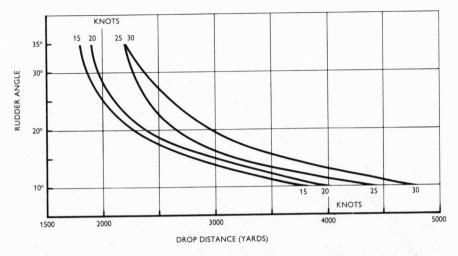

FIG. 14–8. Example of graph showing ground lost by 360-degree turn at various speeds and rudder angles

3. If there is insufficient time to turn through 360 degrees the ship may drop distance by making a broad zigzag. This is a smarter and more rapid method than by a reduction of speed, and in war it enables the ship to maintain a better defensive capability against surprise air or submarine attack. The method is known as making a *fishtail*. A certain amount of wheel is applied to alter course by a specified angle; the ship may or may not be steadied on the new course, and then the same amount of wheel is applied in the opposite direction to bring the ship's head back through the original heading by the same amount as the initial swing. As the original track is approached the same amount of wheel is used to steady on the course ordered. The data for such manoeuvres to drop various distances may be plotted from Turning Trials results and then tabulated as shown below, or a graph (Fig. 14–9) may be constructed.

DROP DISTANCE	FISHTAIL MANOEUVRE USING 25° WHEEL AT 15 KNOTS
300 yards	Out 30° — steady for 30 seconds — back 60° — return to original track.
600 yards	Out 60° — back 120° — return to original track.
1000 yards	Out 60° — steady for 30 seconds — back 120° — return to original track.
1500 yards	Out 90° — back 180° — return to original track.

Data of this type can only give a rough approximation of the distance lost, because the precise behaviour of the ship when turning is influenced by the prevailing weather, etc. and cannot be deduced exactly from

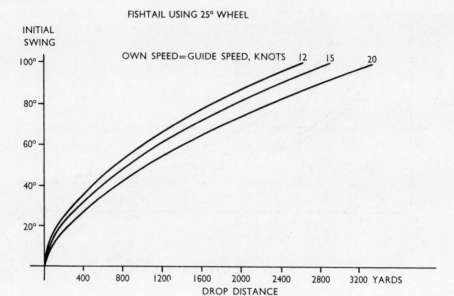

FIG. 14–9. Example of graph showing drop distance by zigzag (fishtail) for a particular class of ship

The manoeuvre consists of an initial swing out, followed by a swing of twice the amount back, and then a final alteration to the original course. A period of 30 seconds on a steady course was allowed between turns

Turning Trials results. Furthermore, the manoeuvre can only be executed if there is sufficient room to port or to starboard without inconvenience to other ships.

Taking station from a position ahead or on the bow

The turn through 360 degrees in two 180-degree stages, described under 2 on page 434 must be elaborated for the case when the ship has time to turn right round and proceed to her new station practically astern. As the ship proceeds on a nearly opposite course towards the unit on which she is to be stationed, fine judgement will be required to estimate the point at which to apply wheel to turn into the new station. If the ship has been stationed several miles ahead or on the bow of the guide there may be time to work out this point by calculation and plotting, but such methods must be used in conjunction with a trained eye which can be developed only by practice. Various methods of calculation from previously prepared data and tables, and by the use of radar, etc. exist, and some of these are described below.

If the calculation has to be made from first principles during the manoeuvre the following factors must be taken into account:

1. The time taken to turn from the approach course to the guide's course, and distance travelled by the guide during this period.

2. The advance and transfer during this turn.

3. The speed lost during this turn.

4. The allowance of a safety margin in case of miscalculation.

Plotting the turning-point is simpler if the approach is made on the reciprocal of the guide's course, but the principles are exactly the same if approach is from the bow, so an example of the latter is given.

EXAMPLE

In Fig. 14–10 the guide, X, is steering 340 degrees at 14 knots. Own ship, A, stationed 5 miles bearing 300 degrees from the guide, is ordered to take station in column 800 yards astern of her. Speed available is 20 knots.

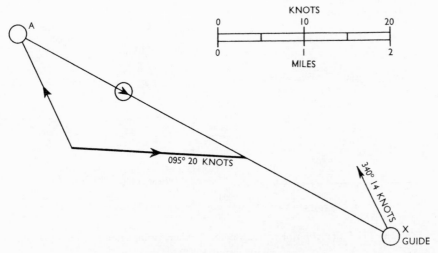

FIG. 14–10. Example of taking station from a position on the bow — first estimation of approach course

1. The shiphandler of ship *A* first plots the course to steer to intercept the guide at 20 knots, alters course to it (095 degrees), and increases speed to 20 knots.

2. Next he plots a safety distance (say, a quarter to one-third of the tactical diameter of his final turn) laterally — *BC* in Fig. 14–11 (300 yards). He now proceeds to find the point at which to turn so as to finish up in position *C*.

3. He decides to take the estimate for the amount of his final turn into column as 120 degrees, for which he has advance and transfer data (the assumption in this case being that he will approach the turning-point on a course of 100 degrees).

4. The final turn is now plotted back from *C*, on the assumption that it will be made at 14 knots. The transfer *CD* for a 120-degree turn at 14 knots using, say, 15 degrees of wheel is plotted at right-angles to the final assumed approach course of 100 degrees — that is, in this case, in a direction 190 degrees from *C*.

5. The corresponding advance is plotted back from *D* to *E* along the final assumed approach course of 100 degrees.

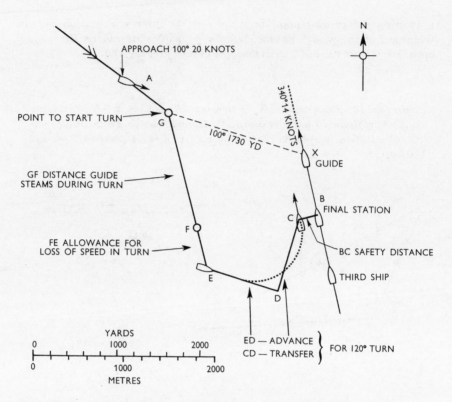

F<small>IG</small>. 14–11. Calculation of turning-point *G* when taking station from a position on the bow of the guide

6. To allow for loss of speed during the turn the *distance correction EF* is plotted back along the guide's course from *E*. This correction is the distance required to make good the speed lost during the turn and it is calculated from the ship's acceleration and deceleration characteristics (see page 352).

7. The distance *FG* steamed by the guide during the turn is then laid off in the direction the guide is steaming.

8. *G* gives the point at which to put the wheel over, in this case when the guide bears 100 degrees at a distance of 1730 yards.

The distance correction *EF* can be neglected by making the final turn at a speed greater than the guide's speed by an amount equal to *A*'s loss of speed during the turn (e.g. at, say, 17 knots in this case) and then reducing to the guide's speed just before arrival in station.

If during the final turn it is seen that the ship is certainly going to attain the intended final position *C*, the wheel can be eased as necessary and revolutions adjusted so as to edge into the line and complete the manoeuvre in the proper station *B*. On the other hand, if the ship has made a bad shot the safety distance *BC* should at least keep her clear of the column, even if ahead or astern of her intended station.

In the example it is found that by adjusting the initial course from 095 degrees to 100 degrees the ship should pass through point *G*. If a much larger adjustment had been required it might have been necessary (time permitting) to make a second approximation. However, the calculation may take at least five minutes, by which time the shiphandler in *A* will have covered half the distance to the turning-point without being able to take his eyes from his plotting. A more rapid method of finding the turning-point is clearly desirable.

The essential feature of the manoeuvre is that the ship should pass *exactly* through the pre-determined turning-point on *approximately* the course for which that turning-point has been calculated. An error of a few degrees in the amount of final turn will make little difference to the advance and transfer. On the other hand, if the ship, even though on the correct approach course, starts to turn, say, 100 yards from the intended turning-point, then she will obviously finish up about 100 yards from her intended station.

Quick methods of plotting the turning-point

By plotting out beforehand a number of turns for different speeds and amounts of final turn, a table similar to that shown below may be prepared for the ship. In the table no allowance is normally made for safety distance which must be plotted separately. The table gives the relative bearing and distance of the turning-point from the new station. This must first be plotted, and then the true bearing and distance of the guide from the turning-point may be obtained.

TAKING STATION FROM THE BOW USING 25 DEGREES OF WHEEL

GUIDE SPEED = OWN SPEED	RELATIVE BEARING AND DISTANCE (*yards*) OF TURNING-POINT FROM NEW STATION WHEN FINAL ALTERATION OF COURSE IS:					
	180°	150°	120°	90°	60°	45°
knots						
10	24°	29°	38°	41°	50°	50°
	2000	1600	1160	760	360	200
12	23°	29°	38°	42°	50°	50°
	2080	1660	1200	800	420	240
14	22°	28°	37°	42°	49°	50°
	2200	1760	1300	860	460	300
16	22°	27°	37°	42°	49°	51°
	2320	1860	1400	920	520	340
18	21°	27°	36°	42°	48°	51°
	2420	2000	1480	960	560	360
20	20°	27°	35°	42°	48°	51°
	2520	2100	1600	1000	600	380

Note. A safety distance should be applied when turning into column.

An alternative method is to plot the data (on the same scale as a manoeuvring form) on a tracing (Fig. 14–12). This tracing can be aligned with the position and course of the guide on a manoeuvring form, and the appropriate turning-point pricked through.

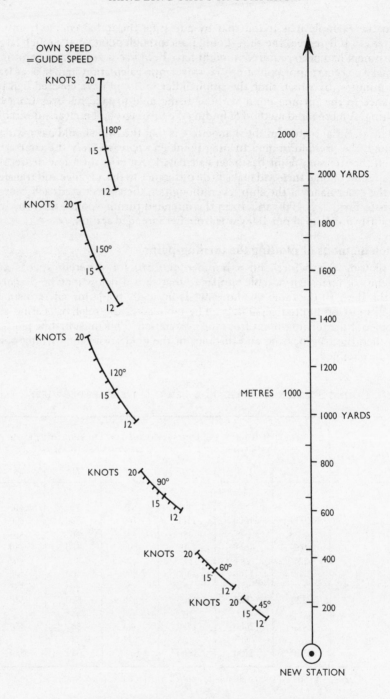

FIG. 14–12. Example of data for estimating the turning-point when taking station
from the bow, as plotted on a tracing of a manoeuvring form
The position of the guide must be plotted relative to the new station, and a safety
distance allowed when turning into column

Reversing the order of ships in column

A description of this manoeuvre when carried out from rest is given on page 449. If carried out when under way, the manoeuvre takes longer to complete and more sea room is required. When a column is ordered to reverse order of ships in column in succession from the rear, the rear ship automatically becomes guide and increases to one knot less than stationing speed, passing the ships ahead of her on the side indicated. Other ships reduce to 7 knots or as indicated. At the appropriate time each ship in succession from the rear increases speed and takes station in the wake of the ship that was previously next astern of her.

It is difficult to estimate exactly the time and sea room that will be required to complete the manoeuvre. Basically the need is to estimate the *time* occupied by the rear ship in traversing twice the length of the column at a relative speed equal to the difference between 7 knots and a speed of one knot less than stationing speed. The *distance* required ahead of the rear ship is that traversed by the rear ship during this time at one knot less than stationing speed. However, a little reflection will reveal that account must be taken of acceleration and deceleration in the various ships in the column. For example the leading ship does not at once drop to her new speed of 7 knots and may not in fact reach it before it is time for her to accelerate again.

A formula that gives an *approximate* time T for the manoeuvre is:

$$T = \frac{[2L + 2(S \times C)] \times 60}{S \times 2000} \text{ minutes}$$

where:

S is the difference in speeds in knots between one-knot-less-than-stationing speed and 7, or between the two speeds ordered;

L is the length of the line in yards;

C is the correction in yards per knot, for gain and loss of speed for the class of ship concerned.

EXAMPLE

A column of four ships steaming at 12 knots is ordered to invert the line. Stationing speed is 20 knots and ships are 800 yards apart. Yards-per-knot correction is 50. Estimate the time and sea room required.

$$T = \frac{[2 \times 2400 + 2(12 \times 50)] \times 60}{12 \times 2000} \text{ minutes,}$$

$$= 15 \text{ minutes.}$$

In 15 minutes the rear ship will cover 4.75 miles at 19 knots. Thus a distance of 3.55 miles is required ahead of the original guide in order to complete the manoeuvre. However, since the formula can give only an approximate time, it would be wise to add at least 25 per cent to the calculated distance ahead of the original guide, and for example call it in this case 4.5 miles. Remember that at the end of the manoeuvre all ships will be proceeding at one knot less than stationing speed and, if it is then necessary to reduce speed, time will be required to signal the new speed and reduce to it.

During the manoeuvre each ship must judge the moment to increase speed so as to fall into correct station on the new guide, bearing in mind that her own speed and that of the ship being stationed on may be anywhere between 7 knots and one-knot-less-than-stationing speed at the time. In Fig. 14–13 it will be seen that ship C will probably require to increase before D draws abeam. Ships A and B should therefore base

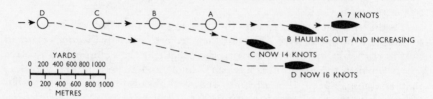

FIG. 14–13. Example of reversing order of ships in column
Initial speed was 12 knots, final speed 17 knots. Typical situation of four heavy ships after 7 minutes, showing need for new guide to haul well clear of column

their timing on the new guide D rather than on the ship due to be next ahead after the manoeuvre. It is clear from the figure that the new guide should haul well out to allow for the fact that several ships may be very nearly abreast one another at some stage.

USE OF RADAR IN FLEETWORK

Radar may be used to great advantage in solving many manoeuvring problems.

The modern radar, with its high rate of aerial rotation and great accuracy, gives an up-to-date picture of other ships' positions, their bearings and ranges, and their approximate relative tracks, from the afterglow tails on the plan position indicator (PPI) display.

The PPI display

The type of PPI display used for navigation purposes has a mechanical bearing cursor fitted over the face of the tube. The cursor is engraved with parallel lines and can be rotated by a manual control. Range is shown on the face of the display by an electronic range-marker which paints a circular trace and is adjusted as required by the range-marker control. The range to which the marker is set is shown on a digital readout.

Over the face of the display is fitted a reflection plotter which comprises a transparent disc provided with side illumination. Manual plotting with chinagraph pencil on the face of the plotter appears coincident with the radar picture on the face of the tube, i.e. there is no parallax. Further details of radar displays are given in BR 1982, *Warning Radar User Instructions*.

Changing station

Relative-velocity problems are solved by using the bearing cursor and range marker, and by plotting on the face of the reflection plotter.

EXAMPLE

Own ship is ordered to change station from 1 mile on the port bow to 1 mile on the starboard bow of the guide who is steering 315 degrees at 14 knots. If the stationing speed is 24 knots, what is the course to steer?

The display is set to a suitable range scale — in this case, say, 1.5 miles. Own ship, O in Fig. 14–14, is at the centre of the display; the guide is now at F and will be at T on completion of the manoeuvre.

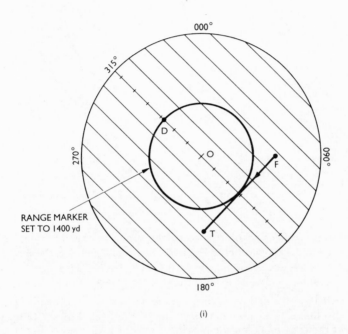

(i)

FIG. 14–14(i). Use of radar display to determine course to new station

Thus the guide's contact must move from F to T, and FT is the guide's relative track. To find the course to steer:

1. On the reflection plotter mark the guide's contact F and its projected position T. Draw the line FT and mark it with an arrowhead in the direction F to T (Fig. 14–14(i)).

2. Rotate the bearing cursor to align the centre line to the guide's course (315 degrees) and set the range marker to a range equivalent to the guide's speed — in this case 1400 yards (Fig. 14–14(i)).

3. On the reflection plotter mark D at the intersection of the bearing cursor centre-line and the range marker (Fig. 14–14(i)).

4. Rotate the bearing cursor so that its lines are parallel to the guide's relative track FT and set the range marker to a range equivalent to the stationing speed — in this case 2400 yards (Fig. 14–14(ii)).

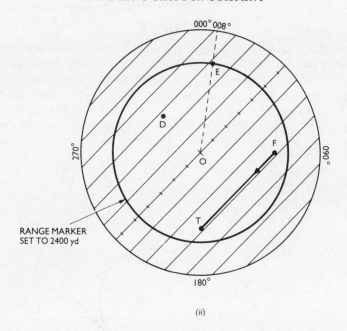

(ii)

FIG. 14–14(ii). Use of radar display to determine course to new station

5. On the reflection plotter mark the range marker at E such that the line ED is parallel to the bearing cursor lines and the direction E to D is the same as the direction F to T. (This procedure is necessary to obviate the alternative, false, position for E.)

6. Finally, rotate the bearing cursor so that the centre line passes through E. The course to steer is then indicated by the outer end of the centre line on the bearing scale of the display — in this case 008 degrees (Fig. 14–14(ii)).

During the manoeuvre the guide's contact should always appear on the relative track FT. However, if the contact appears inside the relative track it is too close and so an adjustment of course to port is necessary; if outside the relative track it is too distant and so an adjustment to starboard is required.

Use of turning data

For precise manoeuvres such as turning into line and taking station on another ship, the position of 'wheel over' must be calculated accurately. The method of plotting to determine this position has already been described on page 437.

When using radar, not only can the position of the guide at 'wheel over' be plotted and the guide's contact be made to pass through it, but the path of the guide, relative to own ship during the turn, can be drawn on the reflection plotter so that the guide's contact may be compared with its planned relative track.

Fig. 14–15 shows a suggested method of obtaining relative curves for varying speeds of own ship and guide. The turn of own ship is first plotted in relation to the centre of the PPI at the scale of the range selected. In most

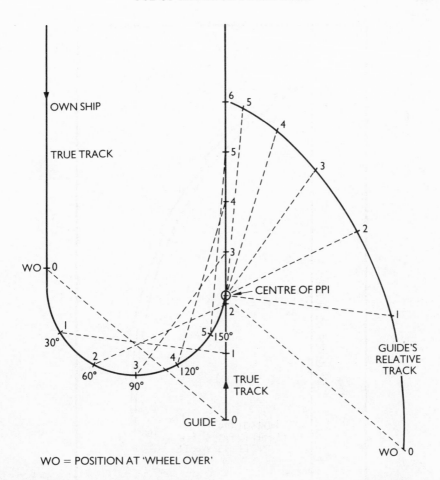

OWN SHIP

TRUE TRACK

WO 0

30°

60°

90°

120°

150°

CENTRE OF PPI

GUIDE'S
RELATIVE
TRACK

TRUE
TRACK

GUIDE 0

WO 0

WO = POSITION AT 'WHEEL OVER'

FIG. 14–15. Method of plotting position of 'wheel over' and guide's relative track

cases the 1.5-mile range scale is recommended although it may be necessary
to use a longer range scale during the early part of the manoeuvre. The
guide's true track is then plotted back from its position when own ship is in
final station. The positions of the guide are then related to own ship, by time
on the turn, at various points throughout the turn. From this information
the guide's relative track may then be plotted.

A simple template may be cut to the curve of the guide's relative track,
marked with the position of 'wheel over', to permit the curve to be drawn
on the reflection plotter of the PPI. The faces of the template are marked
for the direction of turn and the template is turned over to select the
appropriate curve for the direction of turn.

A composite template is shown in Fig. 14–16 where the position of the
guide at 'wheel over' and at intermediate positions for a turn to port of 180
degrees are marked in black figures. The red figures indicate the positions
of 'wheel over' and the relative curves for turns of 150, 120, 90 and 60
degrees.

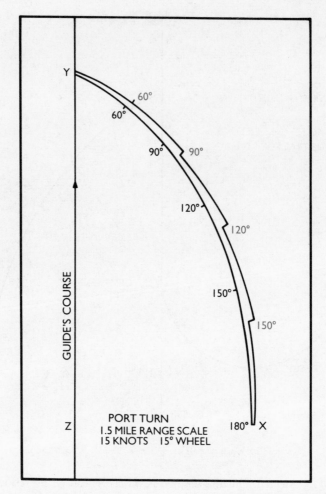

FIG. 14–16. Template for determining position of 'wheel over' and plotting the guide's relative track

Use of the template (Fig. 14–16). Rotate the bearing cursor of the PPI so that the centre line indicates the guide's course, and on the reflection plotter mark the guide's position when in station. Determine the amount and direction of the final turn. Place the template on the reflection plotter so that the guide's course YZ is parallel with the lines of the bearing cursor and point Y is over the marked position of the guide. On the reflection plotter mark the position of 'wheel over' for the appropriate final turn and the remaining curve. Own ship is then steered so that the guide's contact passes through the selected 'wheel over' position; and own ship is then on the correct course for the alteration planned at the moment of 'wheel over'.

Safety. No margin for safety has been allowed in drawing the relative curves shown in Figs. 14–15 and 14–16. The safety distance can be applied by displacing the template laterally by the required distance when marking on the reflection plotter the 'wheel over' position and relative track.

Adjustment of errors (Fig. 14–17). If the guide fails to pass through the planned 'wheel over' position X, or own ship is not on the correct course for the alteration planned, the speed and diameter of the turn must be altered. If the guide is outside the planned relative track, on track YA for example,

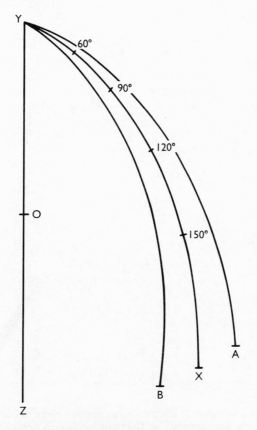

FIG. 14–17. Adjustment of errors during final turn

own ship must use less wheel to produce a larger transfer and must turn earlier to compensate for the extra time on the turn. If the guide is inside (track YB), the turn must be quicker and later. Should own ship fail to be on the planned course at the moment of 'wheel over', the turn must be similarly adjusted to take account of the error.

LEAVING HARBOUR IN COMPANY

Unmooring

When ships are moored it is arranged as a rule that the berths are far enough apart to allow any ship to unmoor independently whatever the direction of wind or stream. But, even so, if all the ships unmoor together it will be necessary for adjacent ships to take care not to hinder one another. If, for example, ships of a column are lying in line with their anchors and one ship

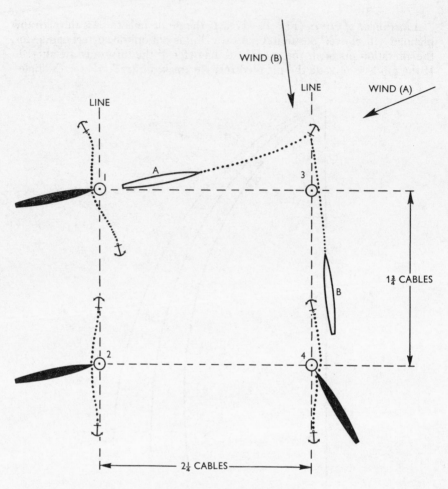

FIG. 14–18. The distance to allow between lines of ships moored, and between berths in the same line, depends on the need for any ship to be able to unmoor independently, whatever the direction of wind or stream

weighs her lee anchor more quickly than her next ahead, she should delay shortening-in her weather cable until her next ahead has also weighed her lee anchor.

Suppose there are two lines of ships moored, as in Fig. 14–18, with the cables laid out along the lines. Each ship has 5 shackles (137.5 metres) of cable on each anchor, so that each ship's anchors will be about 250 metres apart. Consider ship A unmooring independently in the windward line (from berth 3 in Fig. 14–18); it is clear that the distance to the opposite berth in the leeward line (berth 1) must allow for her swinging nearly to the full scope of her weather cable as soon as her lee anchor has been weighed. Thus the lines should be spaced apart at least by this scope (250 metres) plus the length of the ship. Given that all ships are of one class, for this example 120 metres in length, the distance between lines should be at least 370 metres (405 yards or, say, 2¼ cables).

On the other hand, if the wind is blowing not across the lines but along their length, a ship *B* unmooring independently from berth *3* in Fig. 14–18, when lying at the full scope of her weather cable, need not have so much room between her berth and the next berth to leeward. Theoretically, the minimum distance between berths in the same line would be *half* a span of cable (in this case, 137.5 metres) plus the length of the ship (120 metres), which equals 257.5 metres (approximately 280 yards). However, a mooring margin should be allowed, and a reasonable distance for this class of ship would be 1¾ cables (350 yards).

The basic problem of swinging room when moored is outlined in Chapter 13.

Weighing

When ships of a unit in separate berths have weighed together, or slipped from buoys together, they preserve the same bearing and distance from the senior officer of their unit as existed before getting under way, until further orders are received. The senior officer may then order them to cast to port or to starboard or to a particular course. While doing so they should not gather headway or sternway, and they should endeavour to turn at the same rate as the senior officer.

Inverting column when leaving harbour

If the senior officer led his squadron into harbour he will probably order his column to invert the line when leaving. In these circumstances it is preferable to turn at rest together to a heading that is 20 degrees short of the course for leaving harbour, so that each ship, when her turn comes, can go ahead into clear water without having first to turn to avoid her next ahead (Fig. 14–19). Each ship must determine the correct moment to go ahead so as to take station in the column. If ships in the column are of the same class it is a fairly simple matter to calculate this moment as occurring at a certain time interval after the moment at which the senior officer's ship, or ship to be next ahead, has put her engines ahead. The method is based on the assumption that each ship puts her engines to half-speed ahead at the revolutions for the speed ordered in one movement at the calculated moment.

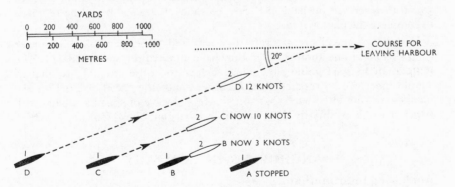

FIG. 14–19. Four ships — *A, B, C* and *D* — inverting the line from rest on leaving harbour. Positions *2* show the situation after 8 minutes if speed ordered is 12 knots

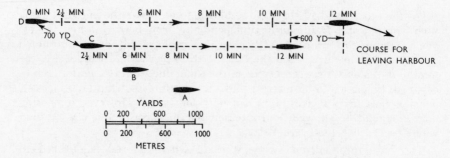

FIG. 14–20. Inverting the line from rest — determination of the correct moment
to go ahead to take up station

Consider ships C and D in Fig. 14–20. C must allow D to gain station-keeping distance (say, 3 cables) plus the distance CD measured at the time D was seen to go ahead. Given that this total is $6\frac{1}{2}$ cables and the speed ordered is 12 knots, then if the ships are of the same class they can be assumed to accelerate at the same rate, and the time interval required is simply the time D takes to cover $6\frac{1}{2}$ cables at 12 knots. In this example the time interval is $3\frac{1}{4}$ minutes, and if C goes ahead at 12 knots, $3\frac{1}{4}$ minutes after D is seen to go ahead, she should fall into correct station.

If ships are of dissimilar class and the ship taking station has a slower rate of acceleration she must obviously go ahead sooner (and vice versa). A simple approximation is to reduce (or increase) the time interval by an amount depending on the difference in the yards-per-knot acceleration values for the two ships. For example, if the value for D is 50 yards per knot and that for C is 100 yards per knot (in Fig. 14–20), the distance to be covered by D (that is, $6\frac{1}{2}$ cables) must be corrected by subtracting $12 \times (100 - 50)$ yards.

In this example the corrected distance is:

$$(6\tfrac{1}{2} \times 200) - [12 \times (100 - 50)] = 700 \text{ yards, or } 3\tfrac{1}{2} \text{ cables.}$$

The corrected time interval is that required by D to cover $3\frac{1}{2}$ cables at 12 knots; that is $1\frac{3}{4}$ minutes.

When the manoeuvre is being executed by ships of slow acceleration the situation is similar to that for reversing the order of ships in column at sea which is described on page 441. Several miles of sea room will be required to complete the manoeuvre.

If ships go ahead prematurely they will find themselves bunched up or even abreast of one another when they have attained the speed ordered. The temptation to start going slow ahead before the time interval has elapsed should therefore be resisted. On the other hand, the speed ordered for the manoeuvre should be such that ships have a reserve of speed available with which to catch up smartly if they find they have gone ahead too late.

ANCHORING IN COMPANY

Anchoring in formation

There are two ways of anchoring a unit as a whole. Either the anchors of all ships are let go simultaneously, in which case the senior officer makes use

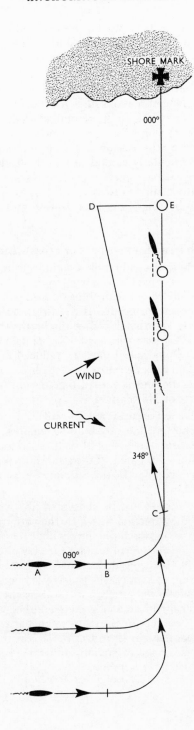

FIG. 14-21. Anchoring a column in a cross wind or cross current

of a signal meaning 'anchor instantly'; or the senior officer leads the unit into harbour so formed and disposed that each ship will pass through her allotted berth, and then orders ships to anchor 'in accordance with previous instructions' as convenient when approaching the berths.

In both methods, but particularly in the former, all ships must maintain station accurately. In the first method ships must maintain exact station until the moment of letting go; while, in the second, ships should maintain station as far as is practicable up to the moment of anchoring, but are at liberty to steer for their assigned berths as soon as the appropriate signal is executed. The guide must be particularly careful to keep a steady course and speed, and must not make any changes in either without signal. Ships should always be ready to anchor individually if ordered, and the Navigating Officer should see that the necessary bearings have been laid off and noted to enable this to be done.

Anchoring a column in a cross current or cross wind

An example of a method of conducting a column to its anchor berths in a cross wind and/or cross current is shown in Fig. 14–21. The guide A approaches, steering 090 degrees with ships on a line of bearing 180 degrees, which is the line of the anchor berths. It is estimated that between the turn to the anchoring course and the arrival in the berths the wind and current will set the unit three cables to leeward — after taking into account that during this period the ships' speed must be reduced first and their engines stopped later. A position D is therefore plotted three cables to windward of the guide's berth, and the unit is turned together on to the anchoring line CE but steering a course of 348 degrees.

If the estimate has been accurate, ships will find themselves slightly to windward of the anchoring line on stopping engines, but as their speed through the water decreases they should drift on to the correct line by the time the signal to anchor is executed. If the guide does not proceed accurately along the first approach course AB, the estimate for point D will be in error and should be adjusted.

A good shore mark ahead must be chosen so that when the ships are on the anchoring course the direction in which they are being set can be seen with ease. If the direction in which the ships will be set is uncertain the senior officer may make two signals, one ordering a turn together of, say, 10 degrees to port and the other of 10 degrees to starboard. He may then execute either one of the signals during the approach, if necessary; or he may find that he needs to execute one, followed after an interval by the other. He will thus have ready a quick means of adjusting course either way during the final approach. If it is not essential for the ships to anchor exactly in the allotted berths, the senior officer may prefer to sacrifice accuracy of berthing position in order to maintain accuracy of station, and if so he will not order any alterations of course during the last mile.

CHAPTER 15

Handling Ships in Heavy Weather

GENERAL CONSIDERATIONS

Avoidance of damage

How best to handle a ship in heavy weather depends so much upon the type, size and capabilities of the particular ship that it would be unwise to lay down precise instructions as to how to act in various circumstances. A seaman studies carefully the reactions of his ship in heavy seas and thereby gains a sympathetic understanding of her sea-keeping qualities. He learns how she should be handled, and how hard she can be driven without incurring danger or damage.

Often, in a warship, the need to carry out the assigned task conflicts with the need to avoid weather damage, but there is no sense in driving a ship in a storm in such a way that she sustains damage to the hull or is placed in danger of foundering. The fact that a modern warship has powerful engines means that in rough weather she has not only the means to extricate herself from danger, but also the means to inflict great damage upon herself. A good seaman does not regard serious weather-damage as an unavoidable misfortune, let alone an honourable wound, but rather as being as culpable as any other damage resulting from careless shiphandling. In heavy weather, superficial damage to boats, davits, guard-rail stanchions, hatches, etc. may have to be accepted for operational reasons, but can usually be avoided without affecting the achievement of the ship's task.

It is important to record information on the ship's behaviour on particular occasions in heavy weather, and any useful advice based on these experiences, in Form S.2677, *Navigational Data Book*. Such information will be invaluable to succeeding captains and officers when they join the ship.

The Officer in Tactical Command (OTC) is responsible for the safety of ships under his command, but he is sometimes in a big ship and may not realise fully how the weather is affecting smaller ships. It is the duty of individual captains to signal the OTC if they expect damage to be caused by maintaining course and speed, particularly at night.

Knowledge of the stability of his ship, and of the various steps that can be taken to improve it, is essential to the seaman if he wishes to preserve her safety in heavy weather. Stability of ships is described in Volume II, Chapter 1, and also in Chapter 1 of this volume.

Precautions

Before leaving harbour the ship should be fully prepared for sea, as described in Volume II, and this work must include the proper securing of everything that is movable, particularly if it is evident that heavy seas will be met as soon as the harbour entrance is passed.

Steps to increase the stability of the ship must be taken in ample time before the weather deteriorates. Such steps include pumping, flooding or ballasting, and jettisoning deck cargo, and clearly they must be done while the ship is still fairly steady otherwise they may endanger her, during the adjustment of stability, by creating free-surface effects of liquids or off-centre loadings.

Consideration of the crew

In heavy weather the Captain and the Officer of the Watch must constantly keep in mind the effects of the motion of the ship upon the members of the ship's company as they go about their various duties. Violent motion may reduce the efficiency of, or slow down, certain operations, such as those concerned with the control of engines or weapons. Seasickness may affect inexperienced men. On exposed decks jackstays should be rigged to help men move forward or aft.

Broadcast the intention to alter course in heavy weather a few minutes before doing so. Men will then be prepared for the new kind of motion; this applies particularly to turning beam-on to a swell. If possible, avoid making alterations of course during meal hours.

When men are working on the forecastle, speed must be reduced to a point at which there is no danger of the ship dipping her bows under. On leaving harbour when a long swell is met but the wind is light, those on the bridge may be deceived as to the amount the ship is likely to pitch. Particular care is required in *Leander* Class and similar frigates, as the generally dry conditions on their forecastles easily encourage a greater sense of security than is justified. Remember that one green sea over the forecastle may sweep men overboard, and that lives have been lost in the past through such lack of foresight.

SEA AND SWELL WAVES

Characteristics of waves in the sea

The formation and action of waves at sea is discussed in some detail in BR 45, *Admiralty Manual of Navigation*. The following are some of the more important facts which emerge:

1. The particles of water in an unbroken wave do not move along with the wave, but oscillate within quite narrow limits, moving upwards as the crest approaches, forwards as the crest passes, downwards as it recedes, and backwards almost to their original positions as the trough passes.

2. Both the length and steepness of waves increase with wind speed, but when the wind rises above 10 knots the rate of increase of height becomes much greater than that of length. No individual wave can, however, attain steepness of more than that which corresponds to a height-to-length ratio of about 1 in 10 without breaking at the crest.

3. A group of waves moves at only half the speed of the individual waves forming the group. Consequently the same wave does not remain the highest of a group, but waves passing through a group attain their maximum height at the centre. 'White horses' do not, therefore, remain on the same waves, and in a simple wave formation a wave only foams

at the crest when passing near the centre of a group. In a cross sea, which is the rule rather than the exception, waves will, however, break more frequently. In deep water, the water forming the broken crest of a wave may be considered as moving forward and downward at about half the speed of the wave.

4. In the most general terms, the fact that a wave attains its maximum height when passing near the centre of a group accounts for the familiar periodic appearance of an extra large wave. The combination of two or more wave patterns similarly results in a fairly regular recurrence of groups of large and small waves, with occasional periods of comparative calm. The number of waves in each group and the interval between successive appearances of extra high groups vary with the type of sea.

An unbroken wave is far less dangerous than a breaking wave. In the former the movement of water is mainly up and down, there being comparatively little forward or backward movement, but in the latter a great mass of water is projected with considerable force forward and downward from the crest; furthermore, a naturally breaking wave is higher and steeper than its unbroken counterpart. An unbroken wave can, however, be broken by impact with the ship, and its potential danger is then nearly as great as the wave which has broken naturally.

Waves running from deep to comparatively shallow water grow steeper and higher and then break up and subsequently re-form into a short, steep sea with breaking waves. If the extent of the shoal water is limited by land a backwash is set up which results in a confused sea with dangerously steep and breaking waves.

A heavy swell caused by a strong and prolonged gale over a large expanse of deep water may travel hundreds of miles without appreciably altering its direction. If it meets seas from a different direction, caused by a local gale, a dangerously confused sea will result.

Broadly speaking, a short steep sea, or a confused sea, is more dangerous to small vessels than to large ships; and conversely, a long, heavy sea is more dangerous to large ships than to small vessels.

Effects of wave motion on a ship

All ships have a natural period of roll and pitch according to their dimensions and conditions of loading.

The *period of roll* is the time a ship takes to roll from one side to the other and back again.

The *period of pitch* is the time the bows of a ship take to rise from the horizontal, fall below the horizontal, and return to it.

The *period of encounter* is the time interval between the passage of two successive wave crests past any given point in the ship.

The movement of a ship in roll or pitch depends on the size of the waves and the relation between the period of encounter and the ship's period of roll or pitch, the greatest movement developing when there is synchronisation. The period of encounter depends on the wave length (which governs the wave speed) and also on the course and speed of the ship relative to the waves. Thus the period of encounter can be varied by alteration of the ship's course and speed.

When the period of the ship is small in comparison with the period of encounter she will tend to ride the waves, keeping her deck parallel to their slope (Fig. 15–1(i)). In a beam sea this will result in rapid, heavy rolling. In a head sea a small period of pitch should result in an easy motion, without much water being shipped.

When the period of the ship is large in comparison with the period of encounter she will roll or pitch independently of the waves. In a beam sea this should mean a comparatively easy motion, though waves slapping against the weather side may make her wet (Fig. 15–1(ii)). In a head sea a comparatively long period of pitch may result in occasional burying of the bows and exposure of propellers and rudder.

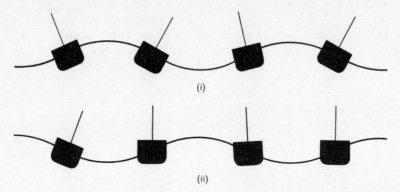

(i)

(ii)

FIG. 15–1. Effect of waves on the motion of a ship

When the period of encounter approaches synchronisation with the period of roll or pitch, the ship's motion will be violent. In a beam sea this may result in dangerously heavy rolling, while in a head sea the severe and rapid pitching movement may cause frequent racing of propellers and unfair hogging and sagging strains.

For a large ship, such as an aircraft carrier, the natural period of roll is about 14 – 15 seconds, and for destroyers and frigates it is from 8 to 10 seconds. Periods of pitch are about half those of roll. As already stated, the period of encounter depends on the length of the waves as well as the speed and direction of the ship, but the values given in the following table, which relate to ships heading into waves of their own length, may be helpful.

PERIOD OF ENCOUNTER FOR SHIPS HEADING INTO
WAVES OF THEIR OWN LENGTH

SHIP SIZE	PERIOD OF ENCOUNTER AT SHIP SPEED OF:	
	15 KNOTS	20 KNOTS
	seconds	seconds
Aircraft carrier (say, 220 m long)	8.2	7.5
Destroyer (say, 160 m long)	6.7	6.0
Frigate (say, 110 m long)	5.2	4.6

An important effect of wave motion on a ship is the loss of stability she suffers as she rides over the crest of a wave. In a ship with a low reserve of stability this may result in a dangerous increase of roll or list, particularly in a high beam-wind.

HEAVY ROLLING — CAUSES AND REMEDIES

Factors contributing to heavy rolling

Light draught. Though a warship is not subject to the great variations in draught of a cargo ship, the effect of expenditure of fuel and ammunition on the propensity to roll may be appreciable. Some ships are fitted with salt-water compensated fuel-storage tanks whereby the expended fuel is replaced by salt water from header tanks, some are fitted with separate ballast tanks, while in others flooding of fuel-storage tanks may occasionally be necessary to avoid weather damage due to excessive rolling.

Free water. The free movement of water from one side of the ship to the other — whether in flooded compartments, below the centre of gravity, or on deck — will increase the period and degree of roll. This effect will be most marked when the free water is high in the ship, e.g. in bulwarked ships with inadequate or inefficient freeing ports. In ships with continuous bulwarks or well decks, such as offshore patrol vessels, the correct functioning of freeing ports is essential to stability in rough weather.

Snow and ice. A considerable coating of snow and ice on rigging, superstructure or on deck will obviously affect the stability of a ship adversely, but to an extent which may not be generally appreciated. For instance, a deposit of 15 centimetres of loosely-packed snow on the flight deck of an aircraft carrier can add a topweight of as much as 70 tonnes, while a coating of 50 millimetres of frozen spray over the exposed area of a destroyer's upperworks may amount to approximately 30 tonnes. When de-icing is impracticable, allowance must be made for the modified sea-keeping qualities of ships in such conditions. For methods of dealing with ice coating see Chapter 17.

Anti-rolling devices

Bilge keels are the simplest form of anti-rolling device, and they are fitted in the majority of HM ships. They are built approximately at right-angles to the hull, at or near the turn of the bilge, and are usually continuous over about half the length of the ship. In general, bilge keels materially decrease the amplitude of roll and slightly increase the period. Their effectiveness increases with the forward speed of the ship, and largely for this reason a ship will usually roll most heavily when stopped and drifting in a beam sea.

Fin stabilisers are fitted in the majority of HM ships. In this system, in its most simplified form, rudder-type fins project almost horizontally through the side of the ship at points near the turn of the bilge on each side. The angle of incidence of the fins to the flow of water past the ship is varied automatically as the ship rolls, the leading edges of the fins on the side which is moving down being turned up, and vice versa. The disadvantage of this system of stabilisation, apart from its complexity and weight, is that the effectiveness of the fins depends on the ship's forward speed through the water, and that their operation involves a small, though appreciable, loss of speed.

Gyroscopic stabilisers have been fitted in some merchant ships and yachts. They are an effective form of stabiliser, but have the disadvantages of great weight and, so far as warships are concerned, the vulnerability of the heavy rotating element. They are not fitted in HM ships.

Anti-rolling tanks, by which the amplitude of roll is reduced by transferring water or fuel between tanks on opposite sides of the ship, have been the subject of experiment since the end of the nineteenth century. Various arrangements have been fitted to ships but the principle is not used in HM ships.

EFFECT OF WIND ON A SHIP

Once a ship has been obliged to reduce to slow speed in a storm the pressure of the wind on her hull will have an increased effect on her handling qualities. The effect is greater if the ship is lightly laden, or is of shallow draught, or has large superstructures. When going very slowly or when stopped, most ships tend to lie broadside-on to the wind, and in exceptionally strong winds it may be difficult to turn them up into the wind, though it may be possible to turn them away down-wind. In a typhoon or hurricane it may be impossible to turn certain ships into the wind, which is one good reason why any seaman avoids such conditions with land or dangers to leeward.

Leeway caused by the wind

The amount of leeway a ship makes in a gale depends on her speed, draught and freeboard, and on her course in relation to the direction of the wind and seas. In winds of gale or hurricane force the leeway with the wind abeam can be very considerable, and may amount to as much as two knots or more, particularly if the ship is steaming at slow speed.

It is a common mistake among inexperienced seamen to make insufficient allowance for leeway, particularly in a prolonged gale when, in addition to the wind, there will be a surface current caused by it. The amount of leeway made by a ship in various circumstances can only be judged by experience, but it is wise to allow a liberal margin of safety when passing dangers to leeward, because cases abound of ships having gone aground through failure to make sufficient allowance for leeway in the course steered.

HANDLING A SHIP IN A SEAWAY

Steaming head to sea

There are three factors to be considered when a ship is heading into a seaway, namely: the force of impact of the waves on her bows; the pitching of the ship and the resultant strains of hogging, sagging and pounding; and waves breaking on board, whether this is caused by their impact with the hull or the pitching of the ship, or both.

The force of impact of the waves varies with the product of the ship's mass and the square of the combined velocity of the ship and the waves, and a small reduction of speed will therefore considerably lessen the force of impact. The larger the area offered to the seas the greater will be the shock of impact, and when ships whose bows are considerably flared, such as aircraft carriers, are pitching, they will be forced to reduce speed sooner than ships with comparatively straight-sided bows. Smaller ships such as frigates and destroyers are liable to incur damage through pounding if driven too fast into head seas; but these ships are designed today with more emphasis on ability to keep up a good speed in heavy weather, and they have higher and longer forecastles than former designs.

The trim of a ship may have a considerable effect on her behaviour when steaming into a head sea. If she is trimmed at all by the head, or if she is heavily laden forward, she will probably pitch sluggishly and tend to bury her bows in the waves. Conversely, if she is trimmed too much by the stern her bows will tend to pay off to one side or the other, and it will be difficult to keep her on her course heading into the seas. The best condition for a ship steaming into a head sea is for her to be trimmed slightly by the stern and lightly laden forward, thus ensuring that her propellers and rudder are well immersed and that her bows are buoyant.

An alteration of speed may have a considerable effect on the pitching of a ship because it alters the period of encounter, but a reduction of speed does not necessarily reduce pitching, nor does an increase of speed necessarily increase pitching. After a reduction of speed on account of the weather the larger ships of a formation are sometimes more uncomfortable and ship more water than their smaller counterparts, and in such circumstances it may be better for the large ships to continue at their original speed but to zigzag, so as to maintain the same speed over the ground as the remainder of the formation. In a short head sea it may be possible to increase speed to a point at which the period of encounter is considerably reduced and the ship rides comfortably over the waves at relatively high speed with little pitching. The decision to order a large speed increase with this result in view is, however, a difficult one to make. If the outcome has been misjudged the ship may sustain damage through pounding, either while attempting the increase or while reducing speed if the attempt is abandoned.

Pitching can sometimes be lessened by altering course so as to bring the seas on the bow, but the resulting motion with both pitch and roll may be more uncomfortable and more water may be shipped. Such action may prove essential, however, in order to prevent the stern being continually lifted out of the water, possibly causing the propellers to race, thus straining the propeller shafts and bearings and the blades of the propellers.

Steaming with the sea abeam
The rolling caused by a beam sea may be so excessive that men have difficulty in keeping their feet, let alone in carrying on with their work efficiently, particularly in a small ship. The best way to reduce the rolling is to alter course so as to prevent the ship's rolling period from being synchronous with the period of encounter. Alterations of speed are unlikely to affect the amount of rolling at all. Ships seldom incur damage to the hull through rolling, but superficial damage to boats or damage caused by seas breaking on to low decks, such as the quarterdeck, may occur. Objects may break loose if they have not been properly secured.

Running before the sea

Running before the sea carries with it certain dangers, but these can usually be avoided by altering the speed and hence the period of encounter. The dangers consist of *broaching-to* or being *pooped* and arise in the following way. If the ship's length is comparable to, and her speed practically the same as, that of the waves, she may find herself running for a considerable time on the crest of a wave. The stern is high in the water, and control by the rudder becomes less effective. If she now pitches on to the forward slope of the wave and the wave breaks, the entire ship is carried forward with the breaking water and she begins to plane along with the wave, or, to use an easily understood expression, she starts *surfing*. The forward motion of the water relative to the rudder and propellers further diminishes steering control, and a yaw may develop rapidly and may be quite impossible to correct. The bow now buries itself deep into the trough and the stern is swung round until the ship lies broadside to the waves. This is the process called *broaching-to*. She now begins to roll heavily, and if a following wave breaks upon her in such a way as to reinforce her roll to leeward, she may be heeled further over and capsize. These stages are shown in simplified form in Fig. 15–2.

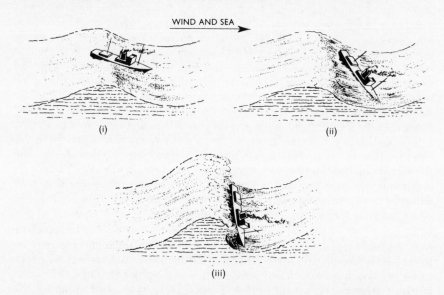

FIG. 15–2. Stages in a vessel being broached-to

If the ship is on the forward slope of a wave that breaks upon her, the water may sweep along her upper decks from aft, causing damage. She is then said to be *pooped* (Fig. 15–3). A ship may be pooped without having lost steerage control, and usually when going slower than the speed of the waves.

Of these dangers it is of paramount importance to avoid surfing and being broached-to; invariably this can be achieved by reducing the speed of the ship to *well below* that of the waves. To be safe, ship speed should be at least 40 per cent below wave speed. For instance, a ship at 20 knots can start surfing on a wave whose speed is 26 knots. A ship may still be pooped if a very heavy sea breaks aboard, and the steering will probably be difficult, but

WIND AND SEA

(i)   (ii)

FIG. 15–3. Stages in a vessel being pooped

many ships have reported that better control is possible and damage can be more easily avoided by steaming down-wind in heavy seas than by attempting to keep head to sea. This applies particularly during replenishment-at-sea operations (see Chapter 16).

To keep the speed of the ship well below that of the waves should not be difficult in a large ship, because waves of 200 metres or more in length usually have a speed of at least 30 knots. Waves of 100 metres and less in length may be travelling at under 15 knots, and in these circumstances small ships such as frigates must watch their speed carefully in a heavy following sea.

If running before the sea towards an estuary or towards shallower water, remember that the waves will become higher and steeper, increasing the danger of broaching-to and adding to it the danger of yawing right out of the navigable channel into shoal water. An attempt to increase speed above the wave speed will involve a period of lack of steering control while the ship's and waves' speeds coincide, and is, in these circumstances, foolhardy.

The possibility of being broached-to or pooped decreases greatly if the length of the waves is either much greater or much smaller than that of the ship. Steering before a heavy sea is, however, always liable to be difficult, and allowance must be made for a certain degree of inevitable yawing on either side of the intended course. Even with bridge steering, constant supervision by the Officer of the Watch is necessary and a reduction of the length of tricks at the wheel may be required. The auto-steering mode, if available, will often prove superior to manual steering in these conditions, provided adequate rudder limits are set.

To avoid being blown along at the speed of the waves small vessels may stream a drogue to reduce their speed and avoid the dangers of surfing.

Turning in a heavy sea
There may be considerable risk in attempting to turn a ship about in a heavy sea, and good judgment is required in selecting the most suitable moment to start the turn.

If you are heading into sea and wish to turn and run before it, the risk of damage will be greatest probably half-way through the turn, when the sea comes abeam. At that moment also the ship will be most reluctant to turn. It has already been mentioned that groups of relatively low waves alternate with groups of higher ones; try, therefore, to get the ship round so that she is beam-on to the sea during one of the calmer periods. Avoid gathering much headway during the first part of the turn, because this may cause heavy pitching. Short bursts of ahead power against a fully angled rudder, possibly combined with reversals of the inner screw, should start the ship turning. From there the turn should be completed as rapidly as possible, using high power for a short time on both screws. The heeling effect caused by relatively high speed in the turn counteracts that due to wind and sea, and makes the ship very stable while turning.

In a following sea, speed should be reduced as far as practicable before starting the turn. Again, if possible, choose a relatively calm period to start the turn and, having got half-way round — which should not be difficult — use plenty of power and full rudder to start the ship turning into the wind. As soon as she starts to answer her wheel, reduce the speed of the engines to the minimum judged necessary to turn her head to wind and keep her there. Be prepared for the ship to roll very heavily to leeward when beam-on to the sea.

HEAVING-TO

The weather may become so violent in the open sea that the performance of the current task, whether it is a passage from one place to another or some operation, must be subordinated to the overriding need to steer and handle the ship in the best possible way to avoid damage and to keep her afloat. The planned course and speed are abandoned and the ship may either run before the sea (see page 460) or *heave-to*. There are, strictly speaking, two ways of heaving-to, the aim in each case being to keep the ship as steady as possible and to prevent seas breaking on board and damaging or flooding her, and, in the last resort, to prevent the ship foundering through flooding or capsizing. The two methods of heaving-to are:

1. Lying with the sea on the bow and steaming ahead at the minimum speed consistent with steerage way.

2. Stopping engines and allowing the ship to drift.

Method 1 — Sea on the bow

The decision to adopt this method may be forced on the Captain because of lack of sea room to leeward. To keep her bows up the ship will require power for a speed of anything from, say 6 to 12 knots, but she may make little headway and even lose ground to leeward. If she has a relatively long and high forecastle the ship may be protected to a certain extent from seas breaking over her decks. The disadvantage of the method is that the engines are being used to drive the ship against the sea, and hence to increase its power to damage her. Heavy pitching and pounding may occur, even if the revolutions/percentage power are reduced to the minimum needed to keep steerage way. Nevertheless, most frigates will find this the safest and most comfortable means of heaving-to. In a ship with a wide flared bow, such as an aircraft carrier, the risk of incurring structural damage forward will be great.

A single-screw ship may find it easier to keep the ship's head up with the wind fine on the port, rather than the starboard, bow because of the sideways force of the propeller.

Method 2 — Drifting with engines stopped

If this method is adopted there must be plenty of room to leeward for the ship to drift. Not only will the wind and breaking seas carry the ship to leeward, but the wind will set up a surface current. The rate of drift in winds of gale force may reach 2 or 3 knots, and at hurricane force it may even reach 5 knots.

It has been argued that if a ship approaches near the centre of a tropical cyclone, this method of heaving-to is the only logical one to adopt because, the sea being confused and not coming from any particular direction, it is impossible to place the ship either head to sea or stern to sea. The use of engines is likely at one moment to push the ship into a huge wave and possibly drive her forecastle under, or at least to cause damage; while at the next moment she may force herself down the crest of a wave approaching from astern and broach-to.

Authentic cases have been reported of ships with engines stopped, successfully riding through, or very near to, the centres of typhoons in the Pacific. In all cases the ships had adequate stability (i.e. metacentric height) and good watertight integrity, and no damage whatsoever was sustained even though pitching and rolling were heavy. When near the centres of the typhoons the ships lay with the wind approximately abeam, but the waves approached from all directions.

Method to adopt

Having considered the above remarks, the Captain, knowing his own ship and her stability and handling qualities, forecasting the future trend of the weather and considering the sea room available, must decide for himself which is the best method to adopt in the prevailing circumstances.

A study of many incidents only serves to demonstrate that similar circumstances do not necessarily produce the same effects, and the presentation of any of these incidents as examples to be followed may only lead to confusion. However, the following paragraphs regarding *Leander* Class frigates are apposite when considering the best approach to bad weather in these and similar ships.

In *Leander* Class frigates it has been found that the worst storms can be ridden out safely and in relative comfort by steaming at minimum speed directly into the sea. Running before the sea has generally been found much less satisfactory, particularly for ships fitted with variable-depth sonar, which are very vulnerable to being pooped.

One such ship, with both steering motors broken down, successfully stayed head to sea in winds up to Force 11 by keeping the engines slow ahead with 100 revolutions set, and by putting the appropriate engine to half ahead when the ship's head began to pay off the wind. In such conditions she made good about one knot directly to windward.

AVOIDANCE OF TROPICAL CYCLONES

Whenever possible the seaman should give a wide berth to a hurricane, cyclone or typhoon because revolving storms of this intensity, especially near their centres, are so violent that small ships may well founder in them and large ships be seriously damaged. Action to avoid such storms should be taken in good time, because once the wind and sea start to rise they usually increase so rapidly that the ship may soon become unmanageable and unable to steer a course for safety. The methods of foretelling the advent of a tropical cyclone and of determining its probable position and course, and the rules for avoiding it, are to be found in NP 100, *The Mariner's Handbook*, which should be studied by every seaman.

SEA ANCHORS

Much has been written about the effectiveness of sea anchors in keeping a vessel head to wind and sea and reducing her rate of drift to leeward, but most of this advice was given in the days of sail when vessels were equipped with heavy wooden spars and stout canvas sails which were eminently suitable for making a sea anchor of effective size. It is doubtful whether a sea anchor of sufficient size to hold any but very small vessels can be constructed with the materials available in the majority of modern ships.

USE OF OIL TO CALM THE SEA

Oil spread in small quantities on the surface of the sea will prevent the waves breaking and damp down the effect of the wind in whipping up the waves into sharp crests. It will not, however, reduce a swell, and its value lies in lessening the probability of shipping water in a heavy, breaking sea. Good results can be obtained from any type of oil, but animal or vegetable oils are more effective than mineral oils, and heavy oils are better than light oils. In cold weather the oil should be warmed to decrease it viscosity. The methods of spreading the oil, either through scuppers or soil-pipes or by means of oil-bags or canvas hoses, are described in Chapter 6. In a single ship, oil is only likely to be effective when drifting with the wind and sea on the beam, and should be distributed through soil-pipes or scuppers, or by oil-bags spaced at intervals of 12 – 15 metres along the weather side.

GENERAL ADVICE ON HEAVY WEATHER AT SEA

From the information given so far in this chapter the reader will realise that no hard-and-fast rules can be laid down relating to the handling of a ship in heavy weather at sea. It depends on the type of ship and her handling qualities, the wind and sea, the room available and other circumstances. Unfortunately, experience shows that there are few generalisations about the behaviour of ships in heavy seas that hold good in all similar circumstances. Cases are on record that show that while the handling of a certain ship in a certain way has proved successful in one instance, yet in another similar instance such handling has apparently led to a ship's foundering. However, it must be emphasised that the design of HM ships always embodies a good margin of safety in stability, and that, by following generally the advice given above, damage can usually — and disaster can always — be avoided. The following summary of this advice, in a series of 'dos and don'ts', may be helpful.

Do

1. Make sure that you are kept informed continually about expected changes of weather.

2. Know the factors affecting the stability of your ship and take steps to improve stability, if necessary, *before* encountering heavy weather. (See Chapter 1 and also Volume II, Chapter 1, on Elementary Stability.)

3. See that the ship is made thoroughly seaworthy before leaving harbour, or before the approach of a storm.

4. Consider the effect of the ship's motion on the activities being carried out by all the various members of the ship's company.

5. Appreciate the signs of an approaching tropical cyclone and take the necessary action to avoid it. (Full information is given in NP 100, *The Mariner's Handbook.*)

6. In a beam sea alter course, if possible, to break the synchronisation of the period of the waves with that of the ship's rolling.

Don't

1. Drive a ship too fast into a head sea — particularly a fast, lightly built ship such as a frigate or destroyer.

2. Fail to reduce speed soon enough in a head sea or swell, through being unable to visualise the consequences or fear of being considered too cautious.

3. Run too fast before a following sea, particularly when the length of the ship and that of the waves are about the same. In these circumstances speed should be reduced judiciously to avoid the grave danger of being pooped.

HEAVY WEATHER IN HARBOUR

Anchoring in a gale

If it is expected that a ship (fitted with two anchors) will have to ride out a strong and prolonged gale both anchors should be used, and they should be let go in such a way that when the ship is riding to the cables the angle between them will be about 20 degrees. To do this the approach should be made with the wind a little before the beam (Fig. 15–4, position *1*) and the weather anchor should be let go first, with headway on the ship. The ship should then be brought to rest when about one-third of the amount of cable intended to be veered eventually has run out (Fig. 15–4, position *2*). At this point the lee anchor should be let go and, with the ship swinging head to wind and drifting to leeward, both cables should be veered and middled at the intended amount (Fig. 15–4, position *3*). While this method of anchoring does make use of the maximum holding power of the two anchors, it also carries with it the danger of getting the cables crossed if the wind shifts direction considerably.

Steaming into the bight of the cables

Having anchored as above in a gale with both anchors down and the cables fully veered and spread about 20 degrees apart, it may happen that despite these precautions the ship starts to drag because of the excessive strength of the wind. A useful expedient in such a case is to steam up to windward between the anchors until the cables are growing aft on either quarter and then to hold the ship there with the engines going slow ahead. Further

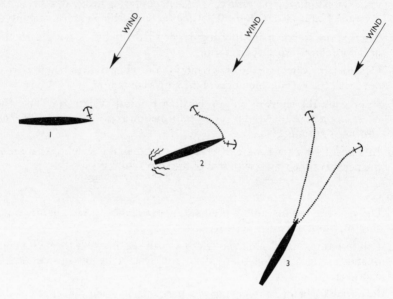

FIG. 15–4. Putting down two anchors in a gale

dragging is prevented and with the constricting effect of the cables it is a fairly simple matter to keep the ship stationary and head to wind until the weather moderates. While maintaining position in this way, take the precaution of fixing the ship's position frequently.

When at single anchor in a gale

If your ship is suddenly overtaken by a gale when at single anchor, the first precaution to take is to veer enough cable to ensure that the stresses of yawing or pitching are absorbed as much as possible by the spring in the cable and that the cable is exerting a horizontal pull on the anchor. At the same time the main propulsion machinery should be brought to immediate notice, an anchor watch set, and the second anchor prepared for letting go.

Even in a very steady gale a ship will not always point dead into wind, and yawing is started by the wind blowing on one side of the ship when she is not heading into wind, so causing her to sail through the water. The combined actions of the wind and the pull of her cable will make the ship yaw, first to one side and then to the other, her stem tracing a figure-of-eight path, as shown in Fig. 15–5. From this illustration it will be seen that the ship presents a large windage area throughout the greater part of the yaw, thus increasing the strain on the cable. Furthermore, an extra heavy load is imposed as the ship rides up on her cable and then falls back at the extremities of her yaw. Ships with their superstructure disposed forward and with a deeper draught aft than forward are more prone to yawing than ships with

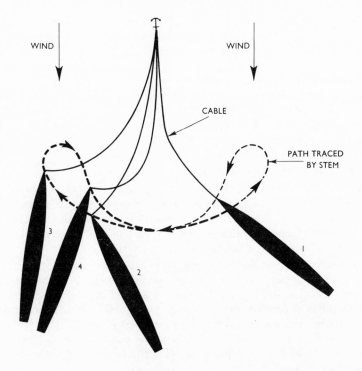

WIND

WIND

CABLE

PATH TRACED
BY STEM

3

4

2

1

FIG. 15–5. Ship at single anchor in a strong wind

their superstructure amidships or aft and trimmed on an even keel. Yawing to any marked degree may cause the anchor to drag and should therefore be prevented when practicable.

Opinion differs among experienced seamen on the best method to check a yaw. Some let go the second anchor underfoot at the middle of the yaw and hold it at short stay, so that the pull of the anchor as it drags along the bottom helps to check the yaw. Others let it go when the ship reaches the limit of her yaw to that side which is farthest from the first anchor. They then veer both cables until the second anchor has sufficient cable to enable it to hold, and the ship then rides to both her anchors. If circumstances allow, however, and if there is a probability of dragging, it is best to steam ahead to a position close abreast the first anchor, drop the second anchor, and then ride to both cables veered an equal amount.

Weighing a single anchor in a gale

If the anchor is being weighed because the ship is dragging in a gale, the anchor may begin to come home well before it is weighed and the ship may begin to drift rapidly to leeward. The engines should then be put ahead boldly and the ship steamed to windward, towing her anchor along the bottom until she is in a position to weigh it and then to anchor again or proceed to sea.

When the ship is dragging at single anchor *beam-on* to a strong gale it may be difficult to get her head to wind to weigh anchor. In these circumstances, if sea room allows, the engines should be put ahead and the ship steamed round her anchor. The drag of the anchor on her bow should bring the ship up into the wind, when she can steam to windward of her anchor and then drift down on it while weighing. In ships with high bows and their superstructure disposed well forward, and in ships with fixed underwater fittings forward, this method may prove impracticable, and the only alternative is to attempt a similar manoeuvre but by going astern instead of ahead and relying on the tendency of all ships to bore up stern to wind when moving astern.

Weighing both anchors in a gale

If both anchors are down in a gale, either the cables should be middled with a fair amount out on each, or one of the anchors should be underfoot. The anchor underfoot can be weighed without difficulty, and this should be done as soon as the wind moderates or begins to back or veer, so as to avoid getting the two cables foul of one another.

If the cables are middled the best method is to heave in both cables together so that both anchors will be weighed simultaneously. If the cables have originally been spanned at 20 degrees this should present no difficulty, and if the ship has dragged so far as to draw both cables together into alignment with the wind, this method will still give the best chance of getting them both up without fouling one another. Thus, if the amounts out on each cable are not equal, it will probably pay to middle the cables first before starting to heave them in together.

Emergency action

If a gale warning is received when in an anchorage where the holding-ground is none too good, where there is little sea room to leeward, or where other ships are berthed nearby, it is best to weigh and anchor again with both anchors in a clear berth well up-wind, or if this impracticable to proceed to sea.

If at anchor in a gale, it may be impossible to weigh because of lack of sea room to leeward with the ship already dragging, and the only safe course in this case may be to slip the cable or cables and proceed to sea. When slipping a cable, the end should be buoyed to enable it and the anchor to be recovered subsequently, the wire-rope buoy pendant used being of sufficient strength to recover the cable.

Approach of a tropical cyclone

If warning of a typhoon or a hurricane is received when the ship is in harbour, the decision whether to ride out the storm or put to sea depends largely on the type of ship, the nature of the holding-ground or strength of the moorings, what sea room is available, and the proximity of the storm and its probable course. If it is decided to put to sea the decision must be made in good time so that the ship may make a good offing and so have plenty of sea room to leeward when the storm overtakes her. It is often inadvisable to put to sea when the storm arrives, because when the ship leaves the shelter of the harbour she may meet mountainous and confused seas set up by the backwash from the coast.

Ships secured to buoys have successfully ridden out a typhoon by using their engines to ease the strain on both bridle and mooring. The buoy is fixed in position and well in sight from the bridge or forecastle, so there should be no danger of overriding the bridles or getting out of position, but the bridles must be kept under a steady strain if possible with no jerking.

Provided there is plenty of sea room to leeward and the ship is not moving into any dangers or into very deep water, dragging in itself does not always call for drastic emergency action such as slipping the cables. Ships anchored in wide bays or open anchorages have dragged slowly and steadily for several days at the rate of about a mile a day without harm while riding out a prolonged gale. Dragging, however, should be avoided because it imposes heavy loads on the cables as the ship rides up and then falls back on them. A method of preventing dragging, by steaming up into the bight of the cable, is described on page 465.

Leaving a head buoy in a gale

If buoy work is impossible, the cables must be broken on deck and the bridles slipped. The strain on the buoy mooring is likely to be such that the buoy will spring back well clear of the ship on slipping, so that there will be no difficulty in avoiding it if the engines are put ahead at once.

Leaving head and stern buoys in a gale

When it is practicable to slip the stern wires and swing to the bow buoy the problem is simple, but in harbours where head and stern moorings are provided it is unlikely that there will be much swinging room. There may also be occasions when it is possible to slip the bow buoy and swing to the stern buoy before proceeding; but more often, when the wind is broad on the beam or abaft the beam, it will be preferable to slip both buoys simultaneously. Every precaution must be taken to ensure that there is no delay at either end, and that the propellers are not fouled by the stern wires or slip rope.

Leaving an alongside berth in a gale

The most difficult situation will be when the wind is blowing on to the jetty. Although tugs may succeed in hauling the ship clear, she will not be able to move ahead or astern so long as they are pulling, for fear of girding them. The essence of the problem therefore is that the ship should be hauled sufficiently clear to ensure that she does not drift back on to the jetty during the period when she is slipping the tugs and gathering way. If a fore spring proves ineffective, a small ship may be able to cast her stern well out by running a wire from right forward to a point well inside the jetty (Fig. 15–6). When the engines are moved astern, the bows will be hauled into the jetty and the ship will pivot on them as she tries to align herself with the pull of the wire. She will gather sternway more rapidly on slipping than she would do if a fore spring had been used, and she is therefore less liable to scrape her bows heavily on the jetty before getting clear. When an anchor has been let go in the process of berthing, the manoeuvre is considerably simplified, but even so the assistance of a tug is essential if the wind is of gale force.

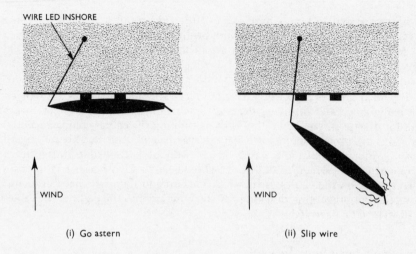

WIRE LED INSHORE

WIND

(i) Go astern

WIND

(ii) Slip wire

FIG. 15–6. Method of getting a small ship away from a jetty with the wind blowing on

CHAPTER 16

Handling Ships while Replenishing at Sea

A description of the methods and gear used for replenishment at sea is given in Volume II. This chapter deals with the problem of how to handle the ship during the process, and the officers of all HM ships and RFAs should read it in conjunction with the advice given in the latest edition of ATP 16, *Replenishment at Sea*, and its UK Supplement. Normally the delivering ship maintains a steady course and speed. The receiving ship approaches her and keeps station either *close aboard* (i.e. steaming abreast the delivering ship at a distance of 25 to 55 metres) or alternatively *close astern*. In neither case are towing or breast lines used, and station is kept entirely by the handling of the ships. The stores, ammunition, fuel or personnel are passed from the delivering to the receiving ship by means of special rigs which are slung between the two ships if they are close aboard (abeam method) or are towed in the water if the receiving ship is astern (astern method). Thus the shiphandling problem is essentially that of approaching very close to another ship, keeping station there for a period that may extend to more than an hour, and then of disengaging.

The differences in water pressure around a moving ship produce forces of acceleration, deceleration, attraction and repulsion between two ships steaming close aboard, or approaching this position: these forces are generally referred to as *interaction* between ships. The forces must be understood and taken into account if collision is to be avoided during replenishment at sea. This chapter deals first with the problem of interaction, then with shiphandling during replenishment by the abeam and astern methods, and finally with the use of liferafts for transferring men or stores in heavy weather when helicopters are not available.

INTERACTION

Some seamen are inclined to consider the difficulties arising from interaction as overstressed. Those with successful experience of handling ships when close aboard are naturally inclined to minimise the difficulties. Serious accidents have occurred through lack of understanding of interaction, or by not making sufficient allowance for its effects. The effects are more pronounced in shallow water and, at normal replenishment speeds, they should be expected to appear if the depth of water is less than 30 metres; at speeds of 15 knots or more, greatly increased interaction effects can be expected up to depths of 40 metres.

Interaction involves many complicated interrelationships, not all of which have been fully explored. Here it is intended to provide a simple explanation to give officers sufficient knowledge to enable them to avoid endangering their ships.

Theory of interaction

The pressure in the water around a ship under way is very different from that when the ship is at rest. Hydrodynamic theory indicates that the pressure is increased near the bow, reduced over the midships portion and increased again near the stern. These three main regions are shown in Fig. 16–1.

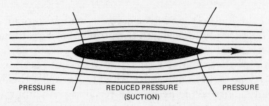

PRESSURE   REDUCED PRESSURE   PRESSURE
                      (SUCTION)

Fig. 16–1. Regions of increased and reduced water pressure around a ship under way at sea

Lines known as *stream-lines* are also shown in Fig. 16–1. In considering stream-lines it is convenient to regard the moving body as at rest and the water as flowing past it. The stream-lines denote the path of individual particles of water, and indicate that those passing near the body are diverted by it into curved paths. The quantity of water flowing between each consecutive pair of lines is the same — thus when the stream-lines are close together the cross-sectional area is reduced and the speed of flow is increased. The particles of water can only move more quickly by the impetus from high pressure to low pressure, and conversely. Thus whenever the speed is greater the pressure is reduced and vice versa. In the case of a single body, the velocities and pressures are the same on each side and there is no resultant force acting sideways. However, when two bodies close together are under consideration the diagram of the stream-lines is altered as shown in Fig. 16–2. Amidships the lines are crowded together; the velocity is increased

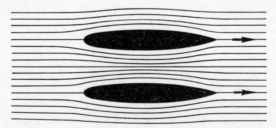

Fig. 16–2. Stream-lines around two ships close aboard at sea

and the pressure reduced so that there is an attraction or suction between the two bodies. At the bow and at the stern the stream-line spacing is greater; the velocity is reduced and the pressure increased.

It appears, therefore, that two symmetrical bodies moving through the water abreast one another would be drawn together because of the zone of reduced pressure lying amidships between them. In the case of two ships steaming close aboard this mutual attraction inwards is accompanied by a turning moment tending to force each stem outwards, probably caused by the bow pressure-zones being opposite one another. If the rudder was left amidships in each ship they would each immediately adopt an angle of yaw outwards, which would produce a force tending to pull them apart because of the water pressure between them. In fact, as the ships approach the close-aboard position the steering is adjusted as necessary to maintain station, and it is found that when they have settled down abreast one another they are carrying some inward wheel and also have adopted a very small angle of yaw outwards.

While approaching the close-aboard position on parallel courses the two ships overlap one another and the pressure zone of one will lie opposite the suction zone of the other. This state of affairs, in either the approach or departure, upsets the stream-line pattern and no exact data are available as to where the boundaries of the pressure and suction zones lie — indeed, they may move as the ships move relative to each other. It is known, however, that in these attitudes larger turning moments arise, which tend to turn the ships, in addition to the forces of attraction and repulsion — and furthermore these turning moments change direction suddenly with only a small change in the relative positions of the ships. This necessitates a rapid change of rudder from one side to the other in order to maintain course while passing through these attitudes when approaching or disengaging.

So far the action of the propellers has not been mentioned. Again, no firm data are available on this topic but it is considered, however, that the effects of propeller action on the interaction between two ships proceeding steadily on parallel courses are probably localised and unimportant.

Interaction between two ships passing close aboard

The stream-lines and pressures can be determined mathematically for oval shapes and also for sharp-ended shapes approximating to ships. It is not yet possible to calculate the forces on a ship exactly from theory, because the shape of a ship cannot easily be expressed mathematically. However, assurance is afforded by experiments using models that the steam-line systems of mathematical shapes exhibit the leading features of the pressure and suction zones around actual ships.

The interaction effects between two ships passing close aboard on parallel tracks are shown in Fig. 16-3. The two sets of curves show the yawing moments and side forces experienced by two ships as one ship A overtakes a larger ship B from the left of the diagram. The values were obtained by experiment using models and, although both ships are large, the same kind of effects would be observed when any ships pass close aboard in this fashion.

It should be noted from Fig. 16-3 that the yawing moments and side forces change in magnitude and direction during the manoeuvre. The side forces on the two ships change more-or-less together whereas the yawing moments change at somewhat different positions.

As A approaches B from astern the effects of interaction are felt even before the bow of A passes the stern of B (position 1); both ships experiencing a bow-inward yawing moment and a force of repulsion. These effects reach a maximum soon after A passes position 1, and then rapidly decrease as A moves farther forward. The effects change direction more-or-less together soon after the midship point of A passes the stern of B (position 2) but the yawing moment of A remains bow-inward rather longer than that of B.

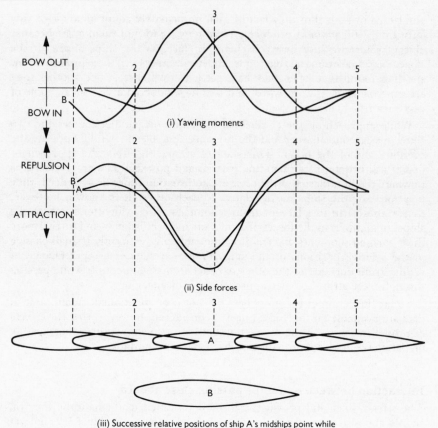

(i) Yawing moments

(ii) Side forces

(iii) Successive relative positions of ship A's midships point while
overtaking ship B

FIG. 16–3. Interaction effects when one ship A passes close aboard
a larger ship B

As A moves forward towards the abeam position (position 3) the effects
on both ships are a bow-out turning moment together with a side force
of attraction, and these effects apply for some distance fore-and-aft of
position 3.

When A moves still farther forward the yawing moments and side forces
reduce and then reverse in direction becoming bow-inward and repulsive
respectively on both ships. The effects reach their maxima as the midship
point of A passes the bow of B (position 4) and they progressively reduce
until, at some stage after the stern of A passes the bow of B (position 5), they
become negligible.

In addition to the yawing moments and side forces, both ships experience
changes in resistance to ahead movement resulting from interaction. When
abreast each other (position 3) both ships probably experience a moderate
increase in resistance. If ship A drops back to position 2 it will experience
a reduction in resistance and if it moves forward to position 4 it will experience
an increase. These two effects can be visualised by considering the smaller

ship A to be riding down the face of the stern wave of ship B when in position 2, and climbing up the rear of the bow wave in position 4. For these reasons this variation of resistance is sometimes called the *up-hill and down-dale* effect. Similarly it can be seen that when moving either forward or aft from position 3, the smaller vessel is approaching a pressure zone created by the larger vessel (see Fig. 16–1) which tends to oppose the relative movement of the vessels. The magnitudes of these changes of resistance depend on speed and separation between the two ships, and the power required to maintain station when very close aboard can be as much as 40 per cent above that normally required for the speed when proceeding singly.

From this description it can be seen that any change in speed, separation or fore-and-aft position will lead to changes in yawing moment, side force and resistance. Continuous particular attention must be paid to helm angle, heading and shaft revolutions/percentage-power, all of which need adjustment to maintain or shift relative position.

Dangerous positions

During the approach and disengaging phases of the overtaking manoeuvre it must be noted that at some positions a bow-in turning moment occurs in combination with an attractive side force. The magnitudes and directions of the moments and forces are changing rapidly in these positions and both ships have to make rapid changes of helm to maintain the correct track. These are potentially dangerous positions because, for example, a steering-gear failure would result in a movement of the ships towards each other.

It is not possible to state the exact locations of change-over from bow-out to bow-in turning moments, or from attractive to repulsive side forces, for particular pairs of ships. However, the interaction effects decrease quite rapidly as separation between the ships is increased, and thus they become more manageable. For these reasons the following precautions should be observed.

1. When overtaking from the quarter, take a path which is not too close to the other ship.

2. When replenishing, adopt a position close to the relatively safe abeam position (i.e. position 3 of Fig. 16–3). The fore-and-aft extent of this position is quite small and the data available suggest, for a warship that is about three-quarters of the length of a replenishment ship, that her midship point should remain between $\dfrac{L}{10}$ forward and $\dfrac{L}{5}$ aft of the midship point of the replenishment ship (where L is the length of the replenishment ship).

3. If it is necessary to replenish from a position where the bow or stern of the smaller ship extends beyond the bow or stern of the larger ship (i.e. the vicinity of positions 2 and 4 of Fig. 16–3), great caution should be exercised. In such cases the separation distance should be kept as great as possible commensurate with an efficient transfer, and the approach should be made from abeam in preference to overtaking on a parallel track.

Summary of interaction effects

The results of the experiments using models on which Fig. 16–3 is based were confirmed by a series of sea trials by three different ships, of destroyer and larger size, and a replenishment ship. The abeam position was found to be generally satisfactory for replenishment because the tendency for the bows to be forced apart increased as the ships closed and thus constituted a safety factor. When approaching or disengaging from the abeam position the ships passed through potentially dangerous positions where the effects of interaction could only be avoided if the separation was increased sufficiently for the ships to be outside the zone of interaction.

The extent of the zone of interaction and the strength of the effects vary with the size, shape and speed of the ships and with the depth of the water. Thus it is difficult to give a general rule for the avoidance of interaction effects when the very nature of the abeam replenishment manoeuvre is conducive to their production.

The forces of interaction are proportional to the square of the speed but, because of the improvement in steering control at higher speed, substantially the same rudder angles are required for station-keeping at any speed between about 10 and 20 knots. However, at the higher speeds less time is available for the correction of mistakes. In shallow water, moreover, the strength of the interaction effects is greatly increased. Frigates refuelling from large tankers have experienced marked interaction effects at 45 metres but generally effects are experienced by small ships when within about 15 metres and by large ships when within about 30 metres of one another. Advice on approach, station-keeping and disengaging is given later in this chapter, and guidance on working-distance apart for HM ships and RFAs appears in ATP 16, *Replenishment at Sea*.

GENERAL CONSIDERATIONS

Choice of course

In winds below Force 5, ships can usually fuel or transfer stores when steaming in any direction. However, if the abeam method is being used it may be an advantage to have the wind and sea slightly on the bow of the delivering ship, or of the larger of two ships, so that small ships such as frigates can replenish from the opposite side and thereby gain some advantage from the lee.

In winds above Force 5, ships can use the astern method if they wish, and this may be advisable for inexperienced crews, because the ships are not in such close proximity as when abeam and the results of steering or conning errors are not so hazardous. However, replenishment astern generally takes longer than abeam and if the hose-line carries away the tanker has to haul in all the gear in order to bend on another line. In heavy weather there is also the possibility of damaging hoses with the forefoot or bilge keels.

Choice of course in heavy weather

The abeam method does not suffer from the disadvantages of the astern method and has been successfully used in very heavy weather. The course recommended in winds above Force 5 is down-swell or down-sea because the ships are generally steadier and men do not have to work with the ships plunging into the seas, with water rushing over the decks and with spray flying everywhere.

It is absolutely essential that the speed chosen is such that the ships' speed is well below the speed of the waves. If the difference is too small there is the very real danger of surfing (see Chapter 15). If this occurs, a small ship may suddenly find herself, in a matter of seconds, on a wave-top a full ship's length ahead of her proper station and losing steering control. Although a reduction of replenishment speed of even one knot may cure this tendency, a reduction to at least 4 knots slower than the speed of the waves is recommended.

When approaching a tanker from the quarter in a following gale, the sight of both ships wallowing and lurching in different troughs can be alarming. When the receiving ship gets abeam at about half a cable, however, both ships are in the same trough, the situation is more comfortable and the receiving ship can finally edge in. Small ships have successfully replenished abeam in the Atlantic down-wind in a full gale at a speed of 10 knots.

Choice of speed

Generally speaking, it is advisable to carry out replenishment at speeds of between 10 and 15 knots. Weather, naturally, influences the choice of speed, as it does the choice of course. Speeds of less than 8 knots are not recommended, because steering control is then greatly diminished. To allow a margin for station-keeping, the speed of the force when replenishing should *not exceed* 1 knot less than the delivering ship's maximum speed, or 2 knots less than the receiving ship's maximum, whichever is the lower.

Replenishment abeam can be conducted safely at speeds of up to 18 knots between warships or if using a fast supply ship. But remember the warnings that at these higher speeds greatly increased interaction effects occur in depths less than about 35 metres and that there is less time available for the correction of mistakes.

Command and control

It is obvious that steering when close aboard must be of the highest standard. The Officer of the Watch should ensure that an experienced helmsman is at the wheel, and should vigilantly supervise his steering. The secondary steering position should be manned, to permit a rapid change-over in the event of failure of the primary system. Some captains prefer to take control personally of both the steering and the revolutions/percentage-power during the approach, and possibly while keeping station during the replenishment. Others have found that it is an advantage for one officer to attend to the revolutions/percentage-power and another to the steering, in the way described below under 'ABEAM METHOD'.

The *distance line* is described in Volume II, and the markings on the line should comply with the instructions given in ATP 16. The line is used to assist in judging the distance between the two ships, by day and by night.

If the replenishment is prolonged those responsible for conning and steering are under considerable strain, and fatigue may cause errors. Steps can be taken to minimise this by arranging reliefs at frequent intervals. A minor point, but one worth considering, is to avoid choosing a course having the same or similar figures to the revolutions, e.g. steering 105 degrees at 106 revolutions per minute. The changes ordered in steering may get transposed with those for speed, with unpleasant results. Another pitfall that has caused difficulties is the danger of ordering a course ten degrees in error after a prolonged period close aboard, e.g. when the replenishment course is 140 degrees, ordering 'Steer 149 degrees' when 139 degrees is intended. To avoid such errors it is preferable, when convenient, to select a replenishment course ending in 5 so that the first two figures are nearly always the same when station-keeping close aboard.

In some ships it is considered useful to have a board prominently displayed on the compass platform, showing the course and revolutions, ordered and attained, and kept up to date by the Navigator's Yeoman. All ships are required to keep a record of wheel and engine orders either in Form S.580, *Wheel and Engine Order Record Book* or by means of a tape recorder.

The use of the auto-pilot may be considered in favourable weather and in the light of the experience of the officers concerned. In particular, where the steering may be adjusted from the bridge wing by means of a portable plug-in unit, the auto-pilot has successfully been used for abeam replenishments.

ABEAM METHOD

Approach

The waiting position will usually be on the beam or fine on the quarter. The approach from abeam is best made by first taking station about one cable on the beam of the delivering ship, and then closing gradually from there. A 5-degree alteration inwards and a slight increase of speed will close the gap to 30 metres or so within a few minutes. A closer approach is not necessary for establishing contact by gun line, and interaction effects may be felt inside this distance. A more spectacular approach with bolder alteration inwards will save little time and could be awkward if misjudged; moreover, the result may well be unsettling to the delivering ship and to ships replenishing on her other side.

The approach from fine on the quarter is normally made with a speed advantage of about 8 knots. The difference between replenishment and approach speeds should not exceed 10 knots. (This advice does not apply to gas-turbine powered ships which can decelerate rapidly under positive control and for which special advice is given in BR 45(4), *Admiralty Manual of Navigation*, Volume IV.) In all cases it is important to make the approach sufficiently far off the track of the delivering ship to avoid interaction, and to allow room for correction of any sheer that may develop. The more shallow the water or faster the speed, the greater should be the distance off track.

In order to avoid interaction effects while the ships are overlapping during the approach, *a track separation of less than 30 metres should never be attempted.* Remember also that some deterioration in steering control will certainly be felt as speed is reduced. Single-screw ships should order 'Slow ahead', rather then 'Stop' or 'Slow astern', to reduce speed when coming in to the replenishment position.

It should be noted that a ship is extremely vulnerable if she reaches a position on the bows of the delivering ship and intends to drop astern to the abeam position. If speed is reduced without some alteration of course outwards to counteract the bow-inward yawing moment, she is liable to yaw inwards and fall across the bow of the delivering ship.

Aircraft carriers normally replenish on their starboard sides, whether delivering or receiving, so that operations can be seen from the bridge. If it is necessary for one of these ships to replenish on her port side she should become the guide.

Track separation when approaching from the quarter

When approaching from fine on the quarter, over-estimation of the separation between the tracks of the receiving and delivering ships can cause the receiving ship to reach a dangerous position during the final stages of the approach. A principal factor contributing to collision is usually found to be the receiving ship estimating the separation to be greater than it really is. Gauging, by eye, the distance off the delivering ship's wake can be useful when taking up the waiting position on the quarter, but it does not provide the greater accuracy needed during the final stages of the approach.

There are two methods by which correct track separation may be obtained during approach:

1. Radar parallel index (Fig. 16–4).
2. Observed range and angle between the delivering ship's course and her bearing observed from the receiving ship (Fig. 16–5).

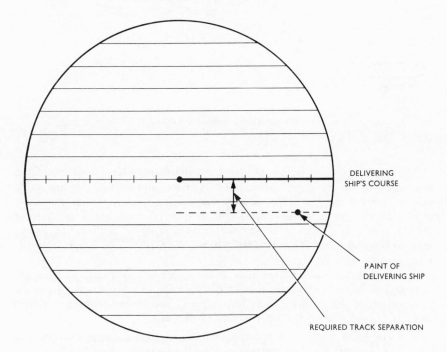

DELIVERING
SHIP'S COURSE

PAINT OF
DELIVERING SHIP

REQUIRED TRACK SEPARATION

FIG. 16–4. Track separation by radar parallel index method

RADAR PARALLEL INDEX METHOD (Fig. 16–4)

The display to be used should be checked for bearing accuracy and linearity, and the radar index (range) error must also be known. Measurement of separation will be required at very short ranges, therefore the display and possibly the receiver may need adjustment to give the optimum picture.

A pecked line is drawn on the display, parallel to the delivering ship's course and at a distance from the centre equal to the required separation. The approaching ship then sets or adjusts its course to maintain the 'paint' of the delivering ship on the pecked line throughout the approach.

OBSERVED RANGE AND ANGLE METHOD (Fig. 16–5)

The track separation is calculated from the range and bearing of the delivering ship and knowledge of its course. The range may be measured by one of the following.

1. Stuart's distance meter.
2. Vertical sextant angle using the Distance by Vertical Angle tables in *Norie's Tables*.
3. Radar.

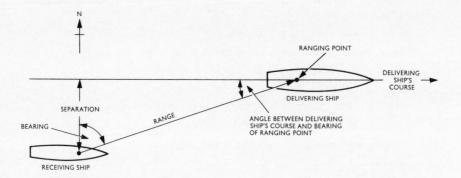

FIG. 16–5. Track separation by observed range and angle method

The *angle* required is that between the delivering ship's course and the bearing of the point being ranged upon. The exact point may not always be easy to observe but the more accurate the bearing the less will be the effect of any compass error. When practicable, it is worth while crossing astern of the delivering ship and observing the exact bearing of her heading before making the approach. The separation in metres can then be found from the table on page 481.

By entering the table horizontally at the range and vertically at the angle obtained at each observation, the track separation in metres is shown at the intersection of the co-ordinates. The stepped line on the table is provided as a rough guide for a track separation of 50 metres.

If a graphical method of interpreting the observed range and angle is preferred, a graph may be constructed from the figures of the table, as shown in Fig. 16–6. When the graph is covered with a transparent surface the

TRACK SEPARATION BY OBSERVED RANGE AND ANGLE
(Separation in metres)

Range yards	cables	\(\) 1	2	3	4	5	6	7	8	9	10	11	12	13	14	15	16
								Angle (degrees)									
100	½	2	3	5	6	8	10	11	13	14	16	17	19	21	22	24	25
200	1	3	6	10	13	16	19	22	25	29	32	35	38	41	44	47	50
300	1½	5	10	14	19	24	29	33	38	43	48	52	57	62	66	71	76
400	2	6	13	19	26	32	38	45	51	57	63	70	76	82	88	95	101
500	2½	8	16	24	32	40	48	56	64	72	79	87	95	103	111	118	126
600	3	10	19	29	38	48	57	67	76	86	95	105	114	123	133	142	151
700	3½	11	22	33	45	56	67	78	89	100	111	122	133	144	155	166	176
800	4	13	26	38	51	64	76	89	102	114	127	140	152	165	177	189	202
900	4½	14	29	43	57	72	86	100	115	129	143	157	171	185	199	213	227
1000	5	16	32	48	64	80	96	111	127	143	159	174	190	206	221	237	252
1100	5½	18	35	53	70	88	105	123	140	157	175	192	209	226	243	260	277
1200	6	19	38	57	77	96	115	134	153	172	190	209	228	247	265	284	302
1300	6½	21	41	62	83	104	124	145	165	186	206	227	247	267	288	308	328
1400	7	22	45	67	89	112	134	156	178	200	222	244	266	288	310	331	353
1500	7½	24	48	72	96	120	143	167	191	215	238	262	285	309	332	355	378
1600	8	26	51	77	102	128	153	178	204	229	254	279	304	329	354	379	403
1700	8½	27	54	81	109	136	162	189	216	243	270	297	323	350	376	402	428
1800	9	29	57	86	115	144	172	201	229	257	286	314	342	370	398	426	454
1900	9½	30	61	91	121	151	182	212	242	272	302	331	361	391	420	450	479
2000	10	32	64	96	128	159	191	223	255	286	317	349	380	411	442	473	504
yards	cables	1	2	3	4	5	6	7	8	9	10	11	12	13	14	15	16
Range								Angle (degrees)									

required track separation for any approach may be drawn as a vertical line with limit lines on either side, and the observations may be plotted during the approach.

Correct station

If ships are of similar size, interaction effects are least noticeable when directly abeam; and if ships are of greatly dissimilar size, the effects are least noticeable when the smaller ship is in the intermediate area between the bow and stern pressure zones of the larger ship (see also page 475). Although the precise position of one ship relative to the other during replenishment will be influenced by the positions of the gear in both ships, great care must be taken to ensure that one ship is not stationed close to the boundary between the high and low pressure zones of the other ship, especially when the ships are of greatly dissimilar size. Furthermore, it must be remembered that the

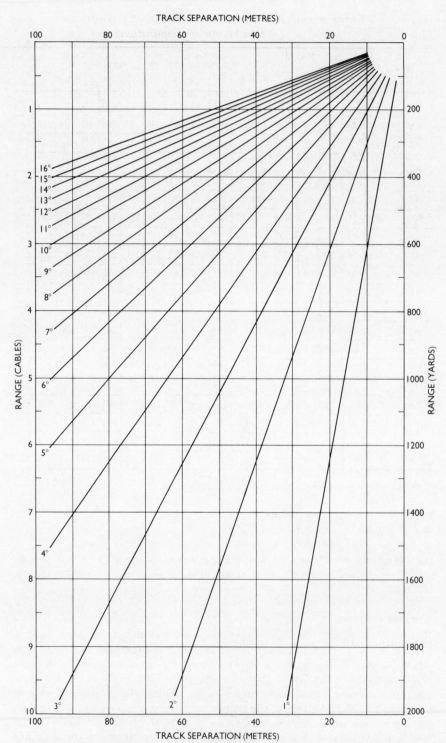

FIG. 16–6. Graphical method of determining track separation by observed range and angle

positions of these boundaries vary with distance apart, dimensions and hull forms of the ships, courses and speeds of the ships, depth of water, height of sea or swell, and the relative directions of wind and sea.

Maintaining station

Usually the receiving ship keeps station on the delivering ship, but there may be occasions when the receiving ship is the less manoeuvrable of the two and the reverse procedure is then preferred. It is of the first importance that the ship being stationed on maintains a steady and accurate course and speed.

Station-keeping close abeam is generally considered to be simplified if two officers are employed: one watches the distance line and adjusts the course, and the other adjusts the speed (either by reference to a mark in the other ship, or the transit of two marks, or by reference to the angle which the distance line makes with the side of either ship). In most ships it is the practice to have the distance line well forward, so that it will indicate a sheer before the distance apart of the ships at the pivoting point has changed. The officer responsible for the course will find it necessary to watch the compass continuously, and to make a frequent check of the helmsman's reactions by noting the movement of the rudder indicator. He must remember that whenever the rudder or course is adjusted, in order to overcome interaction effects, it is probable that the revolutions/percentage-power required to maintain station will also have to be altered.

In good weather conditions by day, station-keeping should present no problem, provided that the importance of using small rudder angles and gradual adjustments of revolutions/percentage-power is appreciated. The course should be steered by compass, and direct rudder orders should not be given except in emergency. Speed adjustments of $\frac{1}{4} - 1$ knot should normally suffice for station-keeping in low sea states.

Keeping station in rough seas is much influenced by the choice of course, and the remarks on this subject earlier in this chapter should be noted (see page 476).

Night replenishment, whether in peace or war, is usually carried out with ships darkened. It is generally found that station-keeping is easier when neither ship is showing any bright sources of light to cause glare and confuse the judgment of distance. A small pin-light forward to indicate the fore-and-aft line from the Pelorus may be helpful in the receiving ship.

Alterations of course

When alterations of course by a force are ordered, individual replenishment units may alter course in steps of 5, 10 or 20 degrees, as ordered by the control ship. Methods of communication include telephone between the bridges of the ships, visual signalling and radio.

Disengaging

Disengagement is best effected by a *slight* alteration outward and a *slight* increase of speed. Although it may be sufficient for the disengaging ship to put her rudder amidships (if she has previously been carrying inward rudder) it is usually better to order a course a few (1 – 5) degrees outwards together with a speed increase of a knot or two to keep abreast the other ship until well clear. Large alterations of speed and large rudder angles should not be used when within half a cable or so of the other ship because the effects are liable to be felt by her and by other ships replenishing from her. The practice of disengaging by a large increase of speed on the present course is particularly objectionable since it may result in a dangerous yaw inwards by the disengaging ship which could prove disastrous.

When disengaging it is important to keep a lookout for traffic astern and on the disengaged side.

Very close aboard

Situations very close aboard (less than 15 – 30 metres depending on the sizes of vessels concerned) should be avoided by keeping a suitable distance off track when approaching from fine on the quarter, by good station-keeping when close aboard, and by altering course away in small steps when disengaging. If a bolas or a heaving line is used to make initial contact, the line should be hove from the windward ship.

In the event of a ship inadvertently finding herself very close aboard or even in an alongside collision, small alterations of course and speed will best suffice to extricate her. Indeed, should a vessel find herself alongside and approximately abeam the replenishment ship, the ships are likely to be forced apart if speed is matched (to minimise damage) and the rudder left amidships. However, in some cases more drastic measures may be required — a prime example is that of a vessel finding herself very close aboard and forward of the pressure and suction zones of a larger ship. Interaction may cause the smaller ship to be accelerated and thereby pushed towards a position close to the stem of the larger, where there is every danger of an enforced yaw across her bows. In this situation the best action may be to order 'Slow ahead', 'Stop' or even 'Slow astern' on both shafts, followed by a resumption of replenishment speed after dropping astern clear of the bow pressure area. It is better to accept the chance of an alongside collision by this manoeuvre than to risk being forced across the stem of the other ship. This principle applies to vessels of all sizes but it is particularly important in the case of a small vessel near the bow of a larger one where the interaction forces may change rapidly and substantially for only minor changes of external influences (see page 481).

ASTERN METHOD

Approach

In the astern method, the normal manner of passing the hose from the delivering ship is by streaming a line with a float on the end, the line being grappled from the receiving ship's forecastle. In this method the approach is made from right astern. Having grappled the hose line, the receiving ship steams ahead and heaves it in. By the time the hose-end reaches the fairlead the marker buoy should be abreast her bridge (Fig. 16–7). This marker buoy is veered by the delivering ship to such a distance that when it does come abreast the receiving ship's bridge the hose will be towing in a bight of about 30 metres.

An alternative method of passing the hose is by gun line, the receiving ship closing the delivering ship's quarter to establish contact. Care must be taken not to overlap excessively, nor to get too close, as interaction effects are particularly noticeable in this position and especially when reducing speed to drop back again to the astern position. Obviously, the gun line method is not practicable when other ships are already replenishing abeam on each side.

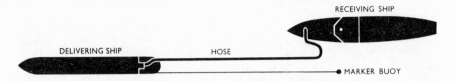

FIG. 16-7. Replenishing by the astern method

Maintaining station

Station-keeping in the astern method is simplified and safer due to the reduction of interaction effects. However, it is not necessarily easier, particularly when exercised down sea and swell if the wave length is such as to cause the receiving ship alternately to close and drop astern of the delivering ship. Furthermore, when hauling the hose end inboard the ship should try to hold a position such that the hose is introduced at nearly 90 degrees to the ship's side and not too steeply, and should avoid falling astern. Once connected, slightly larger margins for station-keeping ahead and astern exist for the astern method than for the abeam method. It is essential, however, to maintain the blight of the hose as narrow as possible, and steering must be carefully watched. The wider the bight the greater the strain on the hose. On the other hand, it is essential to avoid at all costs touching the hose with the forefoot because, if there is any motion on the ship, even a graze is liable to part the hose or damage it.

Speed

In the astern method, speed is restricted by the strength of the hose, but provided the bight is kept fairly narrow — not more than about 12 metres across — speeds of up to 13 knots should be practicable in calm weather. Rough seas will bring greatly increased strains on the hose and station-keeping will be more difficult. Speeds exceeding 10 knots should not normally be attempted when pitching heavily.

Alterations of course

When a single ship is replenishing by the astern method, no special procedure is necessary for altering course. When ships are replenishing astern and abeam simultaneously, it will be necessary to signal alterations in steps, as previously described.

Disengaging

When the hose has been passed by the float method, the receiving ship disengages by dropping astern, veering the bight of hose line as she goes. But she should only drop astern 6 – 9 metres, otherwise there is a danger of parting the gear on the forecastle.

If the gun-line method has been used, the receiving ship must regain station on the quarter of the delivering ship in order to pass back the hose line.

TRANSFER BY INFLATABLE LIFERAFT

In heavy weather at sea, if conditions are too rough for boatwork and a helicopter is not available, a small inflatable liferaft affords a safe and practical method of transferring small quantities of stores or men between two ships under way but stopped. The liferaft is rigged with an outhaul which is passed over to the receiving ship by the delivering ship which retains a similar inhaul. The raft is normally dropped by means of a trip-hook on a purchase slung from a suitable derrick, such as a general-purpose/ammunitioning derrick. Unless specially strengthened, the liferaft should not be hoisted with the load still on board. Details of the rig required are given in Volume II, while the following remarks deal with the handling of the two ships during the transfer.

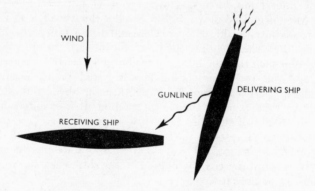

FIG. 16–8. Transfer by liferaft — the approach

The receiving ship remains stopped, lying beam to wind and sea with no way on her. The delivering ship may then approach down-wind and down-sea, passing close to the stern of the receiving ship (Fig. 16–8). As the stern of the receiving ship is passed a gun line is fired to her, and while this is being checked away the delivering ship is brought to rest and held stern to wind and sea. Alternatively, while the ships manoeuvre in the same manner, it may prove easier to fire the gun line from the quarterdeck of the receiving ship across the forecastle of the delivering ship. The delivering ship is then manoeuvred as necessary to keep her stern reasonably clear of the other ship.

The gun line is followed over by the outhaul, and as soon as the strain comes on the outhaul the raft is slipped and veered across on the inhaul to the lee side of the receiving ship (Fig. 16–9). If the stern of the delivering ship now falls off the wind in the direction of the receiving ship (Fig. 16–10) it may be difficult to use the engines to correct this without fouling the gear.

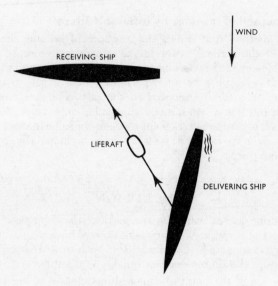

FIG. 16–9. Transfer by liferaft — the transfer

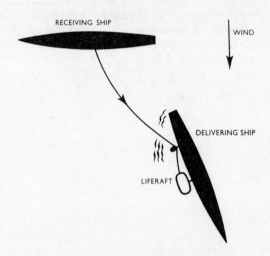

FIG. 16–10. Transfer by liferaft — the recovery

To avoid this difficulty, snatch blocks should be placed in one or two positions abaft the derrick and sufficiently high up on the engaged quarter to enable the inhaul to be snatched in and kept clear of the water when necessary. The use of a derrick situated more nearly amidships than right aft has the advantage of keeping the gear well away from the propellers.

When the transfer has been completed the liferaft should be hauled back (Fig. 16–10) roundly until it is under the derrick of the delivering ship. If the derrick is amidships the delivering ship will now be free to work her engines so as to give a slight lee to the hoist, but should avoid getting beam-on to the wind because heavy rolling will make recovery more difficult.

Alternative method of transfer by inflatable liferaft

An alternative method that avoids the nuisance of keeping the inhaul and outhaul clear of the screws, is for the delivering ship simply to drop the liferaft two cables or so down-wind of the receiving ship and then get clear to windward. There must be an experienced man in the raft, wearing a lifejacket and with a lifeline secured to the raft. The receiving ship then approaches the raft down-wind, stops alongside, embarks the load and gets clear. The delivering ship may then approach in the same manner and recover the liferaft. At night the raft must be fitted with a light and the crew provided with a waterproof torch.

CONCLUSION

While replenishing at sea warships are particularly vulnerable, because of their limited manoeuvrability. Time spent on replenishment is not available for active operations against the enemy. For both these reasons it is clearly desirable that ships should replenish as quickly as possible.

On the other hand, the point of replenishing at sea is to keep ships at sea and minimise their time in shore bases. If collisions occur or gear is damaged through faulty shiphandling, ships will be obliged to return to base for repairs and the aim of the operation will be frustrated. Efficiency is not achieved by speed if it is at the expense of sustaining unnecessary damage. It may therefore be unwise to insist upon too much competition between ships to reduce replenishment times, especially if they have only recently worked up.

CHAPTER 17

Ice Prevention and Handling Ships in Ice

This chapter deals with two related subjects: first, the dangers and prevention of ice accumulating on the superstructure, and second, the handling of ships in sea ice. Warships are not generally designed for operations in ice and should usually try to avoid it. However, on certain occasions it may be essential for them to enter the ice, and the aim of the latter part of this chapter is to advise on how to minimise the hazards entailed.

Other references which enable a more detailed study of ice are: the *Sailing Directions;* NP 100, *The Mariner's Handbook;* and ATP 17, *Naval Arctic Manual.* These publications provide information on the characteristics and extent of ice in the various Arctic and Antarctic regions, ice navigation, weather conditions in high latitudes, and preparations for service in icy conditions. All of these sources should be consulted if operations are planned for sea areas where ice may be expected; Fig. 17–1 gives a dramatic illustration.

F IG. 17–1. Typical North Atlantic iceberg shown with HMS *Bermuda,* a World War II, *Fiji* Class cruiser (length overall 169.3 metres)

ICE ACCUMULATION

Ships operating in high latitudes must be prepared to deal with heavy icing of the superstructure, weather decks and exposed equipment. Under certain conditions sufficient ice can form very rapidly on the upperworks to create a stability hazard, and there are many recorded cases of ships having capsized and been lost with all hands from this cause.

Causes of ice accumulation

Ice accumulation may occur from three causes.

1. Fog, including fog formed by evaporation from a relatively warm sea surface, combined with freezing conditions.

2. Freezing drizzle, rain or wet snow.

3. Sea spray or sea water breaking over the ship when the air temperature is below the freezing-point of sea water (about -2 °C).

It is not often that conditions 1 and 2 cause the accumulation of a heavy weight of ice, but under certain conditions moisture may freeze rapidly on every part of the ship, causing the formation of dangerous topweight on masts and aerials in a few hours. The phenomenon is sometimes called *black frost* or *black ice*. The Officer of the Watch must be on the lookout for this, particularly at night. There may not be time to use the methods of ice removal described below and the only remedy may be to steer quickly away from the area towards warmer air.

It is more common for condition 3 to cause ice accumulation, particularly when strong winds continuously blow much spray or heavy seas over a vessel in temperatures of -2 °C or lower. Frigid winds may blow at gale force for days on end, and the only prudent course may be to steer towards warmer conditions, or to seek shelter, or at the least to steer down-wind for a period and at the same time mobilise all hands to clear the ice.

Dangers of ice accumulation

The danger of additional topweight caused by ice on masts, etc., resulting in loss of stability, is perhaps the most serious. However, there are also the dangers of injury to men by slipping on icy decks or being struck by falling ice which has broken away from aloft. Added to these hazards are the difficulties of handling and working iced-up gear and equipment. Radar aerials and similar apparatus may be damaged by the load of ice formed on them. Methods of combating the dangers consist of: means of preventing the ice forming or, if formed, preventing it adhering to structures; and means of removing the ice when formed.

ICE PREVENTION

Housings, shields and covers

Housings and shields are made to protect armament and other mechanical equipment from exposure to heavy spray. Ships are designed and constructed in a manner either to prevent water entering exposed deck equipment such as davit pedestals, lockers, etc., or to permit rapid drainage. If housings or shields are impracticable, covers of waterproof canvas or PVC are supplied, or should be made up, to cover capstans, windlasses, winches, etc., and exposed parts of armament such as missile launchers and close-range weapons.

For boats' falls it is possible to make a canvas sleeve to cover both blocks when the boat is hoisted. The sleeve should be open at the bottom end, and have a slit through which the hauling part of the fall is led away. It should fit snugly over the upper block so that it can be left in place while the falls are worked. Blocks for signal halyards can be protected with similar covers. Such covers should be coated with a de-icing dressing as described below, and they should be dry when it is applied.

Heating of bridge windows

Screens of special multi-ply glass, heated by means of a fine electric element embedded during manufacture, are generally fitted to the enclosed bridges of HM ships. A power of about 1.5 kilowatts per square metre of exposed glass is sufficient to prevent ice formation under the worst weather conditions likely to be met. Power-operated wipers and fresh-water sprays are also used in conjunction with these heated windows.

De-icing systems and steam heating

In older ships steam heating coils were fitted in certain places to assist in keeping selected weather-deck doors, and exposed armaments and equipments free of ice.

Nowadays selected watertight doors giving access to the weather decks are recessed into the ship's structure to prevent a build-up of ice hindering their operation. Some equipments which are particularly sensitive to icing-up are designed with fitted de-icing systems. These arrangements consist of a tank containing anti-freeze solution which can be heated and then circulated by pump through a pipe system surrounding the parts to be de-iced.

Electric heating

In some ships steam is not available for heating, and in others its use is considered uneconomic or impracticable; as an alternative, electric heating is used. The heating arrangements may be incorporated in the design of particular equipments, but in many cases power is provided at convenient sockets for use with portable heaters. These sockets are fitted to many types of armament, at motor-boat stowage positions and boat booms for warming engines, at stowage positions for mobile cranes, on the fixed structure adjacent to signalling projectors and for any other exposed mechanisms where heating is considered necessary.

Counteractive dressings

Dressings may be applied to surfaces where shielding or heating would be too complicated. These dressings do not prevent the ice from forming but they do prevent it sticking, so that it is easy to remove without damage to the underlying structure. Dressings are not necessary on surfaces bounding heated compartments because the ice layer nearest to the plating melts and ice removal is as easy as if the surface had been dressed.

The following dressings are available:

Grease LG–380. This is used for the lubrication of the mechanisms of armaments, such as guns and torpedoes, at extremely low temperatures but not directly exposed to the weather. It should be liberally applied to prevent water entering the mechanism and freezing there. Exposed mechanisms so lubricated and any openings on equipment should be protected by canvas covers as described on page 490. These covers should be dressed with Grease LG–380 on both sides when dry before use, and they should be re-dressed as necessary when in use.

Grease XG–274. The exposed working surfaces of all weapon and other equipment should be thinly coated with this grease so that snow and ice can be easily removed. If it is found that the grease is too thick at extremely low temperatures, it may be thinned by the addition of a small proportion of mineral vaporising oil (MVO) which should be thoroughly mixed with the grease.

De-icing defrosting fluid. Although described as a fluid this dressing is in fact a compound which is used to protect coarser mechanisms. Such items as the working parts of anchors and cable gear, roller fairleads, door hinges, valves, ventilators, davits, etc., which are directly exposed to spray should be covered with the compound. This dressing is not easily washed off and so it can be applied before leaving harbour. The compound cannot be brushed or melted but should be applied by hand or with a trowel. On plain surfaces the film should be as thin as possible. The compound has no lubricating properties and therefore mechanisms and joints requiring lubrication should first be packed with Grease LG–380 and then covered completely with the compound.

De-icing paste (Kilfrost Marine Paste) can be used for the treatment of large surfaces such as bridge superstructures, gun housings, etc., and for some items of deck machinery. It is a soft mineral jelly that stiffens on exposure to air. It is unnecessary to use it on surfaces bounding heated compartments, as explained above.

Other dressings are provided for particular purposes, e.g. the treatment of exposed missiles and aircraft. Details of these materials and the manner of their use are given in the handbooks related to the equipment.

Precautions. No de-icing dressings should ever be used on cordage. Decks, with the exception of flight decks (see particular instructions below), should not be treated because of the hazard of producing a slippery surface. Any steel wire rope used for hoisting which has been frozen should be thoroughly inspected when thawed in accordance with the instructions given in Volume II.

Removal of dressings. As much as possible of the dressing should be scraped off and the remainder wiped off with rags soaked in MVO. Particular care should be taken to preserve bare steel parts immediately after such treatment because they will rust rapidly.

Treatment of flight decks

In contrast to other decks, flight decks must be treated to maintain sufficient friction for the safe securing, handling and operation of aircraft. The method is briefly described below and full details are given in BR 766A, *Helicopter Operating Handbook (for Ships with Flight Decks)*.

Ice is prevented from forming on flight decks by the application of proprietary anti-icing fluid in solution with urea and water. The solution is sprayed to wet the deck with a very thin even covering. The process is repeated as required but at least every 24 hours in temperatures below freezing-point. Care must be taken that subsequent treatments do not cause slipperiness through a build-up of the anti-icing chemical. Should ice have already formed the deck can be de-iced by using a hot (65 – 80 °C) solution. Where ice forms from over-dilution with snow, it does not bond to the deck and is easy to remove, in contrast to untreated areas.

Ringbolts for securing aircraft, and other fittings such as hinges and clips, are treated with neat, or almost neat, anti-icing fluid, and further applications should be made every 24 hours in adverse weather. Care must be taken to prevent the fluid spreading to the deck and creating a slippery surface.

ICE REMOVAL

By hand

Ice can be broken away and chipped off, using mallets, ice picks and spikes, scrapers and stiff brooms. Caution must be used to avoid damage to metal surfaces such as chains, reels, stanchions or railings. Special care must be employed around electric cables, missile launchers and gun mountings, and other machines or mechanisms. With this method, block ice can be removed by splitting it with sharp-pointed ice picks or spikes which are supplied to ships. Generally, hand-picks weighing about 1.25 kilograms are supplied for clearing large accumulations of ice around launchers, capstan fittings, etc., while ice-spikes with 1.2-metre handles are designed for use in clearing superstructures. The handle of the spike should be shortened as necessary for use in removing ice on decks, while sailmaker's prickers of suitable length should be used in confined spaces where the pick is not suitable.

Very little effort is required to detach large blocks of ice by this method. The procedure is to mark out a line of cleavage with the spike or pick, by jabbing it into the ice a number of times close together; then, by a deeper penetration of the implement in the line of cleavage at one or two points as necessary, split off the block. A narrow channel should first be cleared and then the blocks split off into the clear space, working progressively over the surface.

By hose

Sea water, when applied by hose with standard branch-pipe nozzles, is effective in cutting through and assisting the removal of block ice. Ideally the water temperature should be at least 50 °C but few ships have salt-water heating arrangements; however, with water temperatures down to −1 °C the method is still effective. The normal pressure of the salt-water main is generally suitable but, to maintain a solid jet of water, the pressure should never fall below 2.75 bar (40 lb/in^2). With greater pressures the effectiveness of this technique is appreciably increased, and a nozzle of large diameter will give better results than one of small diameter. The jet should be played on the surface of the block ice until a slot of penetration is achieved. Large masses of ice can then be dislodged easily by playing the jet on the joint line of ice and steel until the adhesion is broken. Dislodged ice must always be removed quickly and not be allowed to build up on the decks.

When using this method all scuppers and drains must be clear to allow a free passage overboard for the water. Caution must be exercised in extremely cold weather because any tendency of the water to freeze will simply add to the ice accumulation.

De-icing of guns

Guns can be fitted with a special harness incorporating a cordtex fuze. The harness is placed over the barrel, and if ice forms on top of it, the ice can be split off by firing the fuze. Thus guns can be prepared initially by fitting the harness in harbour, and later cleared of ice immediately before they are required for action. The harness consists of a canvas muzzle and a number of securing bands which fasten, by means of quick-release buckles, round the barrel. The securing bands are linked by longitudinal strips to which the cordtex fuze is attached. This type of harness is suitable for guns of 76-mm calibre and larger.

Hot air

Moderately hot air (180 °C) tapped from the compression stage of turbine-driven fire pumps can be effectively used for the removal of ice. This method is advantageous for use around instruments and other areas where chance of damage makes other techniques inadvisable. The jet may also be used to undercut or slot other ice so that it can be removed easily by manual means.

Steam jet

As with hot air, a steam jet may be used around instruments, etc., or as an occasional aid to manual methods. Its big disadvantage is its rapid consumption of fresh water.

TYPES OF SEA ICE

As already stated, warships are not generally designed for operations in ice, therefore the following remarks apply only to the rather limited operations in ice likely to be encountered by warships not specially fitted for working in such conditions. The descriptive terms for ice in its many forms are given in NP 100, *The Mariner's Handbook*; ATP 17, *Naval Arctic Manual*; and the *Sailing Directions*. Nevertheless, it may be helpful to begin by restating some of the more common definitions together with remarks on their effects on shiphandling.

Frazil ice. Fine spicules or plates of ice suspended in water. The first stage in the freezing of sea water.

Grease ice. A later stage of freezing than frazil ice when the crystals have coagulated to form a soupy layer on the surface. Grease ice reflects little light, giving the sea a matt appearance.

Slush. Snow which is saturated and mixed with water on land or ice surfaces, or as a viscous floating mass in water after a heavy snowfall.

Shuga. An accumulation of spongy, white ice-lumps a few centimetres across; they are formed from grease ice or slush and sometimes from other ice rising to the surface.

Frazil ice, grease ice, slush and shuga are of little hindrance to navigation although the ship's speed for given revolutions/percentage-power will be reduced. Circulating water inlets, if near the surface, may become choked. Bottom logs and other underwater equipment need not be housed, though a towed log becomes useless. These forms of ice should not be confused with *brash ice* which is an accumulation of floating ice made up of fragments not more than 2 metres across and is the wreckage of other forms of ice.

Pancake ice. Predominantly circular pieces of ice from 30 centimetres to 3 metres in diameter, and up to about 10 centimetres in thickness, with raised rims due to the pieces striking against one another. It may be formed on a slight swell from grease ice, shuga or slush, or by the breaking of other types of ice. It also sometimes forms at some depth, at an interface between water bodies of different physical characteristics, from where it floats to the surface; it may then rapidly cover wide areas of water. In an area of pancake ice the pieces are usually crowded together, but with unfrozen water in the many spaces between their points of contact.

The majority of HM ships will not be able to maintain their normal cruising speed in pancake ice without risk of damage to plating. If forced under the ship this type of ice may damage a bottom log or sonar dome and can bend or break a propeller blade. It is impracticable to use any form of towed sweep in pancake ice.

Floe. Any relatively flat piece of sea ice. Floes are subdivided according to horizontal extent as follows:

Giant	—	Over 10 kilometres ($5\frac{1}{2}$ miles) across
Vast	—	2 – 10 kilometres ($1 - 5\frac{1}{2}$ miles) across
Big	—	500 – 2000 metres across
Medium	—	100 – 500 metres across
Small	—	20 – 100 metres across
Ice cake	—	Less than 20 metres across.

Lead. Any fracture or passage-way through sea ice which is navigable by surface vessels.

Polynya. Any non-linear shaped opening enclosed in ice. Polynyas may contain brash ice and contain or be covered with other types of weak ice, e.g. frazil ice, grease ice, slush, shuga, etc. In submarines the polynyas are referred to as *skylights*.

Pack ice. Term used in a wide sense to include any area of sea ice, other than *fast ice* (i.e. ice which remains fast along the coast), no matter what form it takes or how it is disposed. See Fig. 17 – 2.

The description of pack ice in a defined area is determined by its *concentration* which is the ratio, in tenths, of the area actually covered by ice to the total area under consideration.

Pack Ice

Description	Concentration	Remarks
Open water	Less than 1/10	A large area of freely navigable water. When no sea ice is present the area is termed *ice free* even though icebergs may be present.
Very open pack	1/10 to 3/10	Water predominates over ice. Sometimes referred to as *drift ice*.

FIG. 17–2. Typical Antarctic icebergs surrounded by pack ice

FIG. 17–3. HMS *Endurance* working through Antarctic pack ice

PACK ICE *(cont.)*

DESCRIPTION	CONCENTRATION	REMARKS
Open pack	4/10 to 6/10	Floes not generally in contact with one another, and with many leads and polynyas. See Fig. 17–3.
Close pack	7/10 to 8/10	Floes mostly in contact
Very close pack	9/10 to less than 10/10	
Compact pack	10/10	No water visible
Consolidated pack	10/10	Floes frozen together

In very open pack ice the majority of floes are of greater size and age than pancake ice but are more widely separated, so that the area of clear water is greater than the area of ice. The floes are often soft and in a state of decomposition and they may have relatively hard underwater spurs caused by the melting back of the exposed ice.

HANDLING SHIPS IN ICE

Very open pack ice should be treated with respect, and when the larger floes cannot be avoided they should be approached with caution. Small pieces broken off icebergs, known as *bergy bits*, are much harder than pack ice of any kind and should be avoided, whether in open water or mixed in a field of pack ice. They can usually be distinguished by their more blue appearance compared to that of the pack ice.

In open pack ice a ship can be navigated with caution through the leads between the floes.

In close pack ice the floes are mostly in contact and will block the passage of any but specially strengthened vessels.

Deliberate and routine passages through pack ice should only be attempted by specially equipped vessels, but more or less impromptu operations in very open pack and open pack ice may be required of any class of ship. The majority of HM ships are quite unsuited for forcing a passage through close pack ice, and it must be clearly understood that when such conditions are discussed in subsequent paragraphs, the circumstances in which a ship is compelled to adopt these ice-breaking tactics are assumed to be dictated by emergency.

Poor visibility and ice are common partners. Unstrengthened ships should not penetrate an area with ice if the visibility is poor, as a hazardous situation could very easily arise without sufficient warning to avoid it.

DAMAGE FROM ICE

Shiphandling in ice is best approached by an examination of the type of damage liable to be incurred by a warship in these exceptional conditions. The chief source of weakness is the bow plating which in general, except at very slow speed, will be unsuitable for impact with larger masses of hard ice greater in thickness than 30 centimetres. Although thicker floes may be pushed aside, a large and unyielding floe is liable to bend the stem, or may tear open the plating as the ship slews around after impact. The majority of floes are at least one metre thick and, unless composed of very soft ice, cannot be penetrated with safety.

Propeller blades are very liable to bend or fracture from impact with ice, though in some warships they are so deeply immersed that only an up-ended floe is dangerous. On the other hand, the majority of warships are fitted with multiple screws, which are much more liable to damage than a centre-line screw. Similarly, twin rudders are a great disadvantage when working through ice. Trim by the stern is usually advisable to obtain deeper immersion of propellers and rudders, but an extreme 'bows-light' condition will have an adverse effect on manoeuvrability and should be avoided. Bilge keels are liable to be wrenched away from the hull on impact with ice forced under by the ship's advance. Other hull projections such as scupper guards, eye-bolts, and even rivets, may also be the cause of serious leaks.

In the extreme case of the ship being beset in the ice, the square cross-section of the average warship's hull will render her particularly liable to be crushed.

USE OF RADAR TO DETECT ICE

Modern marine navigational radars will detect ice well. Large icebergs will be detected at ranges commensurate with their size but it will be rarely possible to distinguish them from small islands and vice versa. When bergs are drifting in open water, the speed of drifting is almost imperceptible. Even quite small icebergs will create a radar shadow behind them as observed from the ship. At short range a berg may effectively create a shadow area over a very wide arc, thus any field of icebergs will always look less dense with increasing distance from the ship than is actually the case. Leads between icebergs may appear to be present on the radar display whereas, in reality, they do not exist.

On short range scales, even small pieces of ice will show up well on a modern radar set though detection ranges may be of the order of a mile or so. Sea clutter may well obscure ice contacts.

As a general rule, unless local experience permits a better assessment, ships should seek to avoid hitting, at any speed exceeding dead slow, any piece of ice which is detected by radar.

Pack ice will usually be detected by radar at a range of 4 – 5 miles but the detection range may be as low as 3 miles or even less depending on the thickness, density and sea clutter. There is therefore little time to reduce speed before entering the ice unless early action is taken. Hence it may well be better to turn away until a more reasoned decision can be taken, whether or not to enter the pack. Pack ice will first show as a thin line, often curved, of small contacts across the radar screen. This may not initially be recognised as the edge of a field of pack ice, especially if, in the preceding hours, as is likely, thin tails of small pieces of ice have given similar echoes during the approach to the ice field itself. Because the echoes from pack ice appear less numerous after the first mile or so into the field (a form of radar shadow), one may be led to the conclusion that the pack ice is less dense farther in. This is invariably false and it is very difficult to assess the nature, density and extent of a pack ice field from radar information alone. When surrounded by pack ice, radar is of no use to detect leads in the pack — even if one is detected it is likely to be erroneous because of the radar shadow effect described above. However, bergs in the pack and larger bergy bits will be detected at their normal ranges.

OPERATING IN PACK ICE

Reconnaissance

The leads and lines of weakness in the pack can best be seen from aloft, and it is therefore recommended that an extempore lookout-position should be rigged as high aloft as possible. Every use should be made of helicopters, if available, for reconnaissance, and observers should be carefully briefed. The helicopter track should be followed on the ship's radar so that a local chart of ice conditions relative to the position of the ship can be constructed using the helicopter's reports whilst in the air. Experience suggests that, from the air, pack ice looks less difficult to penetrate than it actually is. A helicopter should therefore always look at the ice from bridge height as well as from several hundred feet so that the scale of the ice can be more easily deduced. Conversely, from a ship's bridge the first view of pack ice may give the impression that it will be difficult to penetrate. As the ship closes the edge of the pack, so the density of the ice will become more apparent.

Operations in very open pack ice

Obviously the only effective way of avoiding damage is to avoid contact with the ice. This may be possible at slow speed in very open pack ice with large areas of clear water between the floes. When the floes cannot be avoided they can often be fended off with long staves. This may not be practicable from the forecastle, because of its height, but should be quite feasible from the quarterdeck, where it is of particular importance owing to the tendency for ice to be drawn in under the counter, especially when the ship is swinging. An extempore propeller-guard rigged at the waterline on each quarter may give some protection, but effective securing arrangements will be difficult to fit. Wooden catamarans, with their outer corners faired off, have been tried, but these are liable to up-end and foul the propellers in much the same manner as a floe.

Very open pack ice may sometimes be soft, so that floes will break up readily with little risk of damage to the ship's hull. Nevertheless, if other considerations permit, evasive action should be the rule. The behaviour of an up-ended floe is unpredictable, and although the ice may not be sufficiently hard to cause direct damage to propellers or rudders, large masses jammed in the vicinity of the 'A' brackets, or between rudder and hull, or on the rudder itself, can be the cause of a breakdown. A propeller dragged through the water for any considerable period is liable to accumulate debris, and the opinion is sometimes expressed that the blades are more liable to fracture when stopped than when turning slowly. Certainly in much ice it will be better to keep the propeller rotating, as it will act as a guard for the rudder, so that only pieces of ice which have been cut up by the propeller will be allowed to pass. In such conditions it is advisable to use only a few degrees of rudder.

When conning the ship in pack ice, it is often difficult to keep even roughly to the desired track. Many leads will take the ship substantially away from the desired course. It is preferable, therefore, to choose as a local headmark either a conspicuous point of land or an iceberg in the distance. Reference to the headmark will assist the conning officer to choose those leads which favour the intended track.

Shiphandling in very open pack ice is largely a matter of careful conning at moderate speed. At high speed, greater concentration and skill are required to avoid the floes, and a small error of judgement may result in serious damage. In this connection it should be noted that 'full speed' in the majority of publications on ice navigation refers to a maximum speed for the average small merchant vessel of some 10 to 12 knots.

This emphasis on manoeuvrability when working in very open pack ice leads to the conclusion that large warships are decidedly unsuitable even for these comparatively easy conditions. Destroyers and frigates also, by reason of their light construction and projecting propellers, come in the category of vessels which are best kept clear of any area of ice unless operational requirements justify the virtual certainty of damage.

Working through open pack ice

When working through open pack ice the need for manoeuvrability is of even greater importance, because the requirements are then not only handiness in negotiating tortuous leads rather than individual floes, but also the ability to select the best points of cleavage and the capacity to back and fill readily.

Working through close pack ice

Pack ice is continuously in motion under the influence of wind, tidal stream, or current. As a result of the varying movement of adjacent masses, there will be a tendency for cracks and leads to open and close from hour to hour and day to day. Swell will also tend to break up the ice, and in narrow or shallow waters the vertical movement of the tide will have the same effect. Conversely, this complex movement of the ice will result in areas of pressure, with the formation of ridges. Entry into an area of ice which is verging on close pack is therefore a step which, in an unprepared ship, should never be taken without preliminary reconnaissance. The choice of the point of entry will be governed primarily by the position of the nearest suitable lead or area of open water.

Breaking through an area of close pack ice

If a ship's destination lies within or beyond an area of close pack ice, there may be a choice of entering the ice from either the windward or leeward side. The latter is preferable, because the ice there will be less concentrated and the sea calmer. Although the dangers of entry into the windward side of the pack may not appear too formidable at the time, it should be assumed that ice conditions in that area are deteriorating and that pressure is building up. When there is no lee, consider lying off and waiting for a change of wind. Entry should be made at the lowest speed that will give steerage way, but once the bow is in the ice and cutting it or pushing it to one side, revolutions/percentage-power should be increased again to avoid losing headway. The ice should always be entered on a course perpendicular to the line of its edge, and the same rule applies when breaking out of the pack into open water.

Once in the pack, the ship will often move in the direction of least resistance, irrespective of the position of the rudder. Bursts of power against full rudder may frequently be necessary to keep her head in the required direction and to prevent the stern swinging against the ice. Do not gather sternway into ice which has closed in astern. Except in specially strengthened ships, movements astern through ice must be avoided.

The ship's bow should never be forced into a narrow lead between large floes if there is any movement tending to bring the floes together. Either one floe should be pushed away to widen the lead, or a part of one floe should be broken off to achieve the same object.

In an unprotected ship it is inadvisable to force on through ice which is becoming so concentrated that the ship seems unlikely to be able to leave a clear lane astern of her. To continue in such conditions may result in the ship being brought to a standstill and yet unable to manoeuvre herself astern, or she may be nipped between two floes. It is better to stop and await more favourable conditions. By so doing, possible damage will be avoided, fuel will be saved, and in all probability no time will be lost. The decision whether or not to keep going is influenced by operational requirements and by whether the ship is entering or breaking out of the ice. If the ship has just entered the ice and it is early in the summer season, it is best to stop and wait; whereas if it is near the end of the season, or if there is only a little way to go to reach open water, it is advisable to keep going. In restricted visibility and at night the ship should always be stopped, since the best direction in which to work can no longer be seen. Even with powerful ice lights it is not recommended to work in close pack at night.

Echo sounders are virtually useless when operating in close pack ice because of the excessive disturbance around the transducers caused by pieces of ice. Ships should not, therefore, attempt to force a passage through pack ice which covers an ill-surveyed area where warning of rocks and shoals cannot be guaranteed.

Stopping in the ice

When stopping, a patch of clear water should be chosen, if possible, and the ship laid alongside the ice so that the wind keeps her against it. No ice anchors are required in these circumstances, and any closing-in of the ice due to the wind will be seen in good time. If no clear water is available the ship should be stopped between small floes rather than large ones, so that if the ice subsequently closes up under pressure, some of the pressure will be absorbed by the small floes rafting or being forced under the ship. Once the ice has met under the ship the danger of being damaged by the pressure is greatly diminished.

Unless it is unable to proceed, the ship must never be stopped between two large floes, particularly if their edges are irregular in shape. If such floes should move together under pressure and a point of ice should bear against the ship's side it will almost certainly damage it, and quite possibly stove it in. If the edges of the floe are straight, the pressure will be borne over more of the side, but even so there will be danger of being crushed.

When stopped in pack ice, a ship will drift down-wind much faster than the floes or icebergs. It is also likely that the ship will gain headway or sternway as well as sideways drift. There is then a danger that floes or bergy bits will pass under the stern and may cause serious damage to the propellers or rudders. The denser the pack, the less the danger because the drifting speed of the ship will be relatively slow but in open pack the ship should not be allowed to drift in strong winds where the rate of drift may become dangerous.

The best place for a ship to winter in is a shallow, enclosed bay — enclosed so that there can be no pressure in the ice, and shallow so that no icebergs can drift in to menace the ship. She should be secured on what is normally the windward side of the bay.

Towing in ice

Should it be necessary to tow a disabled ship through pack ice, the tow should be kept as short as swell conditions permit, so as to give greater control of the towed ship and to minimise the chance of floes drifting between the two ships and parting the towing hawser or damaging the other ship. When there is no swell, it should be possible to keep the tow clear of the water. When towing in this manner, at very short stay, the stern of the towing ship will require to be well fendered, and prompt and skilful action will often be necessary to avoid collision as the tow rides ahead. The wash of full power from the towing ship can sometimes be used effectively to keep the other ship clear of ice.

The behaviour of the ship in tow must be carefully watched, so that alterations of course in leads, or when avoiding floes, may be made without putting her into the ice. When towing at very short stay, two towing hawsers as widely spanned as possible may be used with advantage.

The strain on the towing hawsers will be very severe if the towed ship comes in contact with heavy ice, and special precautions must be taken against nipping and chafing at the lead-in. Bollards should not be used as securing points if this can be avoided; they are liable to be torn out by the sudden jerks caused if ice is encountered when towing at short stay.

Ice-breakers are usually constructed with notched sterns so that, when the pressure of ice is great and the channel closes immediately astern of the ice-breaker, the stem of the towed ship may be hauled close up into the stern indentation. Both ships then work as one unit, thus avoiding the dangers and difficulties of working through close pack with a free tow at short stay.

DANGERS WHEN BESET

Releasing the ship when fast in the ice

The problems of releasing a ship which is fast in the ice are discussed in the *Sailing Directions*. The majority of HM ships will not be prone to run up on the ice, and the remarks on this particular situation will only be applicable to such small ships as have a rounded forefoot. Any of the expedients described may, however, be of assistance in freeing any class of ship, in whatever circumstances, when she is fast or beset. Explosives may sometimes be an effective method of shifting the ice, particularly when the ship has attempted to widen a crack and has become nipped. In such cases, small demolition charges about 3 metres clear of the ship's side where the pressure seems greatest will often cause a temporary movement of the floes that will enable the ship to come astern, provided that her propellers are turning at full speed astern when the charges are detonated. When sunlight is available, it is possible to weaken ice floes by laying a dark-coloured substance across the surface of the ice where a crack is required. This will cause local heating from the sun which effectively cuts the ice. Black oil or even cocoa will suffice.

Risk of damage

The danger to a ship beset depends chiefly on the underwater shape of her hull, the time of year and the locality in which she lies. A ship with deep, straight sides is more likely to be damaged than one with a rounded section, which will rise as the pressure increases and will allow the ice to meet under her. A ship temporarily beset in the spring or summer is unlikely to be damaged if she is caught in an area of little pressure.

A well-built ship beset and forced to winter in the open pack will not necessarily come to any great harm provided she does not subsequently drift into an area of pressure — for instance, an area where the ice is being pressed against a coastline — and provided she has adequate reserves of fuel and stores.

Icebergs are another source of danger to a ship beset, particularly in the Antarctic. Owing to their great size and draught these may not take up the same direction and rate of drift as the pack, and thus they appear to plough through the floes and may build up a 'bow wave' of pressure ice which can crush a ship if she is unable to manoeuvre clear. The smaller Arctic bergs are generally not such a menace in this respect, although a ship must avoid being set down on one. Even though apparently the ship is not moving relative to the pack, the pack will probably be moving relative to even quite small bergs. Ships should beware of stopping, even in dense pack, if there are large bergy bits or small bergs which it would be unwise to hit while drifting.

CONCLUSION

Shiphandling technique in pack ice is dependent basically on the strength, power and manoeuvrability of the individual ship. A lightly-built warship such as a destroyer or frigate will not stand up to impact with heavy floes; her propellers are extremely vulnerable, and her hull will quickly be crushed in pressure ice. Heavier warships are no better-suited to ice operations because their thin bow plating and projecting propellers are generally as vulnerable as those of the smaller ship. Unless specially built for ice operations, a warship must therefore be handled with the object of avoiding impact with thick ice, unless taken at very slow speed directly on the stem. Only the smaller ships have the necessary manoeuvrability to achieve this object.

Patience is essential when in ice-bound waters. Many a difficult situation will resolve itself if only the shiphandler has the patience to await a change of wind or weather. The ability to differentiate between hard ice and soft ice and between passable and impassable pack, to recognise weathered floes with their dangerous underwater spurs, to detect lines of weakness and to select the most suitable leads, etc., can only be gained by experience, and no amount of text-book knowledge will stand in its stead. The use of radar, and its limitations, in the detection of ice should be well understood by all those concerned. Sea ice is a navigational hazard of the first order, and should be accorded all due respect. On the other hand, it is a hazard which can be greatly minimised by skilful shiphandling and a sensitive appreciation of the capacity of the ship to withstand damage.

CHAPTER 18

Offshore Oil and Gas Fields, and Oil Pollution Control Organisation

The increasing dependence of civilisation on mineral oil products and the diminishing supplies from land-based and inshore sources have provided the impetus for the search for new sources of oil farther offshore. The rising value of oil has made the exploration and development of such sources an economic reality despite the difficulties, inherent dangers, high costs and complex equipment required. Wells are now being drilled off every continent, some of them hundreds of miles offshore and in the most storm-ridden waters of the world, and a whole new fast-growing industry has developed to exploit these resources.

A large proportion of the world's maritime trade is devoted to the carriage of oil either as crude oil to refineries or as refined products for distribution. Despite legislation and the best will of all concerned, the bunkering requirements of ships and the large volume of oil in transit constitute a major risk of pollution of the sea, through either accident or disaster. An organisation is therefore required, to marshal and direct resources for the containment and dispersal of pollution however it may occur.

The first part of this chapter provides the background knowledge of the offshore oil and gas production industry which is essential for all mariners, and describes the equipment likely to be encountered in United Kingdom waters: the second part describes the organisation, both national and within the Ministry of Defence, for dealing with oil pollution at sea. Information on oil pollution regulations, and on offshore oil and gas fields, is given in NP 100, *The Mariner's Handbook.*

OFFSHORE OIL AND GAS FIELDS

EXPLORATION AND SURVEY

The exploration of an offshore area thought likely to yield oil or gas commences with an extensive survey to locate magnetic and gravitational anomalies, or possibly with the examination of any visible oil seepages.

Seismic surveys are then undertaken in suitable areas indicated by the initial survey. The seismic-survey vessel tows a detector cable 1 to 2 miles long which is usually submerged to a depth of 7 to 14 metres. The end of the cable is marked with a tail buoy fitted with a radar reflector. 'Air' or 'gas' guns are towed close astern of the vessel and are fired to provide the seismic shock. The explosions of these guns are not visible to other shipping and are harmless to fish. A second vessel may follow the first to keep the way clear of traffic.

Seismic-survey vessels are unable to move freely and they should be given a wide berth of at least 2 miles. The craft generally show the shapes and lights prescribed by Rule 27(b) of the International Regulations for Preventing Collisions at Sea. They may also show the signals PO and IR of the International Code. These ships often keep radio silence to avoid interference with the surveying instruments, and any other ships called by light should answer by the same means and not by radio.

Bottom samples and core samples are then obtained from selected positions to provide more detailed information.

DRILLING RIGS

Test wells are drilled at positions indicated by the surveys, to confirm the possibility that oil or gas may be profitably extracted. As searches have extended into deeper and more exposed waters, larger, more seaworthy and more complicated rigs have been evolved to carry out the drilling operations.

Drilling rigs are not shown on charts because they do not operate for long in any one place, but their positions may be given in *Radio Navigational Warnings* or in *Temporary Notices to Mariners*. Rigs are marked by lights; fog signals are sounded from them; and, on some, flares burn at times to dispose of waste gases. Buoys, lighters and other obstacles are often moored near rigs, and these may not be marked by lights or sound fog signals; wires often extend as far as a mile from rigs — thus it is prudent to give all drilling rigs a wide berth.

The three principal types of drilling rig which may be encountered in offshore fields are described below.

Jack-up rigs

Jack-up rigs are towed into position where their steel legs are lowered to the sea bed. The drilling platform is then elevated on the legs clear of the water. This type of rig is suitable for operations in water to a depth of about 100 metres.

Semi-submersible rigs

Semi-submersible rigs consist of a drilling platform supported on columns which rise from caissons submerged deep enough to minimise the effects of sea and swell. Large semi-submersible rigs may have displacements up to 25 000 tonnes and may be self-propelled, with the capability of proceeding unassisted at speeds of up to 6 – 7 knots. Operating depths are dependent upon the capabilities of the mooring equipment fitted but modern designs of self-propelled rigs incorporate a *dynamic positioning system* which permits drilling operations in depths as great as 2000 metres. A dynamic positioning system comprises a computer, which is fed with information from sensors detecting a mark on the sea bed, and which automatically controls the propulsion system to maintain the vessel's position over the mark.

Drillships

Drillships are ships of conventional form but are distinguished by the tall drilling-rig amidships and they usually have a helicopter platform near the stern. A typical drillship would have a length of about 135 metres, displacement of about 14 000 tonnes and a maximum speed of about 14 knots. When operating in depths to about 200 metres the ship is usually moored by an 8-point anchoring system but in deeper waters to a maximum of about 2000 metres a dynamic positioning system is used to maintain the ship in position. In favourable conditions these vessels can drill to depths of 6000 metres below the sea bed.

WELLS AND WELLHEADS

During exploration numerous wells are drilled to determine the extent of the field. Many of these wells are not required again and so they are sealed with cement below the sea bed and abandoned.

Other wells which may be required in the future but are otherwise left in a dormant state are known as *suspended wells*. A suspended well has its head capped and is left with a pipe and other equipment projecting from the sea bed. These wells are sometimes marked by a buoy to assist recovery and to warn of the hazard to navigation and fishing.

DEVELOPMENT OF OFFSHORE FIELDS

Production platforms

An offshore field is exploited from one or more *production platforms* sited at the most suitable positions. These platforms are of massive construction and built to last the lifetime of the field which may be as much as thirty years.

Two types of structure are commonly used to support the platforms on the sea bed. In one, a *steel jacket structure* is built comprising a number of vertical legs which are braced by lattice-work to form a pylon. The jacket is transported to its position, up-ended and located on the sea bed, and then secured by piling. The other type is the *concrete gravity structure* in which a cellular caisson is built of concrete. The cells are designed for oil storage and some of them extend upwards to form the platform support columns. The structure is towed in its normal attitude to its location and then submerged on to the sea bed. When in position the weight of the structure provides stability and no anchors or piling are required. Concrete and steel skirts project from the underside of the caisson to prevent scouring of the sea bed under the platform. A production platform supported on a concrete gravity structure is illustrated in Fig. 18–1.

A production platform may carry drilling and production equipment, oil and gas separation and treatment plant, oil pumping equipment and electricity generating plant. One or more cranes and a helicopter landing platform are usually fitted, and accommodation and services are provided for a crew of up to 300 men. From such a platform many wells can be drilled, slanting outwards in all directions, to cover a large surrounding area. Even so, the average offshore field usually requires more than one production platform for full development.

A group of platforms in one field is linked together by pipelines measuring 40 – 60 centimetres in diameter. From the production platform or group the oil or gas is delivered, by a trunk pipeline measuring up to 90 centimetres

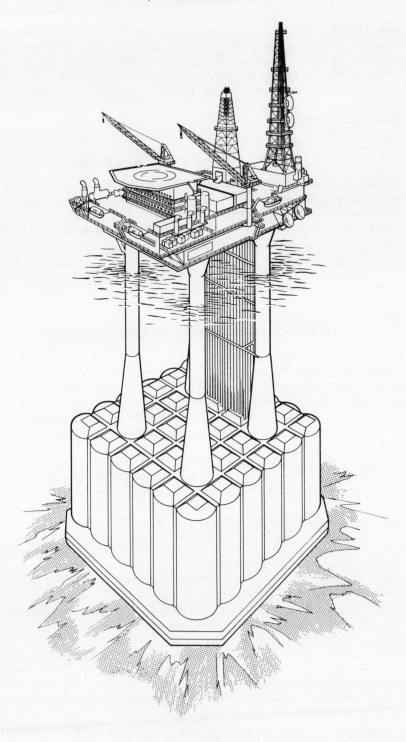

FIG. 18–1. A production platform supported on a concrete gravity structure

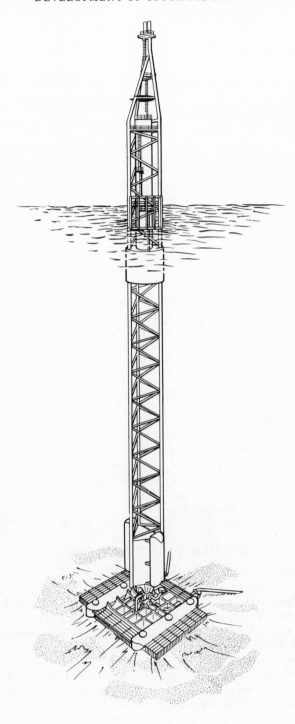

FIG. 18–2. A remote gas vent/flare

in diameter, to shore or to a storage tank, a tanker loading buoy or a floating terminal.

Production platforms are shown on charts and are also mentioned in the *Sailing Directions*. They are marked by lights and they sound fog signals, but mooring buoys, usually uncharted, are often moored at distances up to one mile away and thus production platforms should be given a wide berth whenever practicable.

Underwater completed wells

Some wells, known as *underwater completed wells*, having the wellhead on the sea bed and not on a production platform, are in use on some fields. The oil or gas from these wells is piped to a nearby production platform or floating terminal for processing, or to a tanker loading buoy. Underwater completed wells are either inspected and maintained by divers or encapsulated at atmospheric pressure so that men without diving ability can be taken to them for such work.

Remote gas vent/flare (Fig. 18–2)

Every effort is made to conserve the products of an offshore field. However, in fields which have a high gas-to-oil ratio it may be necessary to incorporate remote gas-vents to dispose of the large volumes of gas involved. The vent is usually situated about two miles away from its associated production platform to which it is connected by a submarine pipeline. The excess gas is either vented to atmosphere or flared off, dependent on the volume concerned.

Transportation

As already stated, usually the oil or gas is mainly delivered to shore by large-bore submarine pipelines. However, in remote fields and fields under development, tankers are often used for transportation although such operations may be hindered by inclement weather. Where tankers are used a variety of *single-point moorings* (SPM) have been developed and set up to allow tankers to load gas or oil.

SINGLE-POINT MOORINGS

In sheltered waters of sufficient depth, tankers of whatever size can load or discharge their cargoes at conventional alongside berths or at berths where they moor head and stern at *conventional buoy moorings* (CBM). However, in offshore waters such as the approaches to ports with insufficient depth of water or on offshore oil and gas fields, a variety of mooring systems has been developed to enable large vessels to moor by the bow and load or discharge their cargoes. These mooring systems, referred to generally as single-point moorings (SPM), vary from large mooring buoys (Monobuoys) to manned floating structures of up to 60 000 tonnes displacement, and include towers and platforms secured in various ways to the sea bed. The largest SPMs are capable of accommodating vessels of up to 500 000 tonnes deadweight.

SPMs are mentioned in *Sailing Directions*, they are shown on charts, and they display lights and sound fog signals. An SPM should always be given a wide berth except by ships intending to use it.

The three basic types of SPM together with their variants are described below.

Catenary anchor leg mooring (CALM)

Various forms of CALM are in service, all of which comprise a large buoy which remains on the surface at all times and is moored by four or more large anchors. Tanker mooring hawsers and cargo hoses are led from a turntable on top of the buoy so that the moored vessel can swing to wind and stream without turning the buoy.

Development of the CALM has led to the following more complex types of mooring.

Exposed-location single-buoy mooring (ELSBM). This type of mooring is designed for use in deep water where bad weather is common, and is capable of accommodating vessels of up to 50 000 tonnes deadweight. A typical ELSBM is shown in Fig. 18–3.

The mooring comprises a large cylindrical buoyant structure which is divided into three sections. The bottom section is a ballast compartment, the middle section provides buoyancy and the upper section contains the operating spaces and emergency accommodation. A helicopter platform is supported

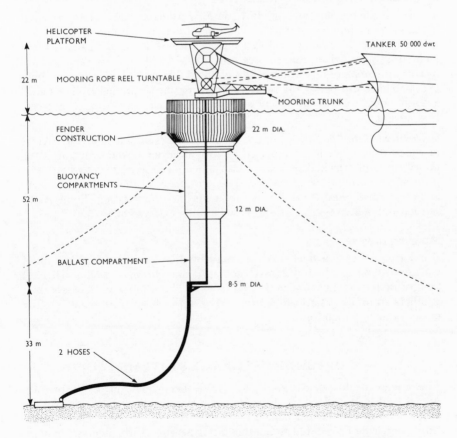

FIG. 18–3. An exposed-location single-buoy mooring (ELSBM)

on the structure by a lattice tower about 20 metres high. Within the tower, reels are fitted for the tanker mooring hawsers and flexible delivery hoses. An ELSBM is usually moored by eight anchors, each of about 15 tonnes, lying up to half a mile away.

SPAR. This type of SPM is similar to the ELSBM but the floating structure is larger, has the facilities to pump, treat and store oil, is permanently manned, and can accommodate the largest tankers. Fig. 18–4 shows the Brent SPAR storage and loading facility, which is moored in the Brent Field in the North Sea. The mooring comprises a large cylindrical buoy, about 17 metres in diameter at the waterline and with a draught of about 110 metres. Below the waterline the diameter of the structure increases to about 30 metres to form the oil storage tanks. The superstructure consists of three decks housing the machinery and control gear, diving equipment and accommodation spaces. The structure is surmounted by a turntable about 30 metres above the waterline, which carries a crane and boom for working the delivery hoses, tanker mooring hawsers and gear, and a helicopter deck. The complete structure has a displacement of about 67 000 tonnes and is moored by six 1200-tonne concrete anchor-blocks laid at about half a mile radius.

Single anchor leg mooring (SALM)

The single anchor leg type of SPM (the SALM) comprises a buoy moored by a single anchor leg of wire or chain, or by a rigid frame or tube, to a universal joint on a large steel or concrete base. The base is ballasted and secured by piles driven into the sea bed. The SALM buoy, usually about 5 metres in diameter and with a height of about 3 metres above the waterline, is designed to dip below the surface. The cargo hoses are led from a swivel assembly near the universal joint and thus a moored vessel can swing freely to wind and stream.

The articulated loading-platform (ALP) is a development of the SALM in which the anchor leg is replaced by a rigid lattice tower, buoyant at the upper end and attached by a universal joint to a base on the sea bed. The tower is surmounted by a helicopter platform, has reels for mooring hawsers and cargo hoses, and is fitted with emergency accommodation. Some ALPs can accommodate vessels of up to 80 000 tonnes deadweight.

Mooring tower

A mooring tower is a steel structure fixed by piles to the sea bed and fitted with a turntable to which the vessel moors. At some towers the oil is delivered by floating hoses which are connected to a swivel assembly on the turntable; at others an underwater loading arm carries a pipe from the turntable to the tanker's midship manifold.

OFFSHORE STORAGE SYSTEMS

The storage facility of a SPAR has already been mentioned. To provide storage and loading facilities in some remote or marginal oil fields, vessels are sometimes moored permanently to an SPM to allow other ships to load either alongside or moored to another SPM nearby. Two such systems are described below.

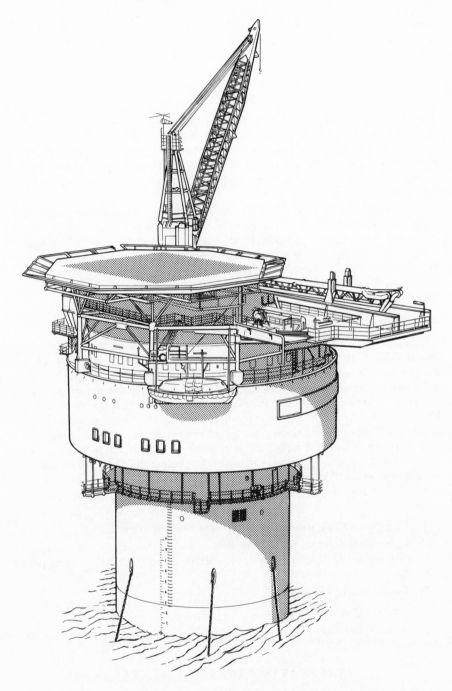

FIG. 18–4. SPAR storage and loading facility (Brent Field, North Sea)

Single-buoy storage (SBS). In this system the storage vessel is moored to a CALM or SALM by a hinged, rigid metal yoke.

Single-anchor-leg storage (SALS). With this system a storage vessel, which may be equipped for separating and treating oil, is moored by a floating metal-yoke and riser-head assembly to an articulated anchor leg. The anchor leg is secured to a base which is fixed by piles to the sea bed.

SAFETY

The development of an offshore field involves the frequent movement of large structures and buoys, and the laying of great lengths of pipeline, all of which are heavily dependent on the weather. Where such operations are liable to occur it should be borne in mind that it is often impossible to give adequate notice of movements, and to keep charts and publications up to date for them.

When passing near an offshore oil or gas field, care must be taken to avoid mistaking the appearance, either visually or on a radar screen, of drilling rigs, fixed platforms, remote gas vents, lights and buoys for shipping or navigational aids. Furthermore, various types of service craft such as anchor-working vessels, supply ships, stand-by boats and pipe-laying vessels may be encountered, not only near rigs and platforms but crossing the main shipping lanes between offshore fields and the coast.

Safety zones

Under international law, coastal states may establish safety zones around any installations that have been constructed on the continental shelf to explore and exploit its resources. These installations include movable drilling rigs, production platforms and gas vents, wellheads, single-point moorings, etc., whether inside or outside the state's territorial waters. An installation may be surrounded by a safety zone extending to 500 metres from its outer edge. *Ships of all nations are required to respect these safety zones* and installation managers are obliged to report infringements of British safety zones to the Ministry of Defence. It is always advisable to assume the existence of a safety zone unless aware of information to the contrary.

Entry into British safety zones is prohibited, except in any of the following cases.

1. To repair a submarine cable or pipeline near the zone.
2. To provide services for an installation within the zone, or to transport persons or goods to or from it, or, with proper authorisation, to inspect it.
3. To save life or property.
4. Under stress of bad weather.
5. When in distress.

LIFESAVING ARRANGEMENTS

The emergency abandonment of an offshore installation calls for special arrangements, because of the height of the platform above the water and the grave probability of an area of fire on the surrounding sea.

Helicopters provide the quickest means of evacuation if they are available and if the nature of the emergency permits use of the helicopter platform.

To reach the water level and gain access to rescue craft some installations are fitted with a boom which has a small platform at its head. The heel is secured to one leg of the rig and the boom is kept topped-up to the rig. In emergency the boom can be lowered so that its platform is near the water level and can be reached by a lifeline running out from the main platform. Other installations may be fitted with inflatable escape chutes similar to those used in large passenger aircraft.

Lifeboats

The provision of specially designed enclosed lifeboats is mandatory on all installations in United Kingdom and Norwegian waters.

These lifeboats are specially constructed to ensure the survival of the occupants should the installation be engulfed in burning oil or gas which also denudes the atmosphere of oxygen. The boats are of GRP construction and are totally enclosed so that the accommodation is gastight and watertight. A compressed-air system is fitted within the boat to provide sufficient breathable air for the occupants while the boat is manoeuvred clear of an area of burning oil or gas. A further important feature is the fitting of equipment to envelop the craft with an umbrella of water spray while passing through a burning sea surface.

OIL POLLUTION CONTROL ORGANISATION

Oil pollution at sea is an ever-increasing hazard requiring a flexible organisation which can react quickly to combat the emergency. This section describes the organisation for dealing with pollution off the coasts and on the beaches of the United Kingdom. Further information is given in BR 8623, *Pollution at Sea*, and also in BR 8514, *Marine Services Manual*.

The primary responsibility for practical measures to overcome oil pollution at sea beyond one mile from the shore lies with the Department of Trade. An organisation with contingency plans is set up in the Department to deal with emergencies such as a major spillage at sea. The one-mile limit is not a rigid demarcation and the Department would organise operations closer to the shore if this were necessary and practicable.

Local authorities are responsible for dealing with oil on beaches and inshore waters and, in this respect, the Ministry of Defence (Navy) has the same responsibilities for tidal waters within naval ports and for the beaches of Navy Department property.

NATIONAL ORGANISATION

The national organisation is best described by listing the government departments and other organisations involved, and briefly stating their functions.

Department of Trade

The *Marine Pollution Control Unit* (MPCU) which has headquarters in London is responsible for all aspects of marine pollution clearance. Overall command throughout an incident rests with the Director of the MPCU.

2L

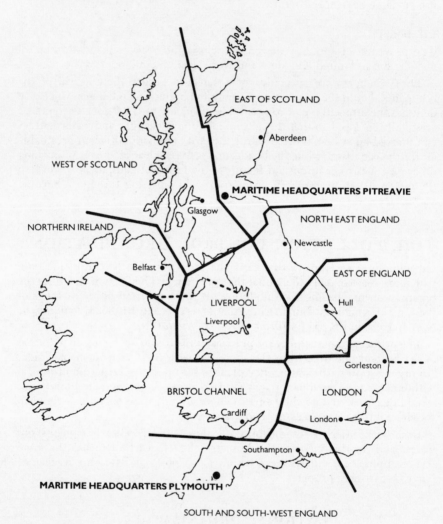

MARITIME HEADQUARTERS PITREAVIE COVER THE AREA
NORTH OF THE LINES BETWEEN BARROW, THE ISLE OF MAN
AND NORTHERN IRELAND AND NORTH OF THE LINE DRAWN
IN AN EASTERLY DIRECTION FROM THE COAST SOUTH OF GORLESTON

MARITIME HEADQUARTERS PLYMOUTH COVER
THE AREA TO THE SOUTH OF THOSE LINES.
THE AREAS EXTEND TO THE MEDIANS BETWEEN NATIONS

EAST OF SCOTLAND

Aberdeen

WEST OF SCOTLAND

MARITIME HEADQUARTERS PITREAVIE

Glasgow

NORTH EAST ENGLAND

NORTHERN IRELAND

Newcastle

EAST OF ENGLAND

Belfast

LIVERPOOL

Hull

Liverpool

Gorleston

BRISTOL CHANNEL

LONDON

Cardiff

London

Southampton

MARITIME HEADQUARTERS PLYMOUTH

SOUTH AND SOUTH-WEST ENGLAND

FIG. 18–5. Division of the United Kingdom into nine districts for dealing with oil pollution at sea

The coastline of the United Kingdom is divided into nine Department of Trade districts (Fig. 18–5) to each of which a Marine Pollution Control Officer (MPCO) is appointed.

Local control at an incident normally rests with the Deputy Director of the MPCU, and he is assisted by the MPCOs who assemble to form the counter-pollution team at or near the incident. Coastguard stations are used as control centres on the coast during pollution emergencies.

HM Coastguard. With stations located at strategic points around the coast, the Coastguard provides the primary communication network. In conjunction with the Ministry of Defence's Maritime Headquarters at Plymouth and Pitreavie and with the Civil Air Traffic Control Centres, HM Coastguards receive and disseminate reports of oil pollution, and assist the MPCU with communication facilities.

Scientific establishments

The Warren Spring Laboratory, at Stevenage, Herts., administered by the Department of Industry, provides scientific and technical advice, and approves equipment and materials for use at sea and on the beaches.

The Laboratory of the Government Chemist analyses samples of oil collected from the sea and from ships to assist in establishing the origin of the spilt oil.

Department of the Environment; Scottish, Welsh and Northern Ireland Offices

The Department of the Environment, and the Scottish, Welsh and Northern Ireland Offices co-ordinate the activities of local authorities within their jurisdiction, in dispersing oil within one mile of shore and in cleaning the beaches. The appropriate departments also arrange the provision of financial assistance for these tasks.

Ministry of Agriculture, Fisheries and Food; Department of Agriculture and Fisheries for Scotland

The Ministry of Agriculture, Fisheries and Food, and the Department of Agriculture and Fisheries for Scotland advise on the toxicological effect of oil on the marine environment, particularly with respect to sea fisheries, shell-fish beds, etc. Advice is also given on the avoidance of adverse effects on fisheries caused by the methods of dealing with pollution. The Fisheries Laboratory at Burnham-on-Crouch is responsible for advising on the toxicity of dispersants used in clearing oil pollution. The Ministry of Agriculture, Fisheries and Food also licenses operators to use dispersants under the terms of the Dumping at Sea Act, 1974.

Ministry of Defence

The Ministry of Defence, through its Maritime Headquarters at Plymouth and Pitreavie, supports the civil departments by providing Service aircraft for surveillance, and suitable vessels, if available, for dispersal operations. If a stricken vessel is involved a Salvage Officer may be seconded and put on board the vessel to advise on the prospects of its salvage.

United Kingdom Offshore Operators Association (UKOOA)

Licences to operate offshore oil and gas installations prescribe the appropriate pollution-prevention methods to be adopted by the operators. The UKOOA has its own contingency plans and equipment to deal with oil spillages. However, should any spillage be beyond the capability of these resources and threaten major coastal-pollution the national organisation described above would be brought into operation.

MINISTRY OF DEFENCE (NAVY) ORGANISATION

Within the Ministry of Defence the professional and technical expertise on all aspects of oil pollution clearance is provided by the Directorate of Marine Services (Naval). The department is charged with the following responsibilities.

1. Advice to all authorities within the Ministry on the clearance of oil pollution from waters controlled by the Ministry.

2. Advice to the Director General Ships on the equipment and materials for oil-pollution clearance to be carried in HM ships, RFAs and RMAS vessels.

3. Liaison with other government departments and commercial organisations to monitor the progress of oil-pollution technology in assessing the Ministry's requirements.

4. Liaison with the appropriate departments of the Ministry of Defence on the policy, financial and operational aspects of oil-pollution clearance measures.

5. Preparation and maintenance of a catalogue of all types of equipment and materials for use in oil-pollution clearance.

Oil clearance at RN ports and installations

Within the area of a dockyard port, the Captain of the Port or the Resident Naval Officer (RNO), as appropriate, is responsible for the recovery and disposal of oil spillages, and for the clearance of oil pollution, arising from incidents in which Ministry of Defence (Navy) vessels are involved. He is empowered to co-opt the assistance of the Principal Supply and Transport Officer (Naval) or other Heads of Departments as necessary to assist in this task. The Captain of the Port or RNO also provides assistance to local authorities or government departments, when requested and on repayment, to clear any oil pollution with which they may be concerned.

In non-tidal basins and docks at naval bases the Yard Services Manager is usually responsible for clearing oil spillages and flotsam, although traditionally at Devonport this duty rests with the Captain of the Port.

At Ministry of Defence (Navy) fuelling installations outside the areas of dockyard ports, the Directorate General of Supplies and Transport (Naval) is responsible for the containment, recovery and dispersal of oil spillages.

Stocks of dispersant

It is Ministry policy to maintain ready for immediate use, stocks of dispersant and associated equipment at naval bases and other locations which are listed in BR 8623.

PROCEDURE IN AN OIL-POLLUTION EMERGENCY AT SEA

It is the duty of all ships and aircraft, whether civil or military, to report incidents of oil pollution at sea around the coasts of the United Kingdom. These reports are initially made to HM Coastguard, Air Traffic Control Centres, or Maritime Headquarters.

The reports are passed to the Marine Division of the Department of Trade and thence to the Director MPCU who has the responsibility to decide on the action required.

Whenever possible, advantage is taken of the natural action of the sea to break up and disperse pollution. However, when an incident poses an imminent threat of heavy coastal pollution the MPCU sends out the necessary aircraft, ships and equipment to deal with the emergency. If necessary, the Ministry of Defence (Navy) is requested to assist in the sea-borne operation.

Control of operations

The Marine Pollution Control Officer of the area concerned takes initial charge of an operation where the prime consideration is oil pollution, pending the arrival of the Deputy Director MPCU and the counter-pollution team. Assistance will be provided as necessary by HM Coastguard. Depending on the location of the incident, and by agreement, a Maritime Headquarters may be used as the incident control centre.

Guidance on pollution clearance

Instructions, information and guidance to HM ships and authorities involved in an oil-pollution incident are promulgated in *Fleet Operating Orders* (FLOOs). These orders describe the roles of various classes of ship, and contain details of the available equipment and materials, advice on their use and precautions to be taken. Courses of instruction are also available to appropriate personnel at the Marine Services School, Rosyth.

INDEX

Printed in the UK by HMSO Press, Edinburgh
Dd 0716842 C100 8/83 (201500)